AA Lifestyle Guides in association with Corus and Regal hotels are giving away

30 relaxing leisure breaks in 6 Free Prize Draws

see overleaf for terms & conditions

Whether you are looking for a short romantic interlude, a family holiday, an active weekend or just a relaxing break away - you'll feel right at home at Corus and Regal hotels.

Make your choice from historic coaching inns, elegant country houses and city centre hotels. Or maybe you'd prefer a traditional seaside resort. With over 100 hotels throughout the UK, we're sure to have somewhere to suit you.

The Rose & Crown Hotel, Salisbury, Wiltshire

corus

Corus and Regal hotels

For more information on Corus and Regal hotels and for your complimentary copy of their 'Leisure Times' brochure call: 01905 730370 quoting 'AA Lifestyle Guides'

HOW TO ENTER

Just complete (in capitals please) and send off this card or alternatively, send your name and address on a **stamped** postcard to the address overleaf (no purchase required). Entries limited to one per household and to residents of the UK and Republic of Ireland over the age of 18. This card will require a stamp if posted in the Republic of Ireland. **Closing date 30th October 2000**

MR/MRS/MISS/MS/OTHER, PLEASE STATE:

NAME:

ADDRESS:

POSTCODE: TEL. NO:

Are you an AA Member? Yes/No Have you bought this or any other AA Lifestyle Guide before? Yes/No

If yes, please indicate the year of the last edition you bought:

The AA Hotel Guide	19___	**AA Camping and Caravanning (Europe)**	19___
AA Best Restaurants	19___	**AA Hotels in France**	19___
AA Bed and Breakfast Guide	19___	**AA Bed & Breakfast in France**	19___
AA Camping & Caravanning (Britain & Ireland)	19___	**AA Best Pubs & Inns**	19___

If you do not wish to receive further information or special offers from

AA Publishing ☐ Corus and Regal hotels ☐ please tick the box(es) BP00

CHRISTMAS CASH BACK OFFER

Offer closes 31 January 2000.

Buy any two of the following AA 2000 Lifestyle Guides, return the cash back vouchers and we'll send you a cheque to the value of the two vouchers up to a maximum of £5.

The Hotel Guide (£2.50 voucher) The Restaurant Guide (£2.50 voucher) Best Pubs & Inns (£1.50 voucher) Bed & Breakfast Guide (£1.50 voucher) The Britain Guide (£1.50 voucher).

HOW TO PARTICIPATE **See overleaf for full terms and conditions.**

Detach vouchers from books and post them, together with a stamped self-addressed envelope, to AA Lifestyle Guides Cash Back, Fanum House (4), Basing View, Basingstoke, Hants RG21 4EA.

CASH BACK £1·50p

Terms and Conditions

1. Five winners will be drawn for each of the six prize draws to take place on 31st December, 1999, 29 February, 28 April, 30 June, 31 August, 31 October, 2000.
2. Closing date for receipt of entries is midday on the relevant draw date. Final close date for receipt of entries is 30 October 2000.
3. Entries received after any draw date other than the final one will go forward into the next available draw. Entries will be placed in one draw only. Only one entry per household accepted.
4. Winners will be notified by post within 14 days of the relevant draw date. Prizes must be booked within 3 months of the relevant draw date. Prizes are not transferable and there will be no cash alternative.
5. This offer cannot be used in conjunction with any other discount, promotion or special offer.
6. Each prize consists of two nights' accommodation, full traditional breakfast and a complimentary bottle of wine on arrival, for two adults sharing a standard twin/double room at participating Corus and Regal hotels. Supplements may be charged for feature and family rooms. All offers of accommodation are made subject to availablity.
7. All hotel accommodation, services and facilities are provided by Corus and Regal hotels and AA Publishing is not party to your agreement with Corus & Regal hotels in this regard.
8. The prize draw is open to anyone resident in the UK or the Republic of Ireland over the age of 18 other than employees of the Automobile Association or Corus and Regal hotels, their subsidiary companies, their families or agents.
9. For a list of winners, please send a stamped, self-addressed envelope to AA Lifestyle Guides Winners, Publishing Admin, Fanum House, Basing View, Basingstoke, Hants, RG21 4EA.
10. If this card is posted in the Republic of Ireland it must have a stamp.

BUSINESS REPLY SERVICE
Licence No BZ 343

PLEASE NOTE: Requires a stamp if posted in Republic of Ireland

AA Lifestyle Guide 2000 Prize Draw

AA PUBLISHING
FANUM HOUSE
BASING VIEW
BASINGSTOKE
HANTS RG21 4EA

CASH BACK £1·50

CHRISTMAS CASH BACK TERMS & CONDITIONS

1. This offer is open only to residents of the UK and Republic of Ireland.
2. Only original vouchers will be accepted and no responsibility will be accepted for vouchers lost or damaged in the post or illegible applications.
3. You may make any number of applications provided two AA Lifestyle Guides 2000 are purchased in each instance.
4. Each application must be accompanied by a clearly legible stamped self-addressed envelope.
5. **Closing date for receipt of vouchers is 31 January 2000.**

AA

Best Pubs & Inns 2000

Over 1600 Pubs & Inns in England, Scotland & Wales

Produced by AA Publishing
Maps prepared by the Cartographic Department of The Automobile Association
Maps © The Automobile Association 1999

Directory generated by the AA Establishment Database, Information Research, Hotel and Touring Services

Editor: David Hancock
Assistant Editors: Lin Hutton, Jim Barker
Cover photograph supplied by Royal Oak, Winsford, Somerset
Title page photograph supplied by The Angel Inn, Hetton, North Yorkshire

Editorial contributors: Jim Barker, Elizabeth Carter, Nick Channer, Julia Hynard

Cover Art: Climpson PHOTOgraphics, Whitchurch

Features: Joshua Smith Graphics, Nailsworth

Advertisement Production
Karen Weeks: Tel 01256 491545

Typeset/Reprographics by Avonset, 11 Kelso Place, Bath BA1 3AU

Printed and bound in Italy by Rotolito, Lombarda SpA

A CIP catalogue record for this book is available from the British Library

Published by AA Publishing, which is a trading name of Automobile Association Developments Limited whose registered office is Norfolk House, Priestley Road, Basingstoke, Hampshire RG24 9NY, Registered number 1878835.

ISBN 0 7495 2246 1

Contents

COUNTY LIST BY REGION

The West Country

Bristol, Cornwall & the Isles of Scilly, Devon, Dorset, Gloucestershire, Wiltshire

South & South East

Bedfordshire, Berkshire, Buckinghamshire, Greater London, Hampshire, Hertfordshire, Kent, London, Surrey, Sussex, East, Sussex, West, Wight, Isle of

Central England & East Anglia

Cambridgeshire, Derbyshire, Essex, Leicestershire, Lincolnshire, Norfolk, Northamptonshire, Nottinghamshire, Oxfordshire, Rutland, Staffordshire, Suffolk, Warwickshire, West Midlands

Wales & The Marches

Bridgend, Caerphilly, Cardiff, Carmarthenshire, Ceredigion, Conwy, Denbighshire, Flintshire, Gwynedd, Herefordshire, Isle of Anglesey, Monmouthshire, Pembrokeshire, Powys, Shropshire, Swansea, Vale of Glamorgan, Worcestershire, Wrexham

Northern England

Cheshire, Cumbria, Co Durham, Greater Manchester, Lancashire, Merseyside, Northumberland, Tyne & Wear, Yorkshire, East Riding of, Yorkshire, North, Yorkshire, South, Yorkshire, West

Scotland

Aberdeen City, Aberdeenshire, Angus, Argyll & Bute, City of Edinburgh, City of Glasgow, Dumfries & Galloway, East Lothian, Falkirk, Fife, Highlands, Moray, Perth & Kinross, Renfrewshire, Scottish Borders, South Ayrshire, Stirling, West Lothian, Western Isles.

TELEPHONE CODE & NUMBER CHANGES

From 22 April 2000 there will be new dialling codes beginning with 02 in London, Cardiff, Coventry, Portsmouth and Southampton. At the same time, all local numbers in these areas will become eight-digit numbers.

Portsmouth Area Telephone Number Changes

From the 22 April 2000, all dialling codes listed as (01705) will change to **(023)**, followed by an eight-digit local number, starting with **92**. For example, **(01705)** 123456 will become **(023) 92**12 3456.

Southampton Area Telephone Number Changes

From 22 April 2000, all dialling codes listed as (01703) will change to **(023)**, followed by an eight-digit local number, starting with **80**. For example, **(01703)** 123456 will become **(023) 80**12 3456.

Coventry Area Telephone Number Changes

From the 22 April 2000, all dialling codes listed as (01203) will change to **(024)**, followed by an eight-digit local number. starting with **76**. For example, **(01203)** 123456 will become **(024) 76**12 3456.

Cardiff Area Telephone Number Changes

From the 22 April 2000, all dialling codes listed as (01222) will change to **(029)**, followed by an eight-digit local number, starting with **20**. For example, **(01222)** 123456 will become **(029) 20**12 3456.

London Telephone Number Changes

From the 22 April 2000, the dialling code for the whole of London with be **(020)**, followed by an eight-digit local number. For example, **(0171)** 123 4567 will become **(020) 7**123 4567, **(0181)** 123 4567 will become **(020) 8**123 4567.

IN CASE OF DIFFICULTIES, PLEASE CONSULT DIRECTORY ENQUIRIES

How to Use this Guide

SYMBOLS AND ABBREVIATIONS

- Accommodation
- Atmosphere
- Children welcome
- Credit cards taken
- Dogs welcome
- Garden
- Horses and their riders welcome
- Quiet location
- Telephone number
- Vegetarian food available
- Walkers welcome

Pubs serving sea food recognised by the Sea Fish Industry Authority (SFIA). For a fuller explanation see page 7. Pubs with a blue tint are regional winners. For a full list see page 18.

Location / Map reference	**TOWN** County *Map 3 F7*
Establishment name/Symbols (*see above*)	**Any Pub**
Town name	*ANY TOWN*
Address & post code / Telephone number	**Any Road GU27 0HZ ☎ 01798 422870**
Description	Very much a dining pub, this popular venue is renowned for its warm welcome and hearty range of good-value and well-cooked meals. Good quality meat, fish, game plus vegetarian dishes vary according to season; puds are always good. **Principal Beers**: Wadworth 6X, Gale's, Broughton, Fullers
Directions	**Directions** 3m E of Any Town
Brewery/Company name or Free House	**Brewery/Company** Free House
Opening times	**Open** 11–3 6–11 (Sun 10.30pm)
Times when food is served / Av. cost of meal	**Bar food** 12–2 7–9.30 Av main course £5 **Restaurant** 12–2 7–9.30 Av 3 course à la carte £15.75 Av 4 course fixed price £8.50
Room tariff	**Accommodation (Min)** s £18 d £30
Credit cards accepted	

REGIONS

Entries are located in one of six regions:

- **West Country**
- **South & South East England**
- **Central England & East Anglia**
- **Wales & The Marches**
- **Northern England**
- **Scotland**

COUNTIES

Counties are listed alphabetically within each Region. See page 4 for full list.

PLACE NAMES

Place names are listed alphabetically within each County.

MAP REFERENCE

The reference number denotes the map page number in the atlas section at the back of the book and the National Grid reference.

TELEPHONE NUMBERS

Some telephone numbers are due to change during the currency of this Guide. See page 5 for details. In case of difficulty check with the operator or Directory Enquiries.

Explanation of the symbols

ATMOSPHERE Expect to find a selection of such features as antique furniture, old beams, open fires, flagstone floors or perhaps a thatched roof.

CHILDREN WELCOME The teddy bear symbol indicates those pubs which welcome children. Usually children are allowed in certain areas and some pubs specify well behaved children only. There may be a children's play area in the garden, but check beforehand. If you have very young children ask about provisions like high chairs or cots if you are staying overnight. Alcohol cannot be bought or drunk until the age of 18.

DOGS WELCOME Well behaved dogs on leads are permitted at the Manager's discretion. Dogs may only be allowed in specific areas.

GARDEN A garden is available for customers' use in good weather. There may be a children's play area or other facilities.

HORSES AND THEIR RIDERS WELCOME There is room in the car park or another specified area for horses and their riders whilst they are taking refreshment. Horses should be attended by a competent handler at all times.

QUIET LOCATION The establishment is considered by the proprietor to be in a quiet and peaceful location.

VEGETARIAN FOOD AVAILABLE Vegetarian meals are always available.

WALKERS WELCOME Although walkers are welcome, their muddy boots may not be and these should be left where indicated by the proprietor.

BREWERY/COMPANY This indicates the name of the Brewery the pub is 'tied' to or the Company the pub is owned by. The extent of the 'tie' depends on whether the pub is managed by employees of the Brewery or leased to a tenant. Tenants generally have more freedom to buy drinks, including beer, from other sources.

FREE HOUSE Free House indicates that the pub is independently owned and run and in theory can buy drinks from any brewery.

DIRECTIONS Directions are given wherever they have been supplied by the proprietor.

OPEN Open indicates the hours when the establishment is open and closed. Times when food is available may be different.

BAR FOOD Bar Food indicates the times when bar food is available, and the average price of a main course as supplied by the proprietor. Last orders may be approximately 30 minutes before the times stated.

RESTAURANT Restaurant indicates the times when restaurant food is available. The average cost of a 3 or 4 course à la carte meal and a 3 or 4 course fixed price menu are shown as supplied by the proprietor. Last orders may be approximately 30 minutes before the times stated.

SEA FISH SYMBOL Shown where a pub serves a minimum of four main course dishes where sea fish is the main ingredient. The Sea Fish Industry Authority have chose seven regional winners and one overall national winner which have their entries highlighted in blue. For a list of winners see page 18.

ACCOMMODATION (MIN) Accommodation prices indicate the **minimum** single room and double room prices per night. En suite bedrooms or adjacent private bathrooms may be available; breakfast may be included in the price, so guests should check when making a reservation. Circumstances and prices may vary during the currency of the Guide.

CREDIT CARDS TAKEN The major credit cards such as Visa and Master Card are taken where C is shown at the end of each entry. Telephone first to check if you wish to use other cards or charge cards.

TRADITIONAL PUB FAVOURITES

Long-established favourites that continue to feature on even the most modern pub menus are home-made pies, in particular steak and ale pie and fish pie. In researching this years guide we mailed out to all the pubs included offering them to submit their steak and ale pie (or pudding) and/or fish pie recipe for a competition to find the best traditional recipes. Ingredients and cooking methods for all the submitted recipes were scrutinised by our inspectors before arriving at a shortlist for both types of pie. Here we feature the top three steak and ale pie and fish pie recipes. Further selected recipes are highlighted on the regional introduction pages. All recipes serve six people.

The Boar's Head Hotel, Ripley, North Yorkshire

Steak & Ripley Crackshot Ale Pudding

Made with an age old recipe found in the Library of Ripley Castle, the ancestral home of the Ingilby family for over 26 generations.

Ingredients:

- 2lb/900g braising **steak** trimmed and diced
- 1lb/450g **lamb** or **ox kidney** (optional) trimmed and diced
- 2oz/50g **beef dripping**
- 4 **celery** sticks diced
- 4 **carrots** peeled and diced
- 6 **onions** peeled and diced
- 8oz/225g **mushrooms** (quartered)
- 1 **Garlic clove** crushed
- 1/2 teaspoon chopped **Thyme**
- 10fl oz/300ml **Crackshot Ale** (Ripley Castle's own label ale)
- 3pts/1.75ltrs good **beef stock**
- **salt** & **Pepper**

Ingredients for the Suet paste:

- 1lb/450g **Plain flour**
- 1oz/25g **Baking powder**
- 4oz/110g Fresh **suet** chopped
- 4oz/110g Dried **suet**
- 10fl oz/300ml **Water**

Method:

Grease six 14floz / 400ml moulds. For **steak** filling: fry **beef** and optional **kidney** in hot **dripping**, allowing to colour well on all sides. In separate large pan, sweat diced **vegetables** and **herbs** for few minutes. Add **Crackshot Ale** and reduce by half. Add **meat** and cover with **beef stock**. Bring to boil, simmer for approx 1.5 hours. Check **seasoning** and allow to cool. **To make suet paste:** sieve **flour**, **baking powder** and pinch of **salt** into bowl. Mix two **suets** then fold in the **water** to form fairly firm **paste**. Allow **paste** to rest for about 20 mins. Roll out **paste** and line moulds, keeping some spare for lids. When **meat** filling is cold, fill moulds making sure you don't overfill with too much liquid. Then cover with lids made from remaining **paste**. Press lid and lining together and cover with buttered foil.

Cooking time:

To cook, stand the puddings in a steamer or pan of water (Half filled). Cover and steam for approximately 1½ hours. The liquid left from the meat casserole can be re-boiled, passed through a sieve and used to accompany the puddings. Serves 6 people.

Top 3 Steak & Ale Pies

The Pear Tree Inn, Woodhouse Eaves, Leicestershire

Steak & Ale Pie

Ingredients for filling:

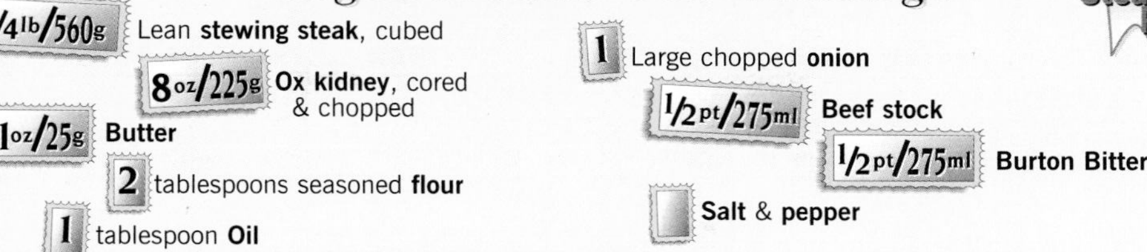

- 1/4lb/560g Lean **stewing steak**, cubed
- 8oz/225g **Ox kidney**, cored & chopped
- 1oz/25g **Butter**
- 2 tablespoons seasoned **flour**
- 1 tablespoon **Oil**
- 1 Large chopped **onion**
- 1/2pt/275ml **Beef stock**
- 1/2pt/275ml **Burton Bitter**
- **Salt** & **pepper**

Ingredients for topping:

- 8oz/225g flour
- 1/4 teaspoon salt
- 2oz/50g lard
- 2oz/50g butter
- cold water to mix

Method for filling:

Toss **steak** and **kidney** on well-seasoned **flour**. Fry in hot **butter** and **oil** until **meat** is browned. Remove to plate. Add **onion** to remaining **butter**. Fry gently until pale golden. Replace **meat** and pour over **ale** and **stock**. Bring to boil, lower heat, cover and simmer for 1 3/4 to 2 hours, or until **meat** is tender. Leave until cold.

Method for topping:

Mix together all ingredients to make basic shortcrust pastry. Roll out half pastry and line 9" pie dish.Trim surplus pastry, roll out remaining pastry for lid. Place cold meat mixture into centre. Moisten edges with water. Cover with pastry lid, trim and decorate if wished. Pinch edges and brush with milk.

Cooking time and oven temp:

Bake at Gas Mark 7/Electric 220°C, for 30-35 minutes or until golden brown. Serves 6 people.

The Plough Inn, Kelmscot, Gloucestershire

Steak & Ale Pie

Ingredients for filling:

- 3lb/1.35kg diced **chuck** steak
- 2 large quartered **onions**
- 2 **bayleaves**
- 1 teaspoon dried **thyme**
- 1pt/570ml **Guinness**
- 1 **Orange**
- 3/4pt/450ml **beef stock**
- 8oz/225g chopped **mushrooms**
- **beef dripping**

Ingredients for topping:

- 12oz/350g **self-raising flour**
- 8oz/225g **suet**
- **water**
- **salt**
- 1 **egg** - slightly beaten

Method for filling:

Brown **chuck steak** in **beef dripping** a small amount at a time. Brown **onions**. Add **bay leaves**, **thyme**, and pared **orange peel**. Add **flour** and cook for 1 minute. Add **orange juice, Guinness, stock, salt** and **pepper**, and cook for approx 1 hour until meat is tender. Pour into large pie dish.

Method for topping:

Sift **salt** and **flour**. Add **suet** and mix with **water** until combined and still quite dry. Top pie dish with **pastry**. Brush with **egg**.

Cooking time and oven temp:

Gas Mark 6/Electric (centigrade) 200 for 30 minutes or until pastry browned. Serves 6 people.

Cairnbaan Inn, Cairnbaan, Argyll & Bute

Fish Pie with Cheese and Paprika Tatties

Ingredients for filling:

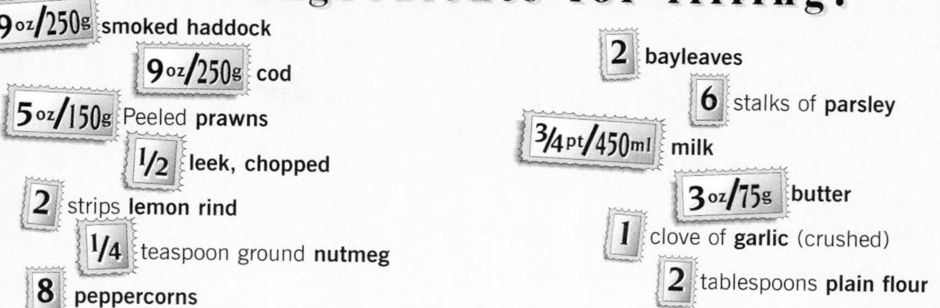

- 9oz/250g **smoked haddock**
- 9oz/250g **cod**
- 5oz/150g Peeled **prawns**
- 1/2 **leek, chopped**
- 2 strips **lemon rind**
- 1/4 teaspoon ground **nutmeg**
- 8 **peppercorns**
- 2 **bayleaves**
- 6 stalks of **parsley**
- 3/4pt/450ml **milk**
- 3oz/75g **butter**
- 1 clove of **garlic** (crushed)
- 2 tablespoons **plain flour**

Ingredients for topping:

- 6 medium sized peeled **potatoes**
- 1/4 **cabbage** (shredded)
- 5oz/150g **butter**
- 1/2 cup of chopped **spring onions**
- 1 tablespoon chopped **parsley**
- 1 tablespoon **sweet paprika**
- 5oz/150g Grated **Cheddar cheese**
- **cream**

Method for filling:

Place the **fish** in a pan and half the **leeks**, **lemon rind**, **nutmeg**, **peppercorns**, and **bay leaves**. Pour in the **milk**, bring to the boil, then turn down and allow to simmer uncovered over a low heat for about 5 minutes or until the **fish** is only just cooked. Carefully remove the **fish** and discard the **lemon rind**, save the **stock** for the sauce. Melt the **butter** in a separate pan and add the crushed **garlic** and the remainder of the **leeks**, and cook over a low heat until the **leeks** become soft. Sprinkle the **flour** over the mixture blending until it becomes smooth. Add the **fish stock** and the **milk**, stirring all the time until it comes to the boil and thickens, reduce the heat and continue to cook for about another minute. Flake the **fish** into chunky pieces and fold it all gently into the **sauce** and check for **seasoning**.

Method for topping:

Cut the **potatoes** into quarters and cook in boiling **salted water** for 15 minutes or until soft. Drain and mash the **potatoes**, seasoning to taste. Wash and shred the **cabbage** and cook in a little boiling **salted water** with the **spring onions** for about 10/15 minutes. Remove the **cabbage** and **spring onions** from the pan and drain well. Combine with the mashed **potatoes** and add the **cheese** and a little **cream** and mix well to achieve a creamy consistency. Pour the **fish** and sauce mixture into a 2 litre shallow casserole dish and spread the mashed **potato** and **cabbage** mixture on top of the **fish** using a fork to create a pattern. Then sprinkle the **paprika** on top and bake in the oven. Sprinkle with chopped **parsley** and serve with crusty bread a chilled glass of Muscadet.

Cooking time and oven temp:

Gas Mark 4/Electric (centigrade) 180 for 20 minutes or until golden brown. Serves 6 people.

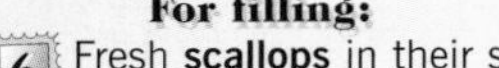

The Froize Inn, Chillesford, Suffolk
Fish Pie

Ingredients:

For filling:

- 6 Fresh **scallops** in their shell. Meat removed
- 24 **Mussels** steamed in their shells with beards removed, then taken out of shell
- 48 Fresh peeled **prawns**
- 8oz/225g **Plaice**
- 8oz/225g **Cod**
- 8oz/225g **Halibut**
- 8oz/225g **Brill**

For béchamel sauce:

- 10 fl oz/300ml full cream **milk**
- 1 1/4oz/30g **butter**
- 3/4oz/20g **plain flour**
- **salt** & **pepper**
- 1 thick **onion**
- 1 **bay leaf**
- 2 fresh **parsley** sprigs
- 2-3 **carrot** slices
- 5 black **peppercorns**

For chicken stock:

- 6lb/2.7kg raw **chicken** carcasses (chopped)
- 10pts/6ltrs cold **water**
- 3 **celery** stalks
- 1 **leek**
- 1 large **onion**
- 2 **carrots**
- 1/2 whole head of **garlic**

For topping:

- 8oz/225g **wholemeal flour**
- 3/4 teaspoon **salt**
- 3/4 teaspoon **sugar**
- 3oz/75g unsalted **butter**
- 1 **egg yolk** beaten
- 1 tablespoon cold **milk**

Methods:

Preparation:

Preheat oven to 200°C / 400°F, Gas Mark 6. Take a large round dish and layer the bottom with the chopped **white fish** (raw) then place a layer of the **prawns** and **mussels**. Arrange **scallops** so everyone will get one when the pie is served. Mix half the **chicken stock** with half the **béchamel sauce** and pour over the fish. Sprinkle with **parsley** and **dill**. Lay the pastry over the pie. Place a pastry fish over every scallop and finish with egg wash. Cook in oven for approx. 20 minutes until fish is cooked and pastry browned. Garnish with fresh coriander and a twist of lemon.

For béchamel sauce:

Put **milk** into pan with **onion**, **bay leaf**, **parsley**, **carrots** and **peppercorns**. Bring very slowly to boil then reduce heat radically and leave to infuse gently for about 10 minutes. Strain and discard flavourings. Melt **butter** in heavy based saucepan. Stir in **flour** and stir over a low heat for about 1 minute. Take off heat and gradually stir in **milk**, a spoonful at a time first, until sauce is runny. Tip in rest of **milk** and stir again. Return to heat and bring gently to boil, stirring. Simmer for at least 10 minutes, stirring frequently. The correct consistency is when sauce will coat back of a spoon. Season with **salt** and **pepper**.

For chicken stock:

Place **chicken carcasses** in large pot, cover with cold **water**, bring to boil and then skim. Keep **vegetables** whole but peel if necessary. Tie **celery** and **leek** together with string. Add all **vegetables** and **garlic** to pot, then bring back to boil. Skim then leave to simmer uncovered for four hours. Pass through fine sieve. The stock should be a light amber colour and clear.

For topping:

Sift **flour** into mixing bowl with **salt**. Stir in **sugar**, cut **butter** into small pieces and add them. Using your fingers, rub together dry ingredients and **butter** until mixture resembles breadcrumbs. Add **egg** and **milk** and bring together to make dough. Wrap in clingfilm and leave one hour in refrigerator.
Serves 6 people.

Cook & Barker Inn, Newton-on-the-Moor, Northumberland

Fish Pie

Ingredients for filling:

- ½lb/750g each of **salmon** & **halibut**
- To garnish **mussels, crayfish** and **prawns (cooked)**
- ½pt/275ml **fish stock**
- 1/4pt/150ml **Chablis**
- 4oz/100g **shallots**
- 3 tablespoons of **parsley** (chopped)
- 1/2 **lemon**
- 6 tablespoons of **crème fraîche**
- 6 **pastry fleurons**

Ingredients for topping:

- ½ oz/125g **plain flour**
- 4 **egg yolks**
- 2 tablespoons of **chives** (chopped)
- **white pepper**
- /150g **Gruyère cheese**
- 1 fresh **spinach** leaf
- 7oz/200g **Cheddar cheese** (grated)
- 4½ oz/125g **butter**
- 2 tablespoons of **crème fraîche**

Method for filling:

Place **fish** with **buttered shallots**. Bring to a simmer with **fish stock, lemon juice** and **Chablis**. Remove fish when cooked through to a warmed baking dish, and reduce liquid and add the **crème fraîche** and **parsley**. Pour reduced sauce over fish

Method for topping:

Melt **butter**, add **flour** and mix in the **Cheddar cheese**, **spinach, egg yolks** and **crème fraîche**.
Cover the **fish** and add the **Gruyère cheese** and bake until golden.
Garnish with **crayfish**, **prawns**, **mussels** and **chives**.

Cooking time and oven temp:

Cook for 15 minutes at Gas Mark 6
Electric (centigrade) 200.
Serves 6 people.

From STEAK and ALE to SHELLFISH and CHABLIS

The English pub is unique: pub, inn, tavern, hostelry, boozer, local, ale house, there are as many varieties of this great institution as we have words to describe them.

The public house is part of our history - descended from both the ancient Saxon ale house where beer was brewed on the premises, and the 13th-century taverns that sold only wine. Over the centuries that distinction has blurred and it is due to that almost inherent ability to change, to reflect the mood of the times, that the pub has survived.

Conjure up an image of your ideal pub and it probably comes thatched, walls bulging heavily with age, a real log fire blazing in the inglenook and not a single beam left unexposed in the ceiling. And it does exist - in the past cottages, farmhouses, blacksmith's forges, even monastic buildings were turned into pubs, but later versions of the genre show equally adept flexibility: the great Victorian/Edwardian gin palaces, the roadside pit-stops of the 20s and 30s, the modern city-centre boozers.

And now change is in the air again. There is no doubt that the Campaign for Real Ale (CAMRA) will be remembered as one of the great British acts of people power versus big business in the 20th century. But as trend setters CAMRA folk were always rather lacking - the beard and sandals-with-socks image that had appeared so worthy and, well, venerable in the early days is not the sort of image to appeal to a design-conscious crowd about to enter a new millennium. Pubs are now sharper, switched on, with beer an option not a fact of life.

Spearheaded by such enlightened individuals as John Hoskins of the East Anglian-based Huntsbridge group who introduced the chef-patron concept and classy wine lists, and renowned chefs such as Steven Doherty who brought a touch of Le Gavroche to his cooking at the Punchbowl Inn in Crosthwaite, Cumbria, pub food is making a considerable impact.

Not a bad thing considering. Who wants to return to that not too far off time when pub food was no better than turd-like sausages ageing on a heated food server, or worse still, the gallon container of pickled onions?

Indeed, for young chefs wanting to start out on their own, a pub is often the only option. To establish or buy into a

restaurant is an expensive business. A pub offers the more cost effective option - while you are establishing your reputation in the restaurant; drinks, bar snacks and, perhaps, a few letting rooms are keeping the bank manager happy.

This has proved a popular route. So much so that the main culinary movement in the final year of the 20th century has been caused by the rush of young chefs to build their solo careers in pubs while the growth of new restaurants, especially outside London, has remained slow.

Take Franck and Kalpana Peigné, a young couple who took over The Blewbury Inn, Blewbury, Oxfordshire in late 1998. To Franck the Blewbury was an obvious move from the three AA Rosetted Lygon Arms at Broadway. A well-heeled location meant the right customers for his 'good food in a relaxed atmosphere', which roughly translates as marinated strips of chicken in five spice with Caesar salad topped with croûtons in the bar and medallions of beef fillet with spinach fondue, shallot confit and Stilton crust in the restaurant.

Or Jonathan Harrison, a former 3 AA Rosetted chef from the Swallow Hotel, Birmingham who was starting his first solo venture just as we went to press. He initially looked at restaurants but the price was against him and he turned to pubs. The Sandpiper Inn at Leyburn in North Yorkshire has given him the right mix of bar, restaurant and letting rooms to make it all viable.

And what of the current restaurant capital of the world? London, often the vanguard in such situations, has been, surprisingly, well to the rear of this food movement. When the breathalyser sucked the life from country pubs there was no choice - darts and the men-only atmosphere had to go, to be replaced by blackboard menus, wine lists, and an emancipated attitude towards women. London pubs, better served by public transport, carried on as they were: boozy, smoky, and still serving the 'tavern fayre' so loved by the British catering industry.

But finally, demands for imaginative food (one-dish grazing rather than three-course blow-outs) and decent wines have been heard. Gastropubs were born. The Anglesea Arms in Chiswick is a case in point. Peer through the windows at the handpumps dispensing Marstons Pedigree and

Theakstons and it could be any corner pub. Within, the low-budget minimalism of bare floor, second-hand tables, DIY paintwork, is offset by breezy young staff, the latest wines, and a kitchen delivering the likes of chargrilled chump of lamb, watercress and chips 'paloise'.

Or The Cow in Notting Hill, which combines the expertise of a Conran - son Tom - and 'the best elements of the Irish bar, French brasserie and English pub'. What you get is lots of seafood and the likes of ham hock, Savoy cabbage and tarragon and mash with salsa verde, while London Pride and ESB keep up the pub image.

Quality is important: not just food and drink, but quality of atmosphere and service, as well. The pub has to be a place you want to spend time in. With this in mind St Peter's Brewery must be one of the success stories of the last few years. It has under its wing two individual pubs - the De la Pole Arms in Wingfield, and the Cornwallis Arms at Brome - both in Suffolk, with an outpost in the Jerusalem Tavern at Clerkenwell in London; the combination of food, wine, atmosphere, service is backed up by imaginative beers - a revival of English fruit beers, stouts, porters, and old fashioned spiced ales. Their bottled ales are sold in very stylish replica 18th-century bottles.

And a brand new pub style is emerging. The glass, steel and granite hard-edged surfaces for the new breed of micro-breweries that combine sleek-lined bars, restaurants and own-brewed beers under one roof are breaking that traditional mould and reaping huge rewards.

Mash & Air (based on brewing terms) pioneered the concept in Manchester before opening Mash in London. The open to-view-brew tanks form part of the design concept, the beers are unusual, and the food as new wave as the wine on offer.

The Freedom Brewing Company picked up the challenge and offer an unprepossessing façade as a foil to their state-of-the-art interior which is dominated by the vast copper brewing vats that provide some superb new-style beers for the increasingly popular bar. Going out for a pint is a lot more exciting these days.

Elizabeth Carter

SEAFOOD - Perfect on any Millennium Menu

There are many great pubs and inns around the country proving that seafood is the ideal choice on any Millennium menu. There is plenty to choose from, with hearty traditional favourites, like fish and chips and seafood pies, or exciting new dishes inspired by Thai, Mediterranean and fusion cooking.

The Sea Fish Industry Authority has sponsored the search for the **Best Seafood Pub in Britain 2000** to highlight where all these great pubs are and to award this prestigious title to the very best we found. We have also awarded special titles to the best seafood pubs in seven regions covering the whole of the country, so you have a wealth to choose from.

Wherever you are travelling you can find out where the nearest seafood pub is by using this Guide. These pubs are marked with the "Good Seafood Served Here" symbol and have all been visited by AA inspectors to ensure that they have a wide range of seafood on the menu. The winners of our Best Seafood Pub competition are further highlighted in the Guide by having a light blue background to their description sections.

Whether you are a devoted fish fan, interested in healthy eating or just looking for a change, you will find that the range of seafood on offer nowadays combines the very best of British traditional and world wide cuisine.

Try the fish - Bon appetit!

Best
on the
Millennium
Menu-
Feast on Fish
Find the perfect seafood pub by looking
for the special symbol in this guide.
SEAFISH
Sea Fish Industry Authority,
18 Logie Mill, Logie Green Road, Edinburgh EH7 4HG
Tel: 0131 558 3331 Fax: 0131 558 1442
E-mail: development@seafish.co.uk

THE BEST SEAFOOD PUBS IN BRITAIN

SPONSORED BY THE SEA FISH INDUSTRY AUTHORITY

NATIONAL WINNER & North Regional winner

The Foresters Arms
Carlton
Leyburn
North Yorkshire DL8 4BB
☎ 01969 640272

REGIONAL WINNERS

West Country

The Harrow Inn
Little Bedwyn
Marlborough
Wiltshire SN8 3JP
☎ 01672 870871

South & South East England

Bryce's at the Old School House
Ockley
Dorking
Surrey RH5 5TH
☎ 01306 627430

London

The Grapes
76 Narrow Street
Limehouse
London E14 8BP
☎ 0171 9874396

Central & East Anglia

The Hoste Arms
The Green
Burnham Market
Norfolk PE31 8HD
☎ 01328 738777

Wales & The Marches

The Penhelig Arms
Aberdyfi
Gwynedd LL35 0LT
☎ 01654 767215

Scotland

Applecross Inn
Shore Street
Applecross
Highland IV54 8LR
☎ 01520 744262

Hotel Services

The AA Hotel Booking Service - Now you have a free, simple way to reserve a place to stay for a week, weekend, or a one-night stopover.

Do you want to book somewhere in the Lake District that has leisure facilities; a city-centre hotel in Glasgow with parking facilities, or do you need accommodation near Dover which is handy for the Eurotunnel? The AA Booking Service can take the hassle out of booking the right place for you.

If you are touring round the UK or Ireland, simply give the AA Hotel Booking Service your list of overnight stops, and from one phone call all your accommodation can be booked for you.

Telephone 0870 5050505

Office hours
Monday - Friday 9am - 6pm
Saturday 9am - 1pm
The service is not available Sundays or Bank Holidays

Full listings of AA recognised accommodation available through the Hotel Booking Service can be found and booked at the AA's Internet Site:

http://www.theaa.co.uk/hotels

Maltsters Arms, Chapel Amble, Cornwall

Libbe's Fish Pie

Ingredients for filling:

- 1lb/450g skinned **white fish** fillet (**whiting, ling, haddock** or **cod**), pin boned and cut into 1 inch square pieces
- 1lb/450g skinned **salmon** fillet, prepared as white fish
- 1/2lb/225g peeled **prawns**
- 1/2lb/225g **scallops**. Cleaned with corals intact
- 3 sticks of **celery,** finely chopped
- 1 bunch of **spring onions** finely chopped using 2 inches of greens ends
- 2 cloves of **garlic**, crushed and smoothed to paste chopped with **salt**
- 1 medium sized **onion** finely chopped
- 2oz/50g **butter**
- 2 **lemons**, zested and juice squeezed
- 1oz/25g **flour**
- 5fl oz/150ml **fish liquor** or **stock**
- 5fl oz/150ml **white wine**
- 7fl oz/350ml double or whipping **cream**
- 1 **bayleaf**
- pinch of **cayenne pepper**
- few drops of **Tabasco**
- 1 tablespoon chopped fresh **parsley**
- **salt** and **black pepper**
- 3 hard boiled **eggs**, sliced
- 1 dessertspoon **olive oil**
- 1 tablespoon **Dijon mustard**

Ingredients for topping:

- 5 large peeled **potatoes**, cooked and mashed
- 2oz/50g **butter**
- 4 tablespoons **cream**
- 8oz/225g **Cornish Yarg cheese**
- 6 tablespoons **breadcrumbs**
- **salt** and **pepper** to taste

Method for filling:

Using a heavy based saucepan, melt **butter** and heat **olive oil** over a low heat, sweat the **celery, garlic, onion, spring onion** until soft. Add the **flour** and cook over a medium heat for approx 1 minute. Add the **stock, white wine, lemon juice** and **Dijon mustard**, cook over a medium heat for approx 5 minutes until the **flour** is cooked in. Turn heat down to low and add the **parsley, seasoning, cayenne pepper, Tabasco, bayleaf** and **cream** (Do not allow to boil). Carefully fold in the raw **white fish and salmon, scallops** and **prawns**. Keep on a low heat for 10-15 minutes until fish is cooked. Add the sliced hard boiled **eggs** and carefully spoon into individual oven-proof serving dishes.

Method for topping:

Add the **cream, salt, pepper** and grated **Cornish Yarg cheese** into the mashed **potato** and beat well. Pipe onto the individual filled dishes and sprinkle with **breadcrumbs.** Serve with a crisp green salad or with garlic bread or granary bread as required.

Cooking time & oven temp:

Gas Mark 2 for 20 minutes
Electric (Centigrade) 150.
Serves 6 people.

Bristol

BRISTOL Bristol *Map 03 ST57*

Highbury Vaults
BRISTOL
164 St Michaels Hill, Cotham BS2 8DE
☎ 0117 9733203
Situated on the outskirts of the city, where public hangings were held, this popular hostelry was once the lock-up for condemned prisoners. (Its original owner came from Highbury, London, hence the name.) All-in-one bowl dishes, such as chilli, curry and casseroles, are offered from a daily menu. **Principal beers:** Smiles Golden, Best & Heritage, Brains SA.
Directions Take main road to Cotham from inner ring dual carriageway
Brewery/Company Smiles
Open 12-11 (Sun 12-10.30)
Bar food 12-2 5.30-8.30 Av main course £3

Cornwall & Isles of Scilly

BOSCASTLE Cornwall & Isles of Scilly *Map 02 SX09*

The Wellington Hotel
BOSCASTLE
The Harbour PL35 0AQ
☎ 01840 250202
Turreted 16th-century coaching inn set in National Trust countryside a few minutes' walk from the Elizabethan harbour and coastal footpaths. Roast chicken, beef curry and steak and kidney pie are popular bar meals, while the restaurant might offer lamb tagine, and brill in vermouth. **Principal beers:** Flowers IPA, St Austell HSD & Dartmoor Best, Whitbread Fuggles Imperial, Wadworth 6X.

Directions A30 onto A395, then A39, R onto B3314, R onto B3266
Brewery/Company Free House
Open 11-3 6-11 (Sun 11-11)
Bar food 12-2.30 6-9.30 Av main course £4.95
Restaurant 7-9.30 Av 3 course à la carte £22.50 Av 3 course fixed price £22.50
Accommodation (Min) s£32 d£58

CHAPEL AMBLE Cornwall & Isles of Scilly *Map 02 SW97*

The Maltsters Arms
CHAPEL AMBLE
PL27 6EU ☎ 01208 812473
Rambling, whitewashed 16th-century inn, situated in a peaceful village close to the Camel estuary. Specialising in fresh fish the menu may list baked medallions of red mullet with garlic, lemon and langoustines, and sea bass on Cornish samphire with Thai curry sauce. Other choices include lamb hotpot and fillet steak with whisky and horseradish sauce. **Principal beers:** Sharp's Cornish Coaster, Fuller's London Pride, Morland Ruddles County, Young's.

Directions From Wadebridge take A39 then 1st L, B3314.Village on R
Brewery/Company Free House
Open 10.30-2.30 6-11 (Sun 12-2.30,7-10.30)
Bar food 12-2 6.30-10 Av main course £5
Restaurant 12-2 6.30-10 Av 3 course à la carte £18

CONSTANTINE Cornwall & Isles of Scilly *Map 02 SW72*

Trengilly Wartha Inn
CONSTANTINE
Nancenoy TR11 5RP ☎ 01326 340332
An old Cornish farmhouse, now a popular country inn located in a beautiful and tranquil area. One of the country's top listed pubs, it offers West Country ales, decent wines and good

food. Competently cooked dishes may include crab cakes with wine sauce, Thai-style sea bass, red pepper lasagne, and pear and blue cheese puff. **Principal beers:** Sharp's Cornish Coaster, St Austell HSD, Skinners, Exmoor Gold.
Directions SW of Falmouth
Brewery/Company Free House
Open 11-3 6.30-11
Bar food 12-2.30 6.30-10.0 Av main course £7
Restaurant 7.30-10. Av 3 course à la carte £22.50 Av 3 course fixed price £22.50
Accommodation (Min) s£39 d£62

CUBERT *Map 02 SW75*
Cornwall & Isles of Scilly

The Smuggler's Den Inn
CUBERT
Trebellan TR8 5PY ☎ 01637 830209
Old-world thatched pub dating from the 16th century, set in a beautiful valley not far from the sea. The kitchen is supplied daily with fresh produce, and a specials board supplements the lunch and evening menus, offering a good choice of fresh fish, seafood and steaks. **Principal beers:** Greene King Abbot Ale, Skinner Cornish Knocker, Sharp's Doom Bar, Cotleigh.
Directions From Newquay take A3075 to Cubert crossroads, then R, then L signed Trebellan, 0.5m
Brewery/Company Free House
Open 11-3 6-11
Bar food 12-2.30 6-9.30
Restaurant 12-2.30 6-9.30

DULOE *Map 02 SX25*
Cornwall & Isles of Scilly

Ye Olde Plough House Inn NEW
DULOE
PL14 4PN ☎ 01503 262050
Family-run, 18th-century inn tucked away in a rural village close to the coast. Specialities served in the neat, slate-floored bars include meat cooked on hot stones at the table, and fresh fish - turbot with mussel provencale and hollandaise. Further choices range from battered cod to beef and Stilton pie and roast guinea fowl. **Principal beers:** Sharps Doom Bar, Butcombe, Bass.
Directions A38 to Dobwalls, take turning signed Looe

Brewery/Company Free House
Open 12-2.30 6.30-11
Bar food 12-2 6.30-9.30 Av main course £4.95
Restaurant 12-2 6.30-9.30 Av 3 course à la carte £13

DUNMERE *Map 02 SX06*
Cornwall & Isles of Scilly

The Borough Arms
DUNMERE
PL31 2RD ☎ 01208 73118
A favoured watering-hole among walkers and cyclists following the Camel Trail from Bodmin to Padstow. Right on the trail and close to the River Camel, it offers good-value pub food. Straightforward dishes range from filled jacket potatoes and steak sandwich, to grills and breaded fish. **Principal beers:** Bass, Sharp's Cornish Coaster, Worthingtons, Boddingtons.
Directions From A30 take A389 to Wadebridge, pub approx 1m from Bodmin
Brewery/Company Greenalls
Open 11-11 (Sun 12-10.30)
Bar food 12-2.15 6.30-9.15 Av main course £4.50
Restaurant 12-2.15 6.30-9.15 Av 3 course à la carte £14 Av 3 course fixed price £10.50

EGLOSHAYLE *Map 02 SX07*
Cornwall & Isles of Scilly

The Earl of St Vincent
EGLOSHAYLE
PL27 6HT ☎ 01208 814807
Dating from the Middle Ages, with colourful floral displays and a collection of old clocks, the Earl of St Vincent is named after Sir John Jervis, the Earl of St Vincent and Nelson's superior officer. There is a comprehensive menu with specialities like tournedos Rossini, chicken in leek and Stilton sauce, and fresh fish. **Principal beers:** St Austell Tinners Ale & HSD.
Brewery/Company St Austell Brewery
Open 11-3 6.30-11

FOWEY *Map 02 SX15*
Cornwall & Isles of Scilly

The Ship Inn
FOWEY
Trafalgar Square PL23 1AZ
☎ 01726 832230
John Rashleigh, cousin to Drake and Raleigh, built this traditional inn before

contd.

setting sail to defeat the Spanish Armada. Quick snacks, an open sandwich selection and a range of special salads form part of the menu, while main courses feature local mussels, vegetarian casserole and locally produced sausages. **Principal beers:** St Austell Tinners Ale & HSD.

Directions From A30,take B3269 & A390.
Brewery/Company St Austell Brewery
Open 11-11
Bar food 12-2 6-9 Av main course £4.95
Accommodation (Min) s£19.50 d£39

GUNNISLAKE Cornwall & Isles of Scilly Map 02 SX47

The Rising Sun Inn NEW
GUNNISLAKE
Calstock Rd PL18 9BX ☎ 01822 832201

Quaint 17th-century pub with glorious gardens and fine views over the Tamar Valley. Cottagey interior featuring a fascinating collection of china, a wide range of real ales, and home-cooked food. Typical dishes may include filled baguettes and jacket potatoes, pork tenderloin, leg of lamb steak, and traditional Cornish pasties. **Principal beers:** Bass, Sharp's Cornish Coaster.

Directions From Tavistock take A390 to Gunnislake, pub is through village and quarter mile on L
Brewery/Company Free House
Open 12-2.30 5-11
Bar food 12-2 7-9 Av main course £5
Restaurant 12-2 7-9 Av 3 course à la carte £11
Accommodation (Min) s£38 d£55

GUNWALLOE Cornwall & Isles of Scilly Map 02 SW62

The Halzephron Inn
GUNWALLOE
TR12 7QB ☎ 01326 240406

'Halzephron,' an old Cornish word, is derived from Als Yfferin meaning 'Cliffs of Hell.' With fine views across Mounts Bay, this 15th-century pub offers good food prepared from fresh local produce. Expect to find smoked salmon and avocado mousse, beef stew with mustard dumplings, excellent crab sandwiches, and lemon sole on the varied menu. Delightful small bedrooms. **Principal beers:** Sharp's Own & Doom Bar, St Austell Dartmoor Best.

Directions 3m S of Helston on A3083, R to Gunwalloe. Then through village, inn is on L overlooking Mount's Bay.
Brewery/Company Free House
Open 11-2.30 6.30-11 (Sun 6.30-10.30)
Bar food 12-2 7-9.30 Av main course £8
Restaurant 12-2 7-9.30 Av 3 course à la carte £15
Accommodation (Min) s£35 d£64

GWEEK Cornwall & Isles of Scilly Map 02 SW72

The Gweek Inn
GWEEK
TR12 6TU ☎ 01326 221502

Traditional village pub and restaurant, situated at the mouth of the Helford River close to the National Seal Sanctuary. A full range of food is served, from baguettes and basket meals to dishes such as venison forestière and devilled seafood rösti. There is also a blackboard listing home-cooked specials. **Principal beers:** Flowers IPA, Morland Old Speckled Hen, Bass, Greenalls Original.

Directions 2m E of Helston near Seal Sanctuary
Brewery/Company Inn Partnership
Open 12-3 6.30-11
Bar food 12-2.15 6.30-9 Av main course £5
Restaurant 12-2.15 6.30-9 Av 3 course à la carte £15

HELFORD *Map 02 SW72*
Cornwall & Isles of Scilly

Shipwright Arms
HELFORD
TR12 6JX ☎ 01326 231235
Superbly situated on the banks of the Helford River, this small thatched pub is especially popular in summer when customers relax on the three delightful terraces which lead down to the water's edge. Heavy nautical theme inside. Various ploughman's lunches and salads, while other dishes might include home-made pies and steaks. **Principal beers:** Castle Eden, Flowers IPA.
Directions A390 through Truro then A39 to Mabe Burnthouse, A394 to Helston, A3083 to Carminowe, E to Helford
Brewery/Company Free House
Open 11-2.30 6-11
Bar food 12-2 7-9 Av main course £4.75
Restaurant 12-2 7-9 Av 3 course à la carte £13.75

HELFORD PASSAGE *Map 02 SW72*
Cornwall & Isles of Scilly

Ferryboat Inn
HELFORD PASSAGE
TR11 5LB ☎ 01326 250625
Historic pub and eating house on the Helford River, opposite the ferry that runs daily across the river to Helford village. Bar snacks are served along with specials such as seafood lasagne or home-made pies. Local plaice, shell on king prawns, and mixed grills are available in the restaurant. **Principal beers:** St Austell HSD, Tinners & Trelawneys Pride.
Directions From A39 at Falmouth, head toward River Helford
Brewery/Company St Austell Brewery
Open 11-2.30 6.30-10.30 (Summer 11-11)
Bar food 12-2 6.30-9 Av main course £5.50
Restaurant 12-2 6.30-9 Av 3 course à la carte £12

HELSTON *Map 02 SW62*
Cornwall & Isles of Scilly

Blue Anchor Inn
HELSTON
59 Coinagehall St TR13 8EX
☎ 01326 562821
One of the oldest pubs in Britain to brew its own beer, this unpretentious, thatched pub dates from the 15th century when its was a monks' rest home. Sample excellent ales in the low-ceilinged bars, tour the brewery, and tuck into a home-made pasty, fish pie, lamb hotpot, or a crusty filled roll.
Principal beers: Blue Anchor Middle, Best, Special & Extra Special.
Directions A30 to Penzance, then Helston signposted
Brewery/Company Free House
Open 11-11 (Sun 12-10.30)
Bar food 12-4 Av main course £2.95

KINGSAND *Map 02 SX45*
Cornwall & Isles of Scilly

The Halfway House Inn
KINGSAND
Fore St PL10 1NA ☎ 01752 822279
Although no longer the border between Devon and Cornwall, this traditional low-ceilinged pub is still the official border between the conservation villages of Kingsand and Cawsand. Good bar food ranges from fish soup and crab puff with pesto for starters, to roast garlic monkfish, sea bass in pimento sauce and venison casserole, followed by lemon tart. **Principal beers:** Sharp's Doom Bar, Flowers Original, Bass Boddingtons.
Directions from either Torpoint Ferry or Tamar Bridge follow signs to Mount Edgcombe
Brewery/Company Free House
Open 12-4 7-11.20
Bar food 12-2 7-9.30 Av main course £5.30
Restaurant 12-2 7-9.30 Av 3 course à la carte £15
Accommodation (Min) s£25 d£50

LAMORNA *Map 02 SW42*
Cornwall & Isles of Scilly

Lamorna Wink
LAMORNA
TR19 6XH ☎ 01736 731566
Seek out this homely local after completing an invigorating cliff walk along the stunning coastal path. Just a short stroll from the tiny cove, it is a welcome watering-hole, offering simple food such as filled jacket potatoes, fresh local crab, home-made quiche, and locally-made pasties.
Directions 4m along B3315 towards Lands End, then 0.5m to turning on L
Brewery/Company Greenalls
Open 11-11 (evening food summer only)
Bar food 11-3 6-9 Av main course £3.50

contd.

LANLIVERY Cornwall & Isles of Scilly
Map 02 SX05

The Crown Inn
LANLIVERY

PL30 5BT ☎ 01208 872707

12th-century longhouse with three-foot thick exterior walls, large inglenook fireplace and a priest hole. Home-cooked food is served including plenty of fresh fish, rack of lamb and rump steak. The fisherman's lunch is a feature in the bar - a snack of smoked mackerel, salad and bread roll. **Principal beers:** Sharp's Own, Coaster & Doom Bar, Morland Old Speckled Hen, Bass.

Directions From Bodmin take A30 S,follow signs 'Lanhydrock',L at mini r'about.3m take A390, Lanlivery 2nd R

Brewery/Company Free House

Open 11-3 6-11

Bar food 12-2.15 7-9.15 Av main course £4.50

Restaurant 12-2.15 7-9.15 Av 3 course à la carte £14.75

Accommodation (Min) s£27.50 d£45

LOSTWITHIEL Cornwall & Isles of Scilly
Map 02 SX15

Royal Oak Inn
LOSTWITHIEL

Duke St PL22 0AH ☎ 01208 872552

A 13th-century inn with an underground tunnel, reputed to connect the Royal Oak's cellar to the dungeons of Restormel Castle. Dishes include a daily curry, Mrs Hine's cow pie (steak, kidney and real ale), Cornish baked mullet, and duck cooked in orange and ginger sauce. Good sandwiches, salads and ploughman's. **Principal beers:** Bass, Fuller's London Pride, Marston's Pedigree, Sharp's Own.

Directions From Exeter take A30 to Bodmin then onto Lostwithiel or from Plymouth take A38 towards Bodmin then L onto A390 to Lostwithiel

Brewery/Company Free House

Open 11-11

Bar food 12-2 6.30-9.30 Av main course £6.75

Restaurant 12-2 6.30-9.30 Av 3 course à la carte £12

Accommodation (Min) s£33.50 d£55

Ship Inn
LOSTWITHIEL

Lerryn PL22 0PT ☎ 01208 872374

Set in a beautiful riverside village, the 17th-century Ship has slate flagged floors, oak panelled walls and an open fire. The specialitiy is home-cooked pies, and there are lots, from steak and Guinness to leek, fennel and pepper croustade. **Principal beers:** Bass, Sharp's, Skinners, Otter Ale.

Directions 3m S of A390 at Lostwithiel

Brewery/Company Free House

Open 11.30-2.30 6-11

Bar food 12-2 6.30-9 Av main course £6

Restaurant 12-2 6.30-9

Accommodation (Min) s£20 d£40

LUDGVAN Cornwall & Isles of Scilly
Map 02 SW53

White Hart
LUDGVAN

Churchtown TR20 8EY ☎ 01736 740574

Early 14th-century pub with splendid views across St. Michael's Mount and Bay. The specials board typically features New Zealand green lipped mussels, cider braised pork, and toad in the hole. Also on offer are home-made pasta dishes, steak grills, and home-made treacle tart and carrot cake. **Principal beers:** Marston's Pedigree, Flowers IPA, Bass.

Directions From A30 take B3309 at Crowlas

Brewery/Company Greenalls

Open 11-2.30 6-11 (no food Mon eve Oct-Easter)

Bar food 12-2 7-9 Av main course £4.50

Restaurant 12-2 7-9

METHERELL
Cornwall & Isles of Scilly
Map 02 SX46

Carpenters Arms
METHERELL
PL17 8BJ ☎ 01579 350242
A 15th-century building, originally the carpenter's workshop for Cotehele House, with slate floors, an internal well, original beams and fireplace. Home-made steak and kidney pie, curry and lasagne are typical bar fare, with the likes of swordfish with bechamel sauce in the restaurant. **Principal beers:** Sharp's Cornish Coaster, St Austell Dartmoor Best, Skinner's Cornish Knocker Ale.
Directions From Saltash take A338 to Callington, then A390 to Tavistock, follow signs to pub
Brewery/Company Free House
Open 12-3 7-11
Bar food 12-3 7-11 Av main course £6
Restaurant 12-3 7-11 Av 3 course à la carte £12

MEVAGISSEY
Cornwall & Isles of Scilly
Map 02 SX04

Rising Sun Inn
MEVAGISSEY
Portmellon Cove PL26 6PL
☎ 01726 843235
Superbly situated 17th-century inn right on the beach at Portmellon Cove overlooking Chapel Point. There is a friendly bar with an open fire and a restaurant serving the same choice of home-made dishes, such as vegetable balti, seafood lasagne, pan-fried cod, and beef in Guinness. **Principal beers:** Wadworth 6X, Marston's Pedigree, Boddingtons.
Brewery/Company Free House
Open 11.30-3 6-11 (closed Oct-Easter)
Bar food 12-2 6.30-9 Av main course £4.50
Restaurant 12-2 6.30-9 Av 3 course à la carte £13
Accommodation (Min) s£29.50 d£49

MITHIAN
Cornwall & Isles of Scilly
Map 02 SW75

Miners Arms
MITHIAN
TR5 0QF ☎ 01872 552375
Interesting architectural features at this ancient inn include 17th-century decorative ceilings, wall paintings, and a hidden passage to the manor house, once used by monks in difficult times. Straightforward bar food includes chicken tikka masala, smoked haddock and prawn curry, vegetable lasagne, and seafood platter. **Principal beers:** Marston's Pedigree, Flowers IPA, Sharp's Doom Bar & Special.
Directions From A30 take B3277 to St Agnes. Take 1st R to Mithian
Brewery/Company Greenalls
Open 12-3 6-11
Bar food 12-2.30 6.30-9.30 Av main course £6

MORWENSTOW
Cornwall & Isles of Scilly
Map 02 SS21

The Bush Inn
MORWENSTOW
EX2 9SR ☎ 01288 331242
Once the haunt of smugglers and wreckers, this 13th-century pub features low beamed ceilings and lovely old wooden furniture, and enjoys a splendid hamlet location close to the coast path. Home-made soups, Bush Inn stew, ploughman's and pasties are always popular, as is the spotted dick for pudding. **Principal beers:** St Austell HSD.
Brewery/Company Free House
Open 12-3 7-11 (closed Mon)
Bar food 12-2

MOUSEHOLE
Cornwall & Isles of Scilly
Map 02 SW42

The Old Coastguard Hotel NEW
MOUSEHOLE
The Parade TR19 6PR
☎ 01736 731222
Set in sub-tropical gardens with views across Mounts Bay, this informal inn offers an interesting range of dishes, especially fresh fish. Check the chalkboard for specials like carrot and coriander soup, hake with avocado and chilli salsa, and mixed fish grill. Imaginative sandwiches and light bar meals like fishcakes, crab salad and nut and herb rissole.
Principal beers: Flowers Original, Wadworth 6X, Sharp's Doom Bar.
Directions A30 to Penzance, take coast road through Newlyn to Mousehole, pub is 1st building on L
Brewery/Company Free House
Open 12-11

contd.

Old Coastguard Hotel

Bar food 12-2.30 6-9.30 Av main course £5.95
Restaurant 6-9.30 Av 3 course à la carte £18.95 Av 3 course fixed price £18.95
Accommodation (Min) s£27 d£54

Ship Inn
MOUSEHOLE
TR19 6QX ☎ 01736 731234
An old-world inn, with low beams and granite floors, overlooking the harbour. Seafood landed at nearby Newlyn figures prominently, with dishes such as crab bisque, seafood platter and fisherman's lunch (smoked mackerel with salad and brown bread). Other options might be Thai turkey, or pork and cider casserole.
Principal beers: St Austell Trelawneys Pride, HSD & Tinners Ale.
Brewery/Company St Austell Brewery
Open 10.30-11
Bar food 12-2.30 6-9.30 Av main course £4.50
Restaurant 6-9.30 Av 3 course à la carte £15
Accommodation (Min) d£36

MYLOR BRIDGE Cornwall & Isles of Scilly *Map 02 SW83*

Pandora Inn
MYLOR BRIDGE
Restronguet Creek TR11 5ST
☎ 01326 372678
Delightfully situated on the shore of Restronguet Creek, this thatched 14th-century inn is popular with visiting yachtsmen. Good fresh seafood and local fish, including sea bass with anchovy and caper butter, scallops with spring onions, ginger and pak choi, and crab cakes highlight the menus. Further choices range from ham, leek and apricot pie, to pork fillet with apple and cider sauce.
Principal beers: St Austell Tinners Ale, HSD, Bass.

Directions North of Falmouth off the A39
Brewery/Company St Austell Brewery
Open 11-11 (Sun 12-10.30)
Bar food 12-2.30 7-9.30 Av main course £5.50
Restaurant 7-9.30 Av 3 course à la carte £19

PELYNT Cornwall & Isles of Scilly *Map 02 SX25*

Jubilee Inn
PELYNT
PL13 2JZ ☎ 01503 220312
Once known as the Axe Inn, this 16th-century pub changed its name in 1887 to commemorate 50 years of Queen Victoria's reign. Royal memorabilia, spiral staircase, and oak-beamed ceilings. Bar fare includes ploughman's, jacket potatoes and various seafood dishes. Restaurant main courses include pork with madeira and cream, prime fillet garni, and chef's specials. **Principal beers:** Bass, Dartmoor.

Directions take A390 signpsted St Austell at village of East Taphouse, turn L onto B3359 signposted Looe & Polperro. Jubilee Inn on left on leaving Pelynt
Brewery/Company Free House
Open 11-3 5-11

Bar food 11.30-3 5-10 Av main course £5.90
Restaurant 11.30-3 5-10 Av 3 course à la carte £16

PENDOGGETT *Map 02 SX07*
Cornwall & Isles of Scilly

The Cornish Arms
PENDOGGETT
PL30 3HH ☎ 01208 880263

A mile from Port Isaac and a rugged stretch of coast (excellent walks), this 16th-century coaching inn boasts flagstone floors, oak beams, open fires, and a good range of food, in particular fresh local seafood. Expect steak and mushroom pie, rack of lamb, various steaks and, perhaps, scallops, lobster, mackerel, monkfish and brill. **Principal beers:** Bass, Wadworth 6X, Cornish Rebellion, Skinner Betty Stoggs.
Directions From A30 Launceston, R onto A395, then L on to A39, then R onto B3314. Pub 7m along this road.
Brewery/Company Free House
Open 11-11 (Sun 12-10.30)
Bar food 12.30-2 6.30-9.30 Av main course £5
Restaurant 12.30-2 7-12 Av 3 course à la carte £20 Av 4 course fixed price £16.50
Accommodation (Min) s£35 d£49

PENZANCE *Map 02 SW43*
Cornwall & Isles of Scilly

The Turks Head Inn
PENZANCE
Chapel St TR18 4AF ☎ 01736 363093

The oldest pub in Penzance (13th century) and the first in England to be so named, after the Turks who invaded the town in 1233. Friendly, bustling bar serving interesting food. Lookout for seafood (fresh crab, lemon sole, cod in beer batter), and, perhaps, pheasant, steak and kidney pie, and hot filled baguettes. **Principal beers:** Sharp's Cornish Doom Bar, Wadworth 6X, Young's Special, Morland Old Speckled Hen.
Brewery/Company Inn Partnership
Open 11-3 5.30-11
Bar food 11-2.30 6-10 Av main course £4.50
Restaurant 11-2.30 6-10 Av 3 course à la carte £14

PHILLEIGH *Map 02 SW83*
Cornwall & Isles of Scilly

The Roseland Inn
PHILLEIGH
TR2 5NB ☎ 01872 580254

The rural setting in the heart of the Roseland Peninsula is a delightful one for sampling decent sandwiches and salads or, perhaps, scallops with bacon and garlic, shank of lamb with rosemary gravy, steak and mushroom suet pudding, or fresh local crab. Unspoilt and immaculately-kept bars, and a splendid rose-covered front terrace.
Principal beers: Sharp's Doom Bar, Ringwood Best, Bass, Marston's Pedigree.
Brewery/Company Greenalls
Open 11-11
Bar food 12-2.15 6-9 Av main course £4.95
Restaurant 12-2.15 6-9 Av 3 course à la carte £15

POLKERRIS *Map 02 SX05*
Cornwall & Isles of Scilly

The Rashleigh Inn
POLKERRIS
PL24 2TL ☎ 01726 813991

Old-world inn, furnished with antiques, set on the beach with glorious views across St Austell Bay. Daphne du Maurier lived nearby and her novels were based in the area. Fresh fish and seafood figures prominently, with a popular fish pie in the bar and Fowey sea trout with almonds in the restaurant. **Principal beers:** Bass, Sharp's Doom Bar, Badger Tanglefoot, Fuller's London Pride.
Directions off the A3082 outside Fowey
Brewery/Company Free House
Open 11-3 6-11 10
Bar food 11.30-2.30 6-10 Av main course £5.50
Restaurant 11 Av 3 course à la carte £15

PORT GAVERNE *Map 02 SX08*
Cornwall & Isles of Scilly

Port Gaverne Hotel
PORT GAVERNE
PL29 3SQ ☎ 01208 880244

Charming 16th-century inn set back from a spectacular small cove. Flagged floors, beamed ceilings and comfortable bedrooms characterise the traditional interior. Fresh produce provides

contd.

interesting menus, from fish pie and crab soup in the bar, to chicken liver pâté, rack of lamb, and chocolate and hazelnut meringue in the dining room. **Principal beers:** Sharp's Doom Bar, Bass, Flowers IPA.

Port Gaverne Hotel

Directions Signed from B3314, S of Delabole via B3267 on E of Port Isaac
Brewery/Company Free House
Open 11-2.30 6-11
(closed early Jan-mid Feb)
Bar food 12-2 7-9.30
Restaurant 7.30-9.30 Av 3 course à la carte £22.50
Accommodation (Min) s£51 d£102

PORTHLEVEN *Map 02 SW62*
Cornwall & Isles of Scilly

The Ship Inn
PORTHLEVEN
TR13 9JS ☎ 01326 572841

Featured in several advertisements, this atmospheric, 17th-century smugglers inn is situated right on the harbourside. Popular options are 'crusties', - a half loaf with a range of fillings - pan fried dover sole, Cornish fish pie, steak and kidney pie and crab thermidor. **Principal beers:** Courage Best & Directors, Greene King Abbot Ale, Sharp's Doom Bar.
Brewery/Company Free House
Open 11.30-3 7-11 (summer hols 11-11)
Bar food 12-2 7-9 Av main course £9

PORTREATH *Map 02 SW64*
Cornwall & Isles of Scilly

Basset Arms
PORTREATH
Tregea Ter TR16 4NG ☎ 01209 842077

Typical Cornish stone cottage, built as a pub in the early 19th century to serve the harbour workers, with plenty of tin mining and shipwreck memorabilia adorning the low-beamed interior. Homely bar food may include fish pie, steak and kidney pudding, fresh local crab, and 'doorstop' sandwiches.
Principal beers: St Austell Dartmoor Best, Bass.
Directions From Redruth take B3300 to Portreath
Brewery/Company Free House
Open 11-3 6-11 (all day in summer)
Bar food 12-2 6.30-9.30 Av main course £5.25
Restaurant 6.30-9.30 Av 3 course à la carte £15.95 Av 3 course fixed price £15.95

RUAN LANIHORNE *Map 02 SW84*
Cornwall & Isles of Scilly

The Kings Head NEW
RUAN LANIHORNE
TR2 5NX ☎ 01872 501263

With its pretty sun-trap, sunken garden overlooking the tidal River Fal, this popular summer pub enjoys a rural location in the heart of the Roseland Peninsula. Straightforward printed menu fare is supplemented by daily specials such as fish gratin, turkey and ham pie, moussaka, and gooseberry pie. **Principal beers:** Sharp's Special & Doom Bar, Hardy Country, Worthington Best.
Directions 2 1/2m from Tregony Bridge on A3078
Brewery/Company Free House
Open 12-3 7-11 (closed Mon, 1wk Feb/Mar or Oct)
Bar food 12-2 7-9.30 Av main course £5.25

ST AGNES *Map 02 SW75*
Cornwall & Isles of Scilly

Driftwood Spars Hotel
ST AGNES
Trevaunance Cove TR5 0RT
☎ 01872 552428 & 553323

Atmospheric 17th-century smugglers' inn situated a stone's throw from a superb beach. Stone walls, huge beams, shipwreck photographs and granite fireplaces characterise the bars, where you can enjoy fresh fish, grills, steaks and hearty pasties from a varied menu.
Principal beers: Tetley, Bass, Sharp's Own, St Austell HSD.
Directions A30 onto B3285, thru St Agnes, down steep hill, L at Peterville Inn, onto rd signed Trevaunance Cove
Brewery/Company Free House

Open 11-11 (Fri-Sat 11-12)
Bar food 12-2.30 6.30-9.30 Av main course £5
Restaurant 6.30-9.30 Av 3 course à la carte £15
Accommodation (Min) s£30 d£60

ST AGNES (Isles of Scilly) *Map 02 SW17*
Cornwall & Isles of Scilly

Turks Head
ST AGNES (ISLES OF SCILLY)
TR22 0PL ☎ 01720 422434

A 20-minute boat trip from St Mary's brings you to this slate-roofed white cottage, Britain's most south-westerly pub, overlooking the cove and the island quay. Savour wonderful views, good real ales and hearty traditional pub food. Favourites include local crab rolls and salads, beef and Murphy's pie and locally-made pasties. **Principal beers:** St Austell Dartmoor Best, Burton Ale, Flowers Original & IPA, Sharp's Doom Bar.
Directions By boat or helicopter to St Mary's and boat on to St Agnes
Brewery/Company Free House
Open 11-11
Bar food 12-2.30 6.30-9.30 Av main course £4.75
Accommodation (Min) d£47

ST JUST (Near Land's End) *Map 02 SW33*
Cornwall & Isles of Scilly

Star Inn
ST JUST (NEAR LAND'S END)
TR19 7LL ☎ 01736 788767

Small Cornish coastal pub offering a range of soups, filled jacket potatoes and sandwiches. Home-made dishes feature local seafood, especially crab. For vegetarians there is a vegetable curry. And the home-made desserts include hot syrup pudding with cream and ice cream. **Principal beers:** St Austell HSD, Tinners Ale, XXXX Mild.
Brewery/Company St Austell Brewery
Open 11-11 (Mon-Thu Oct-Etr 11-3,6-11) (Sun 12-10.30)
Bar food 12-2 6.30-8.30
Accommodation (Min) s£18 d£30

ST KEW *Map 02 SX07*
Cornwall & Isles of Scilly

St Kew Inn
ST KEW
PL30 3HB ☎ 01208 841259

Attractive stone-built 15th-century inn near the parish church in a secluded valley. Retains much of its original character, notably its large kitchen range and slate floors. Dining room specialities include lobster and game pie, while the bar menu might offer fish pie, and beef in Guinness with herb dumplings. **Principal beers:** St Austell HSD & Tinners Ale.
Directions village signed 3m NE of Wadebridge on A39
Brewery/Company St Austell Brewery
Open 11-2.30 6-11
Bar food 12-2 7-9.30
Restaurant 12-2 7-9.30 Av 3 course à la carte £10

ST MAWES *Map 02 SW83*
Cornwall & Isles of Scilly

The Rising Sun NEW
ST MAWES
The Square TR2 5DJ ☎ 01326 270233

The pretty harbour of St Mawes is the setting for this refurbished inn. Popular with the yachting fraternity, it affords lovely views from the front terrace, brasserie and bedrooms. Imaginative cooking results in a sound selection of dishes, perhaps including egg Florentine, chicken supreme with white wine and grape sauce, and lemon tart. Good bar snacks. **Principal beers:** St Austell range.
Brewery/Company St Austell Brewery
Open 8.30-11
Bar food 12-2 6-8.30
Accommodation (Min) s£35 d£49.50

ST MAWGAN *Map 02 SW86*
Cornwall & Isles of Scilly

The Falcon Inn
ST MAWGAN
TR8 4EP ☎ 01637 860225

15th-century wisteria-clad inn tucked away in a secluded valley. Takes its name

contd.

from a falcon which flew over the village during the time of the Reformation, signalling that a secret Catholic church service was taking place. Choose, perhaps, from spicy lamb casserole, chicken supreme, venison sausages and smoked salmon steak. **Principal beers:** St Austell HSD & Trelawneys Pride.

The Falcon Inn

Directions From A30 8m W of Bodmin, follow signs to Newquay/St Mawgan Airport. After 2m turn R into village, pub at bottom of hill
Brewery/Company St Austell Brewery
Open 11-3 2 6-11 9.30
Bar food 12-2 6.30-9.30 Av main course £4.95
Restaurant 12-2 6.30-9.30 Av 3 course à la carte £14
Accommodation (Min) s£12.50 d£45

SALTASH Cornwall & Isles of Scilly
Map 02 SX45

The Weary Friar Inn
SALTASH
Pillaton PL12 6QS ☎ 01579 350238

Situated deep in remote Cornish countryside, this 12th-century inn originally housed the monks who built adjacent St Odulphus church. Straightforward but appetising bar food includes steak and ale pie and chicken Maryland. In the restaurant lookout for venison, poached salmon and the interestingly-named smokey carpetbag sirloin steak. **Principal beers:** St Austell Dartmoor Best, Sharp's Own & Cornish Coaster, Butcombe, Bass.
Directions 2m W of A388 between Callington & Saltash
Brewery/Company Free House
Open 12-3 6.30-11
Bar food 12-2 7-9.30
Restaurant 7-9 Av 3 course à la carte £15
Accommodation (Min) s£35 d£50

TINTAGEL Cornwall & Isles of Scilly
Map 02 SX08

Mill House Inn
TINTAGEL
PL34 0HD ☎ 01840 770200 770932

Set in seven acres of streamside woods, within walking distance of dramatic cliffs and a popular beach, this 17th-century corn mill is well equipped for families and offers good traditional pub food. Choose from filled baguettes or lasagne, or specials like beef in ale stew, lamb rogan josh, and fresh fish. **Principal beers:** Sharp's Own & Doom Bar, St Austell Tinners Ale, Skinners.
Directions From A39 (Wadebridge/Bude rd) take B3314,then B3263 signed Tintagel
Brewery/Company Free House
Open 11-11
Bar food 0 Av main course £7.95
Accommodation (Min) s£22.50 d£50

The Port William
TINTAGEL
Trebarwith Strand PL34 0HB
☎ 01840 770230

Former harbourmaster's house commanding a superb cliff-top position with glorious views over Trebarwith Strand and out to sea; arguably the best sited pub in Cornwall. Focus on the

blackboard for excellent fresh fish (bass with prawns and mushrooms), and home-cooked dishes like celery and Stilton soup, lamb casserole, and venison in Madeira. Good B&B. **Principal beers:** Bass, St Austell Tinners Ale & HSD, Flowers, Boddingtons.
Directions Off B3263 between Camelford & Tintagel
Brewery/Company Free House
Open 11-11
Bar food 12-2.30 6-9.30 Av main course £7.50
Restaurant 12-2.30 6-9.30 Av 3 course à la carte £12.50
Accommodation (Min) s£43.50 d£57

TORPOINT *Map 02 SX45*
Cornwall & Isles of Scilly

The Edgcumbe Arms NEW
TORPOINT
Cremyll PL10 1NX ☎ 01752 822294
Enjoy a riverside stroll through Mount Edgcumbe Country Park before relaxing at this refurbished old inn. Bag one of the waterside tables (or bow window seats), with their River Tamar and Plymouth Sound views, and tuck into a traditional snack or, perhaps, fresh cod, scallops or lemon sole. **Principal beers:** St Austell HSD, Tinners Ale & Trelawney's Pride.
Brewery/Company St Austell Brewery
Open 11-11
Bar food 12-2.30 7-9 Av main course £5
Restaurant 12-2.30 7-9 Av 3 course à la carte £15
Accommodation (Min) s£32.50 d£50

TREBURLEY *Map 02 SX37*
Cornwall & Isles of Scilly

The Springer Spaniel
TREBURLEY
PL15 9NS ☎ 01579 370424
Civilised country dining pub with a neatly furnished bar and well-run dining room. Named after the owners' springer spaniel, Bertie, it offers imaginative and enjoyable food, in particular dishes like pheasant casserole, lamb fillet with crab apple and wine sauce, and venison and game pie. Decent home-made soups, sandwiches and cold meat platters are also available. **Principal beers:** St Austell Dartmoor Best & HSD.
Directions On the A388 halfway between Launceston & Callington
Brewery/Company Free House
Open 10-3 5.30-11
Bar food 11-2.30 6-10 Av main course £5.95
Restaurant 11.30-3 6.30-11 Av 3 course à la carte £20

TREGADILLET *Map 02 SX38*
Cornwall & Isles of Scilly

Eliot Arms (Square & Compass)
TREGADILLET
PL15 7EU ☎ 01566 772051
Granite creeper-clad coaching inn, established 1625 and modernised 1840. An amazing collection of clocks, horsebrasses, cigarette cards and local photographs add interest to the rambling series of rooms. Favourite dishes include mussels with garlic butter, beef, potato and Stilton pie, home-smoked chicken with barbecue sauce and salmon with crab sauce. **Principal beers:** St Austell HSD & Dartmoor Best, Marston's Pedigree.
Directions Turn of A30 for Tregadillet, Bodmin side of Launceston
Brewery/Company Free House
Open 11-3.00 6-11
Bar food 12-2 7-9.30
Restaurant 12-2 7-9.30 Av 3 course à la carte £10
Accommodation (Min) s£25 d£40

TRESCO *Map 02 SW17*
Cornwall & Isles of Scilly

The New Inn
TRESCO (Isles of Scilly)
New Grimsby TR24 0QQ
☎ 01720 422844
Firmly established as a vital part of life on this delightful island, the New Inn is a welcoming, family-run hostelry offering imaginative menus that make use of quality local ingredients, notably fresh seafood. Expect fish soup, crab cakes, John Dory with ginger and lemon grass, pork tenderloin with Calvados and cream, alongside sandwiches and soups. **Principal beers:** Fuller's London Pride, St Austell HSD, Flowers Original, Whitbread Castle Eden Ale.
Directions by New Grimsby Quay
Brewery/Company Free House
Open 11-11
Bar food 12-2 7-9 Av main course £5

contd.

Restaurant 7-9 Av 3 course à la carte £22 Av 3 course fixed price £22
Accommodation (Min) d£114

TRURO Cornwall & Isles of Scilly
Map 02 SW84

Old Ale House
TRURO
7 Quay St TR1 2HD ☎ 01872 271122
Once a grain store for local farmers this traditional ale house has a relaxed attitude. Peanuts are free and customers are expected to throw the shells on the sawdust-covered floor. There's music three nights a week, and no spirits are sold. Food includes seafood paella, beef and stilton, and spice island chicken.
Principal beers: Skinners, Sharp's, John Smith's, Courage Directors.
Directions A30, Truro City centre
Brewery/Company Greenalls
Open 11-11 (Sun 12-10.30)
Bar food 12-2.30 6-7.45 Av main course £4.95

The Wig & Pen Inn & Olivers Restaurant
TRURO
Frances St TR1 3DP ☎ 01872 273028
Listed building in the centre of Truro dating from 1820. A high standard of food is offered, from traditional lunches and an evening brasserie menu in the bar, to the delights of Olivers restaurant, such as duo of fresh brill and plaice fillets, or pan-fried pheasant with a wild berry reduction. **Principal beers:** St Austell Tinners Ale & HSD.
Directions City centre nr Law Courts
Brewery/Company St Austell Brewery
Open 11-11
Bar food 12-2.30 6-9.30 Av main course £7
Restaurant 12-2 7-9.30 Av 3 course à la carte £20 Av 3 course fixed price £20

VERYAN Cornwall & Isles of Scilly
Map 02 SW93

The New Inn
VERYAN
TR2 5QA ☎ 01872 501362
Superbly situated for exploring the beautiful Cornish coast, this unspoilt village inn concentrates on home cooking and almost everything is prepared from basic ingredients. Various pizzas, jacket potatoes and light snacks feature on the bar menu, while specials might include salmon and cod bake and lamb and mushroom Stroganoff.
Principal beers: St Austell HSD & Tinners Ale.
Directions Off A3078 towards Portloe
Brewery/Company St Austell Brewery
Open 12-3 6.30-11 (no food Mon eve in winter)
Bar food 12-2 7-9 Av main course £6
Accommodation (Min) s£21.50 d£43

Devon

ASHBURTON Devon
Map 03 SX77

The Rising Sun NEW
ASHBURTON
Woodland TQ13 7JT ☎ 01364 652544
Modernised cream-painted pub enjoying a splendid rural position with rolling views across South Hams countryside. Good food ranges from hearty ploughman's with four Devon cheeses, short-crust pastry-topped pies (lamb and apricot), and seafood tagliatelle, to venison with prune compôte, sea bass with basil and tarragon dressing, and plum and almond tart. **Principal beers:** Princetown Jail Ale.

Directions E of Ashburton from the A38 take lane signed to Woodland and Denbury
Brewery/Company Free House
Open 11-3 6-11
Bar food 12-2.15 6-9.15 Av main course £5.95
Restaurant 12-2.15 6-9.15 Av 3 course à la carte £15

Pubs offering a good choice of seafood on the menu

AVONWICK Devon *Map 03 SX75*

The Avon Inn
AVONWICK

TQ10 9NB ☎ 01364 73475

Unassuming, cream-painted pub set beside the River Avon, offering traditional bar food (baguettes, fish and chips), alongside good blackboard specials with a distinct Italian influence. From authentic pasta meals (tagliatelle with smoked chicken and walnuts), the menu extends to Thai-style bass, chargrilled swordfish with pesto, and beef fillet with wild mushrooms and peppers. **Principal beers:** Bass, Badger Best.

Directions From A38 take South Brent turning, Avonwick signed on B3210

Brewery/Company Free House

Open 11.30-2.30 6-11 (closed Sun & 2wks in Jan)

Bar food 12-2 6.45-9.30 Av main course £5.25

Restaurant 12-2 6.45-9.30 Av 3 course à la carte £18

AXMOUTH Devon *Map 03 SY29*

The Ship Inn
AXMOUTH

EX12 4AF ☎ 01297 21838

Attractive creeper-clad inn situated in the centre of the village, displaying Guinness memorabilia and international dolls. Local seafood features strongly, with dishes such as baked fillet of plaice stuffed with crab meat and prawns. There is also a good choice of snacks and home-made puddings. **Principal beers:** Bass, Otter Ale, guest beer.

Directions 1m S of A3052 between Lyme Regis & Exeter

Brewery/Company Inn Partnership

Open 11-2.30 6-11 (Sun 12-3, 7-10.30)

Bar food 12-2.30 7.30-11 Av main course £5.50

Restaurant 12-2.30 7.30-11

BANTHAM Devon *Map 03 SX64*

Sloop Inn
BANTHAM

TQ7 3AJ ☎ 01548 560489

A 16th-century inn with smuggling connections, located a short stroll from the beach. The interior has a flagstone floor and a side bar is made of old boat timbers and retains its boat shape. Special dishes include seafood salad, liver with onion mash and sage gravy, good fresh fish, and treacle tart. **Principal beers:** Blackawton, Theakston, Bass.

Directions From Kingsbridge take A379. At roundabout after Churchstow follow signs for Bantham

Brewery/Company Free House

Open 11-2.30 6-11 (Sun 12/2.30, 7-10.30)

Bar food 12-2 7-10 Av main course £12

Restaurant 12-2 7-10 Av 3 course à la carte £15

Accommodation (Min) s£30 d£60

BARNSTAPLE Devon *Map 02 SS53*

62 The Bank
BARNSTAPLE

62 Boutport St EX31 1HG
☎ 01271 24446

Built as a merchant's house in 1620, this striking building became a coaching inn and a bank before finally becoming bar/bistro. Hot baguettes, grills, interesting burgers, Cajun chicken, salmon and broccoli pasta, and Tex-Mex dishes can be enjoyed inside, complete with vaulted ceilings, panelled walls and original bank features.

Directions A361 from M5, pub in town centre

Brewery/Company Brend

Open 11-10.30 (Fri-Sun 10-10.30)

Restaurant 12-3 6-10.30 Av 3 course à la carte £15

Accommodation (Min) s£54 d£74

BEER Devon *Map 03 SY28*

The Anchor Inn
BEER

Fore St EX12 3ET ☎ 01297 20386

One of Britain's best sited inns, the Anchor overlooks the tiny working harbour and beach in this popular little

contd.

resort. Good summer cliff-top garden and an open-plan bar where you can enjoy pub snacks and excellent fresh fish. From mussels and oysters, the choice extends to red mullet with crab and herb crust and white wine sauce, and sea bass with creamy tarragon and orange sauce. **Principal beers:** Otter Ale, Otter Bitter, Courage Directors.

The Anchor Inn

Directions Turn off A3052 following signs for Beer, continue through the village to slip road for Beach Anchor Inn on the R.
Brewery/Company Old English Inns/Hot
Open 11-2.30 5.30-11 (Summer & w/e 11-11)
Bar food 12-2 7-9.30 Av main course £6
Restaurant 12-2 7-9.30 Av 3 course à la carte £20
Accommodation (Min) s£40 d£55

BERE FERRERS Devon Map 02 SX46

Old Plough Inn
BERE FERRERS
PL20 7JL ☎ 01822 840358
Originally three 16th-century cottages, the inn exudes character with its timbers and flagstones, which on closer inspection are revealed to be headstones. The selection of home-made dishes changes daily, favourites are Maggie's monster pies, chargrilled steaks, and fresh fish from Plymouth. Lovely rear patio overlooking the River Tavy. **Principal beers:** Bass, St Austell Dartmoor Best, Flowers IPA, guest beers.
Directions A386 from Plymouth, A390 from Tavistock
Brewery/Company Free House
Open 12-3 7-11
Bar food 12-3 7.30-11 Av main course £6
Restaurant 12-4 7.30-12 Av 3 course fixed price £12.50

BIGBURY-ON-SEA Devon Map 02 SX46

Pilchard Inn
BIGBURY-ON-SEA
Burgh Island TQ7 4BG ☎ 01548 810514
Atmospheric 14th-century white-walled pub located on a tiny tidal island reached only by giant sea tractor when the tide is in. The main catch off the island was pilchard - hence the name. Ploughman's or salads are available in summer from cafe beneath the bar right on the rocks above the beach. **Principal beers:** Courage Best & Directors.
Directions From A38 turn off to Modbury then follow signs to Bigbury & Burgh Island
Brewery/Company Free House
Open 12-10.30 (11-11 in summer)

BLACKAWTON Devon Map 03 SX85

Normandy Arms
BLACKAWTON
Chapel St TQ9 7BN ☎ 01803 712316
Venture off the beaten track to find this 15th-century inn in a peaceful backwater. Named in honour of the Normandy Landings, for which training exercises took place on nearby Slapton Beach, follow the signpost 'forces tavern' to sample traditional English dishes like Devonish pork and tipsy cake. **Principal beers:** Blackawton Bitter, Burton Ale.
Directions A381 from Totnes, L onto A3122, 1st R to Blackawton after Kingsbridge turning
Brewery/Company Free House
Open 12-2.30 7-11
Bar food 12-1.45 7-9 Av main course £4.50
Restaurant 12-1.45 7-9 Av 3 course à la carte £14
Accommodation (Min) s£30 d£48

BRAMPFORD SPEKE Devon Map 03 SX99

The Agricultural Inn
BRAMPFORD SPEKE
EX5 5DP ☎ 01392 841868
Good honest English cooking, with Eastern influences and speciality days and evenings, are on offer at this 18th-century former cider house situated close to the River Culm. Visitors are also guaranteed good ales and a friendly welocome. **Principal beers:** Exe Valley, Otter Ale, Hardy Royal Oak, Courage Best.

Directions 1st R off A377 Exeter to Crediton, approx 1m N of Exeter
Brewery/Company Free House
Open 11.30-3 6-11
Bar food 12-2 6-10 Av main course £6.50
Restaurant 12-2 6-10 Av 3 course à la carte £15

BRANSCOMBE Devon *Map 03 SY18*

The Masons Arms
BRANSCOMBE
EX12 3DJ ☎ 01297 680300
14th-century inn set in a picturesque village close to the sea and invigorating cliff walks. Beamed and slate-foored with open log fire where joints are spit-roasted. Good food ranges steak and kidney pudding, and venison with cabbage and bacon, to red mullet with oyster stir-fry and spicy tomato sauce, and duck with plum sauce. **Principal beers:** Otter Ale, Masons Ale, Bass, guest ale.

Directions Turn off A3052 towards Branscombe, head down hill, hotel in the valey at the bottom of the hill
Brewery/Company Free House
Open 11-11 (winter 11-3, 6-11)
Bar food 12-2.15 7-9.15 Av main course £8.50
Restaurant 12-2.15 7-8.45 Av 3 course à la carte £22 Av 3 course fixed price £22
Accommodation (Min) s£24 d£44

BROADHEMBURY Devon *Map 03 ST10*

Drewe Arms
BROADHEMBURY
EX14 0NF ☎ 01404 841267
Fish from Newlyn features strongly on the blackboard menus at the 15th-century, cob and thatch Drewe Arms. Seafood includes sea bass steamed with pesto, John Dory with wild mushrooms, and crab thermidor, while meat lovers can choose beef, venison or chicken. Open sandwiches are also available.
Principal beers: Otter Ale, Head, Brew & Bright.
Directions A373 halfway between Cullompton and Honiton
Brewery/Company Free House
Open 11-3 6-11
Bar food 12-2 7-10 Av main course £9
Restaurant 12-2 7-10 Av 3 course à la carte £22.50 Av 3 course fixed price £22.50

BUCKFASTLEIGH Devon *Map 03 SX76*

Dartbridge Inn
BUCKFASTLEIGH
Totnes Rd TQ11 0JR ☎ 01364 642214
Black and white inn, renowned for its colourful floral displays, situated close to the banks of the River Dart. A good range of food is available, from sandwiches to steaks, and fresh local fish and seafood, perhaps grilled whole Brixham plaice, and salmon and broccoli bake. **Principal beers:** Theakston XB, Courage Directors, Marstons Pedigree.
Directions Turn off A38 onto A384, the Dartbridge Inn is 200yrds on the L
Brewery/Company Old English Inns/Hot
Open 11-2.30 6.30-11
Bar food 12-2 7-9.30 Av main course £6.50
Restaurant 12-2 7-9.30 Av 3 course à la carte £16
Accommodation (Min) s£45 d£60

BUCKLAND MONACHORUM Devon *Map 02 SX46*

Drake Manor Inn
BUCKLAND MONACHORUM
The Village PL20 7NA ☎ 01822 853892
Largely 16th century, but with some 12th-century bits, the inn was built by the masons who built the church. It is known for its award-winning floral displays and its collection, now approaching 100, of single malt whiskies. The menu includes Cajun-style chicken and breaded lobster tails. **Principal beers:** Ushers - Best, Founders & Four Seasons, John Smiths.
Directions Off A386 near Yelverton
Brewery/Company Ushers
Open 11.30-2.30 6.30-11 (Sun 12-3, 7-10.30)
Restaurant 12-2 7-10 Av 3 course à la carte £12

CHERITON BISHOP Devon Map 03 SX79

The Old Thatch Inn
CHERITON BISHOP
EX6 6HJ ☎ 01647 24204
Old-World charm and modern comforts are effectively combined at this 17th-century listed inn. The menu is supported by an interesting specials board and might offer pan-fried duck breast with black Brie and redcurrant sauce, sea bream with coriander salsa, and rack of lamb with port and rosemary. **Principal beers:** Branscombe Vale Branoc, Sharps Own & Special + guest beers.
Directions Take A30 from M5, about 10m turning on L signed Cheriton Bishop
Brewery/Company Free House
Open 11-3 6-11 (closed 1st 2 wks Nov)
Bar food 12-2 7-9.30 Av main course £6.75
Accommodation (Min) s£34.50 d£46

CHUDLEIGH KNIGHTON Devon Map 03 SX87

The Claycutters Arms
CHUDLEIGH KNIGHTON
TQ13 0EY ☎ 01626 853345
Thatched village pub, originally three Quaker cottages, on the flanks of Dartmoor, complete with beams, an open fire and an abundance of hanging baskets in summer. Dishes range from home-made pigeon pie, wild boar sausages and cider apple sauce , to duck with leeks and port, and venison with honey and juniper. **Principal beers:** Bass, Morland Old Speckled Hen, Marston's Pedigree, Wadworth 6X.
Directions Turn off the Devon Expressway at Chudleigh Knighton
Brewery/Company Heavitree
Open 11-3 6-11
Bar food 12-2.30 6.30-10.00 Av main course £5.95
Restaurant 12-2.30 6.30-10 Av 3 course à la carte £20

CLYST HYDON Devon Map 03 ST00

The Five Bells Inn
CLYST HYDON
EX15 2NT ☎ 01884 277288
Summer flowers adorn the facade and cottagey front garden of this thatched 16th-century longhouse. Fresh local produce, notably fish and game, is used in preparing such home-cooked dishes as chicken liver and brandy pâté, rack of lamb with apricot sauce, and bread-and-butter pudding. Sandwiches and ploughman's platters are also available. **Principal beers:** Wadworth 6X, St Austell Dartmoor Best, Cotleigh Tawny.
Directions B3181 1m out of Cullompton, L to Clyst Hydon then R to Clyst St Lawrence. Pub on R
Brewery/Company Free House
Open 11.30-2.30 (Sun 12-2.30 7-10.30) 7-11
Bar food 12-2 7-10 Av main course £7.25
Restaurant 12-2 7-10 Av 3 course à la carte £20

COCKWOOD Devon Map 03 SX98

The Anchor Inn
COCKWOOD
EX6 8RA ☎ 01626 890203
A haven for seamen and smugglers for 450 years, this bustling inn overlooks a landlocked harbour. It has three snug areas with plenty of brass and bric-a-brac. Fish and seafood predominate, including oysters with an impressive choice of sauces, bouillabaisse, and lobster thermidor. Meat-eaters should find steak and kidney pie, or lamb curry on the menu. **Principal beers:** Bass, Flowers Original, Wadworth 6X, Hardy Royal Oak.
Directions Off A379 between Dawlish & Starcross

Brewery/Company Heavitree
Open 11-11
Bar food 12-3 6.30-10 Av main course £5.95
Restaurant 12-3 6.30-10 Av 3 course à la carte £20

CORNWORTHY Devon Map 03 SX85

Hunters Lodge Inn
CORNWORTHY
TQ9 7ES ☎ 01803 732204
Tucked away in a sleepy village close to the River Dart, this small 17th-century inn draws a loyal dining clientele for the interesting range of food available. Chalkboard menus may list monkfish in cream and garlic, roast pheasant, venison in red wine, Cumberland sausage and mash, or seafood pie, followed by treacle tart. **Principal beers:** Princetown

Dartmoor IPA, Otter Ale.
Directions Off A381 S of Totnes
Brewery/Company Free House
Open 11.30-2.30 6.30-11
Bar food 12-2 7-9 Av main course £4.95
Restaurant 7-9 Av 3 course à la carte £14

CREDITON Devon *Map 03 SS80*

The New Inn
CREDITON
Coleford EX17 5BZ ☎ 01363 84242

Thatched 13th-century building situated beside the River Cole in a conservation village. Captain, the chatty resident parrot is a popular character in the low-beamed bar. Good home-cooked food includes beef and venison casserole, fish soup, brill with lime and coriander beurre blanc, fish and dill pie, and duck with blueberry sauce. **Principal beers:** Wadworth 6X, Otter Ale, Badger.
Directions from Exeter take A377, 1.5m after Crediton turn L for Coleford. Pub in 1.5m
Brewery/Company Free House
Open 12-3 6-11
Bar food 12-2.30 7-11.30
Restaurant 12-2.30 7-11.30
Accommodation (Min) s£46 d£60

DALWOOD Devon *Map 03 ST20*

The Tuckers Arms
DALWOOD
EX13 7EG ☎ 01404 881342

Historic thatched pub with flagstone floor and inglenook fireplace, situated in a beautiful, quiet corner of East Devon. Daily-changing menu might feature venison steak and Stilton with port, lamb cutlets, rib-eye steak with pepper sauce, and good seafood, including king scallops with cider, cream and tarragon, and sea bream with oysters.. **Principal beers:** Otter Bitter, Otter Ale, Courage Directors.
Directions off A35 between Honiton & Axminster
Brewery/Company Free House
Open 12-3 6.30-11
Bar food 12.30-3 Av main course £5
Restaurant 12-2 6-12 Av 3 course à la carte £15
Accommodation (Min) s£27.50 d£45

DARTINGTON Devon *Map 03 SX76*

Cott Inn
DARTINGTON
TQ9 6HE ☎ 01803 863777

Built during the reign of Edward II, this charming inn, which takes its name from a local Dutch shepherd, has been licensed since 1320. A selection of typical main courses includes chargrilled sirloin steak, pork cobbler, paupiette of plaice filled with asparagus, and leek and oyster mushroom risotto. **Principal beers:** Bass, Courage Directors, Courage Best.
Directions On A384 between Totnes & Buckfastleigh
Brewery/Company Old English Inns/Hot
Open 11-2.30 5.30-11
Bar food 12-2.15 6.30-9.30 Av main course £10
Restaurant 12-2.15 6.30-9.30 Av 3 course à la carte £25
Accommodation (Min) s£55 d£65

DARTMOUTH Devon *Map 03 SX85*

The Cherub Inn
DARTMOUTH
13 Higher St TQ6 9RB ☎ 01803 832571

Dating from 1380, this interesting pub near the quay is the oldest building in Dartmouth. A timber-framed frontage leads to a small bar with exposed beams and low ceilings. Fish features strongly on the menu, from sea bass to lobster, and typical bar meals include chilli, steak and chips, and mushroom Stroganoff. **Principal beers:** Wadworth 6X, Morland Old Speckled Hen.
Brewery/Company Free House
Open 11-11
Bar food 12-2 7-10 Av main course £6.50
Restaurant 7-9.30 Av 3 course à la carte £18

Royal Castle Hotel
DARTMOUTH
11 The Quay TQ6 9PS ☎ 01803 833033

Historic coaching inn situated on the quayside, with a central courtyard, bustling ground-floor bars, and an elegant restaurant overlooking the River Dart. From filled jacket potatoes and fresh crab salad in the bar, the menu extends to duck with cranberry sauce, and good range of fish dishes in the restaurant. Delightful bedrooms.

contd.

Royal Castle Hotel

Principal beers: Flowers Original, Wadworth 6X, Courage Directors.
Brewery/Company Free House
Open 11-11
Bar food 11-6.30 6.30-10 Av main course £6
Restaurant 12.30-2.00 8.30-10 Av 3 course à la carte £19 Av 3 course fixed price £15
Accommodation (Min) s£51.45 d£99.90

DODDISCOMBSLEIGH Devon *Map 03 SX88*

The Nobody Inn
DODDISCOMBSLEIGH

EX6 7PS ☎ 01647 252394

A previous landlord reputedly locked the door to this splendid 16th-century inn and when customers knocked he would call out: 'nobody in.' Speciality dishes include the Nobody soup, pork sausage with mash and onion gravy, chicken with orange marmalade, and excellent West Country cheeses. Good restaurant and an extensive wine list. **Principal beers:** Bass, Teign Valley Tipple, Nobody's.
Directions From A38 follow signs for Dunchideock and Doddiscombeleigh
Brewery/Company Free House
Open 12-2.30 6-11 10
Bar food 12-2.30 7-10.30 Av main course £6.80
Restaurant 7.30-9 Av 3 course à la carte £15
Accommodation (Min) s£22 d£33

DOLTON Devon *Map 02 SS51*

The Union Inn
DOLTON

Fore St EX19 8QH ☎ 01805 804633

Built of traditional cob and situated in North Devon's glorious rolling countryside, this 19th-century village inn features fresh fish on its imaginative menu. Expect tuna with tomato, chilli and red peppers, cod in beer batter, hake with salsa verde, and mixed seafood stir-fry, alongside duck with port and juniper and rack of Devon lamb. **Principal beers:** Sharp's Doom Bar, St Austell HSD, Barum Original.
Directions From A361 take B3227 to S Moulton, then Atherington. L onto B3217 then 6m to Dalton. Pub on R
Brewery/Company Free House
Open 12-2.30 6-11 (closed Wed & 1st 2wks Feb)
Bar food 12-2 7-9 Av main course £4.50
Restaurant 7-9.30
Accommodation (Min) d£45

DREWSTEIGNTON Devon *Map 03 SX79*

The Drewe Arms
DREWSTEIGNTON

The Square EX6 6GQ ☎ 01647 281224

Picturesque thatched pub tucked away in a sleepy village square high above the wooded Teign Valley. Ales from the cask and home-cooked meals attracts a loyal clientele. Dishes on the interesting blackboard menus range from venison hotpot, corned beef hash, and crab and mushroom bake, to stuffed sea bass with lime and coriander **Principal beers:** Flowers IPA, Bass, Fullers London Pride, Wadworth 6x.
Directions Leave A30 for Cheriton Bishop at Woodleigh jct, follow signs for Castle Drogo
Brewery/Company Whitbread
Open 11-2.30 6-11
Bar food 12-2 6-9.30 Av main course £5
Restaurant 12-2 7-9 Av 3 course à la carte £20
Accommodation (Min) d£50

EXETER Devon *Map 03 EX99*

Double Locks Hotel NEW
EXETER

Canal Bank EX2 6LT ☎ 01392 256947

Difficult to find but well worth the effort involved for the real ale connoisseur, this red-brick Georgian pub enjoys a peaceful canalside setting within sight of Exeter cathedral. A splendid summer destination (ideal for families), it also offers traditional bar food, including ploughman's, salads, popular curries, lasagne, and feta cheese and spinach pie.

Principal beers: Adnams Broadside, Everards Old Original, Smiles Best, Branscombe Branoc.
Directions From M5 follow signs for Marsh Barton Trading Est, R at 2nd rdbt, then onto slip rd to L of incinerator, R after bridge across canal
Brewery/Company Smiles
Open 11-11 (Sun 12-10.30) (bar food 11-10.30, Sun 12-10)

EXMINSTER Devon Map 03 SX98

Turf Hotel
EXMINSTER

Turf Lock EX6 8EE ☎ 01392 833128
Remotely situated on the Exeter Canal, this is one of only a few pubs in the country that cannot be reached by car. Follow the paths or travel there on the inn's own boat. Lasagne and homity pie are on the menus goodies section and there are various blackboard specials.
Principal beers: Marston's Pedigree, Morland Old Speckled Hen, St Austell Dartmoor Best.
Directions Off A379 turn L at end of Exminster by-pass/over rail bridge. Park by canal (pub is 0.75m on foot)
Brewery/Company Free House
Open 11-3 6-11 (Jul-Aug 11-11, closed Nov-Feb)
Bar food 12-2.30 6.30-9 Av main course £5.50
Accommodation (Min) s£25 d£50

HARBERTON Devon Map 03 SX75

The Church House Inn
HARBERTON

TQ9 7SF ☎ 01803 863707
A fine 12th-century building, built to house masons working on the adjacent church, tucked away in a sleepy village. Character interior and a wide-ranging menu that may feature game terrine, rabbit casserole, pheasant in red wine, mushroom and Stilton sauce, and freshly battered cod and chips, in addition to traditional snacks. **Principal beers:** Bass, Wells Bombardier.
Directions From Totnes take A381 S. Take turn for Harbeton on R
Brewery/Company Free House
Open 12-3 6-11 (Sat 12-4,6-11 Sun 12-3,7-10.30)
Bar food 12-3 7-11 Av main course £6
Restaurant 12-3 7-11 Av 3 course à la carte £15
Accommodation (Min) s£25 d£40

HATHERLEIGH Devon Map 02 SS50

Tally Ho Inn & Brewery NEW
HATHERLEIGH

14 Market St EX20 3JN
☎ 01837 810306
Character 15th-century pub situated on the steep main street, complete with beamed bar, cosy dining room, and micro-brewery. Beyond a varied printed menu (lunchtime sandwiches, ploughman's, freshly-made pizzas), daily specials may feature herb-crusted rack of lamb with rosemary jus, mixed grill, and sea bass with ginger. Comfortable overnight accommodation. **Principal beers:** Tally Ho! Pot Boilers Brew, Tarka's Tipple, Thurgia & Nutters Ale.
Brewery/Company Free House
Open 11-3 6.30-11.30
Bar food 11-2.30 6.30-9.30 Av main course £5
Restaurant 11-2.30 6.30-9.30 Av 3 course fixed price £16
Accommodation (Min) s£30 d£50

HAYTOR VALE Devon Map 03 SX77

The Rock Inn
HAYTOR VALE

TQ13 9XP ☎ 01364 661305
Delightful 16th-century inn situated in a tranquil village below Haytor, the best known of Dartmoor tors. Its beamed rooms are perfect for relaxing in after a walk and for enjoying some honest cooking, in particular local game and seafood. Imaginative dishes include duck and port pate, pheasant with wild mushrooms, seafood ragout, and rabbit with mustard sauce. **Principal beers:** Hardy Royal Oak, St Austell Dartmoor Best, Bass.
Directions A38 from Exeter, at Drum Bridges rdbt take A382 for Bovey Tracey, 1st ex at 2nd rdbt (B3387), 3m L to Haytor Vale.
Brewery/Company Free House
Open 11-11
Bar food 12-2.30 7-9.30 Av main course £9.95
Restaurant 12-2.15 7-9.30 Av 3 course à la carte £25 Av 3 course fixed price £25.95
Accommodation (Min) s£47.50 d£65.95

HOLBETON Devon Map 03 SX65

Mildmay Colours Inn
HOLBETON

PL8 1NA ☎ 01752 830248

Close to a scenic beach, this 17th-century village pub is named after a famous Grand National jockey, the late Lord Mildmay. The racing theme is taken up on the menu. From typical pub favourites, the choice extends to seafood chowder, beef and mustard pie, butterscotch tart, and the ever-popular restaurant carvery. **Principal beers:** Mildmay Colours, Mildmay SP, Gale's HSB, Skinners Skillwidden.

Directions S from Exeter on A38, ex at Nat Shire Horse Centre, S past Ugborough & Ermington R onto A379. After 1.5m

Brewery/Company Free House

Open 11-3 6-11 (Sun 12-3, 7-10.30)

Bar food 12-2/2.30 6-9/9.30 Av main course £6

Restaurant 12-2 7-9 Av 3 course à la carte £12

Accommodation (Min) s£30 d£50

HOLNE Devon Map 03 SX76

Church House Inn
HOLNE

TQ13 7SJ ☎ 01364 631208

Head for the village centre to find this 14th-century inn with traditional bars and two dining areas. Once a resting place for pilgrims, and Oliver Cromwell reputedly stayed here during the Battle of Totnes. Local growers and suppliers ensure the freshest ingredients for home-cooked English and French regional dishes. **Principal beers:** St Austell Dartmoor Best, Butcombe, Hall & Woodhouse, Badger Tanglefoot.

Directions Turn off A38 at Buckfast, take road signed for Two Bridges & Princetown

Brewery/Company Free House

Open 11.30-3 6.30-11

Bar food 12-2.30 7-9.30 Av main course £6.50

Restaurant 12.15-1.45 7-8.30 Av 3 course à la carte £17

Accommodation (Min) s£19.50 d£22.50

HONITON Devon Map 03 ST10

The Otter Inn
HONITON

Weston EX14 0NZ ☎ 01404 42594

14th-century inn, formerly a cider house, named after the river which runs through its pretty two and a half acre grounds. Spacious bar and restaurant, inglenook fireplace and quaint alcoves. Among the home-made meals on offer are bangers and mash, fresh baked trout, steak and kidney pie and fresh salmon in Cajun seasoning. **Principal beers:** Bass, Hardy Country.

Directions Just off A30 W of Honiton

Brewery/Company Heavitree

Open 11-3.30 6-11.30

Bar food 12-2 7-10 Av main course £5.95

Restaurant 12-2 7-10 Av 3 course à la carte £14.95 Av 1 course fixed price £7.95

HORNDON Devon Map 02 SX58

The Elephant's Nest Inn
HORNDON

PL19 9NQ ☎ 01822 810273

Isolated, 400-year-old hostelry on the western flanks of Dartmoor. Named after a previous portly landlord who, when seated on his bar stool, looked like an elephant guarding its brood. Expect Tavy trout, local game pie, fisherman's lunch and chilli on the blackboard menu, in the rambling series of rustic bars.

Principal beers: Boddingtons, Palmers IPA, St Austells HSD.

Directions Off A386 N of Tavistock

Brewery/Company Free House

Open 11.30-2.30 6.30-11

Bar food 11.30-2 6.30-10 Av main course £5

HORSEBRIDGE Devon Map 02 SX47

The Royal Inn
HORSEBRIDGE

PL19 8PJ ☎ 01822 870214

Originally a nunnery, the 15th-century Royal Inn is so named after Charles 1 visited the pub and left his seal in the granite doorstep. In a lovely spot by the Tamar river, the pub has a micro-brewey and offers ham, egg and chips, fish pie, and pheasant casserole, among other dishes. **Principal beers:** Royal Inn - Tamar, Right Royal & Inn Heller, Wadworth 6X, Sharps Doombar.

Directions South of B3362 Launceston/Tavistock road
Brewery/Company Free House
Open 12-3 7-11 (Sun 7-10.30)
Bar food 12-2 7-9 Av main course £5

KINGSBRIDGE Devon *Map 03 SX74*

Church House Inn
KINGSBRIDGE
Churchstow TQ7 3QW ☎ 01548 852237

Rebuilt in the 15th century, this historic inn originated as a rest house for Cistercian monks in the 13th century. New owners continue to operate the ever-popular hot carvery with a choice of roasts and fresh vegetables, in addition to home-made fish pie, steak and kidney pie, and fresh haddock in beer batter.
Principal beers: Bass, Fullers London Pride, St Austell Dartmoor Best.
Directions On A379 1 1/2m W of Kingsbridge
Brewery/Company Free House
Open 11-2.30 6-11
Bar food 12-2.30 6.30-9 Av main course £5.35
Restaurant 7-9 Av 3 course à la carte £11.50

KINGSKERSWELL Devon *Map 03 SX86*

Barn Owl Inn
KINGSKERSWELL
Aller Mills TQ12 5AN ☎ 01803 872968

Period features at this 16th-century former farmhouse include beams, inglenook fireplaces, flagged floors, a black leaded range, oak panelling and ornate plasterwork. The menu offers plenty of fresh fish, home-made steak and kidney pie, and a range of French-influenced dishes. **Principal beers:** St Austell Dartmoor Best, Marstons Pedigree, Murphys.
Brewery/Company Free House
Open 11.30-2.30 6.30-11
Bar food 11.45-2 6.30-10 Av main course £8.50
Restaurant 7-9.30 Av 3 course à la carte £17.75 Av 2 course fixed price £14.75
Accommodation (Min) s£45 d£60

KINGSTEIGNTON Devon *Map 03 SX87*

Old Rydon Inn
KINGSTEIGNTON
Rydon Rd TQ12 3QG ☎ 01626 354626

A feature of this atmospheric Grade II listed farmhouse is a conservatory full of tropical plants, and a cosy bar with crackling log fire. Inventive bar food ranges from warm salads, smoked fish and leek chowder, and filled baguettes, to lamb steak on roast vegetable couscous, and nasi goreng. Restaurant fare may include fish soup, monkfish ravioli, and beef Stroganoff. Lovely sheltered garden.
Principal beers: Bass, Wadworth 6X, Fullers London Pride, Teignworthy Reel Ale.
Directions From A380 take B3193 into Kingsteignton
Brewery/Company Free House
Open 11-2.30 6-11
Bar food 12-2.30 6.30-11 Av main course £5.95
Restaurant 7-12 Av 3 course à la carte £21 Av 2 course fixed price £12.50

KINGSTON Devon *Map 03 SX64*

The Dolphin Inn
KINGSTON
TQ7 4QE ☎ 01548 810314

A 16th-century inn in the heart of the beautiful South Hams countryside. All meals are freshly prepared using local produce, with fish featuring prominently. Typical dishes include ocean rolls - plaice fillets with crab and prawn stuffing in cream sauce - and steaks from the charcoal grill. **Principal beers:** Ushers - Founders & Four Seasons Ale, Courage Best.
Brewery/Company Ushers

Open 11-2.30 6-11 (Sun 12-3,7-10.30)
Bar food 12-2 6-10 Av main course £5.95
Accommodation (Min) s£37.50 d£49.50

Pubs offering a good choice of seafood on the menu

West Country

KNOWSTONE Devon *Map 03 SS82*

Masons Arms Inn
KNOWSTONE
EX36 4RY ☎ 01398 341231 & 341582
Tiny, 13th-century thatched inn nestling in a sleepy village in the foothills of Exmoor. Rustic beamed bars, lovely garden with views, and a good menu offering a daily curry and a home-made pie, and specials like Devon cider cassoulet, seared monkfish with tomato salsa, and lemon posset with summer fruits coulis. **Principal beers:** Badger Dorset Best, Cotleigh Tawny.

Directions M5 J27 Off A361 between Tiverton & S Molton
Brewery/Company Free House
Open 11-3 6-11
Bar food 12-2 7-9 Av main course £5.25
Restaurant 12-2 7-9
Accommodation (Min) s£18 d£42

LIFTON Devon *Map 02 SX38*

The Arundell Arms NEW
LIFTON
PL16 0AA ☎ 01566 784666
Creeper-covered 18th-century coaching inn on the banks of the Tamar close to Dartmoor. With 20 miles of fishing waters it is a leading country sports hotel and draws discerning guest for its relaxing atmosphere and first-class food in the elegant dining room. Bar food is equally enjoyable, perhaps including smoked salmon, asparagus and dill linguine, gammon with Cumberland sauce, mixed sea fish grill, and delicious sandwiches. Separate locals' bar with real ales and simple snacks.
Directions 2/3m off the A30 dual carriageway, 3m E of Launceston
Brewery/Company Free House
Open 11.30-3 6-11
Bar food 12-2.30 6-9.30 Av main course £9.50
Restaurant 12.30-2 7.30-9.30 Av 3 course à la carte £35.50 Av 5 course fixed price £28.50
Accommodation (Min) s£44 d£88

LITTLEHEMPSTON Devon *Map 03 SX86*

Tally Ho Inn
LITTLEHEMPSTON
TQ9 6NF ☎ 01803 862316
A 14th-century, Grade II listed inn with open fires in winter and a fine, flower-adorned patio for summer alfresco drinking. An extensive menu lists traditional pub meals alongside good home-cooked specials, such as fisherman's pie, whole local plaice, rabbit casserole, and steak and kidney pie. **Principal beers:** St Austell Dartmoor Best, Teignworthy Reel Ale.
Directions off the A38 at Buckfastleigh
Brewery/Company Free House
Open 12-3 6-11
Bar food 12-2 6.45-10 Av main course £7.50
Accommodation (Min) s£38 d£50

LOWER ASHTON Devon *Map 03 SX88*

Manor Inn
LOWER ASHTON
EX6 7QL ☎ 01647 252304
Traditional rural pub set in the Teign Valley with views across fields to the hills. It retains the atmosphere of a local pub while offering a good range of food and real ales. Sandwiches and filled jacket potatoes are offered alongside beef and red wine casserole, and grilled salmon steak. **Principal beers:** Teignworthy Reel Ale, Wadworth 6X, Theakston XB, Princetown Jail Ale.
Directions A38, Teign Valley turning, follow signs for B3193, pub 5m on R
Brewery/Company Free House
Open 12-2.30 6-11 (Sat & Sun 7-11; closed Mon ex BH)
Bar food 12-1.30 7-9.30 Av main course £5.95

LUSTLEIGH Devon *Map 03 SX78*

The Cleave
LUSTLEIGH
TQ13 9TJ ☎ 01647 277223
Thatched 15th-century inn set in a beautiful village on the flanks of Dartmoor. It has a large inglenook fireplace, exposed granite walls, flagstones, and old settles for seating.

Food ranges from sandwiches and home-made soup, to roasts and good daily dishes such as spaghetti Bolognese, grilled sea bass, and local venison.
Principal beers: Flowers Original, Bass, Wadworth 6X.
Directions Off A382 between Newton Abbot and Moretonhampstead
Brewery/Company Heavitree
Open 11-3 6.30-11 (summer 11-11)
Bar food 12-2.30 6.30-9 Av main course £6
Restaurant 7-9 Av 3 course à la carte £16

LYDFORD Devon *Map 02 SX58*

Castle Inn & Hotel
LYDFORD
EX20 4BH ☎ 01822 820242 & 820241
Pretty, pink-washed and wisteria-clad village inn situated next to a Saxon castle and near to Lydford Gorge (NT). Character interior dating from the 16th century and good food. Dishes from a choice of menus include imaginative snacks, Thai crab cakes, pheasant casserole with cream and brandy sauce, and bourride of monkfish, salmon and langoustine with Noilly Prat.

Principal beers: Blackawton Bitter, Fullers London Pride.
Directions Off A386 S of Okehampton
Brewery/Company Free House
Open 11-3 6-11
Bar food 12-2.30 6.30-9.30 Av main course £6.75
Restaurant 7-9.30 Av 3 course à la carte £22.85 Av 3 course fixed price £16.95
Accommodation (Min) s£36.25 d£65

For Pubs with AA food rosettes see page 430

LYNMOUTH Devon *Map 03 SS74*

Rising Sun Hotel
LYNMOUTH
Harbourside EX35 6EQ
☎ 01598 753223
Sheltering beneath steep wooded slopes, overlooking picturesque Lynmouth Harbour, this 14th-century thatched smugglers inn is where Shelley supposedly stayed with his teenage bride in 1812. Expect beef Stroganoff, spicy chicken stir-fry and smoked haddock risotto among the lunchtime specialities, while grilled cod and best end of lamb feature on the evening menu.

Principal beers: Exmoor - Gold & Fox, Theakston XB, Courage Directors.
Directions From M5 J25 to Minehead, A39 to Lynmouth
Brewery/Company Free House
Open 11-2.30 6-11
Bar food 12-2 7-9 Av main course £4.75
Restaurant 12-2 7-9 Av 3 course à la carte £27.50 Av 3 course fixed price £27.50
Accommodation (Min) s£55 d£84

MEAVY Devon *Map 02 SX56*

The Royal Oak Inn
MEAVY
PL20 6PJ ☎ 01822 852944
A 15th-century village inn on the edge of Dartmoor, with a large fireplace and bread oven. It is named after an oak tree outside on the village green, some 900-1,000 years old. Main meals include roast beef, rump steak, cockles and mussels in garlic and white wine sauce, and an extensive vegetarian choice. **Principal beers:** Bass, Courage Best.
Directions Off A386 between Tavistock & Plymouth
Brewery/Company Free House
Open 11.30-3 6.30-11
Bar food 11.30-2.30 6.30-9.30 Av main course £5.50

contd.

NEWTON ST CYRES Devon *Map 03 SX89*

Crown and Sceptre
NEWTON ST CYRES
EX5 5DA ☎ 01392 851278
Over 30 years ago this 16th-century inn was destroyed by fire, and was subsequently rebuilt in traditional style. A selection of home-cooked dishes is offered from the daily blackboard menus, including a range of popular pies, salmon en croûte, chicken Wellington and a good choice of vegetarian dishes.
Principal beers: Bass.
Directions 2m NW of Exeter on A377
Brewery/Company Heavitree
Open 11.30-3 6-11
Bar food 12-2 7-9.30 Av main course £5.75
Restaurant 12-2 7-9.30 Av 3 course à la carte £16

NORTH BOVEY Devon *Map 03 SX78*

Ring of Bells Inn
NORTH BOVEY
TQ13 8RB ☎ 01647 440375
Originally built to house the masons constructing the church, this 13th-century thatched inn offers a welcoming atmosphere with good local gossip. Ingredient conscious dishes feature fresh West Country fare including fish from Brixham and local game. Vegetarians are well catered for, and the dining room is no-smoking. **Principal beers:** Butcombe, St Austell HSD, Teignworthy Reel Ale, guest beers.
Brewery/Company Free House
Open 11-3 6-11 (Summer 11-11)
Bar food 12-2 6.30-9 Av main course £8
Restaurant 12-2 6.30-9 Av 3 course à la carte £16
Accommodation (Min) s£35 d£50

PETER TAVY Devon *Map 02 SX57*

The Peter Tavy Inn
PETER TAVY
PL19 9NN ☎ 01822 810348
15th-century stone inn, originally a cottage and smithy, situated in the heart of a tranquil Dartmoor village. Good choice of real ales, open fires and home-cooked meals, including port and Stilton pate, game casserole, cashew nut paella, and evening dishes like rack of lamb with minted plum sauce, and monkfish in cream and garlic. **Principal beers:** Princetown Jail Ale, St Austell Dartmoor Best, Cotleigh Tawny, Bass.
Directions Off A386 NE of Tavistock
Brewery/Company Free House
Open 11.30-2.30 (Fri-Sun 12-3) 7-11 (Fri-Sat 6-11, Sun 7-10.30)
Bar food 12-2 7-9
Restaurant 12-2 7-9 Av 3 course à la carte £12.50

PLYMOUTH Devon *Map 02 SX45*

The China House
PLYMOUTH
Marrowbone Slip, Sutton Harbour PL4 0DW ☎ 01752 260930
Built as a warehouse in the mid-17th-century, this waterfront pub has also been used as a gun wharf, a bakehouse, even a prison. Nowadays, its menu features duck with honey sauce, lamb with redcurrant and wine sauce, and char-grilled steaks. Delicious desserts include poached fresh oranges in Grand Marnier. **Principal beers:** St Austell Dartmoor Best, Tetley, Marstons Pedigree.
Directions A38 to Plymouth centre, follow Exeter St to Sutton Rd, follow signs for Queen Anns Battery
Brewery/Company Allied Domecq
Open 11-11 (Fri-Sat 11-12.30,Sun 12-10.30)
Bar food 12-3 7-10.30
Restaurant 12-3 7-10.30 Av 3 course à la carte £16

Langdon Court Hotel
PLYMOUTH
Down Thomas PL9 0DY
☎ 01752 862358
Once owned by Henry VIII, this historic manor became the home of his last wife Catherine Parr. Close to outstanding coastal scenery. Freshly cooked bar meals range from home-made soup and fish, to steaks, Swedish gammon and various daily specials. Restaurant dishes might feature rack of lamb and citrus sea bass.
Principal beers: Wadworth 6X, Bass, Flowers Original.
Directions On A379 from Elburton follow brown tourist signs, also HMS Cambridge signs

Brewery/Company Free House
Open 12-2.30 6.30-11 9
Bar food 12-2.30 6.30-11 Av main course £6
Restaurant 7-11 Av 3 course à la carte £19.50 Av 3 course fixed price £19.50
Accommodation (Min) s£37.50 d£62.50

POSTBRIDGE Devon *Map 03 SX67*

Warren House Inn
POSTBRIDGE
PL20 6TA ☎ 01822 880208
Old tin miners' inn, one of the highest in England, offering breathtaking views over the moors from its isolated position. The fire here has burned continuously since 1845. Enjoyable home-cooked dishes include some popular pies, Warrener's pie, steak and ale pie and apple pie.
Principal beers: Gibbs Mew Bishops Tipple, Butcombe, Badger Tanglefoot, guest beer.
Directions Take B3212 through Moretonhampstead on for 5m
Brewery/Company Free House
Open 10-3 6-11 (Summer 10-11)
Bar food 12-2.30 6-9.30 Av main course £6

ROCKBEARE Devon *Map 03 SY09*

Jack in the Green Inn
ROCKBEARE
London Rd EX5 2EE ☎ 01404 822240
Unassuming roadside inn offering innovative food and wines, and a good atmosphere within its neatly refurbished interior. Freshly prepared dishes range from excellent ploughman's and beef stew in the bar, to duck leg confit and potato rosti, rib-eye steak with red wine and shallot sauce, and pigeon with black pudding, cabbage and bacon in the restaurant.
Principal beers: Bass, Cotleigh Tawny, Hardy Country, Otter Ale.
Directions 5m E of Exeter on A30
Brewery/Company Free House
Open 11-3 6-11
Bar food 12-2.30 6-10 Av main course £6
Restaurant 12-2.30 6-10 Av 3 course à la carte £16.95 Av 3 course fixed price £16.95

SHEEPWASH Devon *Map 02 SS40*

Half Moon Inn
SHEEPWASH
EX21 5NE ☎ 01409 231376
In the same family for over 40 years, this friendly pub enjoys a peaceful position in the village square. Home-made food, served in the civilised main bar with its fishing pictures and open fire, includes Annie's pasties, home-made soups, ploughman's and salads, The restaurant serves traditional English fare, prepared from fresh local produce. **Principal beers:** Courage Best, Marstons Pedigree, Jollyboat Mainbrace.
Directions from M5 take A30 to Okehampton then A386, at Hatherleigh, L onto A3072, after 4m R for Sheepwash
Brewery/Company Free House
Open 11-2.30 6-11
Bar food 12-2 Av main course £4
Restaurant 8-9 Av 5 course fixed price £19.50
Accommodation (Min) s£32.50 d£57.50

SLAPTON Devon *Map 03 SX84*

The Tower Inn
SLAPTON
TQ7 2PN ☎ 01548 580216
The inn was built in 1346 to provide accommodation for artisans working on the Chantry Tower, the ruins of which stand adjacent. It has low ceilings, open fires, a beautiful walled garden and a good range of real ales. Typical dishes include Dartmouth smokey, and pork tenderloin with apricots and cider.
Principal beers: St Austell Dartmoor Best, Exmoor Ale, Badger Tanglefoot, Gibbs Mew Bishops Tipple.
Directions Off A379 south of Dartmouth, turn L at Slapton Sands
Brewery/Company Free House
Open 12-3 6-11
Bar food 12-3 6-11 Av main course £4.50
Restaurant 12-3 6-11 Av 3 course à la carte £13
Accommodation (Min) s£20 d£20

SOUTH POOL Devon *Map 03 SX74*

Millbrook Inn
SOUTH POOL
TQ7 2RW ☎ 01548 531581
Customers can arrive at this quaint 16th-century pub close to Salcombe estuary by

contd.

West Country

boat when the tide is high. The attraction is the sunny rear terrace overlooking Millbrook stream, and decent simple bar food, notably the delicious fresh crab sandwiches, pasta with pesto and parmesan, fisherman's pie, chilli, or halibut au poivre. **Principal beers:** Bass, Ruddles Best, Wadworth 6X.
Directions Take A379 from Kingsbridge to Frogmore then E
Brewery/Company Free House
Open 11.30-2.30 5.30-11 (winter 12-2.30, 6.30-11)
Bar food 12-2 7-9 Av main course £4.50

SOUTH ZEAL Devon *Map 03 SX69*

Oxenham Arms
SOUTH ZEAL
EX20 2JT ☎ 01837 840244
15th-century inn, formerly the Dower House of the Burgoynes whose heiress brought it into the Oxenham family, after whom it is named. Main course dishes typically include lamb curry madras, salmon fillet poached in white wine and tarragon, and Oxenham steak, kidney Guinness and mushroom pie.
Principal beers: Princetown Dartmoor IPA, Sharps.
Directions just off A30 4m E of Okehampton in the centre of the village
Brewery/Company Free House
Open 11-2.30 6-11
Bar food 12-2 7-9.15 Av main course £5.75
Restaurant 12-2 7.30-9 Av 3 course à la carte £15 Av 3 course fixed price £15
Accommodation (Min) s£40 d£60

SPREYTON Devon *Map 03 SX69*

The Tom Cobley Tavern
SPREYTON
EX17 5AL ☎ 01647 231314
According to legend this is the pub that 'Uncle Tom Cobley and all' set off from in 1882 - it also has wonderful views of Dartmoor. Hearty home-cooked food includes lasagne, sandwiches and good pies, perhaps chicken and mushroom, game, or fish pie. Good summer alfresco drinking; Cotleigh Tawny ale tapped from the cask. **Principal beers:** Cotleigh Tawny, Bass.
Directions From Merrymeet roundabout take B3219 north
Brewery/Company Free House
Open 12-2.30 6-11.30 (closed Mon)
Bar food 12-2 7-9 Av main course £5.50
Restaurant 1 7-9 Av 3 course à la carte £13
Accommodation (Min) s£18 d£36

STAVERTON Devon *Map 03 SX76*

The Sea Trout NEW
STAVERTON
TQ9 6PA
Attractive, 15th-century village inn peacefully set close to Totnes and the River Dart. A firm favourite for its friendly welcome, good home cooking and comfortable accommodation. An extensive bar menu is enhanced by blackboard specials, perhaps fresh local fish, guinea fowl with port and orange, and lamb steak with red wine sauce. Also, expect tip-top ales and imaginative restaurant food.

Principal beers: Bass, Fullers London Pride, Princetown Dartmoor IPA.
Directions off A384 NW of Totnes
Brewery/Company Free House
Open 11-3 6-11
Bar food 12-2 7-9.45 Av main course £6.50
Restaurant 12-2 (sun only) 7-9.30 Av 3 course à la carte £18, Av 3 course fixed price £18.75.
Accommodation (Min) s£42.50 d£58

STOCKLAND Devon *Map 03 ST20*

Kings Arms
STOCKLAND
EX14 9BS ☎ 01404 881361
Pre-1700 Grade 11 listed coaching inn on the Great West Way, in what is very much a farming community. Home-made soups, decent pies and scrumpy pork are popular lunchtime dishes, while evening blackboard fare extends the choice to crispy roast duck, rack of lamb, and fillet of ostrich. Good wines and malt whisky choice.

Principal beers: John Smith, Marston Pedigree, Otter Ale, Exmoor Ale.
Brewery/Company Free House
Open 12-3 6.30-11.30
Bar food 12-3 Av main course £5.50
Restaurant 12-3 6.30-11 Av 3 course à la carte £18 Av 3 course fixed price £18
Accommodation (Min) s£25 d£40

THURLESTONE Devon *Map 03 SX64*

The Village Inn
THURLESTONE
TQ7 3NN ☎ 01548 560382

Built in 1533, the inn was the original farmhouse building for Thurlestone Hotel. Home-cooked specials include the paella, monkfish Wellington with lobster sauce, and prime steak in Guinness pie. On the snack side, there's the popular Village Inn BLT, a triple decker sensation. **Principal beers:** Palmers IPA, Bass, Marstons Pedigree, Courage Directors.
Directions A381 from Kingsbridge, R thru South Milton
Brewery/Company Free House
Open 11.30-3 6-11
Bar food 12-2 6.30-9.30 Av main course £4.95

TORCROSS Devon *Map 03 SX84*

Start Bay Inn
TORCROSS
TQ7 2TQ ☎ 01548 580553

14th-century thatched pub situated between Slapton Ley and the panoramic sweep of Start Bay. Fish is delivered from a local trawler and the landlord scuba dives for plaice and scallops. Try the superb jumbo haddock and chips, one of four different sized Dover soles, or perennial favourites like the crab salads and sandwiches. **Principal beers:** Flowers Original, Bass.
Directions between Dartmouth & Kingsbridge on the A379
Brewery/Company Heavitree
Open 11.30-2.45 6-11.20 (Summer 11.30-11.30)
Bar food 11.30-2 6-9 Av main course £5

TOTNES Devon *Map 03 SX86*

Durant Arms
TOTNES
Ashprington TQ9 7UP ☎ 01803 732240

Immaculate 18th-century Grade II listed inn, originally owned by the Sharpham House estate. Strong emphasis on interesting changing menus, with cottage pie and seafood flaky bake among the bar meals. Pork tenderloin, casseroled venison, and duck with gooseberry sauce are typical evening specials. Home-made puddings include rhubarb and apple crumble. **Principal beers:** Flowers Original, Wadworth 6X.
Directions Leave A38 at Totnes Jct, proceed to Dartington & Totnes, at 1st set of traffic lights R for Knightsbridge on A381, after 1m L for Ashprington
Brewery/Company Free House
Open 11.30-2.30 6.30-11
Bar food 12-2.30 7-9.15 Av main course £6.45
Restaurant 12-2.30 7-9.15 Av 3 course à la carte £15.95
Accommodation (Min) s£30 d£50

The Watermans Arms
TOTNES
Bow Bridge, Ashprington TQ9 7EG
☎ 01803 732214

Former smithy and brewhouse, this stone-built inn is peacefully situated at the head of Bow Creek next to the ancient Bow Bridge. In addition to the candlelit restaurant, there is a fine riverside terrace for summer dining. Food ranges from decent snacks to cod and chips, chicken with olive tapenade, and duck with five spices. **Principal beers:** Bass, Flowers Original, Morland Old Speckled Hen, Shepherd Neame Spitfire.
Directions A38, A381, follow signs for Kingsbridge out of Totnes, at top of hill turn L for Ashprington and Bow Bridge
Brewery/Company
Open 11-11
Bar food 12-2.30 6.30-10 Av main course £7.95
Restaurant 12-2.30 7-10 Av 3 course à la carte £16.95
Accommodation (Min) s£40 d£49.90

The White Hart Bar NEW
TOTNES
Dartington Hall TQ9 6EL
☎ 01803 866051/866303

Situated in the 14th-century courtyard on the Dartington Hall Estate, with its 30-acres of gardens and splendid riverside walks, this stylish bar and dining venue offers organic produce and west country ales. Menu choices range from lunctime baguettes (local ham and mustard), and

contd.

short-crust pastry-topped pies, to crab fritters, and Cornish organic lamb steak with game chips and Madeira jus. **Principal beers:** Princetown Jail Ale, Butcombe Bitter, Blackawton Bitter.
Directions Totnes turning on A38 to Plymouth, approx 4m
Brewery/Company Free House
Open 11-11 (closed 24 Dec-6 Jan)
Bar food 12-2.30 6-9 Av main course £7.95
Restaurant 12-2.30 6-9 Av 3 course à la carte £15 Av 4 course fixed price £15.95
Accommodation (Min) s£22.50 d£45

TRUSHAM Devon Map 03 SX88

Cridford Inn
TRUSHAM
TQ13 0NR ☎ 01626 853694
Britain's oldest domestic dwelling, originally a Saxon house, rebuilt as a hall in 1081. Local produce features in dishes such as battered Brixham cod and roast duckiling with port and orange sauce. The proprietor spent many years in S E Asia and also offers a range of authentic Mayalsian dishes. **Principal beers:** Trusham Ale, Teign Valley Tipple, Courage Directors, guest beers.
Brewery/Company Free House
Open 12-2.30 6.30-11
Bar food 12-2.30 7-9.30 Av main course £7.50
Restaurant 7-9.30 Av 3 course à la carte £22
Accommodation (Min) s£40 d£70

TUCKENHAY Devon Map 03 SX85

The Maltsters Arms
TUCKENHAY
TQ9 7EQ ☎ 01803 732350
Beautifully situated overlooking tidal Bow Creek, this 18th-century pub is a must for wildlife enthusiasts. Look out for kingfishers, redshanks and herons as you relax in the riverside restaurant, sampling chestnut and saffron soup, pan-fried parrot fish, game casserole, rack of lamb with honey and mustard glaze, and plum tarte tatin from the excellent menu.
Principal beers: Princetown Dartmoor IPA, Blackawton 44 Special & Headstrong, Youngs, Otter.
Brewery/Company Free House
Open 11-11 (closed 2.30-6 in winter)
Bar food 12-2.30 7-9.30
Restaurant 12-2.30 7-9.30
Accommodation (Min) d£45

UMBERLEIGH Devon Map 02 SS62

The Rising Sun Inn
UMBERLEIGH
EX37 9DU ☎ 01769 560447
A 12th-century sporting inn overlooking the River Taw, with an abundance of fishing memorabilia. Bar food includes venison sausage with a warm roll, home-made pies, and chicken in white wine sauce, while the restaurant might offer pork in cider and apple sauce or hot peppered mackerel fillet. **Principal beers:** Courage Directors, St Austells Dartmoor Best, Tetleys, Wadworth 6x.
Directions Situated at Umberleigh Bridge on the A377, Exeter/Barnstaple road, at the junc of the B3227
Brewery/Company Free House
Open 11-2.30 6-11
Bar food 12-2.30 6.30-10 Av main course £4.50
Restaurant 12.30-2.30 7-10 Av 3 course à la carte £15 Av 3 course fixed price £15
Accommodation (Min) s£40 d£77

WIDECOMBE-IN-THE-MOOR Devon Map 03 SX77

Rugglestone Inn
WIDECOMBE-IN-THE-MOOR
TQ13 7TF ☎ 01364 621327
Unspoilt Dartmoor farm cottage, converted to an inn in 1832, surrounded by peaceful moorland views. Simple, hearty, home-cooked dishes, such as steak and kidney pie, beef in red wine casserole, cheesy leek and potato bake, or hot salt beef roll can be enjoyed in the two, tiny beamed rooms, or in the streamside garden, and washed down by ales tapped from the cask. **Principal beers:** Butcombe Bitter, St Austell Dartmoor Best.
Directions A38 Drumbridges exit towards Bovey Tracey, L at 2nd rdbt, L at sign Haytor & Widecombe, village is 5m
Brewery/Company Free House
Open 11-2.30 (Sat-Sun 11-3) 6-11 (6.30-11 in winter,6-10.30 Sun)
Bar food 12-2 7-9 Av main course £4
Restaurant 12-2 7-9

YARCOMBE Devon Map 03 ST20

The Yarcombe Inn
YARCOMBE
EX14 9BD ☎ 01404 861676
Once owned by Sir Francis Drake, this historic pub offers a range of

imaginatively devised chef's specials. Expect home-made steak and kidney pie, warm onion and potato tart, lobster and tiger prawn ravioli, stuffed guinea fowl with port jus, and farmhouse mixed grill on the interesting menu. Ploughman's and open sandwiches are always available. **Principal beers:** Cotleigh Tawny, St Austell Dartmoor Best.
Directions On A30 between Chard and Honiton, 1m from A303
Brewery/Company Free House
Open 11-3 6-11 (Sun 12-10.30)
Bar food 12-2 6.30-10 Av main course £5
Restaurant 12-2 6.30-10 Av 3 course à la carte £20

Dorset

BLANDFORD FORUM Dorset *Map 03 ST80*

The Cricketers
BLANDFORD FORUM

Shroton, Iwerne Courtney DT11 8QD ☎ 01258 860421

Nestling in a sleepy village below Hambleton Hill, this homely village local is popular with local cricketers, and walkers hiking the Wessex Way. Expect fresh fish and good local game, perhaps pigeon with whisky and cream sauce, fish soup, cod in beer batter, and lobster and scallop thermidor on the blackboard menu. Baguettes and lasagne are always available.

Principal beers: Courage Directors, Cottage Brewery, Fullers London Pride, Flowers.
Directions Off the A350 Shaftesbury to Blandford road
Brewery/Company Free House
Open 11.30-2.30 7-11 (Sun 12-3, 7-10.30)
Bar food 12-2 7-9.45 Av main course £5.95
Restaurant 12-2 7-9.30 Av 3 course à la carte £16

The Crown Hotel
BLANDFORD FORUM

West St DT11 7AJ ☎ 01258 456626

Classic Georgian coaching house with plenty of period atmosphere, overlooking Blandford's handsome red-brick-and-stone town centre. Ideal base for touring Dorset. Bar fare includes venison sausages, grilled ribeye steaks and hot baguettes, while lemon sole, fillet steak, chicken with Stilton, and lamb cutlets feature on the restaurant menu.
Principal beers: Badger Tanglefoot, McMullen Country Best.
Directions M27 W onto A31 to junction with A350 W to Blandford. 100 metres from town bridge
Brewery/Company Hall & Woodhouse
Open 10am-11pm
Bar food 12-2 6.30-9.15 Av main course £6
Restaurant 12.30-2 7.15-9.15 Av 3 course à la carte £15 Av 3 course fixed price £15
Accommodation (Min) s£50 d£70

BOURTON Dorset *Map 03 ST73*

The White Lion Inn
BOURTON

High St SP8 5AT ☎ 01747 840866

The epitomy of an English pub, this stone-built village inn features old beams, flagstones, real fires and fishing mementoes. Good range of home-cooked food and traditional pub favourites. Apart from hot baguettes and jacket potatoes, there are steaks, duck with orange sauce, rack of lamb and grilled lemon sole. **Principal beers:** Ushers Best, Wadworth 6X, Courage Directors.
Directions Off A303, opposite B3092 to Gillingham
Brewery/Company Inntrepreneur
Open 12-3 5-11 (Sun 12-10.30)
Bar food 12-3 6.30-11
Restaurant 12-2.30 6.30-9.30 Av 3 course à la carte £25
Accommodation (Min) d£38

BRIDPORT Dorset *Map 03 SY49*

The Anchor Inn
BRIDPORT

Seatown DT6 6JU ☎ 01297 489215

Idyllically situated on the coast path below Golden Cap, the highest point on

contd.

the South Coast, this attractive beachside pub is popular with both locals and holidaymakers. Good value bar meals include seafood platter, crab sandwiches, monkfish kebabs, local lobster, and steak and kidney pie. Front terrace with sea views. **Principal beers:** Palmers - Bridport, IPA & Tally Ho!.
Directions On A35 turn S in Chideock opp church & follow single track rd for 0.75m to beach
Brewery/Company Palmers
Open 11-2.30 7-11 (Whit-end Aug 11-11. Food all day)
Bar food 12-2 7-9.30 Av main course £6

The George Hotel
BRIDPORT
4 South St DT6 3NQ ☎ 01308 423187
Handsome Georgian town house in the town centre. The old-fashioned, Victorian-style bar, complete with piped classical music, open fire and a mellow atmosphere, bustles all day, and offers decent morning coffee and croissants, and a good menu featuring fish and crab from West Bay, home-made rabbit pie, Welsh rarebit, and lambs' kidneys in Madeira. **Principal beers:** Palmers - IPA, Bridport Bitter & 200.
Directions Town centre
Brewery/Company Palmers
Open 8.30-11
Bar food 12-2.30 7-9 Av main course £4
Accommodation (Min) s£25 d£50

Shave Cross Inn
BRIDPORT
Shave Cross, Marshwood Vale DT6 6HW ☎ 01308 868358
Thatched, 14th-century cob and flint inn tucked away down narrow lanes in the heart of the beautiful Marshwood Vale. Once a resting place for pilgrims and travelling monks, it retains many original features and a delightful suntrap garden. Standard bar food includes chargrilled steaks, ploughman's lunches, Shave burger, and chicken, ham and mushroom pie. **Principal beers:** Hardy Royal Oak, Badger Best, Otter Ale.
Directions From Bridport take B3162 2m turn L signed 'Broadoak/Shave Cross' then Marshwood
Brewery/Company Free House
Open 12-3 7-11 (closed Mon, ex BHs, & Feb)
Bar food 12-2 7-9.30 Av main course £4
Restaurant 12-2 7-9.30

BUCKLAND NEWTON Dorset — *Map 03 ST60*

Gaggle of Geese
BUCKLAND NEWTON
DT2 7BS ☎ 01300 345249
Built in 1834 as a village shop, the Gaggle of Geese became a pub in 1846, changing its name from the Royal Oak 18 years ago when the previous landlord started breeding geese. Strictly other poultry on the menu, however, including chicken tikka along with other traditional pub dishes. **Principal beers:** Badger Dorset Best, Ringwood Best, Ringwood 49er, Oakhill.
Directions On B3143 N of Dorchester
Brewery/Company Free House
Open 12-2.30 6.30-11
Bar food 12-2 7-10 Av main course £5
Restaurant 12-2 7-10 Av 3 course à la carte £12

CERNE ABBAS Dorset — *Map 03 ST60*

The Red Lion
CERNE ABBAS
24 Long St DT2 7JF ☎ 01300 341441
Following a fire in the 1890s, parts of this 16th-century cottagey pub have been rebuilt in the Victorian style. Note the impressive original fireplace and picturesque south-facing garden. Appetizing home-cooked bar food includes steak and kidney pie, swordfish steaks, chicken filled with salmon mousse and crab salad. **Principal beers:** Wadworth IPA & 6X, Bass, Adnams Extra.
Brewery/Company Free House
Open 11.30-2.30 6.30-11
Bar food 11.30-2.30 6.30-11 Av main course £6.80
Restaurant 11.30-2.30 6.30-11 Av 3 course à la carte £12

The Royal Oak
CERNE ABBAS
23 Long St DT2 7JG ☎ 01300 341797
Thatched, creeper-clad, 16th-century inn, formerly a coaching inn and blacksmiths, situated in a picturesque village below the Dorset Downs. Home-cooked food is served in the cosy, traditional interior. Expect pub favourites and specialities like rough Dorset paté, venison in port, country chicken pie and local pheasant. **Principal beers:** Morland Old Speckled Hen, Butcombe, Hardy Royal Oak, Oakhill.

Directions On A352 N of Dorchester
Brewery/Company Free House
Open 11-3 6-11
Bar food 12-2 7-9.30 Av main course £6.95
Restaurant 12-2 7-9.30 Av 3 course à la carte £12.50

CHIDEOCK Dorset Map 03 SY49

The George Inn NEW
CHIDEOCK
Main St DT6 6JD ☎ 01297 489419
300-year-old thatched inn, formerly the village hall, not far from the coast. An impressive range of snacks and light lunches is available, plus steak and pasta dishes. The interesting vegetarian selection features nut roast Portuguese, and chestnut patties. Calamari, salmon, trout and lemon sole are among the seafood attractions. **Principal beers:** Palmers IPA & 200.
Directions On A35
Brewery/Company Palmers
Open 11-11
Accommodation (Min) s£17.50 d£37.50

CHRISTCHURCH Dorset Map 04 SZ19

Fishermans Haunt Hotel
CHRISTCHURCH
Salisbury Rd, Winkton BH23 7AS
☎ 01202 477283
Overlooking the sparkling waters of the River Avon, this old-world inn, dating back to 1673, is a popular base for those who enjoy angling and walking. Familiar dishes on the bar menu include steak and kidney pie and deep-fried plaice. Imaginative restaurant menu may offer rack of lamb, rump steak and Dover sole.
Principal beers: Gales IPA & HSB, Bass.
Directions 2.5m north on B3347(Christchurch/Ringwood rd)
Brewery/Company Gales
Open 10.30-2.30 5-11 (Sun 12-10.30)
Bar food 12-2 7-10 Av main course £6
Restaurant 12-2 7-10 Av 3 course à la carte £13.95
Accommodation (Min) s£48 d£64

CHURCH KNOWLE Dorset Map 03 SY98

The New Inn NEW
CHURCH KNOWLE
BH20 5NQ ☎ 01929 480357
Overlooking the Purbeck Hills and only a gentle country walk from Corfe Castle, this 16th-century thatched inn is a popular destination among visitors exploring this unspoilt area. Fresh fish - roast cod, haddock in beer batter, bouillabaisse - and traditional pub food (game pie, Blue Vinny ploughman's, local lamb dishes) are among the attractions.
Principal beers: Wadworth 6X, Morland Old Speckled Hen, Flowers Original.
Brewery/Company Free House
Open 11-3 6-11 (closed Mon Jan-Mar)
Bar food 12-3.15 6-9.15 Av main course £7.50
Restaurant 12-3.15 6-9.15

CORSCOMBE Dorset Map 03 ST50

The Fox Inn
CORSCOMBE
DT2 0NS ☎ 01935 891330
Idyllic, rose-adorned thatched pub tucked away down winding lanes in deepest Dorset. Dating from 1620 it features unspoilt beamed bars, a splendid rear conservatory, and three delightful cottagey bedrooms. Well worth seeking out for the excellent fresh fish dishes on the imaginative daily menus. Expect Galician-style cod, monkfish with red pepper salsa, Moroccan lamb tagine, venison in red wine, and rich chocolate torte.

contd.

Principal beers: Exmoor Ale, Shepherd Neame Spitfire, Fullers London Pride.
Directions From A37, between Yeovil & Dorcester, follow signs for Halstock/Corscombe on R
Brewery/Company Free House
Open 12-2.30 7-11
Bar food 12-2 7-11 Av main course £8
Restaurant 12-2.30 7-11 Av 3 course à la carte £16
Accommodation (Min) s£45 d£70

EAST CHALDON Dorset *Map 03 SY78*

The Sailors Return
EAST CHALDON
DT2 8DN ☎ 01305 853847
Splendid 17th-century thatched country inn tucked away in rolling downland, close to Lulworth Cove and miles of cliff walks. Comfortable beamed and flagstoned bar where a blackboard lists the food available. Expect lasagne, fresh cod, whole plaice, game pie, scallop and mussel Stroganoff and, perhaps, saddle of rabbit, and pig roasts. **Principal beers:** Flowers IPA, Fuller's London Pride, Wadworth 6X, Hook Norton Old Hooky.
Directions 1m S of A352 between Dorchester & Wool
Brewery/Company Free House
Open 11-2.30 6-11
Bar food 12-2 6-9 Av main course £4
Restaurant 12-2 6-9 Av 3 course à la carte £13.50

EAST KNIGHTON Dorset *Map 03 SY88*

The Countryman Inn
EAST KNIGHTON
Blacknoll Ln DT2 8LL ☎ 01305 852666
Tucked away just off the A352 in the heart of Hardy country, this attractive whitewashed pub offers a warm welcome and an extensive menu. The choice ranges from filled rolls, jacket potatoes and grills, to home-made specials like pan-fried turkey steak, deep fried butterfly prawns, and mushroom and leek tagliatelle. There is also a carvery.
Principal beers: Morland Old Speckled Hen, Courage Directors, Ringwood Best & Old Thumper, Theakston XB.
Directions On A352 between Warmwell Cross & Wool
Brewery/Company Free House
Open 10.30-3 6-11
Bar food 12-2 6.30-9.30 Av main course £6
Restaurant 12-2 6.30-9.30 Av 2 course fixed price £10.75

EAST MORDEN Dorset *Map 03 SY99*

The Cock & Bottle
EAST MORDEN
BH20 7DL ☎ 01929 459238
Occupying a lovely rural setting, this traditional village inn is an original cob-walled Dorset longhouse, parts of which date back 300 years. A seasonally-changing menu highlights good International cooking and wholesome country fare. Expect leek and mushroom crumble, home-made curries, roast pheasant, red bream with Cajun spices, and tuna with sun-dried tomatoes.
Principal beers: Badger Dorset Best & Tanglefoot.
Directions From A35 W of Poole take B3075. Pub 2m on R
Brewery/Company Hall & Woodhouse
Open 11-3 6-11
Bar food 12-2 6-9 Av main course £6.95
Restaurant 12-2 6-9 Av 3 course à la carte £17.50

EVERSHOT Dorset *Map 03 ST50*

The Acorn Inn
EVERSHOT
DT2 0JW ☎ 01935 83228
A perfect rural base from which to explore the beautiful Dorset coast and countryside, this 16th-century coaching inn enjoys a quaint, historic village setting. Expect comfortable accommodation and interesting home-cooked food. Menus range for traditional pub snacks, to cockle chowder, pork with onion and cider marmalade, and sea bass with caramelised shallot and red wine sauce. **Principal beers:** Fullers London Pride, Otter Ale.

Directions A303 to Yeovil, Dorchester Rd, on A37 R to Evershot
Brewery/Company Free House
Open 11.30-2.30 6.30-11

Bar food 11.30-2 6.30-9 Av main course £6
Restaurant 11.30-2 6.30-9 Av 3 course à la carte £15
Accommodation (Min) s£45 d£80

GILLINGHAM Dorset *Map 03 ST82*

The Kings Arms Inn
GILLINGHAM
East Stour Common SP8 5NB
☎ 01747 838325

200-year-old coaching inn set in the beautiful Blackmore Vale, opposite the conical Duncliffe Hill. Good base from which top explore the heart of Dorset. Traditional pub food ranges from toasted sandwiches and ham, egg and chips, to leek and Stilton bake, chicken, bacon and mushroom pie, lemon sole, and beef in red wine. **Principal beers:** Bass, Worthington Best.
Directions 4m W of Shaftesbury on A30
Brewery/Company Free House
Open 12-2.30 5-11
Bar food 12-2 Av main course £4.95
Restaurant 12-2 6-9.30 Av 3 course à la carte £6.95
Accommodation (Min) s£22.50 d£45

GUSSAGE ALL SAINTS Dorset *Map 04 SU01*

The Drovers Inn
GUSSAGE ALL SAINTS
BH21 5ET ☎ 01258 840084

16th-century free house where the home-made selection includes steak and mushroom pie, scrumpy pork, and chicken chasseur. Other main courses feature trout almondine, various steak grills, and for vegetarians there's mushroom Stroganoff and pasta with creamy white wine and Stilton sauce. Plus a selection of special coffees to finish. **Principal beers:** Marston's Pedigree, Ringwood Best.
Directions A31 Ashley Heath rdbt, R onto B3081
Brewery/Company Free House
Open 11-3 6-11
Bar food 12-2.30 7-9 Av main course £5
Restaurant 12-2.30 7-9 Av 3 course à la carte £10

Pubs offering a good choice of seafood on the menu

LODERS Dorset

Loders Arms NEW
LODERS
DT6 3SA ☎ 01308 422431

Unassuming stone-built local tucked away in a pretty thatched village close to the Dorset coast. Arrive early to bag a seat in the bar or in the homely (and tiny) dining room. Interesting blackboard menus may list fish soup, smoked haddock fishcakes and filled baguettes for bar diners, with the likes of scallops in Pernod, rack of lamb, and sea bass with salsa verde available throughout. Lovely summer garden. **Principal beers:** Palmers Bridport Bitter, Palmers IPA, Palmers 200.
Directions off the A3066, 2m NE of Bridport
Brewery/Company Palmers Brewery
Open 11.30-2.30 6-11
Bar food 12.30-2 7.15-9
Restaurant 12.30-2 7.15-9
Accommodation (Min) s£25 d£45

MARSHWOOD Dorset *Map 03 SY39*

The Bottle Inn NEW
MARSHWOOD
DT6 5QJ ☎ 01297 678254

Simply furnished 16th-century thatched pub situated on the edge of the Marshwood Vale. Specialises in organic food and drink and a good range of vegetarian meals. From natural breaded plaice, and organic baguettes, the specials menu may list Moroccan lamb and apricot tagine, pheasant in red wine, steak, stout and chestnut pie, and homity pie. **Principal beers:** Otter Ale, Marston Old Speckled Hen.

Directions 5m inland from Lyme Regis on the B3165
Brewery/Company Free House
Open 12-3 6.30-11
Bar food 12-2 7.30-9

MILTON ABBAS Dorset *Map 03 ST80*

The Hambro Arms
MILTON ABBAS

DT11 0BP ☎ 01258 880233

The thatched whitewashed appearance of this 18th-century longhouse completes the picturesque scene of an idyllic village street. Enjoy a traditional bar snack or, perhaps, noisettes of lamb, pheasant with mushrooms and red wine, or whole lemon sole from the specials board, in the comfortable lounge bar or on the pretty patio. **Principal beers:** Bass, Boddingtons.
Brewery/Company Greenalls
Open 11-3 6.30-11
Bar food 12-2 7-9
Restaurant 12-2 7-9
Accommodation (Min) s£35 d£55

MOTCOMBE Dorset *Map 03 ST82*

The Coppleridge Inn
MOTCOMBE

SP7 9HW ☎ 01747 851980

Tastefully converted 18th-century farm set in 15 acres with beautiful views across the Blackmore Vale. Choose, perhaps, ploughman's, crab salad, venison casserole, or fresh fish - cod with herb and cheese crust - in the bar, or scallops with bacon and cream, paella, or partridge with port sauce and game chips in the cosy bistro. **Principal beers:** Butcombe Bitter, Hook Norton, Fullers London Pride.
Brewery/Company Free House
Open 11-3 5-11
Bar food 11.30-3 5-11 Av main course £6.25
Restaurant 11.30-3 7-12 Av 3 course à la carte £17.50 Av 3 course fixed price £10
Accommodation (Min) s£42.50 d£75

NETTLECOMBE Dorset *Map 03 SY59*

Marquis of Lorne
NETTLECOMBE

DT6 3SY ☎ 01308 485236

Tucked away along narrow country lanes, this friendly 16th-century inn, formerly a farmhouse, enjoys peaceful rural views and offers good home-cooked food. Traditional snacks are supplemented by daily specials such as steak, ale and mushroom pie, pork schnitzel with sweet and sour sauce, fresh battered cod, and lamb Valentine. **Principal beers:** Palmers - Bridport, IPA & 200.
Directions 3m E of A3066 Bridport-Beaminster rd, after Mangerton Mill & West Milton
Brewery/Company Palmers
Open 11-2.30 6-11 (Sun 11-2.30, 7-10.30)
Bar food 11.30-2.30 7-10 Av main course £6.50
Accommodation (Min) s£40 d£60

NORTH WOOTTON Dorset *Map 03 ST61*

The Three Elms
NORTH WOOTTON

DT9 5JW ☎ 01935 812881

Overlooking the beautiful Blackmoor Vale, this country pub boasts a collection of over 1200 model cars. Extensive choice of real ales, club sandwiches and tasty snacks, while more substantial dishes include battered cod, home-made fish pie, beef and Guinness casserole, and a good range of vegetarian meals.
Principal beers: Fullers London Pride, Butcombe Bitter, Shepherd Neame Spitfire, Otter Ale.
Directions From Sherborne take A352 to Dorchester then A3030. Pub 1m on R
Brewery/Company Free House
Open 11-2.30 6.30-11
Bar food 12-2 6.30-10 Av main course £5
Restaurant 12-2 6.30-10 Av 3 course à la carte £10.50
Accommodation (Min) s£25 d£40

PIDDLEHINTON Dorset *Map 03 SY79*

The Thimble Inn
PIDDLEHINTON

DT2 7TD ☎ 01300 348270

The pub is so called because it was once as small as a thimble. It is a 250-year-old thatched property with a river running through the garden and a 22-foot well indoors. Good traditional food is on offer including steak and oyster pudding, several fresh fish dishes and curries.
Principal beers: Badger-Best & Tanglefoot, Hardy Country, Ringwood Old Thumper.
Directions A35 westbound, R onto B3143, Piddlehinton 4m
Brewery/Company Free House
Open 12-2.30 7-11 (Sun 12-2.30 7-10.30)
Bar food 12-2 7-9 Av main course £6
Restaurant 12-2 7-9 Av 3 course à la carte £10 Av 4 course fixed price £12

PLUSH Dorset *Map 03 ST70*

Brace of Pheasants
PLUSH

DT2 7RQ ☎ 01300 348357

Thatched 16th-century inn, originally a row of brick and flint cottages, enjoying an idyllic hamlet location surrounded by open downland. Lamb and rosemary pie and smoked haddock mornay are offered in the beamed bar, while restaurant fare includes trio of game breasts with port and redcurrant sauce, and crab and prawn thermidor. **Principal beers:** Fullers London Pride, Smiles Best, Bass, Wadworth 6X.

Directions A35 onto B3143, 1m to Piddletrenthide, then R to Mappowder & Plush

Brewery/Company Free House

Open 12-2.30 7-11 (Sun 12-3 7-10.30)

Bar food 12-2 7-9.30 Av main course £6.50

Restaurant 12-2 7-9.30 Av 3 course à la carte £17

POWERSTOCK Dorset *Map 03 SY59*

Three Horseshoes Inn
POWERSTOCK

DT6 3TF ☎ 01308 485328

Well worth the tortuous drive down narrow country lanes, this stone and thatch village inn offers superior pub food and fine valley views. Blackboard menus list local seafood (cracked Lyme Bay crab, sea bass with roasted peppers and saffron), alongside pheasant broth, game terrine, rack of lamb with caper and redcurrant sauce, and sticky toffee pudding. **Principal beers:** Palmers-Bridport & IPA.

Directions E of A3066 (Bridport/Beaminster rd)

Brewery/Company Palmers

Open 12-3 6-11

Bar food 12-2 7-9.30 Av main course £5.95

Restaurant 12-2 7-9.30 Av 3 course à la carte £20

PUNCKNOWLE Dorset *Map 03 SY58*

The Crown Inn
PUNCKNOWLE

Church St DT2 9BN ☎ 01308 897711

Picturesque 16th-century thatched inn, once a popular haunt of smugglers from nearby Chesil Beach, with a traditional atmosphere within its rambling, low-beamed bars. Hearty pub food ranges from sandwiches and scampi, to home-cooked pork and pigeon casserole, steak and kidney pie, and salmon with avocado and herb butter. **Principal beers:** Palmers-Bridport, IPA, Tally Ho! & 200.

Directions From A35, into Bride Valley, thru Litton Cheney. From B3147, inland at Swyre.

Brewery/Company Palmers

Open 11-3 7-11 (Sun 12-3,7-10.30)

Bar food 12-2 7-9.30 Av main course £6

Accommodation (Min) s£20 d£40

SHERBORNE Dorset *Map 03 ST61*

Skippers Inn
SHERBORNE

Horsecastles DT9 3HE ☎ 01935 812753

Old cider house, always busy, and recently refurbished to provide larger bars and a diners' area with a naval helicopter theme. Skippers is renowned for its fish, with at least ten fresh fish dishes on the menu, along with prime steaks, gammon, duck and the usual bar snacks. **Principal beers:** Wadworth 6X, Henrys IPA, & Valentines Old Malt Ale.

Directions From Yeovil A30 to Sherborne

Brewery/Company Wadworth

Open 11-2.30 6.30-11

Bar food 11.30-2 6.30-9.30 Av main course £6.75

Restaurant 12-2 6.30-9.30 Av 3 course à la carte £15

White Hart
SHERBORNE

Bishops Caundle DT9 5ND
☎ 01963 23301

On the site of a monks brewhouse, infamous Judge Jeffries held court at this historic inn, which boasts stone walls and beams. A wide range of functions are very willingly catered for. Typical menu includes White Hart chicken, Dorset blue steak, and a variety of curries. **Principal beers:** Badger Dorset Best, Tanglefoot, & IPA.

Directions On A3030 between Sherborne & Sturminster Newton

Brewery/Company Hall & Woodhouse

Open 11.30-2.30 6.30-11

Bar food 12-2 7-9.30 Av main course £6

Restaurant 12-2 7-9.30 Av 3 course fixed price £12

STUDLAND Dorset *Map 04 SZ08*

The Bankes Arms Hotel
STUDLAND
Watery Ln BH19 3AV ☎ 01929 450225
Just 500 yards from the beach and outstanding coastal walks, this creeper-clad stone inn overlooks Studland Bay. A simple menu highlights local fish such as sea bass, pollock and pan-fried plaice, and fresh crab and lobster. You will also find cottage pie and ploughman's on the menu. **Principal beers:** Six changing guest ales.
Directions B3369 from Poole, across on Sandbanks chain ferry, or A35 from Poole, A351 then B3351
Brewery/Company Free House
Open 11-11 (mid Nov-mid Mar 11-3,7-11) (Summer food all day)
Bar food 12-2.30 7-9/9.30 Av main course £10
Accommodation (Min) s£20 d£40

TARRANT MONKTON Dorset *Map 03 ST90*

The Langton Arms
TARRANT MONKTON
DT11 8RX ☎ 01258 830225
Thatched 17th-century inn with a bistro in a converted stable and a good choice of real ales in the rustic, beamed bar. Old English game dishes, faggots and steak pie are served in the bar, while the daily restaurant menu might offer herb-crusted cod baked with coriander cream sauce, or peppered fillet of pan-fried steak. **Principal beers:** Ringwood Best & 4 changing guest beers.
Directions A31 from Ringwood, or A357 from Shaftesbury, or A35 from Bournemouth
Brewery/Company Free House
Open 11.30-11 (Sun 12-10.30)
Bar food 12-2.30 6-9.30 Av main course £6.95
Restaurant 12-2.30 7-9 Av 3 course à la carte £19
Accommodation (Min) s£40 d£60

THREE LEGGED CROSS Dorset *Map 04 SU00*

Old Barn Farm
THREE LEGGED CROSS
Ringwood Rd BH21 6RE
☎ 01202 812901
Located on the edge of Cranbourne Chase, and less than a mile from Moors Valley Country Park, this converted 19th-century farm building is ideal for getting away from it all. It also has its own pond and a dovecote. **Principal beers:** Bass, Worthington.
Directions From Ashley Heath rdbt on A31, head toward Three Legged Cross, & pub is just over 2m to L
Brewery/Company Vintage Inns
Open 11-11 (Sun 12-10.30)

TOLPUDDLE Dorset *Map 03 SY79*

The Martyrs Inn
TOLPUDDLE
DT2 7ES ☎ 01305 848249
Originally the Crown Inn, the pub was renamed in honour of the six local farm labourers deported for their union activities. Tolpuddle Martyrs' memorabilia is strongly featured. Home-cooked fare includes fresh grilled trout with lime and dill butter, and rabbit in mustard and tomato sauce. **Principal beers:** Badger Dorset Best & Tanglefoot.
Directions Off A35 between Bere Regis (A31/A35 Junction)
Brewery/Company Hall & Woodhouse
Open 11-3 6.00-11 (Sun 6-10.30)
Bar food 12-2.30 6.30-9.30 Av main course £7.50
Restaurant 12-2.30 6.30-9.30 Av 3 course à la carte £7.50

TRENT Dorset *Map 03 ST51*

Rose & Crown Inn
TRENT
DT9 4SL ☎ 01935 850776
Unspoilt, beamed and flagstoned, stone and thatch village pub converted from two cottages in 1720. It reputedly once hid France-bound Charles II. Modern-day visitors come for the bistro-style food on offer, in particular fresh fish and local game. Typical dishes may include West Bay plaice with home-made tartare sauce, Thai chicken, and brochette of monkfish with couscous. **Principal beers:** Shepherd Neame Spitfire, Butcombe Bitter.
Directions A30 W on A30 towards Yeovil. 3m from Sherborne R to Over Compton/Trent, 1.5m downhill, then R. Pub opp church
Brewery/Company Free House
Open 12-2.30 7-11
Bar food 12-1.45 7-9 Av main course £7.75
Restaurant 12-1.45 7-9 Av 3 course à la carte £14

WEST BEXINGTON Dorset *Map 03 SY58*

The Manor Hotel NEW
WEST BEXINGTON
DT2 9DF ☎ 01308 897616
Just a short stroll from Chesil Bank and exhilarating coast path walks, this ancient manor house features a stone-walled cellar bar, oak-beamed lounges and imaginative cooking. Expect good fresh fish, rabbit casserole, steak and kidney pudding, rack of lamb with rosemary and mint crust, baked cod with cranberry sauce, and winter vegetable pudding. **Principal beers:** Hardy Royal Oak & County, Wadworth 6X.
Brewery/Company Free House
Open 11-11

Bar food 12-2 6.30-10 Av main course £8.55
Restaurant 12.15-1.30 7.15-9.30
Accommodation (Min) s£52 d£88

WEST KNIGHTON Dorset *Map 03 SY78*

The New Inn
WEST KNIGHTON
DT2 8PE ☎ 01305 852349
A 200-year-old pub with listed archway, formerly a row of farm cottages. Good base for walks and exploring the surrounding countryside. Meals are listed on the blackboard and, as well as sandwiches and baguettes, there is a range of wholesome meals, including Dorset mixed grill, rump steak and wholetail scampi. **Principal beers:** Ringwood - Best, Fortyniner & Old Thumper.
Brewery/Company Inn Partnership
Open 11-3 7-11.30 (Winter 12-3,7-11.30)
Bar food 12-2.30 7-9.30 Av main course £5
Restaurant 11.30-2.30 7-9.30 Av 3 course à la carte £11.50
Accommodation (Min) s£18 d£36

WEST STAFFORD Dorset *Map 03 SY78*

The Wise Man Inn
WEST STAFFORD
DT2 8AG ☎ 01305 263694
Set in the heart of Thomas Hardy country, this village pub displays a large collection of brass, pipes and Toby jugs, and local Morrismen meet and dance here in the summer. The menu features local meat, ham and fresh fish, and ploughman's with freshly baked bread. **Principal beers:** Bass, Marstons Pedigree, Ringwood Best & Fortyniner, guest beers.
Directions 2m from A35
Brewery/Company Free House
Open 11-3 6-11
Bar food 12-2.30 7-9.30 Av main course £4.50
Restaurant 12-2 7-9.30 Av 3 course à la carte £10

Gloucestershire

ANDOVERSFORD Gloucestershire *Map 04 SP01*

The Kilkeney Inn
ANDOVERSFORD
GL54 4LN ☎ 01242 820341
Charming character pub with a civilised dining ambience and delightful views of Cotswold countryside. Specials change daily and might include beef medallions with Madeira sauce, and herb-crusted rack of lamb. Expect fisherman's pie and warm croissant filled with bacon and black pudding with Stilton dressing on the light lunch menu. **Principal beers:** Ruddles Best, Tetley.
Directions On A436 1m W of Andoversford
Brewery/Company Free House
Open 11.30-2.30 6.30-11
Bar food 12-2 Av main course £6.50
Restaurant 12-2 7-9 Av 3 course à la carte £17

AWRE Gloucestershire *Map 03 SO70*

The Red Hart Inn NEW
AWRE
GL14 1EW ☎ 01594 510220
Built to house workers constructing the church opposite, this unusually tall country inn lies close to the Forest of Dean. Expect a friendly welcome and good value food. Menu choices range from Thai crab cakes and home-baked ham on the pub menu, to braised

contd.

pheasant, and rack of lamb with rosemary and red pepper jus. **Principal beers:** 4 guest beers.
Directions E of A48 between Gloucester & Chepstow, access is from Blakeney or Newnham villages
Brewery/Company Free House
Open 12-3 6.30-11 (Sat 12-3, 6-11/Sun 12-3, 7-10.30)
Bar food 12-2 7-9 Av main course £6.25
Restaurant 12-2 7-9 Av 3 course à la carte £22
Accommodation (Min) d£55

BARNSLEY Gloucestershire
Map 04 SP00

The Village Pub
BARNSLEY
GL7 5EF ☎ 01285 740421
Well placed for visitors to Barnsley House & Garden, this traditional Cotswold stone pub features open fires, antique settles and a collection of farming implements. Home-cooked food ranges from ploughman's and bagels, to salmon terrine, lamb and apricot casserole, grilled Bibury trout, leek mushroom and pasta bake, and beef in Guinness. **Principal beers:** Hook Norton Bitter, Wadworth 6X.
Directions On B4425 3m NE of Cirencester
Brewery/Company Free House
Open 10.30-3 6-11
Bar food 12.00-2 6.30-9.30 Av main course £7
Restaurant 12.00-2 6.30-9.30
Accommodation (Min) s£25 d£35

BISLEY Gloucestershire
Map 03 SO90

The Bear Inn
BISLEY
George St GL6 7BD ☎ 01452 770265
A priest hole, a bread oven and a huge inglenook fireplace are among the fascinating features at this charming village inn, supposedly used by gunpowder conspirators. Extensive bar menu features Bear burgers, a selection of home-made pies and casseroles and a wide choice of filled baguettes. **Principal beers:** Bass, Tetley, Flowers Original, Whitbread Castle Eden Ale.
Directions E of Stroud off B4070
Brewery/Company Pubmaster
Open 11-3 6-11
Bar food 12-2.30 7-10.30 Av main course £5.50
Accommodation (Min) d£36

BLEDINGTON Gloucestershire
Map 04 SP22

Kings Head Inn & Restaurant
BLEDINGTON
The Green OX7 6XQ ☎ 01608 658365
A 15th-century inn in a lovely setting facing the village green. Food is to be savoured here, with dishes such as smoked eel, steaks from the chargrill and extras to the menu including a fresh fish selection with whole baked grey mullet, game choice with local rabbit, and a pasta bowl with salad options. Comfortable B&B. **Principal beers:** Hook Norton Bitter, Wadworth 6X.
Directions On B4450 4m from Stow-on-the-Wold
Brewery/Company Free House
Open 11-2.30 6-11 9.45

Bar food 12-2 7-9.45 Av main course £4.95
Restaurant 12-2 7-9.45 Av 3 course à la carte £12 Av 3 course fixed price £10.95
Accommodation (Min) s£45 d£65

BLOCKLEY Gloucestershire
Map 04 SP13

The Crown Inn
BLOCKLEY
High St GL56 9EX ☎ 01386 700245
Mellow, 16th-century coaching inn set in one of the most attractive of the Cotswold villages. Charming interior with old beams, log fires and exposed stone walls. Interesting brasserie fare might offer chicken liver parfait, halibut with Burgundy sauce, or pork stir-fry with hoisin sauce. Decent snacks are served in the bustling bar.

Principal beers: Goff Jouster, Hook Norton Bitter, Fullers London Pride.
Brewery/Company Free House
Open 11-3 5-12
Bar food 12-2.30 7-10.30 Av main course £9.95
Restaurant 12-2.30 7-10.30 Av 3 course à la carte £25
Accommodation (Min) s£64 d£99

BROCKWEIR Gloucestershire — Map 03 SO50

Brockweir Country Inn
BROCKWEIR
NP6 7NG ☎ 01291 689548
A village pub, dating back some 400 years, situated on Offa's Dyke by the River Wye and Brockweir Bridge. Popular dishes include pork in cider, fresh local trout and Cajun chicken, followed perhaps by home-made cheesecake or steamed chocolate pudding.
Principal beers: Thwaites Bitter, Hook Norton Bitter.
Brewery/Company Free House
Open 12-2.30 6-11 (Sat 12-11)
Bar food 12-2.30 7-8.30 Av main course £4.50
Restaurant 12-2.30 7-8.30 Av 3 course à la carte £10
Accommodation (Min) s£28 d£40

CHEDWORTH Gloucestershire — Map 04 SP01

Hare & Hounds
CHEDWORTH
Foss Cross GL54 4NN ☎ 01285 720288
Surrounded by beautiful Cotswold countryside on a remote stretch of the Fosse Way, this ancient pub features flagged floors and open fires. Well respected new tenants (see Churchill Arms, Paxford) now offer innovative food, perhaps including salmon and sole terrine, pork with red cabbage and Thai spices, and cod with spiced couscous and red pepper pesto. **Principal beers:** Arkells 3B & Kingsdown.
Directions On A429(Fosse Way), 6m from Cirencester
Brewery/Company Arkell's
Open 11-3 6-11
Bar food 12-3 7-9.15 Av main course £8

Seven Tuns
CHEDWORTH
Queen St GL54 4AE ☎ 01285 720242
In the case of this unspoilt Cotswold village pub, the seven tuns refers to chimneys rather than beer barrels. There is a daily-changing menu, examples from which might be natural smoked haddock and chive fishcakes with Cheddar cheese sauce, lamb cutlets on a bed of gnocchi, and sea bass with wild rice and cep sauce.
Principal beers: Ruddles County, Georges Bristol Premium.
Directions A40 then A429 towards Cirencester, after 5m R for Chedworth, 3m then 3rd turning on R

Brewery/Company Free House
Open 12-3 6.30-11
Bar food 12-2 6.30-9 Av main course £8
Restaurant 12-2 6.30-9 Av 3 course à la carte £16

CHELTENHAM Gloucestershire — Map 03 SO92

The Little Owl
CHELTENHAM
Cirencester Rd, Charlton Kings GL53 8EB ☎ 01242 529404
Named after the 1981 Cheltenham Gold Cup winner, this double-fronted pub is situated near the popular Cotswold Way long-distance trail. Bar meals include wild boar sausages made to the inn's own recipe, and daily specials, perhaps including Italian risotto, turkey escalope, and pan-fried fillet of salmon. **Principal beers:** Wadworth 6X, Hook Norton Bitter.
Directions M5 (J11a) take A417 E,A436 then L onto A435. Approx 2m to pub
Brewery/Company Whitbread
Open 11.30-2.30 5.30-11.30
Bar food 12-2 6-10 Av main course £5.50
Restaurant 12-2 6-10 Av 3 course à la carte £15
Accommodation (Min) s£25 d£50

CHIPPING CAMPDEN Gloucestershire — Map 04 SP13

The Bakers Arms NEW
CHIPPING CAMPDEN
Broad Campden GL55 6UR ☎ 01386 840515
Located in one of the region's lesser-known villages, this small Cotswold inn has been licensed for the last 200 years.

contd.

Several open fires add to the cosy atmosphere. Straightforward pub food ranges from cottage pie and chicken curry, to spinach and mushroom lasagne and smoked haddock bake. **Principal beers:** Marstons Pedigree, Adnams Bitter, guest ales.
Brewery/Company Free House
Open 11.30-2.30 6.30-11
Bar food 12-2 6.30-9 Av main course £5

The Churchill Arms NEW
CHIPPING CAMPDEN
Paxford GL55 6XH ☎ 01386 594000
Quality cooking using fresh seasonal produce, decent wines and an informal atmosphere attract discerning diners to this charming Cotswold village pub. Interesting, daily-changing chalkboard menus may list goat's cheese soufflé with coriander and walnut pesto, followed by lamb with haricot beans, bacon and thyme, or gurnard with red pepper sauce, and sticky toffee pudding. **Principal beers:** Hook Norton Bitter, Arkell's, 3B & Kingsdown.
Directions 2m E of Chipping Campden, 4m N of Moreton-in-Marsh
Brewery/Company Free House
Open 11-3 6-11
Bar food 12-2.15 7-9.15 Av main course £9
Accommodation (Min) s£40 d£60

Eight Bells Inn
CHIPPING CAMPDEN
Church St GL55 6JG ☎ 01386 840371
A 14th-century inn of Cotswold stone with open fires and old beams, providing warm, comfortable surroundings. Dishes on offer from the ever popular Mr Lashford's sausages with mash and onion gravy to loin of lamb with aubergine and basil cream. **Principal beers:** Marstons Pedigree, guest beers.
Brewery/Company Free House
Open 11-3 5.30-11
Bar food 12-2.30 5.30-9.30 Av main course £8.50
Restaurant 12-2.30 6-9.30 Av 3 course à la carte £15
Accommodation (Min) s£30 d£50

The Noel Arms Hotel NEW
CHIPPING CAMPDEN
High St GL55 6AT ☎ 01386 840317
A 14th-century coaching inn with a stunning village setting in the heart of the Cotswolds. The inn is noted for its excellent food, with a separate area for bar food, such as Cotswold platter, rump steak, or chicken and mushroom pie. Restaurant dishes include sea bass, magret of duck, and assiette of chocolate. **Principal beers:** Hook Norton Bitter, Bass.
Brewery/Company Free House
Open 11-11 (Sun 11-10.30)
Bar food 12-2 7-9 Av main course £6
Restaurant 12-2 7-9.30 Av 3 course à la carte £20
Accommodation (Min) s£70 d£99

CIRENCESTER Gloucestershire
Map 04 SP00

The Crown of Crucis
CIRENCESTER
Ampney Crucis GL7 5RS
☎ 01285 851806
Traditional Cotswold village inn, the name of which refers to the very old cross in the churchyard. An award-winning ploughman's lunch is served in the bar along with shank of lamb with honey and rosemary, and steak and kidney pie. Interesting restaurant fare might include pork with caramelised onions, and red snapper with roasted tomatoes. **Principal beers:** Wadworth 6X, Archers Village, Theakston XB.

Directions On A417 to Lechlade, 2m E of Cirencester
Brewery/Company Free House
Open 10-11
Bar food 12-2.30 6-10 Av main course £5.60
Restaurant 12-2.30 7-10 Av 3 course à la carte £18 Av 3 course fixed price £17

CLEARWELL Gloucestershire Map 03 SO50

Wyndham Arms
CLEARWELL

GL16 8JT ☎ 01594 833666

A stone's throw from the glorious Wye Valley and the Forest of Dean, this splendid 13th-century inn oozes charm and character, especially in the stone-walled bar with its impressive inglenook. Good bar food includes soup and sandwiches, fresh salmon from the Wye, lasagne, Dover sole, and lamb's liver and bacon. **Principal beers:** Bass.

Directions In centre of village on the B4231

Brewery/Company Free House

Open 11-11 (Sun 12-10.30)

Bar food 12-2 6.45-9.30 Av main course £9.50

Restaurant 12-2 6.45-9.30 Av 3 course à la carte £21.25 Av 3 course fixed price £21.25

Accommodation (Min) s£58.50 d£80

COLESBOURNE Gloucestershire Map 04 SP01

The Colesbourne Inn
COLESBOURNE

GL53 9NP ☎ 01242 870376

An 18th-century coaching inn with exposed beams and log fires, and a large garden overlooking wooded hills. Appetising main courses include beef fillet with Stilton and horseradish, and salmon with bearnaise. Chocolate cheesecake and lemon ginger crunch are among the home-made puddings. **Principal beers:** Wadworth 6X, Henrys IPA & Farmers Glory.

Directions On A435 (Cirencester to Cheltenham road)

Brewery/Company Wadworth

Open 11.30-3 6.30-11

Bar food 12-2.30 7-10 Av main course £7.50

Restaurant 12-2.30 7-10 Av 3 course à la carte £20

Accommodation (Min) s£20 d£30

COLN ST-ALDWYNS Gloucestershire Map 04 SP10

The New Inn
COLN ST-ALDWYNS

GL7 5AN ☎ 01285 750651

Offering a successful blend of modern ideas and old English recipes, the menu at this imposing Elizabethan coaching inn features some innovative dishes. In addition to steak and kidney pudding and glazed Welsh rarebit with beetroot relish, restaurant choices might comprise Caesar salad with chargrilled swordfish, and fricassee of guinea fowl with olives, bacon and herbs.

Principal beers: Hook Norton Bitter, Wadworth 6X, Butcombe Bitter.

Directions Between Bibury (B4425) & Fairford(A417), 8m E of Cirencester

Brewery/Company Free House

Open 11.30-11

Bar food 12-2 7-9 Av main course £9.50

Restaurant 12-2 7.30-9.00 Av 3 course à la carte £26.50 Av 3 course fixed price £26.50

Accommodation (Min) s£68 d£96

CRANHAM Gloucestershire Map 03 SO81

The Black Horse Inn
CRANHAM

GL4 8HP ☎ 01452 812217

Traditional 17th-century inn with open fires and flagstone floors. Food evenings are regularly staged, offering cuisine with a distinctly international theme. Dishes are home-cooked, using locally supplied meat and vegetables. Beef and Guinness pie, fresh haddock, and sausage and bacon toad-in-the-hole are typical examples of the varied menu.

Principal beers: Wickwar Brand Oak, Hook Norton, Marstons Pedigree, Flowers Original.

Directions A46 towards Stroud, follow signs for Cranham

Brewery/Company Free House

Open 11.30-2.30 6.30-11

Bar food 12-2 7-9

EWEN Gloucestershire Map 04 SU09

The Wild Duck
EWEN

Drakes Island GL7 6BY ☎ 01285 770310

An Elizabethan inn of Cotswold stone set in a quiet corner on the edge of the village. In addidition to steaks, scampi and ploughman's, there's a daily blackboard menu offering market fresh fish, vegetarian options and specials such as roasted stuffed duck leg with bramble sauce. **Principal beers:** Theakstons Best & Old Peculier, Courage Directors, Smiles Best.

contd.

The Wild Duck

Directions From Cirencester take A429, at Kemble take L turn to Ewen, pub in village centre
Brewery/Company Free House
Open 11-11 (Sun 12-10.30)
Bar food 12-2 7-10 Av main course £6
Restaurant 12-2 7-10 Av 3 course à la carte £15
Accommodation (Min) s£49.50 d£69.50

FORD Gloucestershire *Map 04 SP02*

Plough Inn NEW
FORD
GL54 5RU ☎ 01386 584215
Long a favourite of Cotswold walkers, the idyllic, little 13th-century Plough, with its flagstone floors, open fires and sturdy pine furnishings, has all the atmosphere one could wish for. Home-made bar food ranges from lunchtime sandwiches and ploughman's, to lasagne, 16oz cod in beer batter, steak and fries, and pork tenderloin with mustard sauce. **Principal beers:** Donnington BB & SBA.
Directions 4m from Stow-on-the-Wold on the Tewkesbury road
Brewery/Company Donnington
Open 10.30-11 (Sun 12-10.30)
Bar food 12-2 6.30-9.15
Accommodation (Min) d£50

FOSSEBRIDGE Gloucestershire *Map 04 SP01*

Fossebridge Inn
FOSSEBRIDGE
GL54 3JS ☎ 01285 720721
Handsome Tudor and Regency coaching inn situated on the banks of the River Coln, boasting a fine lakeside terrace and gardens, and picturesque valley walks. Expect Thai chicken, breast of duck on red cabbage, beer-battered cod and speciality sausages on bubble and squeak on the enterprising menu, served in the civilised bars. **Principal beers:** Hook Norton Bitter, Bass, Wadworth 6X.
Directions From M4 J15, take A419 towards Cirencester, then take A429 towards Stow, pub approx 7m on L
Brewery/Company Free House
Open 12-2.30 7-9.30

Bar food 12-2.30 7-9.30 Av main course £9.95
Restaurant 12-2.30 7-9.30 Av 3 course à la carte £17
Accommodation (Min) s£49.50 d£69.50

GREAT RISSINGTON Gloucestershire *Map 04 SP11*

The Lamb Inn
GREAT RISSINGTON
GL54 2LP ☎ 01451 820388
Mellow stone-built former farmhouse dating from the 17th century, overlooking the Windrush Valley in the heart of the Cotswolds. Home-cooked bar meals range from French onion soup and chicken liver pate, to salmon pasta and steak and kidney pie. Separate restaurant menu and pretty, individually decorated bedrooms. **Principal beers:** Fullers London Pride, Ruddles County & guest beers.
Directions Between Oxford & Cheltenham off A40
Brewery/Company Free House
Open 11.30-2.30 6.30-11
Bar food 12-2 6.30-9.30 Av main course £5.50
Restaurant 12-2 6.30-9.30 Av 3 course à la carte £15
Accommodation (Min) d£50

For Pubs with AA food rosettes see page 430

GREET Gloucestershire *Map 04 SP03*

The Harvest Home
GREET

Evesham Rd GL54 5BH
☎ 01242 602430

Popular country inn built around the same time as the famous Great Western Railway which served the village. Well placed for visiting medieval Sudeley Castle, it offers honest home-cooking. Typical dishes include steak and mushroom pie, local Gloucester sausages, rack of lamb, sea bass with dill and vermouth sauce, and German specialities.

Principal beers: Hook Norton Bitter, Fullers London Pride, Boddingtons.
Directions M5 J9 take A435 towards Evesham, then B4077 & B4078 towards Winchcombe
Brewery/Company Whitbread
Open 11-3 6-11
Bar food 12-2 6.30-9.30 Av main course £6.25
Restaurant 12-2 6.30-9 Av 3 course à la carte £8

GUITING POWER Gloucestershire *Map 04 SP02*

The Hollow Bottom
GUITING POWER

GL54 5UX ☎ 01451 850392

An 18th-century building constructed of Cotswold stone, the pub has a horse racing theme and is frequented by racing personalities. The same menu is available in the bar and restaurant, and offers filled baguettes, chicken and mushroom pie, steaks, fresh fish, pasta and Sunday roasts. **Principal beers:** Goffs Jouster, Hook Norton Bitter, Bass.
Directions From Stow-on-the-Wold take B4068 (approx 5m) past golf course, next R signed Guitings at T-junc, R again, L at pub
Brewery/Company Free House
Open 11.30-11.30 (12-10.30 Sun)
Bar food 12-2.30 7-9 Av main course £7
Restaurant 12-2.30 7-9 Av 3 course à la carte £15
Accommodation (Min) s£25 d£45

HINTON Gloucestershire *Map 03 ST77*

The Bull Inn
HINTON

SN14 8HG ☎ 0117 937 2332

Beams, flagstone floors and a vast peaceful garden characterise this sturdy, stone-built, 450-year-old country pub, situated close to Dyrham Park (NT). Expect traditional pub food, including decent home-made curries, Wiltshire ham, egg and chips, hearty soups, steak and mushroom pie, and the classic Bull sandwich. **Principal beers:** Wadworth 6X & Henrys IPA, Bass, Adnams Broadside.
Directions From M4, A46 to Bath for 1m then R, 1m down hill, Bull on L
Brewery/Company Wadworth
Open 11.30-3 6-11
Bar food 12-2 6-9.30 Av main course £4
Restaurant 12-2 6-9.30 Av 3 course à la carte £16.50

HYDE Gloucestershire *Map 03 SO80*

Ragged Cot Inn
HYDE

Cirencester Rd GL6 8PE
☎ 01453 884643

17th-century free house with unusual undressed stone walls; hence the name Ragged Cot. Close to 600 acres of National Trust common land. Daily specials are displayed on the blackboard menu. Wide selection of filled jacket potatoes, sandwiches and rolls, and ploughman's lunches. Main course staples regulars salmon, gammon, and lamb curry. **Principal beers:** Bass, Theakston Best, Uley Old Spot.
Directions From M5 take A429 for Cirencester, Hyde 2m after Stroud on R
Brewery/Company Free House
Open 11-2.30 6-11
Bar food 12-2 7-9 Av main course £5.50
Accommodation (Min) s£40 d£58

LECHLADE Gloucestershire — Map 04 SU29

The Five Bells NEW
LECHLADE

Broadwell GL7 3QS ☎ 01367 860076

Attractive, 16th-century Cotswold stone inn overlooking the Manor and parish church. Character beamed and flagstoned bars, and conservatory leading to a pretty garden, ideal for summer alfresco dining. Extensive menus list salads, cod and chips, steak and kidney pie and salmon and prawn gratin, alongside specials like pheasant in red wine. **Principal beers:** Wadworth 6X, Hampshire King Alfred's, Archers Village.

Directions A351 from Lechlade to Burford, after 2m R to Kencot & Broadwell, then R after 200m, then R at crossrds

Brewery/Company Free House

Open 11.30-2.30 6.30-11 (Sun 12-3, 7-10.30)

Bar food 12-1.45 7-9 Av main course £4.35

Restaurant 12-1.45 7-9 Av 3 course à la carte £13 Av 3 course fixed price £12.95

Accommodation (Min) s£40 d£80

The Trout Inn
LECHLADE

St Johns Bridge GL7 3HA

☎ 01367 252313

Worth seeking out for its lovely position by the Weir Pool at a lock on the Thames, this 15th-century stone building was once an almshouse and is a popular refreshment stop among walkers strolling the Thames Path. Traditional bar food includes soups, casseroles and home-made pies. **Principal beers:** Courage Best & Directors, John Smiths.

Directions From A40 take A361 then A417. From M4 to Lechlade then A417 to Trout

Brewery/Company Courage

Open 10-3.30 6-11 (Summer 11-11)

Bar food 12-2 7-10

LOWER APPERLEY Gloucestershire — Map 03 S082

The Farmers Arms
LOWER APPERLEY

Ledbury Rd GL19 4DR ☎ 01452 780307

Traditional country pub in the heart of Gloucestershire, between the Cotswolds and the Malverns. The Farmers Arms serves two real ales brewed on the premises - Mayhems Odda's Light and Sundowner Heavy. The menu may include duck stir fry, Cajun chicken, beef and ale pie, or paprika pork. **Principal beers:** Farmers Arms Oddas Light & Sundowner, Wadworth 6X and guest beers.

Directions On B4213 SE of Tewkesbury (off A38)

Brewery/Company Wadworth

Open 11-3 6-11

Bar food 12-2 6-10 Av main course £5.95

Restaurant 12-2 6-10 Av 3 course à la carte £15

LOWER ODDINGTON Gloucestershire — Map 04 SP22

The Fox
LOWER ODDINGTON

GL56 0UR ☎ 01451 870555

Very pretty 15th-century village pub with a cottage garden, situated in the heart of the Cotswolds. Relax in the tastefully refurbished bars and sample some good bar food. A typical meal may feature curried parsnip and apple soup, or smoked mackerel mousse, followed by rack of lamb with onion sauce, fish pie, or salmon fishcakes, and double chocolate sponge pudding. **Principal beers:** Hook Norton Best, Marstons Pedigree, guest ale.

Directions A436 from Stow-on-the-Wold then R to Lower Oddington

Brewery/Company Free House

Open 12-3 6.30-11

Bar food 12-2 7-10 Av main course £7.95

MEYSEY HAMPTON Gloucestershire — Map 04 SP10

The Masons Arms NEW
MEYSEY HAMPTON

28 High St GL7 5JT ☎ 01285 850164

Cotswold stone building dating from the 17th century located beside the village green. Hot baguettes and salad platters are served in the bar with dishes such spicy lemon chicken or ham and eggs. Typical restaurant fare includes pork Stroganoff and rack of lamb with herb crust and redcurrant sauce. **Principal beers:** John Smiths, Wadworth 6X & Flowers IPA, Wychwood Shires XXX.

Directions A417 from Cirencester toward Fairford, after 6m R into village, pub on R by village green

Brewery/Company Free House

Open 11.30-2.45 6-11
Bar food 12-2 7-9.30
Restaurant 12-2 7-9.30
Accommodation (Min) s£36 d£52

MINCHINHAMPTON Gloucestershire — Map 03 SO80

The Old Lodge Inn NEW
MINCHINHAMPTON
Minchinhampton Common GL6 9AQ
☎ 01453 832047
Former 16th-century hunting lodge set in the middle of a 600 acre common. Pleasing rural outlook from pine-furnished rooms, good real ales and an imaginative choice of food. From sandwiches and jacket potatoes, the menu may also feature lamb and vegetable broth, stuffed saddle of lamb with port and redcurrant gravy, and beef ragout. **Principal beers:** Marstons Pedigree, Theakstons Best, Taylor Landlord, Fullers London Pride.
Brewery/Company Free House
Open 11-3 6.30-11 (closed Mon)
Bar food 12-2 7-9.30 Av main course £8.50

MISERDEN Gloucestershire — Map 03 SO90

The Carpenters Arms
MISERDEN
GL6 7JA ☎ 01285 821283
Dating from about 1700 and taking its name from the old carpenter's workshop on the premises, this historic inn stands on the Miserden Park Estate. Traditional Gloucestershire menu may include rump steaks, home-made faggots and mashed potato, braised mixed game sausages and deep-fried crispy cod. **Principal beers:** Brakspear Bitter, Wadworth 6X, Marston Pedigree.

Directions Leave A417 at Birdlip, take B4010 toward Stroud, after 3m Miserden signed.
Brewery/Company Free House
Open 11.30-3 6-11.20
Bar food 12-3 7-10 Av main course £5.50
Restaurant 12-3 7-10 Av 3 course à la carte £12.50

NAILSWORTH Gloucestershire — Map 03 ST89

Egypt Mill NEW
NAILSWORTH
GL6 0AE ☎ 01453 833449
Well-converted 16th-century flour mill with comfortable bedrooms, attractive riverside patio and many original features, including two working water wheels. Good bistro fare features fresh Cornish fish, chicken liver, pork and bacon terrine, honey-roast pork hock with wine and mustard sauce, tagliatelle with pesto, and chocolate and brandy mousse. **Principal beers:** Wadworth 6X.
Brewery/Company Free House
Open 10.30-11
Bar food 12-3 6.30-11 Av main course £9
Restaurant 12-3 6.30-11 Av 3 course à la carte £20
Accommodation (Min) s£45 d£75

NEWLAND Gloucestershire — Map 03 SO50

The Ostrich Inn
NEWLAND
GL16 8NP ☎ 01594 833260
The existing structure of this atmospheric pub is late 16th century, and it's situated opposite the fine 13th-century 'Cathedral of the Forest. Ever-changing blackboard menus may highlight Thai vegetable curry, venison with wild mushrooms, Mexican chicken, and unusual fish dishes like pike with lime masala, and zander with roasted peppers.
Directions Follow Monmouth signs from Chepstow (A466), Newland is signed from Redbrook
Brewery/Company Free House
Open 12-2.30 6.30-11
Bar food 12-2.30 7-9.30 Av main course £6
Restaurant 12-2.30 7-9.30 Av 3 course à la carte £18
Accommodation (Min) s£25 d£40

OAKRIDGE Gloucestershire
Map 03 SO90

The Butcher's Arms
OAKRIDGE

GL6 7NZ ☎ 01285 760371

Traditional Cotswold country pub with stone walls, beams and log fires in the renowned Golden Valley. Once a slaughterhouse and butchers shop. A full and varied restaurant menu offers steak, fish and chicken dishes, while the bar menu ranges from ploughman's lunches to home-cooked daily specials. **Principal beers:** Archers Best, Taylor Landlord, Tetleys, Hook Norton Best.

Directions From Stroud take A419 turn L for Eastcombe. Then follow signs for Bisley. Just before Bisley turn R to Oakridge

Brewery/Company Free House

Open 11-3 6-11

Bar food 12-3 6.30-11 Av main course £5

Restaurant 12-3 7.30-11 Av 3 course à la carte £16.50

OLDBURY-ON-SEVERN Gloucestershire
Map 03 ST69

The Anchor Inn
OLDBURY-ON-SEVERN

Church Rd BS35 1QA ☎ 01454 413331

Traditional pub built on the site of a mill with open fireplaces and large garden, close to the River Severn. Home-made bar food ranges from various salads, lasagne and moussaka, to honeyed Welsh lamb, Madras beef and cashew nut curry, pork au poirve, and smoked haddock with mustard and bacon sauce. **Principal beers:** Bass, Theakston Best & Old Peculiar, Worthington, Butcombe Bitter.

Directions From N A38 towards Bristol, 1.5m then R, village signed. From S A38 through Thornbury

Brewery/Company Free House

Open 11.30-2.30 6.30-11 (Sat 11.30-11, Sun 12-10.30)

Bar food 11.30-2 6.30-9.30 Av main course £5.95

Restaurant 11.30-2 6.30-9.30

PAINSWICK Gloucestershire
Map 03 SO80

The Falcon Inn
PAINSWICK

New St GL6 6UN ☎ 01452 814222

Built in 1554, this handsome coaching inn and former courthouse stands in a picturesque village on the route of the popular Cotswold Way. Home-cooked food includes everything from chargrilled Barnsley chop and lobster and tiger prawn ravioli, roast partridge in game sauce, and kangaroo casseroled in red wine.

Principal beers: Hook Norton Best, Greene King Abbot Ale, Wadworth 6X, Brakspear.

Directions On A46 in centre of Painswick

Brewery/Company Free House

Open 11-11

Bar food 12-3.30 7-11 Av main course £5.50

Restaurant 12-3 7-11 Av 3 course à la carte £14

Accommodation (Min) s£35 d£46

SHEEPSCOMBE Gloucestershire
Map 03 SO81

The Butchers Arms
SHEEPSCOMBE

GL6 7RH ☎ 01452 812113

Situated deep in Laurie Lee's Cider with Rosie country, this 17th-century inn has a famous sign depicting a butcher sipping a pint of beer with a pig tied to his leg. Mixed grills and pork escalope topped with pineapple, bacon and cheese are among the house specialities. **Principal beers:** Hook Norton Best, Archers Best, Uley Old Spot.

Directions 1.5m south of A46 (Cheltenham to Stroud road), N of Painswick

Brewery/Company Free House

Open 11.30-3 6-11.30

Bar food 12-2.30 7-11 Av main course £5.50
Restaurant 12-2.30 7-11 Av 3 course à la carte £14

SIDDINGTON Gloucestershire *Map 04 SU09*

The Greyhound
SIDDINGTON
Ashton Rd GL7 6HR ☎ 01285 653573
Village pub, formally a coach house, built of Cotswold stone with flagstone floors inside. A new function room incorporates an original well. Main course dishes include salmon steaks, rolled beef stuffed with horseradish, and breast of chicken with a cream and white sauce. **Principal beers:** Wadworth 6X & Henry's IPA, Badger Tanglefoot.
Directions A419 from Swindon, turn at sign for industrial estate, L at main rdbt, follow Siddington signs, pub at far end of village on R
Brewery/Company Wadworth
Open 11.30-3 6.30-11
Bar food 12-2 7-10 Av main course £7.50

SOUTHROP Gloucestershire *Map 04 SP10*

The Swan
SOUTHROP
GL7 3HU ☎ 01367 850205
Creeper-clad Cotswold pub with a busy public bar and skittle alley. Civilised dining areas offering good pub food with an emphasis on fresh ingredients. The short menu may list tiger prawns with coconut and lemon grass, and Stiton and onion soup, folowed by beef Wellington, pheasant with red wine and bacon, and treacle pudding. **Principal beers:** Morland Original, Archers Best.
Directions Off A361 between Lechlade and Burford
Brewery/Company Free House
Open 12-2.30 6.45-11.30
Bar food 12-2.30 7-9.30 Av main course £5.95
Restaurant 12-2.30 7-9.30

STOW-ON-THE-WOLD Gloucestershire *Map 04 SP12*

Coach and Horses
STOW-ON-THE-WOLD
Ganborough GL56 0QZ
☎ 01451 830208
Built of Cotswold stone and set beside an old coach road, this 250-year-old inn boasts a welcoming bar with beams, flagstones and an open fire. Well-kept Donnington ales and freshly-cooked bar food, including monkfish with cream and garlic sauce, seafood pancake, and hot filled baguettes. **Principal beers:** Donnington Best & SBA.
Directions On A424 2.5m from Stow-on-the-Wold
Brewery/Company Donnington
Open 11.30-2.30 6-11
Bar food 12-2 6.30-9.30 Av main course £4.50
Restaurant 12-2 6.30-9.30

STROUD Gloucestershire *Map 03 SO80*

Bear of Rodborough Hotel NEW
STROUD
Rodborough Common GL5 5DE
☎ 01453 878522
300-year-old coaching inn situated high above Stroud with magnificent views. Worth seeking out for the comfortable accommodation, and some sound home cooking. Using the best Cotswold produce, including good local cheeses, the varied menus may offer shank of lamb with mint and rosemary, vegetable curry and beef fillet with mustard crumble and thyme and shallot confit. **Principal beers:** Bass, Uley Bitter.
Directions From M5 J13 follow signs for Stonehouse then Rodborough
Brewery/Company Free House
Open 11-11
Restaurant 12-2.30 7-10 Av 3 course à la carte £19.95 Av 4 course fixed price £19.95
Accommodation (Min) s£65 d£90

The Ram Inn
STROUD
South Woodchester GL5 5EL
☎ 01453 873329
Built in 1601 from mellow Cotswold stone, this atmospheric inn, with huge open fire and excellent real ales, enjoys beautiful valley views from its summer patio. Interesting daily menus may list filled rolls, ham hock with creamy cider sauce, leek and lentil pie, chicken balti, and lamb and apricot pie, with toffee cheesecake for pudding. **Principal beers:** Uley Old Spot, Archers Best, Gales, John Smiths.
Directions A46 from Stroud to Nailsworth, R after 2m into S.Woodchester (brown tourist signs)
Brewery/Company Free House
Open 11-11 (Sun 12-10.30)
Bar food 12-2.30 6-9.30 Av main course £5.95
Restaurant 12-2.30 6-9.30 Av 3 course à la carte £11.80

Rose & Crown Inn
STROUD
The Cross, Nympsfield GL10 3TU
☎ 01453 860240
A 17th-century coaching inn of Cotswold stone, where good-value food is offered from a menu of over 70 items. There's something for everyone - snacks, curries, pies, fish and steaks - including a vegetarian choice and children's favourites. Puddings range from knickerbocker glory to treacle sponge.

Principal beers: Uley Old Spot, Wickwar BOB, Theakston Old Peculiar, Wadworth 6X.
Directions M5 J13 off B4066 SW of Stroud
Brewery/Company Free House
Open 11.45-11
Bar food all day
Accommodation (Min) s£32.50 d£55

TETBURY Gloucestershire
Map 03 ST89

Gumstool Inn
TETBURY
Calcot GL8 8YJ ☎ 01666 890391
The inn is Calcot Manor's own local, where the hotel's chefs provide food of a simpler, more rustic style. Local produce is used where appropriate, and representative dishes are Thai-spiced crab cakes, and wild boar steak and kidney pie, orange and sage sausages. To finish try the Calcot bread-and butter-pudding. **Principal beers:** Bass, Fullers London Pride, Wickwar Brand Oak Bitter & Coopers WBA.
Directions In Calcot (on jct of A4135 & A46, 4m W of Tetbury)
Brewery/Company Free House
Open 11.30-2.30 6-11 (Sat-Sun 11.30-11)
Restaurant 12-2.30 7-11 Av 3 course à la carte £25
Accommodation (Min) s£115 d£120

Hunters Hall
TETBURY
Kingscote GL8 8XZ ☎ 01453 860393
Dating back to 1650, this ancient hostelry has a wealth of charm and character, which is enhanced by stone-flagged floors and and exposed stone walls. From an extensive menu you may choose chicken liver pate for starters, followed by steak and ale pie, hake with pesto, or peppered rump steak. **Principal beers:** Uley Hogs Head, Bass, Ruddles Best, Theakstons.
Directions 5m W along A4135 from Tetbury
Brewery/Company Old English Inns/Hot
Open 7am-11pm
Bar food 12-2.30 6.30-9.30 Av main course £6.95
Restaurant 12-2.30 6.30-9.30 Av 3 course à la carte £15 Av 3 course fixed price £15
Accommodation (Min) s£41 d£61

Trouble House Inn
TETBURY
Cirencester Rd GL8 8SG
☎ 01666 502206
The distinctive sign at this Cotswold inn depicts a hanging, a drowning and a riot which took place during the Agricultural Revolution. Very low ceiling inside and three open fires. Interesting menu has a

racing theme and offers daily specials such as Suffolk hotpot, mushroom and cheese tagliatelle, and sirloin steak.
Principal beers: Wadworth 6X & Henrys IPA.
Directions On A433 between Tetbury & Cirencester
Brewery/Company Wadworth
Open 11-3 6-11
Bar food 12-2.30 6.30-9.30 Av main course £6

TORMARTON Gloucestershire — *Map 03 ST77*

Compass Inn
TORMARTON
GL9 1JB ☎ 01454 218242
Busy country inn well placed on the village edge and convenient for M4 (J18) travellers. The original 18th-century building has been extended to offer accommodation and a choice of restaurants. Game in season, fresh fish and local produce are featured in the Avon Room. Bar fare includes pies, steaks and daily specials. **Principal beers:** Bass, Smiles, Archers.
Directions From M4 take A46 towards Stroud for 100yds then R
Brewery/Company Free House
Open 11-11 (Sun 12-10.30)
Bar food all day
Restaurant 7pm-9.15 Av 3 course à la carte £20
Accommodation (Min) s£69.50 d£79.50

WINCHCOMBE Gloucestershire — *Map 04 SP02*

Royal Oak NEW
WINCHCOMBE
Gretton GL54 5EP ☎ 01242 602477
Lovely views across the Malvern Hills can be enjoyed from the extensive gardens and conservatory at this old Cotswold inn, complete with beamed and flagstoned bars, and steam train at the bottom of the garden. Excellent real ales and blackboard menu listing mussels grilled with Stilton, leg of lamb baked with mustard and garlic, ploughman's platters, and home-made puddings.
Principal beers: Morland Old Speckled Hen, Goff's Jouster, John Smiths, Wickwar Brand Oak.
Brewery/Company Free House
Open 11-3 6-11
Bar food 12-2 7-9.30 Av main course £7
Restaurant 12-2 7-9.30

WOODCHESTER Gloucestershire — *Map 03 SO80*

The Royal Oak
WOODCHESTER
Church Rd GL5 5PQ ☎ 01453 872735
Overlooking the Nailsworth Valley, the 17th-century Royal Oak features exposed Cotswold stone, oak beams and ancient flagstones throughout its neat interior. Imaginative home-made food ranges from corned beef hash and smoked salmon and scrambled eggs, to brill with white wine sauce, scallops on puréed celeriac, and pan-fried fillet steak.
Principal beers: Hook Norton Best, Uley Old Spot, Archers Best, Berkeley Old Friend.
Directions Take A46 south from Stroud, R at N Woodchester sign onto Selsley Road. Church Rd on L
Brewery/Company Free House
Open 11-11
Bar food 12-2 6.30-9.30 Av main course £4.50
Restaurant 6-9.30 Av 3 course à la carte £18

Somerset

APPLEY Somerset — *Map 03 ST02*

The Globe Inn
APPLEY
TA21 0HJ ☎ 01823 672327
Located in undulating Devon and Somerset border country, this 500-year-old inn is built of slate and familiar West Country cob. Good country walks nearby. Main courses include a good selection of steaks, breast of local chicken, lamb curry, fillet of pork, smoked haddock with bacon chowder, and seafood pancake. **Principal beers:** Cotleigh Tawny.
Directions From M5 J6 take A38 towards Exeter. Village signposted in 5m
Brewery/Company Free House
Open 11-3 6.30-11 (closed Mon lunch)
Bar food 12-2 7-10 Av main course £8
Restaurant 12-2 7-10 Av 3 course à la carte £15

ASHCOTT Somerset Map 03 ST43

Ring O Bells
ASHCOTT
High St TA7 9PZ ☎ 01458 210232
Ever-changing real ales and hearty, home-cooked food are among the attractions of this friendly 18th-century pub tucked away by the parish church. Typical blackboard specials may include cheese, ale and onion soup, sausage and bacon casserole, beef carbonade, fresh cod in batter, and coffee and walnut tart. **Principal beers:** Moor Withycutter.
Directions From M5 follow signs A39 & Glastonbury
Brewery/Company Free House
Open 12-3 7-11 (Sun 7-10.30)
Bar food 12-3 7-11 Av main course £5.50
Restaurant 12-3 7-11 Av 3 course à la carte £11

ASHILL Somerset Map 03 ST31

Square & Compass
ASHILL
Windmill Hill TA19 9NX
☎ 01823 480467
A traditional country pub specialising in good food and drink, with no fruit machines or juke box. The grounds enjoy magnificent views, and there is room in the garden for children to play. Dishes include breaded plaice, prawn and halloumi stir-fry, spaghetti Marinara, and a variety of ploughman's, sandwiches and salads.
Principal beers: Exmoor Ale.
Directions 1 mile off A358 between Taunton & Ilminster near to village of Ashill
Brewery/Company Free House
Open 12-3.30 6.30-11 (Sun 7-11)
Bar food 12-3 7-10 Av main course £6

AXBRIDGE Somerset Map 03 ST45

The Oak House
AXBRIDGE
The Square BS26 2AP ☎ 01934 732444
Parts of this inn date from the 11th century, and much of its historic character is retained in the beams, stone walls, inglenook fireplaces and an ancient well linked to the Cheddar caverns. Dishes in the bistro include fresh Brixham salmon and a trio of Axbridge sausages. **Principal beers:** Smiles.
Directions From M5 J22, take A38 to Bristol. Turn onto A371 to Cheddar/Wells, then L at Axbridge. Town centre
Brewery/Company Old English Inns/Hot
Open 12-3 7-11
Bar food 12-3 Av main course £3.85
Restaurant 12-3 7-11 Av 3 course à la carte £14
Accommodation (Min) s£42 d£57

BATH Somerset Map 03 ST76

The Olde Green Tree
BATH
12 Green St BA1 2JE ☎ 01225 448259
Bustling oak-panelled pub dating from 1752, with a genuinely unspoilt interior and up to five real ales from local breweries on handpump. Home-cooked lunchtime food ranges from bangers and mash, filled baps, and ploughman's, to fresh pesto spaghetti, fish pie and beef rogan josh. **Principal beers:** changing guest beers.
Directions Town centre
Brewery/Company Phoenix Inns
Open 11-11 (Sun 7-10.30)
Bar food 12-2.15 Av main course £4.80

BATHAMPTON Somerset Map 03 ST76

The George Inn
BATHAMPTON
Mill Ln BA2 6TR ☎ 01225 425079
A traditional country pub on the Kennet and Avon Canal in a quiet village location just a mile from Bath. Home-cooked food using fresh local produce includes Thai stir-fries (the house speciality), fresh fillet of salmon in a filo basket with Pernod sauce, and steaks from the grill. **Principal beers:** Wadworth 6X, Courage Best.
Directions M4 J18 onto A46 L at traffic lights & follow signs for Bathampton
Brewery/Company Scottish & Newcastle
Open 11-3 6-11.30
Bar food 12-2 6.30-9.30 Av main course £7.50

BECKINGTON Somerset Map 03 ST85

Woolpack Inn NEW
BECKINGTON
BA3 6SP ☎ 01373 831244
Relaxing 16th-century coaching inn featuring an attractive, flagstoned bar

and various cosy dining areas. Noted locally for good food, the wide range of freshly prepared dishes may include crab cakes with red Thai curry sauce, sea bass on squid with Parma ham, herb-roasted chicken on pumpkin risotto with port and tarragon jus, and lemon tart.
Principal beers: Greene King IPA, Wadworth 6X, Courage Directors.
Directions Just off A36 near junction with A361
Brewery/Company Old English Inns/Hot
Open 11-3 6-11
Bar food 11-2 6-9
Restaurant 11-2 7-9
Accommodation (Min) s£55 d£65

BLAGDON Somerset *Map 03 ST55*

The New Inn
BLAGDON
Church St BS19 6SB ☎ 01761 462475
Open fires, traditional home-cooked food and magnificent views across fields to Blagdon Lake are among the attractions at this welcoming 17th-century inn, tucked away near the church in a pleasant village. Dishes range from grills, fresh fish and ploughman's to steak and kidney pie and home-made apple crumble. **Principal beers:** Wadworth 6X, Henry's IPA & Summersault.
Directions From Bristol take A38 S then A368 towards Bath
Brewery/Company Wadworth
Open 11.30-3 7-11
Bar food 12-2 7-9 Av main course £5.95

BRADFORD-ON-TONE Somerset *Map 03 ST12*

White Horse Inn
BRADFORD-ON-TONE
TA4 1HF ☎ 01823 461239
Incorporating both the village stores and post office, this homely country pub enjoys a pretty setting opposite the parish church. Expect a friendly welcome and good-value traditional bar food, perhaps battered cod, steak and kidney pie, ham, egg and chips, ploughman's, and fresh mussels. **Principal beers:** Cotleigh Tawny & Barn Owl, Boddingtons.
Directions N of A38 between Taunton & Wellington
Brewery/Company Free House
Open 11.30-3.30 5.30-11
Bar food 12-2.30 6.30-9.30 Av main course £4.95
Restaurant 12-2.30 6.30-9.30 Av 3 course à la carte £11.50

BRIDGWATER Somerset *Map 03 ST33*

Ashcott Inn
BRIDGWATER
50 Bath Rd, Ashcott TA7 9QH
☎ 01458 210282
Pleasant 16th-century coaching inn featuring an oak beamed bar and pretty walled garden with children's adventure plays areas. Home-made bar food ranges from filled baguettes, cider-baked ham ploughman's, beef and ale pie and battered cod, to mixed grill, pork tenderloin with Dijon mustard sauce, and old English fillet steak. **Principal beers:** Butcombe, Wadworths 6X, Boddingtons.
Directions M5 J23 follow signs for A39 to Bridgwater
Brewery/Company Heavitree
Open 11-11 (Sun 12-10.30)
Bar food 12-2.30 6.30-9.30 Av main course £5.50
Restaurant 12-2.30 6.30-9.30 Av 3 course à la carte £15

BUCKLAND DINHAM Somerset *Map 03 ST75*

The Bell Inn
BUCKLAND DINHAM
High St BA11 2QT ☎ 01373 462956
A 16th-century creeper-clad stone village inn, with walled gardens and a terrace, surrounded by beautiful countryside. The bar serves a bistro menu, with baguettes, baked potatoes and burgers, while the restaurant offers fish, game, Mediterranean and Oriental dishes - typically Dijon roasted cod, and griddled wild boar steak. **Principal beers:** Morland Old Speckled Hen, Marstons Pedigree, Courage Best, John Smiths.

contd.

Directions 2m from Frome on A362,(S of M4, N of A303)
Brewery/Company Enterprise Inns
Open 11.45-3 6-11
Bar food 12-3 6.45-9.30 Av main course £9.50
Restaurant 12-3 6.45-9.30 Av 3 course à la carte £18

CASTLE CARY Somerset *Map 03 ST63*

The George Hotel
CASTLE CARY
Market Place BA7 7AH ☎ 01963 350761
Built of stone and thatch, this lovely 15th-century inn blends perfectly into this pretty and historic market town. From spacious bedrooms and cosy bars, it offers an imaginative range of dishes using fresh local produce, including, perhaps, rustic duck terrine, succulent pork tenderloin, scallops and samphire with basil butter, and a zesty lemon tart. **Principal beers:** Butcombe, Morland Old Speckled Hen.
Directions From A303 take A371 at Wincanton, then N to Castle Cary
Brewery/Company Old English Inns/Hot
Open 10-3 6-11
Bar food 12-2 7-9 Av main course £7.95
Restaurant 12-2 7-9 Av 3 course à la carte £20 Av 3 course fixed price £20
Accommodation (Min) s£45 d£65

CHARD Somerset *Map 03 ST30*

The Happy Return
CHARD
East St TA20 1EP ☎ 01460 63152
Run by the Welch family for over 40 years, this unassuming local, formerly the Railway Hotel, offers a warm welcome and a straightforward selection of bar food, including home-made lasagne, beef curry, whole lemon sole, sausage and bean bake, pork Stroganoff, filled jacket potatoes and an award-winning steak and kidney pie.
Principal beers: Butcombe Bitter.
Directions From M5 Taunton J, take Ilminster rd then follow signs to Chard, L at junct with A30 into East Street. Pub on R
Brewery/Company Free House
Open 12-3 7-11
Bar food 12.15-2.15 7-9.30 Av main course £3
Restaurant 12.15-2.15 7-9.30 Av 3 course à la carte £12
Accommodation (Min) s£17.50 d£35

Hornsbury Mill
CHARD
Eleighwater TA20 3AQ ☎ 01460 63317
Situated in five acres of landscaped water gardens, this 200-year-old corn mill and museum still has a water-driven working wheel. Varied menus range from lamb casserole and roasted root vegetable terrine in the bar, to Highland game terrine, Lyme Bay lemon sole or duck with masala and wild berries in the restaurant. **Principal beers:** Wadworth 6X, Shepherd Neame, Badger, Butcombe.
Directions A358 to Chard. Pub 2m
Brewery/Company Free House
Open 10.30-4 6.30-11 (closed Jan)
Bar food 12-4 Av main course £6.95
Restaurant 12-4 6.30-11 Av 3 course à la carte £19.50
Accommodation (Min) s£55 d£75

CHURCHILL Somerset *Map 03 ST45*

Crown Inn
CHURCHILL
The Batch, Skinners Ln BS25 5PP ☎ 01934 852995
Unspoilt gem of a stone-built pub on the edge of the Mendip Hills, with stone walls, flagstone floors, open log fires, and invigorating local walks. Freshly prepared food includes locally caught trout and salmon when available, in addition to decent sandwiches, filled jacket potatoes, cauliflower cheese, Stilton and pepper quiches and popular casseroles. **Principal beers:** Cotleigh Tawny, Palmers IPA, Smiles Golden, Bass.
Directions Take A38 S of Bristol.Turn R at Churchill traffic lights, then 1st L
Brewery/Company Free House
Open 11.30-11
Bar food 12-2.30 Av main course £3.95

CHURCHINFORD Somerset *Map 03 ST21*

The York Inn
CHURCHINFORD
Honiton Rd TA3 7RF ☎ 01823 601333
Character village inn dating from the 16th century and well worth the detour for the range of interesting, home-cooked food. Choose, perhaps, from smoked haddock with Welsh rarebit, herb-crusted rack of lamb, local game and fresh fish from Brixham. Light snacks available lunchtime. For pudding try the sticky toffee pudding.

Principal beers: Otter Ale.
Directions Exit M5 J26, towards Wellington for 0.5m, 1st L at rdbt. 1m L onto Ford St, 2m at top of hill L, 4m phone box, R to Inn
Brewery/Company Free House
Open 12-3 6-11
Bar food 12-3 7-11 Av main course £6
Restaurant 12-3 7-11 Av 3 course à la carte £20
Accommodation (Min) s£30 d£56

COMBE HAY Somerset Map 03 ST75

The Wheatsheaf
COMBE HAY
BA2 7EG ☎ 01225 833504
Fronted by an attractively landscaped garden, the 17th-century Wheatsheaf overlooks a peaceful valley south of Bath. A huge blackboard hangs in the stone-walled bar and lists home-cooked dishes such as game terrine, pheasant with juniper, redcurrant and port sauce, and bread-and-butter pudding. Cottagey bedrooms in a converted stable block.
Principal beers: Courage Best, John Smith.
Directions Take A369 Exeter rd from Bath to Oddown, turn L at park towards Combe Hay. Follow lane for approx 2m to thatched cottage & turn L
Brewery/Company Free House
Open 11-2.30 6-10.30 (Sun 12-3,7-10.30)
Bar food 12-2 6.30-9.30 Av main course £5.25
Restaurant 12-2 6.30-9.30 Av 3 course à la carte £15
Accommodation (Min) s£45 d£68

CRANMORE Somerset Map 03 ST64

Strode Arms NEW
CRANMORE
BA4 4QJ ☎ 01749 880450
Rambling, mostly 15th-century coaching inn, formerly a farmhouse, with splendid front terrace overlooking the village pond. Enjoy a drink with the daily papers, or order a meal from the interesting menus. Choose, perhaps, duck liver terrine, followed by chicken and ham pie or pheasant en croûte, and finish with orange and chocolate mousse.
Principal beers: Flowers IPA, Fuller's London Pride, Marston's Pedigree.
Directions S of A361, 3.5m E of Shepton Mallet, 7.5m W of Frome
Brewery/Company Free House
Open 11.30-3 6.30-11.30
Bar food 12-3 7-11 Av main course £6.50
Restaurant 12-2 7-9.30 Av 3 course à la carte £15

CREWKERNE Somerset Map 03 ST40

The Manor Arms
CREWKERNE
North Perrott TA18 7SG
☎ 01460 72901
Charming 16th-century hamstone-built pub overlooking the village green. Traditional home-cooked fare, served in the rambling, low-beamed bars, ranges from seafood crumble or chicken curry, to pan-fried monkfish or rack of lamb in the small restaurant. Puddings include treacle sponge and light lemon mousse.

Principal beers: Butcombe, Smiles.
Directions From A30 (Yeovil/Honiton rd) take A3066 towards Bridport, N Perrott 1.5m further on
Brewery/Company Free House
Open 11.30-2.30 6.45-11.30
Bar food 12-2 7-10 Av main course £5.25
Restaurant 12-2 7-10 Av 3 course à la carte £15
Accommodation (Min) s£35 d£38

DINNINGTON Somerset Map 03 ST41

Rose & Crown Inn
DINNINGTON
TA17 8SX ☎ 01460 52397
Licensed for over 250 years, this genuine village pub serves good value home-cooked food, including roast dishes, casseroles, fresh crab and lobster in season, and emphatically no fries. Sweets include apple and redcurrant crumble, and pear and ginger upside down pudding.

contd.

Principal beers: Butcombe Bitter, Wadworth 6X, Charles Wells Bombardier.
Directions N of A30 between Crewkerne & Chard
Brewery/Company Free House
Open 11-4 6-11
Bar food 12-3 7-10.45 Av main course £4.25
Restaurant 12-3 7-10.45 Av 3 course à la carte £7.50

DITCHEAT Somerset *Map 03 ST63*

The Manor House Inn NEW
DITCHEAT
BA4 6RB ☎ 01749 860276
Red-brick-built early 18th-century inn located in an unspoilt village close to the Bath & West Showground. Well placed for exploring Somerset, it offers ploughman's platters, filled granary rolls, and spaghetti Bolognese at lunchtime; evening fare includes rack of lamb with redcurrant sauce, whole lemon sole, chargrilled steaks, and fruit crumble.

Principal beers: Butcombe, Courage Directors.
Directions from Shepton Mallet take the Castle Cary road, after 3m R to Ditcheat
Brewery/Company Free House
Open 12-2.30 6-11
Bar food 12-2
Restaurant 12-2 7-10
Accommodation (Min) s£30 d£50

EXEBRIDGE Somerset *Map 03 SS92*

Anchor Inn
EXEBRIDGE
TA22 9AZ ☎ 01398 323433
A 17th-century coaching inn, mentioned in R D Blackmore's 'Lorna Doone', ideally located for exploring Exmoor. It is situated on the banks of the River Exe, and trout fishing can be arranged. Popular dishes include 12oz sirloin steak, fresh river trout and lasagne.
Principal beers: Wadworth 6X, Exmoor Ale, Fuller's London Pride, guest beers.
Directions On B3222
Brewery/Company Old English Inns/Hot
Open 11-11 (Sun 12-10.30)
Bar food 12-2 6.30-9 Av main course £5.95
Restaurant 7-9 Av 3 course à la carte £11
Accommodation (Min) s£40 d£60

EXFORD Somerset *Map 03 SS83*

The Crown Inn
EXFORD
TA24 7PP ☎ 01643 831554
A 300-year-old hotel overlooking the village green, in the middle of Exmoor National Park. Expect above average food, from bar meals like Exmoor lamb with thyme dumplings, and salmon and crab fishcake with turmeric sauce, to restaurant options like sea bass with tapenade, and partridge supreme on a celery and foie gras croustade. **Principal beers:** Exmoor Ale, Brakspear Special, Wadworth 6X.
Directions From M5 J25 follow signs for Taunton. Take A358 then B3224 via Wheddon Cross to Exford
Brewery/Company Free House
Open 11-3 6-11
Bar food 12-2 6.30-9.30
Restaurant 12-3 7-9.30 Av 3 course à la carte £27.50 Av 3 course fixed price £27.50
Accommodation (Min) s£45 d£80

FITZHEAD Somerset *Map 03 ST12*

Fitzhead Inn NEW
FITZHEAD
TA4 3JP ☎ 01823 400667
Cosy village pub hidden away in the Vale of Taunton. Expect a relaxed atmosphere, good real ales, and interesting home-cooked food. Typical dishes may include braised oxtail in red wine jus with celeriac and coriander mash, game casserole, stuffed teal, and fresh fish and seafood - shellfish platter, sea bass with prawn butter sauce. **Principal beers:** Cotleigh Tawny, Butcombe Bitter, Fullers London Pride, Juwards Ales.
Directions 1½m from Milverton
Brewery/Company Free House
Open 12-2.30 7-11
Bar food 12-2 7-10 Av main course £4.95
Restaurant 12-2 7-10 Av 3 course à la carte £13.70

FRESHFORD Somerset *Map 03 ST76*

The Inn at Freshford
FRESHFORD
BA3 6EG ☎ 01225 722250

A traditional country inn with extensive gardens and a pleasant setting by an ancient stone river bridge. There are delightful waterside walks to the Kennet & Avon Canal. Typical dishes include Stilton pork, lamb steaks, and oak-smoked chicken and toffee crisp pie for dessert. The specials board changes weekly and there are childrens meals too.
Principal beers: Courage.
Directions 1m from A36 between Beckington & Limpley Stoke
Brewery/Company Lanona Leisure
Open 11-3 6-11
Bar food 12-2 6-9.30 Av main course £7
Restaurant 12-2 6-9.30 Av 3 course à la carte £13

FROME Somerset *Map 03 ST74*

The Horse & Groom
FROME
East Woodlands BA11 5LY
☎ 01373 462802

There's an imaginative selection of appetising and regularly changing dishes at this country pub, such as home-smoked chicken with a lemon and tarragon dressing, oriental mushroom dumplings with plum sauce & rice, and duck served with black cherry and port sauce. Vegetarians might like to try the wild mushroom tagliatelle. **Principal beers:** Brakspear, Wadworth 6X, Greene King IPA, Butcombe.
Directions Just off Frome by-pass (A361 Shepton Mallet/Devizes rd)
Brewery/Company Free House
Open 11.30-2.30 6.30-11 (closed Mon lunch)
Bar food 12-1.45 6.30-9 Av main course £5.50
Restaurant 12-1.45 6.30-9 Av 3 course à la carte £14

The Talbot Inn
FROME
High St, Mells BA11 3PN
☎ 01373 812254

Rambling, 15th-century coaching inn with cobbled courtyard and beamed bars, nestling in a timeless feudal village. Expect a friendly welcome, real ales and real food, the latter ranging from cauliflower cheese and smoked salmon and prawn pasta, to pheasant in red wine, fresh sea bass, and chargrilled steaks.

Principal beers: Bass, Butcombe Bitter.
Directions From A36(T), R onto A361 to Frome, then A362 towards Radstock, 0.5m then L to Mells 2.5m
Brewery/Company Free House
Open 12-2.30 6-11
Bar food 12-2.30 7-12 Av main course £5
Restaurant 12-2.30 7-12 Av 3 course à la carte £16
Accommodation (Min) s£30 d£50

GLASTONBURY Somerset *Map 03 ST53*

The Who'd a Thought It Inn
GLASTONBURY
17 Northload St BA6 9JJ
☎ 01458 834460

18th-century building with lots of local artefacts and interesting memorabilia. One wall is covered in old photographs and there is even an award-winning gents loo. Typical fare available throughout the pub includes steak, Stilton and Guinness pie, game pudding, tenderloin of pork and whole grilled trout. **Principal beers:** Palmers IPA & 200.
Directions Bottom of High St, 100yds from Abbey ruins
Brewery/Company Palmers Brewery
Open 11-11 (Sun 12.30-2.45, 7-10.30)
Bar food 12-2.15 5.45-9.15 Av main course £5.25
Restaurant 12-2.15 5.45-9.15
Accommodation (Min) s£32.50 d£49

For Pubs with AA food rosettes see page 430

HASELBURY PLUCKNETT Somerset *Map 03 ST41*

The Haselbury Inn NEW
HASELBURY PLUCKNETT

North St TA18 7RJ ☎ 01460 72488

Originally used for the manufacture of sails and rope, this extended roadside pub enjoys an attractive village setting on the Dorset and Somerset border. From authentic curries, steaks and grills, the varied menu may list pheasant casserole, wild mushroom and pesto tagliatelle, stuffed pork tenderloin, and excellent fresh fish - roast cod on saffron mash. **Principal beers:** Wadworth 6X, Palmers IPA, Hardy Country Ale, Ringwood Best.
Directions Just off A30 between Crewkerne & Yeovil on B3066
Brewery/Company Free House
Open 11.45-2.30 6.45-11 (closed Mon)
Bar food 12-2 7-9.30 Av main course £7.95
Restaurant 12-2 7-9.30 Av 3 course à la carte £16 Av 3 course fixed price £10.95

HINTON ST GEORGE Somerset *Map 03 ST41*

The Lord Poulett Arms NEW
HINTON ST GEORGE

High St TA17 8SE ☎ 01460 73149

A 17th-century thatched hamstone inn nestling in a beautifully kept village. Strong enphasis on home-cooked food in the refurbished main bar. Dishes range from ploughman's, chicken liver paté with gooseberry relish and mixed fish gratin, to rabbit stuffed with apple and pistachio nuts, and beef in ale with caramelised onions. **Principal beers:** Butcombe Bitter, Otter Ale, Fullers London Pride, Whitbread Flowers.
Directions 2m N of Crewkerne, 1.5m S of A303
Brewery/Company Free House
Open 12-2.30 7-11
Bar food 12-2 Av main course £4
Restaurant 12-2 7-9 Av 3 course à la carte £16

ILCHESTER Somerset *Map 03 ST52*

Ilchester Arms
ILCHESTER

The Square BA22 8LN ☎ 01935 840220

Elegant, ivy-clad Georgian building in the town square, featuring flagstone floors, oak beams and open fires throughout its neat interior. Under new owners the menu now lists goat's cheese salad, home-made soups, hot filled baguettes, duck with honey and orange, or, perhaps, venison with port and juniper. **Principal beers:** Cottage - Our Ken & Golden Arrow, Butcombe Bitter.

Directions From A303 take A37 to Ilchester/Yeovil, L towards Ilchester at 2nd sign marked Ilchester. Hotel 100yds on R
Brewery/Company Free House
Open 11-11
Bar food 12-2.30 7-10 Av main course £8.95
Restaurant 12-2.30 7-10 Av 3 course à la carte £20
Accommodation (Min) s£55 d£70

ILMINSTER Somerset *Map 03 ST31*

New Inn
ILMINSTER

Dowlish Wake TA19 0NZ
☎ 01460 52413

A 350-year-old stone pub tucked away in a quiet village close to Perry's thatched cider mill. Neatly-kept beamed bar liberally bedecked with hops and featuring sturdy furnishings and a warming wood-burning stove. Good bar food includes pheasant casserole, rack of lamb, paella, and the Swiss landlady's specialities - fondue, carbonnade and raclette are all popular. **Principal beers:** Butcombe Bitter, Theakston Old Peculier, Wadworth 6X.
Directions From Ilminster follow signs for Kingstone then Dowlish Wake
Brewery/Company Free House
Open 11-3 6-11
Bar food 12-2.30 6.30-9.30 Av main course £4.95
Restaurant 12-2.30 6.30-9.30 Av 3 course à la carte £16

KILVE Somerset Map 03 ST14

The Hood Arms
KILVE
TA5 1EA ☎ 01278 741210
At the foot of the Quantock Hills, this 17th-century coaching inn is especially suitable for families. A meal may include venison casserole with apricot brandy, crispy duck in black cherry sauce, or Stilton and spinach lasagne. **Principal beers:** Exmoor Ale, Butcombe Bitter, Wadworth 6X.
Directions Off A39 between Bridgwater & Minehead
Brewery/Company Free House
Open 11-3 6-11
Bar food 12-2.30 6.30-10 Av main course £6
Restaurant 12-2.30 6.30-10 Av 3 course fixed price £13.95
Accommodation (Min) s£30 d£48

KINGSDON Somerset Map 03 ST52

Kingsdon Inn
KINGSDON
TA11 7LG ☎ 01935 840543
A 200-year-old thatched building with beams and log fires. Well-placed for weary A303 travellers. Its provides interesting food while maintaining a lively pub atmosphere. Seafood mornay and liver and bacon are typical bar meals, while the restaurant might offer roast duck in scrumpy sauce or grilled whole brill. **Principal beers:** Cotleigh Tawny, Otter Ale, Cottage Golden Arrow, Fullers London Pride.
Directions From A303 take A372 towards Langport then B3151 toward Street, 1st R and R again
Brewery/Company Free House
Open 11-3 6-11
Bar food 12-2 7-10 Av main course £5.50
Restaurant 7-10 Av 3 course à la carte £16

KNAPP Somerset Map 03 ST32

The Rising Sun Inn
KNAPP
TA3 6BG ☎ 01823 490436
The original building dates back to the 15th century, though it has been a pub for less than 40 years. Lookout for the excellent fresh fish dishes, though options range from traditional bar snacks to fillet steak. Typical examples are monkfish with curry sauce and rice, and scallops poached in a brandy and cream sauce. **Principal beers:** Exmoor Ale, Bass, Boddingtons.
Directions M5 J25, A358 then A378 follow signs for North Curry/Knapp

Brewery/Company Free House
Open 11.30-2.30 6.30-11
Bar food 12-2 7-9.30 Av main course £5
Restaurant 12-2 7-9.30 Av 3 course à la carte £25
Accommodation (Min) s£25 d£36

LANGLEY MARSH Somerset Map 03 ST02

The Three Horseshoes
LANGLEY MARSH
TA4 2UL ☎ 01984 623763
Handsome 300-year-old sandstone village inn close to Exmoor. Charming character bars full of old motoring memorabilia and a rustic mix of sturdy furnishings. Good food is genuinely home-made, with vegetables from the garden, and definately no chips! Expect filled baps, vegetable and lentil soup, rabbit casserole, cheesy-baked hake fillet, and fish pie. **Principal beers:** Palmers IPA, Otter Ale, Fullers London Pride, Wadworth 6X.
Directions M5 J25 take B3227 to Wiveliscombe. From square follow signs for Langley Marsh. 1m
Brewery/Company Free House
Open 12-2.30 7-11 (closed Mon Oct-Mar)
Bar food 12-2.30 7-11 Av main course £4.95

LANGPORT Somerset Map 03 ST42

Rose & Crown NEW
LANGPORT
Huish Episcopi TA10 9QT
☎ 01458 250494
Affectionately known as 'Eli's', after the present landlady's father, this individual pub has been in the Pittard family for 130 years. Thatched and with church-like windows and a stone floor, it is an unspoilt gem. Expect good ale from the barrel and simple, home-cooked food such as pork, apple and cider casserole, lamb hotpot and hearty soups.
Principal beers: Teignworthy Reel Ale, Bass, Hop Back Summer Lightning, Branscombe Vale Summa That.
Brewery/Company Free House

contd.

Open 11-2.30 5.30-11 (Fri-Sat 11-11, Sun 12-10.30)
Bar food 12-3 6-8.30 Av main course £5.50

LUXBOROUGH Somerset Map 03 SS93

Royal Oak Inn
LUXBOROUGH
TA23 0SH ☎ 01984 640319
Truly rural and unspoilt 14th-century inn nestling in a peaceful village deep in the Brendon Hills. Rustic, flagged-floor bars, neat dining areas, and pine-furnished bedrooms characterise the inn. Sample local real ales and ciders and hearty home-cooked food such as pork and Stilton pate, venison casserole, steak and ale pie, and roast cod fillet. **Principal beers:** Flowers IPA, Exmoor Gold, Cotleigh - Tawny & Harrier, Flowers IPA.
Directions From A38 (Taunton/Minehead) at Washford take minor rd S thru Roadwater
Brewery/Company Free House
Open 11-2.30 6-11
Bar food 12-2 7-10 Av main course £4.95
Restaurant 12-2 7-10 Av 3 course à la carte £20
Accommodation (Min) s£45 d£55

MONKSILVER Somerset Map 03 ST03

The Notley Arms NEW
MONKSILVER
TA4 4JB ☎ 01984 656217
White-painted roadside village pub with a stream in the garden, a charming interior and a bustling, friendly atmosphere. Good wholesome cooking is the attraction here, the short blackboard menu offering wild mushroom strudel, bacon, leek and cider pudding, cod with red pepper relish and mash, salmon fishcakes with crème fraîche, and, perhaps, treacle tart. **Principal beers:** Exmoor Ale, Wadworth 6X, Smiles Best.
Brewery/Company Unique Pub Co
Open 11.30-2.30 6.30-11 (closed 2 wks Jan/Feb)
Bar food 12-2 7-9.30 Av main course £5.75

MONTACUTE Somerset Map 03 ST41

Kings Arms Inn
MONTACUTE
Bishopston TA15 6UU ☎ 01935 822513
Delightful 16th-century hamstone inn, situated close to Montacute House (NT) in an unspoilt village, offering comfortable accommodation and a varied selection of bar meals (salmon and leek fishcakes, beef, Guinness and mushroom pie) in the Pickwick Bar. More imaginative fare, perhaps duck confit or monkfish with mustard sauce, is available in the restaurant. **Principal beers:** Bass, Courage Directors & Best.
Directions Turn off A303 at A3088 roundabout signposted Montacute. Hotel by church in village centre
Brewery/Company Old English Inns/Hot
Open 11-11
Bar food 12-3 7-10.30 Av main course £8.50
Restaurant 7-10.30 Av 3 course à la carte £19.50 Av 3 course fixed price £14.95
Accommodation (Min) s£55 d£70

The Phelips Arms
MONTACUTE
The Borough TA15 6XB
☎ 01935 822557
Overlooking the village square close to historic Montacute House (NT), this attractive, 17th-century hamstone building has a tranquil walled garden and character bars. Reliable bar food ranges from home-made soup and filled rolls, to boozy beef pie, sweet and sour pork, chicken curry, whole plaice, and treacle tart. **Principal beers:** Palmers IPA & 200.
Directions From Cartgate roundabout on A303 follow signs for Montacute
Brewery/Company Palmers
Open 11-2.30 6-11 (Sun 12-3,7-10.30)
Bar food 12-2 6-10 Av main course £6
Accommodation (Min) s£25 d£40

NETHER STOWEY Somerset Map 03 ST13

The Cottage Inn
NETHER STOWEY
Keenthorne TA5 1HZ ☎ 01278 732355
Dating from the 16th century, the Cottage is an old coaching inn and traditional cider house where cider was made until about 15 years ago. There is a bar menu of which includes fish dishes and char-grill specialities. The daily

specials might include rib-eye steak or a pasta bake. **Principal beers:** Whitbread Best, Worthington.
Directions M5 J23 follow A39 signs for Cannington/Minehead. Inn on A39
Brewery/Company Free House
Open 11-11 (Sun closed 3-7)
Bar food 12-2.15 6.15-9.30 Av main course £5

NEWTON ST LOE Somerset *Map 03 ST76*

The Globe Inn
NEWTON ST LOE
BA2 9BB ☎ 01225 875951
Believed to have been built in the 18th century, The Globe was first mentioned in the Bath Journal of March 1786. It was the setting for many local social events including a shooting match which offered two pairs of boots as prizes.
Principal beers: Bass, Worthington.
Directions On the junction of the A4 & A39, W of Bath
Brewery/Company Vintage Inns
Open 11-11 (Sun 12-10.30)

NORTH CURRY Somerset *Map 03 ST32*

The Bird in Hand NEW
NORTH CURRY
1 Queen Square TA3 6LT
☎ 01823 490248
Friendly 16th-century village inn with large stone inglenook fireplaces, flagstone floors, exposed beams and studwork. Food is prepared from fresh local produce and ranges from traditional bar snacks to hearty soups, Provencal beef casserole, Cajun spiced salmon, lemon sole pan-fried with herbs, and lemon tart.
Principal beers: Badger Tanglefoot, Exmoor Gold, Otter Ale, Cotleigh Barn Owl.
Directions village off A361, 4m W of Taunton & M5 J25
Brewery/Company Free House
Open 12-3 7-11 (Sat 12-4, 7-11. Sun 12-5, 7-10.30)
Bar food 12-2 7-11 Av main course £6

NORTON ST PHILIP Somerset *Map 03 ST75*

George Inn NEW
NORTON ST PHILIP
High St BA3 6LH ☎ 01373 834224
Built in the 13th century as a Carthusian guest house, the George, a striking stone and timbered building with a galleried courtyard, is one of the finest surviving medieval inns in the land. Recently refurbished and oozing atmosphere and historic charm, it offers lunchtime snacks, alongside crab and cod fishcakes, beef and ale pie and braised shank of lamb. **Principal beers:** Wadworth 6X, Henrys IPA, Old Timer & Summersault.

Directions From Bath take A36 to Warminster, after 6m take A366 on R to Radstock, village 1m
Brewery/Company Wadworth
Open 11-11
Bar food 12-2.30 6.30-9.30 Av main course £8.50
Restaurant 12-2.30 6.30-9.30 Av 3 course à la carte £16.50
Accommodation (Min) s£65 d£95

NUNNEY Somerset *Map 03 ST74*

The George at Nunney
NUNNEY
Church St BA11 4LW ☎ 01373 836458
Opposite a 13th-century castle in a historic conservation village, this rambling old coaching inn boasts a pretty walled garden. The George's steaks are a well-known local dish and are made from top grade Scotch beef. Other dishes include fillet of Brixham plaice, vegetable bake, chicken Wellington and chicken cordon bleu.
Principal beers: Highgate Saddlers, Wadworth 6X, Bass, Greene King.
Directions 0.5m N off A361, Frome/Shepton Mallet
Brewery/Company Free House
Open 12-3 6.30-11
Bar food 12-3 7-9
Restaurant 12-2 7-9 Av 3 course fixed price £5
Accommodation (Min) s£44 d£62

OVER STRATTON Somerset *Map 03 ST41*

The Royal Oak
OVER STRATTON

TA13 5LQ ☎ 01460 240906

A stone and thatch building, formerly three cottages, dating back some 400 years. Sit in the peaceful garden or in the character bars, complete with old beams, flagged floors and dried flower displays, and sample fresh cod in beer batter, peppered venison steak, smoked haddock, leek and Gruyère tartlet, seared king scallops with sweet chilli sauce, or beef Oakie.. **Principal beers:** Badger Best, IPA & Tanglefoot.

Directions A3088 from Yeovil, L onto A303, Over Stratton on R after S Petherton

Brewery/Company Hall & Woodhouse

Open 11-3 6-11

Bar food 12-2.30 7-10 Av main course £6

Restaurant 12-2.30 7-10 Av 3 course à la carte £20

PORLOCK Somerset *Map 03 SS84*

The Ship Inn
PORLOCK

High St TA24 8QT ☎ 01643 862507

13th-century thatched coaching inn nestling at the foot of Porlock Hill, between Exmoor and the sea. Mentioned in Lorna Doone, and Coleridge and Southey reputedly drank here. Traditional pub fare and a small but selective menu featuring venison sausages, lasagne, steak and ale pie and a range of seafood dishes. **Principal beers:** Cotleigh Barn Owl, Bass, Courage Best, guest beer.

Directions A358 to Williton, then A39 to Porlock

Brewery/Company Free House

Open 10.30-11

Bar food 12-2 6.30-9.30 Av main course £6

Restaurant 12-2 6.30-9.30 Av 3 course à la carte £9.50 Av 3 course fixed price £9.50

Accommodation (Min) s£27.50 d£50

For Pubs with AA food rosettes see page 430

PRIDDY Somerset *Map 03 ST55*

New Inn
PRIDDY

Priddy Green BA5 3BB ☎ 01749 676465

Overlooking the village green high up in the Mendip Hills, this 15th-century former farmhouse is popular among walkers, riders and pot-holers. Freshly prepared food may include lamb and apricot pie, pork and cider casserole, cheese souffle with roasted vegetables, halibut with orange and thyme sauce, decent soups and traditional bar snacks. **Principal beers:** Bass, Fullers London Pride, Wadworth 6X.

Directions From M4 J18 take A39 R to Priddy 3m before Wells. From J19 through Bristol onto A39. From M5 J21 take A371 to Cheddar, then B3371

Brewery/Company Free House

Open 11.30-2.30 7-11

Bar food 12-2 7-10 Av main course £6

Restaurant 12-2 7-10 Av 3 course à la carte £12

Accommodation (Min) s£21 d£32.50

RUDGE Somerset *Map 03 ST85*

The Full Moon at Rudge
RUDGE

BA11 2QF ☎ 01373 830936

There's been a coaching inn or hostelry on this site, at the crossroads of the old drovers' routes, since the early 1700s. The inn retains its small rooms, stone floors and scrubbed tables. Fresh fish is a feature, with dishes such as marlin and tomato salsa and tuna with chilli mayonnaise. **Principal beers:** Butcombe Bitter, Bass, Fullers London Pride.

Directions From A36 (Bath/Warminster rd) follow signs for Rudge

Brewery/Company Free House

Open 12-3 6-11

Bar food 12-3 Av main course £5.50

Restaurant 6.30-9.30 Av 3 course à la carte £20

Accommodation (Min) s£35 d£55

SHEPTON MALLET Somerset *Map 03 ST64*

The Three Horseshoes
SHEPTON MALLET

Batcombe BA4 6HE ☎ 01749 850359

A former toll house and smithy built in 1600, situated beside the parish church in the very rural Batcombe Vale. New

owners offer an interesting choice of food, such as orange and ginger soup, pork with garlic and thyme jus, salmon with sun-dried tomato and olive butter, and duck with wild berry sauce.
Principal beers: Butcombe Bitter, Wadworth 6X, Adnams.
Directions Take A359 from Frome to Bruton. Batcombe signed on R
Brewery/Company Free House
Open 12-3 6.30-11
Bar food 12.30-2 6.30-9.30
Restaurant 12-2 6.30-9.30 Av 3 course à la carte £20

The Waggon and Horses NEW
SHEPTON MALLET
Frome Rd, Doulting Beacon BA4 4LA
☎ 01749 880302
Dating from about 1790, this fine stone building was originally a coaching inn. Robust food with lots of flavour characterises the varied menu which has a strong Central European and Mediterranean theme and features Chinese and Thai cuisine. Representative main courses include braised pheasant, peppered steak, and baked sea bass.
Principal beers: Ushers Best, Founders & Seasonal Ales.
Directions 1.5m N of Shepton Mallet at crossroads with Wells-Frome road
Brewery/Company Ushers
Open 11-3 6-11.20 (Sun 12-3.30, 7-11)
Bar food 12-3 6.30-10.30
Restaurant 12-3 6.30-10.30 Av 3 course à la carte £15

SHEPTON MONTAGUE Somerset *Map 03 ST63*

The Montague Inn
SHEPTON MONTAGUE
BA9 8JW ☎ 01749 813213
Refurbished country inn with an attractive summer terrace with rural views, and a welcoming log fire in the bar. Food options range from decent bar snacks to more imaginative meals in the Red Room. Typical dishes may include casket of kidneys in Madeira, pan-fried cod on basil pesto, and nicoise onion tart. **Principal beers:** Butcombe Bitter, Greene King IPA, Fullers London Pride, Oakhill Best.

Pubs offering a good choice of seafood on the menu

Directions R off A371 between Wincanton & Castle Cary towards Shepton Montague
Brewery/Company Free House
Open 12-2.30 6-11 (closed Mon lunch)
Bar food 12-2.30 Av main course £6
Restaurant 7.30-11 Av 3 course à la carte £25 Av 3 course fixed price £25
Accommodation (Min) s£30 d£45

SOMERTON Somerset *Map 03 ST42*

The Globe
SOMERTON
Market Square TA11 7LX
☎ 01458 272474
Fresh fish at weekends and hearty English cooking draw local diners to this 17th-century former coaching inn in the market square. From salads, ploughman's and home-made soups, the main seasonally-changing menu lists grills, lamb steak with garlic and rosemary, and chicken supreme. **Principal beers:** Bass, Butcombe Bitter, Boddingtons.
Directions 4m from A303
Brewery/Company Punch Taverns
Open 11-2.30 5.30-11
Bar food 12-2 7-9.30 Av main course £4.50
Restaurant 12-2 7-9.30 Av 3 course à la carte £15

SPARKFORD Somerset *Map 03 ST62*

The Sparkford Inn
SPARKFORD
High St BA22 7JN ☎ 01963 440218
Antiques, pictures and oak settles create a cosy atmosphere at this high street coaching inn. Bar food includes soup, sandwiches and salad platters and there is a daily carvery at lunchtime with three roasts. The restaurant offers popular dishes such as grills, burgers and a fisherman's platter. **Principal beers:** Bass, Otter Ale, Fullers London Pride, Badger Tanglefoot.
Directions just off A303, 400yds from rdbt at Sparkford
Brewery/Company Free House
Open 11-3 6.30-11
Bar food 12-2 7-10 Av main course £5.80
Restaurant 12-2 7-10 Av 3 course à la carte £14 Av 2 course fixed price £8.65
Accommodation (Min) s£29 d£39

STANTON WICK Somerset Map 03 ST66

The Carpenters Arms
STANTON WICK
BS39 4BX ☎ 01761 490202

Civilised honey-coloured stone inn, formerly a row of 17th-century miners' cottages, overlooking the Chew Valley. Imaginative dishes are served in the informal Coopers Parlour. Look out for chargrilled loin of pork served with bubble and squeak, stir-fried fillet of beef, Thai chicken curry, and pan-fried skate. **Principal beers:** Bass, Butcombe, Otter, Courage Best.
Directions From A37(Bristol/Wells rd) take A368 towards Weston-s-Mare take 1st R
Brewery/Company Buccaneer Holdings
Open 11-11
Bar food 12-2.15 7-10 Av main course £7
Restaurant 12-2 7-9.30 Av 3 course à la carte £20
Accommodation (Min) s£52.50 d£69.50

STOKE ST GREGORY Somerset Map 03 ST32

Rose & Crown
STOKE ST GREGORY
Woodhill TA36 6EW ☎ 01823 490296

A pretty cottage-style pub with a popular front terrace and sitting area, and a 60ft well in the beamed bar. Expect the likes of scrumpy chicken and shepherd's pie in the bar, while the restaurant offers venison casserole, duck with orange sauce, and fresh fish from Brixham each day. **Principal beers:** Hardy Royal Oak & Hardy Country, Exmoor Ale.
Directions M5 J25, A358/A378 then 1st L through North Curry to Stoke St Gregory church on R. Pub 0.5m on L
Brewery/Company Free House
Open 11-3 7-11
Bar food 12.30-2 7-10 Av main course £6
Restaurant 12.30-2 7-10 Av 3 course à la carte £12.99 Av 3 course fixed price £12.99
Accommodation (Min) s£25 d£38

WAMBROOK Somerset Map 03 ST20

The Cotley Inn NEW
WAMBROOK
TA20 3EN ☎ 01460 62348

Good local walks, lovely views, a friendly welcome, and a peaceful village location are among the attractions at this long, stone-built pub. Cosy plush bar and adjoining dining room offering a wide range of meals, from a traditional snack menu and 'small eats' (chicken curry, lasagne), to 'big meaty eats' and vegetarian choices. **Principal beers:** Otter Ale, Boddingtons.
Brewery/Company Free House
Open 11.30-11
Bar food 12-3 7-11 Av main course £10
Restaurant 12-3 7-11 Av 3 course à la carte £10
Accommodation (Min) s£25 d£35

WATERROW Somerset Map 03 ST02

The Rock Inn
WATERROW
TA4 2AX ☎ 01984 623293

400-year-old former coaching inn built into the rock face, in a lovely green valley beside the River Tone. Sit in the peaceful bar, with winter log fire and traditional furnishings, and accompany steak and kidney pie or beef in red wine with a well-kept pint of Somerset ale. **Principal beers:** Cotleigh Tawny, Exmoor Gold.
Directions From Taunton take B3227.Waterrow approx 14m west
Brewery/Company Free House
Open 7-3 6-12
Bar food 11-2.30 6-11 Av main course £3.20
Restaurant 11-2.30 6-11 Av 3 course à la carte £12
Accommodation (Min) s£22 d£44

WELLS Somerset Map 03 ST54

The Fountain Inn/Boxers Restaurant
WELLS
1 St Thomas St BA5 2UU
☎ 01749 672317

This 15th-century inn once housed the labourers who helped to build Wells Cathedral, just 50 yards away. Bar food includes Mediterranean open toasted sandwiches, English doorsteps and dishes such as stir-fry of chicken and beef. A typical restaurant dish is monkfish kebab on a bed of couscous.

Principal beers: Ushers Best & Founders Ale.
Directions City centre, at junc of A371 & B3139
Brewery/Company Ushers
Open 10.30-2.30 6-11 (Sun 12-3,7-10.30)
Bar food 12-2.30 6-11 Av main course £5
Restaurant 12-2.30 6-11 Av 3 course à la carte £15 Av 2 course fixed price £5.95

The Pheasant Inn NEW
WELLS
Worth, Wookey BA5 1LQ
☎ 01749 672355
Situated at the foot of the Mendips with marvellous countryside views, this country pub has flagstone floors and a cosy beamed restaurant. Also features a large garden and a skittle alley. Menu may include Dover sole Cleopatra, chicken princess and penne Alfredo.
Principal beers: Butcombe, Bass, Morland Old Speckled Hen, Exmoor Gold.
Directions W of Wells on the B3139
Brewery/Company Free House
Open 11-3 6-11
Bar food 12-2 6.30-9.30 Av main course £5
Restaurant 12-2 6.30-9.30 Av 3 course à la carte £13.50

WEST CAMEL Somerset *Map 03 ST52*

The Walnut Tree
WEST CAMEL
Fore St BA22 7QW ☎ 01935 851292
Tucked away in an attractive village a minute's drive off the A303, this neatly refurbished inn offers well-equipped accommodation and interesting food. Local specialities and fresh fish feature on the menu, including Dorset crab, sea bass with tarragon and shallot sauce, lamb hock with rosemary and garlic sauce, fillet Rossini, and Thai fishcakes.
Principal beers: Bass, Butcombe.
Directions Off A303 between Sparkford & Yeovilton Air Base
Brewery/Company Free House
Open 11-3 6.30-11.30
Accommodation (Min) s£46 d£70

WEST HUNTSPILL Somerset *Map 03 ST34*

Crossways Inn
WEST HUNTSPILL
TA9 3RA ☎ 01278 783756
Handy for both M5 travellers (J23) and families returning from the beach, this 17th-century inn offers a relaxed atmosphere in its low-ceilinged bars, and good bar meals, notably home-made pies and chargrilled steaks. Traditional dishes include rabbit casserole, liver and bacon, beef and Guinness pie, and ploughman's lunches. **Principal beers:** Hardy Royal Oak, Flowers Original & IPA.
Directions On A38 3.5m from M5 J22/23
Brewery/Company Free House
Open 12-3 5.30-11
Bar food 12-2.30 6.30-9.30 Av main course £5
Restaurant 12-2.30 6.30-9.30 Av 3 course à la carte £9 Av 3 course fixed price £10
Accommodation (Min) s£24 d£34

WEST PENNARD Somerset *Map 03 ST53*

Apple Tree Inn
WEST PENNARD
BA6 8ND ☎ 01749 890355
Old stone building surrounded by open fields with views of the Mendip Hills. Regular dishes include chargrilled steaks and chops, home-made chicken Kiev and lasagne, and mussels. Cashew and nut paella, and pasta and vegetable crumble are on offer to vegetarians.
Principal beers: Butcombe.
Directions On A361(Glastonbury/ Shepton Mallet)between West Pennard & Pilton
Brewery/Company Free House
Open 11-2.30 6-11
Bar food 12-2 6.30-10 Av main course £6
Restaurant 12-2 2.30-10 Av 3 course à la carte £14

West Country

WINSFORD Somerset *Map 03 SS93*

The Royal Oak Inn NEW
WINSFORD
TA24 7JE ☎ 01643 851455
Ancient, impressive thatched inn set in the heart of an Exmoor village. Popular with locals and the hunting, shooting and fishing set, it offers 'country house' style accommodation and good country cooking in both the convivial bar and smart dining room. Expect hearty snacks and dishes like venison with port wine sauce, red mullet with capers, fillet of pork with cider sauce, and banana and toffee crumble on the daily menus.
Principal beers: Exmoor Ale, Whitbread Flowers Original and IPA, Shepherd Neame Spitfire.
Directions village off A396, 10m S of Dunster
Brewery/Company Free House
Open 11-3 6-11
Bar food 12-2 6.30-9.30 Av main course £7.50
Restaurant 12.15-2.30 7.30-11
Accommodation (Min) d£65

WITHYPOOL Somerset *Map 03 ST56*

Royal Oak Inn
WITHYPOOL
TA24 7QP ☎ 01643 831506 831236
Situated in the Exmoor National Park, this friendly, 300-year-old country inn has boasted some famous guests, including President Eisenhower and R D Blackmore, author of Lorna Doone. Expect the likes of steak and kidney pudding or fresh fillet of plaice in the bar, and roasted quail or escalope of venison in the restaurant.
Principal beers: Exmoor Ale & Fox Bitter, Tetley, Oakhill Yeoman.

Directions From M5 thru Taunton on B3224, then B3223 to Withypool

Brewery/Company Free House
Open 11-11
Bar food 11-2.30 6.30-9.30 Av main course £7
Restaurant 12-2 7-9 Av 3 course à la carte £19.50
Accommodation (Min) s£41 d£82

Wiltshire

ALDERBURY Wiltshire *Map 04 SU12*

The Green Dragon
ALDERBURY
Old Rd SP5 3AR ☎ 01722 710263
There are fine views of Salisbury cathedral from this 14th-century pub, which is mentioned in Martin Chuzzlewit by Charles Dickens. Interesting bar food ranges from salmon and coriander fishcakes and chilled ginger, carrot and lime soup, to sea bass with mint, ribeye steak with tomato and lime salsa, and sticky toffee pudding.
Principal beers: Badger Dorset Best & Tanglefoot.
Directions 1m off A36 (Southampton/Salisbury rd)
Brewery/Company Hall & Woodhouse
Open 11.30-2.30 6-11
Bar food 12-2 7-9 Av main course £5.95
Restaurant 12-2 7-9 Av 3 course à la carte £17

AXFORD Wiltshire *Map 04 SU27*

Red Lion Inn
AXFORD
SN8 2HA ☎ 01672 520271
17th-century brick and flint inn enjoying peaceful views across the lush Kennet Valley. Fresh fish and game (in season) feature on the blackboard menus. Choose from monkfish, baked sea bass, pheasant in red wine and cranberry or casseroled wild duck with sage and blueberries, or opt for lamb and apricot pie, rack of lamb or a decent steak. **Principal beers:** Hook Norton Best, Wadworth 6X, guest beers.
Directions M4 J15, A246 Marlborough centre. Follow signs for Ramsbury. Inn 3m
Brewery/Company Free House
Open 11-3 6.30-11
Bar food 12-3 7-10 Av main course £4.95
Restaurant 12-3 7-10 Av 3 course à la carte £20
Accommodation (Min) s£35 d£50

BARFORD ST MARTIN Wiltshire *Map 04 SU03*

Barford Inn
BARFORD ST MARTIN
SP3 4AB ☎ 01722 742242

Atmospheric, 16th-century coaching inn with welcoming lounge, lower bar area and intimate snug. Among the bar menu choices are home-made salmon fishcakes, and vegetable brushetta with grilled goat's cheese and pine kernel pesto. The regularly changing restaurant menu might feature pork tenderloin with apricot, mushroom and smoked bacon and apricot wine sauce or chargrilled veal with a garlic and herb crust. **Principal beers:** Badger Dorset Best, Badger Tanglefoot.
Directions on B3089 5m W of Salisbury
Brewery/Company Hall & Woodhouse
Open 11-11
Bar food 12-2.30 7-9.30 Av main course £6
Restaurant 12-2.30 7-9.30 Av 3 course à la carte £16
Accommodation (Min) s£35 d£45

BECKHAMPTON Wiltshire *Map 04 SU06*

Waggon & Horses
BECKHAMPTON
SN8 1QJ ☎ 01672 539418

A beautiful thatched coaching inn dating back 400 years located close to the Avebury Stone circles. It was mentioned in Dickens''Pickwick Papers', and offers the same friendly, informal atmosphere today. Favourite dishes include home-made soups, beef and ale casserole and beef and Stilton pie. **Principal beers:** Wadworth Henrys IPA, 6X, Old Timer & Summersault.
Brewery/Company Wadworth
Open 11-3 5.30-11.30 (Sun 6-10.30)
Bar food 12-2 5.30-11.30 Av main course £5.50

BOX Wiltshire *Map 03 ST86*

The Quarrymans Arms
BOX
Box Hill SN13 8HN ☎ 01225 743569

There are splendid views of the Colerene Valley from this 300-year-old miners' pub. Blackboard menus in the bar might list Quarryman's platter, spicy Boxhill bangers, Stilton and asparagus crepe, tuna with pepper sauce, and duck with grand marnier and orange sauce. Separate vegetarian selection and home-made puddings like treacle tart and chocolate terrine. **Principal beers:** Butcombe, Wadworth 6X, Abbey Bellringer, Moles and guest beers.
Directions Phone the pub for accurate directions
Brewery/Company Free House
Open 11-11 (Win Thu-Sun 11-11,Mon-Wed 11-3.30 6-11)
Bar food 11-3 6.30-9.30 Av main course £5.95
Restaurant 11-3 6.30-9.30 Av 3 course à la carte £15
Accommodation (Min) s£25 d£45

BRADFORD ON AVON Wiltshire *Map 03 ST86*

The Canal Tavern
BRADFORD ON AVON
49 Frome Rd BA15 1LE
☎ 01225 867426 865232

Kennet and Avon canalside pub displaying all manner of waterways memorabilia. A selection of steak grills is available, including prime fillet with pâté and Stilton in a rich wine sauce. Other main course dishes are roast duckling with apricot and brandy sauce, vegetarian moussaka, and couscous and cranberry lattice. **Principal beers:** Wadworth 6X, Wadworth Henrys Original IPA, Wadworth Old Timer, Bass.
Directions From Bath A4 to Bathford roundabout then A363
Brewery/Company Wadworth
Open 11-3 6-11
Bar food 12-2.30 7-10 Av main course £4.50
Restaurant 12-2.30 7-10 Av 3 course à la carte £14

BRINKWORTH Wiltshire *Map 04 SU08*

The Three Crowns
BRINKWORTH
SN15 5AF ☎ 01666 510366

A stone-built 200-year-old inn, on the village green close to the church, with a stone-flagged conservatory. Exotic meats - crocodile and ostrich - are a feature, alongside an array of imaginative dishes, such as tuna en croute with white wine and cream sauce, and guinea fowl with red wine and chocolate sauce. Lighter snacks are available.

contd.

Principal beers: Wadworth 6X, Bass, Boddingtons, Archers Village.
Directions A3102 to Wootton Bassett, then B4042, 5m to Brinkworth
Brewery/Company Whitbread
Open 10-3 6-11
Bar food 12-2 Av main course £5
Restaurant 12-2 6-9.30 Av 3 course à la carte £15

BROAD CHALKE Wiltshire — Map 04 SU02

The Queens Head Inn
BROAD CHALKE
1 North St SP5 5EN ☎ 01722 780344
Attractive stone-built inn, once the village bakehouse, overlooking the Ebble chalk stream. Relax in the homely beamed bars, or in the sheltered rear courtyard, and enjoy good sandwiches, sardines with lime and coriander butter, stilton and beef pie, peppered ribeye steak, or local game like partridge or jugged hare in season.
Principal beers: Greene King IPA & Triumph, Wadworth 6X.
Directions Take A354 from Salisbury toward Blandford Forum, at Coombe Bissett turn R toward Bishopstone, follow rd for 4m
Brewery/Company Free House
Open 11.30-3 6-11
Bar food 12-2 7-9 Av main course £6
Restaurant 12-2 7-9 Av 3 course à la carte £13.50
Accommodation (Min) s£30 d£50

BROMHAM Wiltshire — Map 03 ST96

The Greyhound Inn
BROMHAM
SN15 2HA ☎ 01380 850241
The landlord at this friendly 300-year-old pub used to be a diver, which explains the collection of miniature bottles and seashells. Large 36ft-deep well in the back bar. One menu is available throughout, ranging from red snapper and Dover sole, to fiery pork, and ham, egg and chips.
Principal beers: Wadworth 6X.
Directions Chippenham rd from Devizes for 4m. L into Bromham
Brewery/Company Free House
Open 11-2.30 6.30-11 (Sun 12-2.30, 7-10.30)
Bar food 12-2 7-10 Av main course £7
Restaurant 12-2 7-10 Av 3 course à la carte £15

BURBAGE Wiltshire — Map 04 SU26

Three Horseshoes Inn
BURBAGE
Stibb Green SN8 3AE ☎ 01672 810324
Good old-fashioned country cooking can be enjoyed at this thatched 200-year-old pub decorated with railway artefacts. From hearty snacks like Wiltshire ham and eggs, and ploughman's, the menu lists poacher's pie, lamb and watercress bake, fisherman's hotpot, and Italian chicken. **Principal beers:** Wadworth Henrys IPA & 6X.
Brewery/Company Wadworth
Open 12-2.30 6-11.30
Bar food 12-1.45 7-9 Av main course £5.75

BURTON Wiltshire — Map 03 ST87

The Old House at Home
BURTON
SN14 7LT ☎ 01454 218227
Authentic beamed pub on the edge of the Cotswolds. It may be in deepest Wiltshire but the choice of food makes the effort of getting there worthwhile. Dublin pheasant, steak bordelaise, woodland duck and griddled cod are typical examples of the inn's highly original menu. There are also pasta dishes and numerous puddings. **Principal beers:** Wadworth 6X, Smiles Best, Bass.
Directions On B4039 NW of Chippenham
Brewery/Company Free House
Open 11.30-2.30 7-11 (closed Tue lunch)
Bar food 12-2 7-10 Av main course £10

CALNE Wiltshire — Map 03 ST97

Lansdowne Arms
CALNE
Derry Hill SN11 9NS ☎ 01249 812422
Enjoying scenic views along the Avon Valley to Bath, this Victorian coaching house located close to Bowood House, offers an extensive menu. Home-cooked options include poached haddock fillet, chicken and smoky bacon fusilli, Moroccan lamb tagine, a variety of steaks, and mushroom and asparagus lasagne verdi. **Principal beers:** Wadworth 6X, IPA, Summersault, & Farmers Glory; Adnam Best.
Brewery/Company Wadworth
Open 11.30-2.30 6-11
Bar food 12-2 7-9 Av main course £7

CASTLE COMBE Wiltshire *Map 03 ST87*

The White Hart
CASTLE COMBE
Castle St SN14 7HS ☎ 01249 782295
A pub of great antiquity, with a history even more ancient than that of the 14th-century market cross it faces, the White Hart claims to have been an ale house since 1250. Crowded in summer and cosy in winter, both the character bar and patio garden are perfect for enjoying a pint and traditional bar snacks. **Principal beers:** Wadworth 6X, Adnams Best.
Brewery/Company Wadworth
Open 11-3 6-11
Bar food 12-2 6.30-9 Av main course £6.15
Restaurant 12-2 6.30-9

COLLINGBOURNE DUCIS Wiltshire *Map 04 SU25*

The Shears Inn & Country Hotel
COLLINGBOURNE DUCIS
The Cadley Rd SN8 3ED
☎ 01264 850304
A traditional thatched country inn with beams and brick floors, the Shears is well situated for both Marlborough and Salisbury. Bar food includes baguettes, jacket potatoes, and Wiltshire ham ploughmans', while restaurant fare may include fresh poached salmon, warm duck breast salad and chargrilled marlin.
Principal beers: Theakstons Best, Marstons Pedigree, Gales HSB.
Directions On A338 NW of Andover & Ludgershall
Brewery/Company Free House
Open 11-3 5.30-11
Bar food 12-2.15 7-9.30 Av main course £5.95
Restaurant 12-2.15 7-9.30
Accommodation (Min) s£35 d£50

CORSHAM Wiltshire *Map 03 ST87*

Methuen Arms Hotel

CORSHAM
2 High St SN13 0HB ☎ 01249 714867
The building began as a nunnery in the 14th century, and mullioned windows can still be seen in the long bar skittle alley, though the front part of the building is Georgian. A full range of snacks is served, along with Thai curry, seafood medley, and Barbary duck breast.
Principal beers: Wadworth 6X, Boddingtons, Bass.
Directions Town centre,on A4 between Bath & Chippenham
Brewery/Company Enterprise Inns
Open 11-2.30 6-11
Bar food 12-2 7-9.45 Av main course £5
Restaurant 12-2 7-9.45 Av 3 course à la carte £15
Accommodation (Min) s£43 d£55

CORSLEY HEATH Wiltshire *Map 03 ST84*

The Royal Oak Inn
CORSLEY HEATH
BA12 7PR ☎ 01373 832238
Situated on the edge of the Longleat estate, this 16th-century inn was built on the site of a 15th-century monk's retreat and is owned by the Marquis of Bath. Food includes salmon fishcakes, duck with peppercorn sauce and the pub's speciality, Royal Oak sausage made from lamb, game, spices and Wadworth 6X.
Principal beers: Wadworth 6X, Bass.
Directions On A362 between Warminster & Frome
Brewery/Company Wadworth
Open 12-2.30 6-11 (open all day Sun Etr-Sep)
Bar food 12-2.30 6.30-9 Av main course £6.25

CORTON Wiltshire *Map 03 ST94*

The Dove Inn NEW

CORTON
BA12 0SZ ☎ 01985 850109
Delightful Victorian pub with dovecote and sheltered courtyard nestling in a quiet hamlet in the picturesque Wylye Valley. Stylish blackboard menus listing baguettes, steak and stout pie, cod in beer batter, and evening choices like red snapper on buttered spinach with shellfish cream sauce, and lambs' liver on garlic mash with mushroom and Madeira sauce.
Principal beers: Oakhill Best, Brakspear, Wadworth 6X, Fullers London Pride.
Directions Between Salisbury & Warminster on minor rd (parallel to A36)
Brewery/Company Free House
Open 12-3.30 6-11 (wknd 12-11)
Bar food 12-2.30 7-9.30 Av main course £6.50

contd.

West Country

The Dove Inn

Restaurant 12.30-2.30 7-9.30 Av 3 course à la carte £17.50
Accommodation (Min) s£40 d£49.50

DEVIZES Wiltshire Map 04 SU06

The Bear Hotel NEW
DEVIZES
The Market Place SN10 1HS
☎ 01380 722444
Centrally located coaching inn dating back to 1559, and offering old-fashioned hospitality, light snacks in the cosy, low-beamed bar, and interesting restaurant fare. Expect ploughman's, soups and salads, and main meals like seared salmon on spring onion mash with vermouth cream sauce, and duck on red cabbage with port and redcurrant sauce. **Principal beers:** Wadworth 6X & Henry's IPA.
Brewery/Company Wadworth
Open 7-11.30
Bar food 11-2.30 7-9.15 Av main course £5.50
Restaurant 12.30-1.45 7-9.15 Av 3 course à la carte £16.50 Av 3 course fixed price £16.50
Accommodation (Min) s£54 d£80

The Elm Tree
DEVIZES
Long St SN10 1NJ ☎ 01380 723834
A 16th-century coaching inn with a function room for hire and a courtyard garden. Italian cooking is a speciality, and the menu offers a wide range of pizza and pasta dishes, including lasagne al forno, Arrabbiata, and a risotto Bolognese. Followed perhaps by tiramisu for dessert. **Principal beers:** Wadworth 6X, Henrys IPA & Farmers Glory.
Brewery/Company Wadworth
Open 12-3 6-11 (closed BH Mon)
Accommodation (Min) s£25 d£50

Fox & Hounds
DEVIZES
Nursteed Rd SN10 3HJ ☎ 01380 723789
Thatched former farmhouse located near its owning brewery - customers are guaranteed a tip-top pint of Wadworth 6X. Accompany it with a hearty snack, perhaps ham, egg and chips or a filled baguette, or choose home-made lambs' liver, bacon and onions, or roast pheasant with redcurrant sauce from the specials board. **Principal beers:** Wadworth 6X, Henrys IPA & Summersault.
Directions On A342 between Devizes & Andover, 1m from Devizes town boundary
Brewery/Company Wadworth
Open 11.30-2.30 6-11
Bar food 12-2 6-9 Av main course £5.75
Restaurant 12-2 6-9 Av 3 course à la carte £20

EAST KNOYLE Wiltshire Map 03 ST83

The Fox and Hounds
EAST KNOYLE
The Green SP3 6BN ☎ 01747 830573
Originally three cottages, dating from the late 15th century, this thatched pub overlooks the Blackmore Vale with fine views for up to 20 miles. A good choice of food ranges from sandwiches to steaks, with daily specials such as sweet and sour prawn balls, and pheasant casserole with Madeira wine. **Principal beers:** Fullers London Pride, Wadworth 6X, Smiles Golden, Butts Barbus Barbus.
Directions Off A303 onto A350 for 200yds, then R. Pub 1 0.5m on L
Brewery/Company Free House
Open 11-2.30 6-11
Bar food 12-2.30 7-10

EBBESBOURNE WAKE Wiltshire Map 03 ST92

The Horseshoe
EBBESBOURNE WAKE
Handley St SP5 5JF ☎ 01722 780474
Old farming implements adorn the homely bars of this traditional, unspoilt 17th-century village inn, peacefully situated in the rural Ebble Valley. Bar food is good value and freshly prepared from local produce. Expect fish bake, liver and bacon casserole, game pie and excellent Sunday lunches. Alfresco eating in the flower-filled garden.

Principal beers: Wadworth 6X, Ringwood Best, Adnams Broadside.
Brewery/Company Free House
Open 12-3 6.30-11
Bar food 12-2 7-9.30 Av main course £6.50
Restaurant 12-2 7-9.30 Av 3 course à la carte £15

FONTHILL GIFFORD Wiltshire *Map 03 ST93*

Beckford Arms
FONTHILL GIFFORD

SP3 6PX ☎ 01747 870385

Located opposite Fonthill Estate, this 18th-century stone-built inn provides a good base from which to explore the unspoilt Nadder Valley. Filled baguettes (smoked salmon and prawn), home-made soup or tagliatelle carbonnara followed by home made treacle sponge or apple pie will satisfy the heartiest of appetites.
Principal beers: Courage Best, Tisbury.

Directions 2m from A303 (Fonthill Bishop turning) halfway between Hindon & Tisbury at crossroads next to Beckford Estate
Brewery/Company Free House
Open 11-11
Bar food 12-2.30 7-9.30 Av main course £6.50
Accommodation (Min) s£35 d£65

FORD Wiltshire *Map 03 ST87*

The White Hart
FORD

SN14 8RP ☎ 01249 782213

Nestling beside the babbling Bybrook river, this rambling, mellow-stone, 16th-century coaching inn provides good ale and imaginative food within its cosy, half-panelled bar and adjoining dining areas. Interesting menus may list lunchtime ploughman's, salmon and prawn fishcakes, ham hock with herbed butter beans and parsley sauce, and glazed lemon tart.
Principal beers: Badger Tanglefoot, Marston's Pedigree, Wadworth 6X.

Directions From M4 J17 take A429 then A420, Ford is situated alongside A420
Brewery/Company Lionheart Inns
Open 11-3 5-11.30
Bar food 12-2 7-9.30 Av main course £6
Restaurant 12-2 7-9.30 Av 3 course à la carte £18
Accommodation (Min) s£55 d£79

GREAT HINTON Wiltshire *Map 03 ST95*

The Linnet
GREAT HINTON

BA14 6BU ☎ 01380 870354

Village pub with a front patio festooned in summer with colourful flower displays. Food ranges from Hawaiian-style gammon in the bar to navarin of lamb in the restaurant. There is a good choice of fish, such as fresh local trout with hazelnuts and tarragon butter.
Principal beers: Wadworth 6X & Henrys IPA.
Directions Just off the A361 Devizes to Trowbridge rd
Brewery/Company Wadworth
Open 11-2.30 6.30-11
Bar food 12-2 Av main course £5.95
Restaurant 12-2 6.30-9.45 Av 3 course à la carte £14.50

HEYTESBURY Wiltshire *Map 03 ST94*

The Angel Inn
HEYTESBURY

High St BA12 0ED ☎ 01985 840330

Former 17th-century coaching inn with a secluded courtyard garden. Typical menu options range from warm salad of pigeon breast with cranberry dessing, Venison steak with three mustard mash to fish dishes such as sautéed salmon on wild

contd.

mushroom and leek Stroganoff and fresh lobster with basil mayonnaise. **Principal beers:** Ringwood Best, Marstons Pedigree, Taylor Landlord.
Directions From A303 take A36 toward Bath, 8m, Heytesbury on L
Brewery/Company Free House
Open 11.30-3 6.30-11
Bar food 12-2.15 7-9 Av main course £6.95
Restaurant 12-2.15 7-9 Av 3 course à la carte £16
Accommodation (Min) s£37.50 d£49

HINDON Wiltshire *Map 03 ST93*

Grosvenor Arms
HINDON
SP3 6DJ ☎ 01747 820696
White-painted Georgian building situated in a pretty village close to the A303. Good accommodation and imaginative brasserie-style food served throughout the beamed bars. Expect warm salads, home-made soup and, perhaps, herb-crusted rack of lamb, rabbit wrapped in Parma ham with mustard cream sauce, and turbot with parsley and lemon jus. **Principal beers:** Wadworth 6X, Bass, Stonehenge Bitter.

Directions 1.5m from A303, on B3089 towards Salisbury
Brewery/Company Free House
Open 11-3 6-11
Bar food 12-2 7-9.30 Av main course £5.50
Restaurant 12-2 7-9.30 Av 3 course à la carte £20
Accommodation (Min) s£45 d£65

The Lamb at Hindon
HINDON
SP3 6DP ☎ 01747 820573
Situated in picturesque Hindon, this 17th-century posting inn is a handy refreshment stop for A303 travellers. A weekly market was held here until 1862, with business transactions conducted in the bar. Civilised restaurant serves local produce, including game in season, while bar food may feature hearty ploughman's lunches, venison and mushroom casserole, and whole Dover sole.

Principal beers: Tisbury Archibald Beckett, Ash Vine, Wadworth 6X, Exmoor Gold.
Directions 1m from A303 & B3089 in the centre of the village
Brewery/Company Free House
Open 11-11
Bar food 12-2 7-10 Av main course £7.95
Restaurant 12-2 7-9.30 Av 3 course à la carte £18.95 Av 3 course fixed price £18.95
Accommodation (Min) s£40 d£55

HORNINGSHAM Wiltshire *Map 03 ST84*

The Bath Arms
HORNINGSHAM
BA12 7LY ☎ 01985 844308
Puchased from Glastonbury Abbey and converted into a public house in 1763, the Bath Arms is situated at the driveway of Longleat House. A varied menu may feature crab and halibut in a filo basket, pan-fried monkfish, wild mushroom risotto, or pot roasted pork fillet.
Principal beers: Smiles .
Directions Off B3092 S of Frome
Brewery/Company Smiles
Open 12-3 6-11
Bar food 12-2.30 7-9.30 Av main course £7.50
Restaurant 12-2.30 7-9.30 Av 3 course à la carte £25

Pubs offering a good choice of seafood on the menu

HORTON Wiltshire *Map 04 SU06*

The Bridge Inn
HORTON
SN10 2JW ☎ 01380 860273
Spacious renovated pub, with well furnished bars, log fires, welcoming atmosphere, large garden with barbeque, situated next to the Kennet and Avon Canal. Homely bar food ranges from filled baguettes and lambs liver and bacon with bubble and squeak, to mint-crusted lamb, seafood tagliatelle, tuna with spicy salsa, and crème brûleé.
Principal beers: Wadworth Henry's & 6X.
Directions A361 from Devizes, R at 3rd roundabout
Brewery/Company Wadworth
Open 12-3 6.30-11
Bar food 12-2 7-9 Av main course £6
Restaurant 7-9 Av 3 course à la carte £15.95 Av 3 course fixed price £15.95

KILMINGTON Wiltshire *Map 03 ST73*

The Red Lion Inn
KILMINGTON
Kilmington BA12 6RP ☎ 01985 844263
Creeper-clad 15th-century coaching inn owned by the National Trust and handy for Stourhead Estate visitors. Cosy low-ceilinged bar, with open fires and old settles, in which to enjoy real ale and simple meals like game pie, lasagne, ploughman's, and fish pie. Good garden with views; popular with walkers.
Principal beers: Butcombe.
Directions B3092 off A303 N towards Frome. Pub 2.5m from A303 on R on B3092 just after turning to Stourhead Gardens
Brewery/Company Free House
Open 11.30-2.30 6.30-11 (Sun 7-10.30)
Bar food 12-2.30 Av main course £4
Accommodation (Min) s£25 d£30

LACOCK Wiltshire *Map 03 ST96*

The George Inn

LACOCK
4 West St SN15 2LH ☎ 01249 730263
Charming 14th-century pub, complete with large open fireplace and curious dogwheel operated spit, situated in an historic National Trust village. Traditional pub food ranges from sandwiches and ploughman's, to warm chicken and bacon salad, steak and kidney pie, lasagne, and wild boar steak with peppercorn sauce.
Principal beers: Wadworth 6X, Henrys IPA, Old Timer & Farmers Glory.
Directions M4 J17 take A350 S
Brewery/Company Wadworth
Open 10-2.30 5-11
Bar food 12-1.45 5.30-9.45 Av main course £5.95
Restaurant 12-1.45 5.30-9.45 Av 3 course à la carte £11
Accommodation (Min) s£25 d£35

Red Lion Inn
LACOCK
1 High St SN15 2LQ ☎ 01249 730456
With its timber buildings and gabled roofs, Lacock survives as a perfect example of medieval England. Adjacent to the Fox Talbot Museum of Photography, this historic inn has been refurbished to reflect its splendid Georgian past. Typical restaurant dishes might include seafood bake, beef in red wine and garlic, and spicy lamb casserole.
Principal beers: Wadworth Henry's IPA & 6X, Badger Tanglefoot.
Directions just off A350 between Chippenham & Melksham
Brewery/Company Wadworth
Open 11.30-3 6-11
Bar food 12-2.30 6-9 Av main course £6.95
Restaurant 12-2 6-9 Av 3 course à la carte £13
Accommodation (Min) s£55 d£75

LIMPLEY STOKE Wiltshire *Map 03 ST76*

The Hop Pole Inn
LIMPLEY STOKE
Woods Hill, Lower Limpley Stoke BA3 6HS ☎ 01225 723134
The Hop Pole dates from 1580, the name coming from the hop plant, which still grows outside the pub. Home-made pies, including steak and ale, are a speciality of the house, and there's a choice of fish, steaks and vegetarian dishes. Bar snacks encompass chip butties and samosas with salad. **Principal beers:** Courage Best, Butcombe, Bass.
Directions Off A36 (Bath to Warminster road)
Brewery/Company Free House
Open 11-2.30 6-11
Bar food 11.30-2.30 6.15-9.15 Av main course £5.50
Restaurant 11.30-2.30 6.15-9.15 Av 3 course à la carte £8 Av 3 course fixed price £14

LITTLE BEDWYN Wiltshire
Map 04 SU26

The Harrow Inn
LITTLE BEDWYN

SN8 3JP ☎ 01672 870871

Elegantly refurbished Victorian pub situated near the Kennet and Avon Canal, formerly a basic village local and post office. Expect inspired daily-changing menus featuring fresh fish and seafood and local game in season. Imaginative dishes range from Thai fishcakes and steak sandwiches, to confit of duck, turbot with cockles, garlic and lime, and mallard with pear and game jus. **Principal beers:** Wadworth 6X, Archers Village, Brains SA.

Directions From M4, A338 to Hungerford then R on A4 to Marlborough. After 2m L to Little Bedwyn
Brewery/Company Free House
Open 12-3 6-12 (closed Sun eve & all Mon)
Bar food 12-3 Av main course £4.95
Restaurant 12-3 7-12 Av 3 course à la carte £25

LITTLE CHEVERELL Wiltshire
Map 03 ST95

The Owl
LITTLE CHEVERELL

Low Rd SN10 4JS ☎ 01380 812263

19th-century local in a tiny hamlet, surrounded by farm land with views of Salisbury Plain, and a garden that runs down to Cheverell Brook. Today's specials may be cod fillet fried in olive oil, whole knuckle end of lamb with Cumberland sauce, or honey roast gammon with parsley sauce.
Principal beers: Wadworth 6X.
Directions A344 from Stonehenge, then A360, after 10m L onto B3098, R after 0.5m, Owl signposted
Brewery/Company Free House
Open 12-2.30 7-11 (closed all Mon, & Sun eve in winter)
Bar food 12-2 7-9.30 Av main course £5.95

LOWER WOODFORD Wiltshire
Map 04 SU13

The Wheatsheaf
LOWER WOODFORD

SP4 6NQ ☎ 01722 782203

Popular 18th-century inn nestling in the charming Woodford Valley overlooking the River Avon. Delightful riverside garden and good value home-cooked food. Typical meals include a range of steaks, Wiltshire ham and eggs, and fresh fish and vegetarian options listed on a daily specials board, and home-made apple pie. **Principal beers:** Badger Dorset Best & Tanglefoot.
Directions Take A360 N of Salisbury. Village signposted 1st R
Brewery/Company Hall & Woodhouse
Open 11-2.30 6.30-11
Bar food 12-2 6.30-9.30 Av main course £5.50

MALMESBURY Wiltshire
Map 03 ST98

Horse & Groom
MALMESBURY

The Street, Charlton SN16 9DL
☎ 01666 823904

Handsome 16th-century stone coaching inn set back from the road, with stone-floored bars and well-appointed bedrooms. Favoured by local hunting and shooting parties. Interesting food options range from filled rolls and decent ploughman's, to beef, Stilton and Guinness pie, sole Veronique, Normandy pork, and duck and bacon salad.
Principal beers: Wadworth 6X, Archers Village.
Directions from M4 head toward Malmesbury, 2nd rdbt go R towards Cricklade on B4040, premises through the village on the left
Brewery/Company Free House
Open 12-3 7-11
Bar food 12-2 7-10 Av main course £6
Restaurant 12-2 7-10 Av 3 course à la carte £20
Accommodation (Min) s£60 d£75

The Smoking Dog
MALMESBURY
62 The High St SN16 9AT
☎ 01666 825823
Refined 18th-century town centre pub with stone floors and log fires. Expect daily papers, decent wines, a relaxing atmosphere, and an interesting range of food. Choose from home-made burgers and steak ciabatta or, perhaps, fresh tuna with guacamole, roast cod with sweet chilli sauce, and venison in rich ale sauce.

Principal beers: Wadworth 6X, Marstons Pedigree, Archers Best & Black Jack Porter, Bass.
Brewery/Company Free House
Open 11.30-11 (Sun 12-10.30)
Bar food 12-2 7-9.30 Av main course £6.95
Restaurant 12-2 7-9.30 Av 3 course à la carte £22

MARTEN Wiltshire *Map 04 SU26*

Tipsy Miller
MARTEN
SA8 3SH ☎ 01264 731372
Isolated downland free house close to Wilton Windmill, the Kennet and Avon Canal and lovely walks. Menu choices range from baguettes and ham and chips on the traditional snack menu, to

vegetarian pasta dishes, rack of lamb, beef Stroganoff and, on the specials board, home-made pies and fresh fish.
Principal beers: Bass, Butts.
Directions 6m SW of Hungerford on A338
Brewery/Company Free House
Open 11.30-3 6.30-11
Bar food 11-3 6.30-11 Av main course £5
Restaurant 11-3 6.30-11 Av 3 course à la carte £20
Accommodation (Min) s£20 d£35

MELKSHAM Wiltshire *Map 03 ST96*

Kings Arms Hotel
MELKSHAM
Market Place SN12 6EX
☎ 01225 707272
Once an important coaching house on the London to Bath route, warmth and hospitality are offered by this traditional market place inn. Choose from the set menu or the carte, perhaps pan-fried sardines followed by chicken coriander, in the comfort of the dining room.
Principal beers: Wadworth 6X, Wadworth Henrys Original IPA, John Smiths.
Directions In the town centre opposite Lloyds Bank
Brewery/Company Wadworth
Open 11-2.30 5-11
Bar food 12-2 6-9 Av main course £6
Restaurant 12-2 7-9 Av 3 course à la carte £16
Accommodation (Min) s£32 d£60

MERE Wiltshire *Map 03 ST83*

Old Ship Inn
MERE
Castle St BA12 6JE ☎ 01747 860258
You are assured of a warm welcome at this 16th-century coaching inn. Architectural features include stone walls, flagstone floors and an original elm stairway. Home-cooked dishes are served in the bar, and there is a full carte in the oak-beamed restaurant. **Principal beers:** Badger Tanglefoot & Dorset Best.
Directions W of Stonehenge just off A303
Brewery/Company Hall & Woodhouse
Open 11-11 (Sun 12-10.30)
Bar food 12-2 6.30-9 Av main course £5.95
Restaurant 7.30-9 Av 3 course à la carte £20
Accommodation (Min) s£25 d£50

NUNTON Wiltshire Map 04 SU12

The Radnor Arms
NUNTON
SP5 4HS ☎ 01722 329722
A popular pub in the centre of the village dating from around 1750. Bar snacks are supplemented by an extensive fish choice and daily specials, typically including black bream with spring onion, lemon grass and ginger, or roast haunch of venison with red wine and juniper sauce. Fine summer garden with rural views.

Principal beers: Badger Tanglefoot & Dorset Best.
Directions From Salisbury ring road take A338 to Ringwood. Nunton signposted on R
Brewery/Company Hall & Woodhouse
Open 11-3 6-11
Bar food 12-2.30 7-9.30 Av main course £7
Restaurant 12-2.30 7-9.30 Av 3 course à la carte £15

PEWSEY Wiltshire Map 04 SU16

The French Horn
PEWSEY
Marlborough Rd SN9 5NT
☎ 01672 562443
During the Napoleonic War, French POWs building this stretch of the Kennet and Avon Canal were called to eat at this attractive canalside pub by french horn. Two specials boards supplement the menu, one for home-made bar meals and one with at least five fresh fish dishes.
Principal beers: Wadworth 6X, Henry's IPA & Summersault, Bass.
Directions A338 thru Hungerford, at Burbage take B3087 to Pewsey
Brewery/Company Wadworth
Open 12-2.30 6-11
Bar food 12-2.30 6.30-9.30 Av main course £6.50
Restaurant 12-2.30 6.30-9.30 Av 3 course à la carte £17 Av 3 course fixed price £12.95

The Seven Stars
PEWSEY
Bottlesford SN9 6LU ☎ 01672 851325
Set in the heart of the Pewsey Vale, down narrow lanes with views of the White Horse, the Seven Stars is a splendid, thatched and creeper-clad pub offering imaginative food in its rambling, beamed bars. Good food includes French-inspired dishes such as Brittany seafood platter, cassoulet, bouillabaisse, and traditional fare - jugged hare, venison and mushroom casserole, and whole Dover sole. **Principal beers:** Wadworth 6X, Badger Dorset Best.
Directions Off A345
Brewery/Company Free House
Open 12-3 6-11 (closed Sun eve & all Mon)
Bar food 12-2 7-9.30
Restaurant 12-2 7-9.30 Av 3 course à la carte £25

The Woodbridge Inn
PEWSEY
North Newnton SN9 6JZ
☎ 01980 630266
Formerly a bakery, toll house, and later a brewhouse, this 16th-century building is situated amid four acres of riverside meadows. Bar menu offers a fine selection of baguettes, club sandwiches, vegetarian light pasta dishes and fishcakes. Imaginative main courses include swordfish with lime and caper sauce, and pork forestière.
Principal beers: Wadworth 6X, Farmers Glory & Henrys IPA.
Directions 2m SW on A345
Brewery/Company Wadworth
Open 11-3 5.30-11
Bar food 11-3 5.30-11 Av main course £5.50
Restaurant 11-3 5.30-11 Av 3 course à la carte £18

PITTON Wiltshire Map 04 SU23

The Silver Plough
PITTON
White Hill SP5 1DZ ☎ 01722 712266
Attractive long building, formerly a 200-year-old farmhouse, with neat front lawns and beamed bars full of interesting old artefacts. Good range of bar food, including ploughman's lunches,

sandwich platters, seafood tagliatelle, beef stew and dumplings, hot chicken salad, and ribeye steak.
Principal beers: Badger Tanglefoot, Dorset Best, Wadworth 6X & Henry's IPA.
Directions From Salisbury take A30 towards Andover, Pitton signposted (approx 3m)
Brewery/Company Hall & Woodhouse
Open 11-3 6-11 (Sun 12-3, 7-10.30)
Bar food 12-2.30 7-10 Av main course £6
Restaurant 12-2 7-9.30 Av 3 course à la carte £19

RAMSBURY Wiltshire Map 04 SU27

The Bell
RAMSBURY
The Square SN8 2PE ☎ 01672 520230
A well-travelled Swedish proprietor and a Swedish chef offer authentic dishes from a variety of traditions at this 17th-century coaching inn. Gravadlax and home-made ice creams are particularly popular. A monthly carte and twice daily blackboard menu are offered throughout and there is a choice of some 20 varieties of schnapps. **Principal beers:** Wadworth 6X, Hook Norton Best, Shepherd Neame Spitfire.
Directions off A4 W of Hungerford

Brewery/Company Free House
Open 12-3 6-11
Restaurant 12-2.30 6.30-10

REDLYNCH Wiltshire

Kings Head NEW
REDLYNCH
SP5 2JT ☎ 01725 510420
Adorned in summer with hanging baskets, this atractive, cottagey, 17th-century pub is a convenient for visitors exploring the Avon valley and the New Forest. Low beams and open fires add to the charm and hearty food ranges from toasted bacon sandwich and seafood crepes, to herb-crusted salmon, and ham hock glazed in honey and mustard.
Principal beers: Ushers Best, Spring Fever & Founders.
Directions on B3080 8m NW of M27 J1, 6m S of Salisbury
Brewery/Company Ushers
Open 11-11
Bar food 12-3 6-10 Av main course £6.50

ROWDE Wiltshire Map 03 ST96

The George and Dragon
ROWDE
High St SN10 2PN ☎ 01380 723053
Inspired and inventive modern cooking can be found at this informal village pub, complete with wooden floors, old school tables and an impressive fireplace. Dishes run from imaginative spinach and walnut soup, goose and pork rillettes with spiced oranges, and ribeye steak, to excellent fresh seafood, perhaps, Thai squid salad, monkfish with bacon, cucumber and mustard, turbot with red wine and shallots, and whole Dover sole. AA/Seafish Authority Seafood Pub of the Year 1999.

Principal beers: Hop Back Summer Lightning, Ash Vine Challenger, Butcombe, Wadworth 6X.
Brewery/Company Free House
Open 12-3 7-11 (closed Mon lunch)
Bar food 12-2 7-10
Restaurant 12-2 7-10 Av 3 course à la carte £25 Av 2 course fixed price £8.50

SALISBURY Wiltshire Map 04 SU12

The Coach & Horses NEW
SALISBURY
Winchester St SP1 1HG
☎ 01722 336254
Many changes have taken place in its 500-year history, but the black and white timbered facade of Salisbury's oldest inn remains. Complete with slate-floored bar and cobbled courtyard, it offers a varied menu, including home-made soup, corned beef hash, steak and kidney pie, chargrilled salmon, and smoked haddock and leek bake.
Brewery/Company Free House
Open 11-11
Accommodation (Min) s£39.50 d£49.50

The Old Mill at Harnham
SALISBURY
Town Path, West Harnham SP2 8EU
☎ 01722 327517
Listed building which became Wiltshires first papermaking mill in 1550. Tranquil meadow setting with classic views of Salisbury Cathedral. Crystal clear water diverted from the River Nadder cascades through the restaurant. English cooking based on quality and simplicity. Uses fresh produce from local farms. Good fish selection.

Principal beers: Hop Back, Ringwood.
Directions near city centre, on River Avon
Brewery/Company Old English Inns/Hot
Open 11-11
Bar food 12-2.30 6.30-9.30 Av main course £5.50
Restaurant 12-2 7-10 Av 3 course à la carte £20
Accommodation (Min) s£45 d£75

SEEND Wiltshire Map 03 ST96

The Barge Inn
SEEND
Seend Cleeve SW12 6QB
☎ 01380 828230
The pub has an unusual barge theme decor, with Victorian painted flowers covering the ceilings. After a leisurely towpath stroll, relax in the lovely waterside garden and watch the narrowboats on the Kennet & Avon Canal. Dishes range from salmon and crab fishcakes to salmon with ginger sauce, and pasta with pesto.
Principal beers: Wadworth 6X & Henry's IPA, Badger Tanglefoot.
Directions Off A365 between Melksham & Devizes
Brewery/Company Wadworth
Open 11-2.30 6-11
Bar food 12-2 7-9.30 Av main course £7.90
Restaurant 7-9.30 Av 3 course à la carte £17

Bell Inn
SEEND
Bell Hill SN12 6SA ☎ 01380 828338
Cromwell and his troops supposedly breakfasted here during the Civil War, on their way to attack Devizes Castle. Wholesome pub fare features home-cooked Wiltshire ham, eggs and chips, and shepherd's pie. Restaurant meals feature Thai green chilli chicken with wild rice, lamb with port and redcurrant sauce, and beef and Stilton pie. **Principal beers:** Wadworth 6X & Henry's IPA, Murphys.
Brewery/Company Wadworth
Open 11-3 5.45-11
Bar food 11.45-2.15 6.15-9.30 Av main course £5.50
Restaurant 11.45-2.15 6.15-9.30 Av 3 course à la carte £11.50

SHERSTON Wiltshire Map 03 ST88

The Rattlebone Inn
SHERSTON
Church St SN16 0LR ☎ 01666 840871
16th century village inn, named after local hero John Rattlebone, slain in the Battle of Sherston (1016). A good choice of imaginative food is served in the rambling series of beamed rooms, including spicy crab and mushroom bake, a range of steaks, salmon topped with toasted parmesan and tomato coulis, and home-made crumble.
Principal beers: Smiles Best & Golden, Youngs Special, Everards Tiger, Bass.
Directions M4 J18 take A46 towards Stroud,then R onto B4040 through Acton Turville & onto Sherston. Or N from M4 J17 & follow signs
Brewery/Company Smiles
Open 10-11
Bar food 12-2 7-10 Av main course £5
Restaurant 12-2 7-10 Av 3 course à la carte £13.50

STAPLEFORD Wiltshire Map 04 SU03

The Pelican Inn
STAPLEFORD
Warminster Rd SP3 4LT
☎ 01722 790241
A 250-year-old coaching inn with stone walls, an inglenook fireplace, stables

converted into a restaurant, and a large rear garden popular with families. Dishes on the extensive main menu may include smoked trout paté, ploughman's, fresh battered fish and chips, mixed grill, and lentil and nut casserole. **Principal beers:** Ringwood Best & Fortyniner, Otter Bitter.
Directions On A36 7m W of Salisbury
Brewery/Company Free House
Open 11-2.30 6-11 (Sun 12-3, 7-10.30)
Bar food 12-2 6.30-9.30
Restaurant 12-2 6.30-9.30 Av 3 course à la carte £15
Accommodation (Min) d£45

STOURHEAD Wiltshire *Map 03 ST73*

Spread Eagle Inn
STOURHEAD
BA12 6QE ☎ 01747 840587
Fine 18th-century brick inn peacefully located in the heart of Stourhead Estate (NT), just yards from the magnificent landscaped gardens, enchanting lakes and woodland walks. Popular all day with visitors seeking refreshment, it offers traditional pub food, including lasagne, steak and kidney pie and sandwiches, and comfortable bedrooms.
Principal beers: Courage Best.
Directions N of A303 off B3092
Brewery/Company Free House
Open 9am-11pm
Bar food 12-9 6-9 Av main course £5
Restaurant 12-9 6-9 Av 3 course à la carte £12
Accommodation (Min) s£60 d£85

TOLLARD ROYAL Wiltshire *Map 03 ST91*

King John Inn
TOLLARD ROYAL
SP5 5PS ☎ 01725 516207
A Victorian building, opened in 1859, the King John is a friendly and relaxing place. An interesting menu (you won't find chips here) includes chicken liver and brandy pate, salmon fishcakes with tomato and basil, bubble and squeak, lemon sole meuniere and lemon and elderflower syllabub. **Principal beers:** Smiles Best, Greene King Abbot Ale, Fullers London Pride.
Directions On B3081 (7m E of Shaftesbury)
Brewery/Company Free House
Open 12-2.30 6.30-11
Bar food 12-2 7-9 Av main course £5
Restaurant 12-2 7-9 Av 3 course à la carte £12.95 Av 3 course fixed price £12.95
Accommodation (Min) d£40

UPTON LOVELL Wiltshire *Map 03 ST94*

Prince Leopold
UPTON LOVELL
BA12 0JP ☎ 01985 850460
Village inn frequented by Queen Victoria's youngest son when he lived in nearby Boyton - hence the name. Warm filled baguettes, balti curries, and fish of the day are offered in the bar. Restaurant dishes might include swordfish with garlic, wine and pesto, or fillet steak.
Principal beers: Ringwood, Fullers London Pride, Wychwood.
Directions S of A36 between Warminster & Salisbury
Brewery/Company Free House
Open 12-2.30 7-11 (closed Sun eve & Mon lunch)
Bar food 12-3 7-11 Av main course £5.90
Restaurant 12-3 7-11 Av 3 course à la carte £14
Accommodation (Min) s£25 d£38

WHITLEY Wiltshire

The Pear Tree Inn NEW
WHITLEY
Top Ln SN12 8QX ☎ 01225 709131
Lovingly restored, 18th-century stone-tiled pub set in four acres in the heart of peaceful Whitley. Expect log fires, a relaxing atmosphere, decent wines and imaginative modern cooking. Dishes range from ploughman's and seared scallops with langoustine and lemon grass sauce at lunch, to confit of duck with peppercorn and herb sauce, and calves' liver with curried onion marmalade. **Principal beers:** Wadworth 6X, Bass, Abbey Bellringer, Oakhill Best.

contd.

Directions A365 from Melksham toward Bath, at Shaw R on B3353 into Whitley, 1st L in lane, pub is at end of lane.
Brewery/Company Free House
Open 11-3 6-11
Bar food 12-2 6.30-9.30
Restaurant 12-2 6.30-9.30 Av 3 course à la carte £18

WOODFALLS Wiltshire Map 04 SU12

The Woodfalls Inn
WOODFALLS
The Ridge SP5 2LN ☎ 01725 513222
Built in 1868 as an ale house and coaching inn on the northern edge of the New Forest, this attractively refurbished inn offers well-equipped bedrooms and a good range of food. Fish from local harbours is a speciality (grouper, sea bass, red mullet), along with honey-roast duck, calves' liver, and shank of lamb. **Principal beers:** Courage Directors & Best, Gale's HSB, Fuller's London Pride.
Directions B3080 to Woodfalls
Brewery/Company Free House
Open 11-11
Bar food 12-2.15 7-9.30 Av main course £8.95
Restaurant 7-9 Av 3 course à la carte £17.95 Av 4 course fixed price £17.95
Accommodation (Min) s£49.95 d£59.90

WOOTTON RIVERS Wiltshire Map 04 SU16

Royal Oak
WOOTTON RIVERS
SN8 4NQ ☎ 01672 810322
Thatched and timbered 16th-century inn situated 100 yards from the Kennet and Avon Canal in one of Wiltshire's prettiest villages The same menu is offered throughout the heavily beamed bars, ranging from ploughman's to seafood salad or Porterhouse steak. Home-made puddings include sticky treacle and almond tart, and sherry trifle. **Principal beers:** Wadworth 6X, Ushers Best.
Directions 3m S from Marlborough
Brewery/Company Free House
Open 10.30-3.30 6-11
Bar food 11.30-2.30 6-9.30 Av main course £6.50
Restaurant 11.30-2.30 6-9.30 Av 3 course à la carte £13.50 Av 3 course fixed price £10
Accommodation (Min) s£20 d£40

Best
on the
Millennium
Menu-
Feast on Fish
Find the perfect seafood pub by looking for
the special symbol in this guide.
SEAFISH
Sea Fish Industry Authority,
18 Logie Mill, Logie Green Road, Edinburgh EH7 4HG
Tel: 0131 558 3331 Fax: 0131 558 1442
E-mail: development@seafish.co.uk

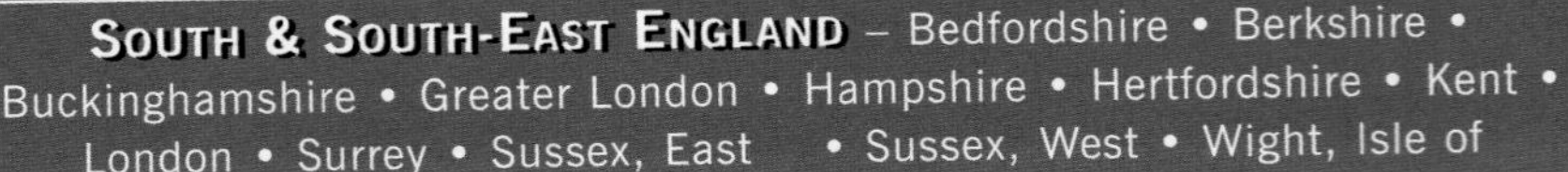

Wykeham Arms, Winchester, Hampshire

Seafood Pie

Ingredients for filling:

mussels, cooked

prawns, cooked

cod fillet (poached, save cooking liquid)

salmon, poached

large **leek**

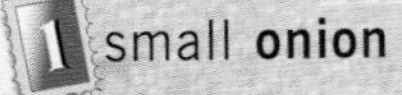

small **onion**

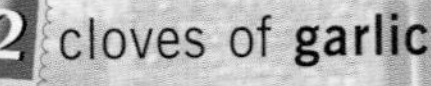

cloves of **garlic**

glass of dry **white wine**

white sauce made with the fish stock

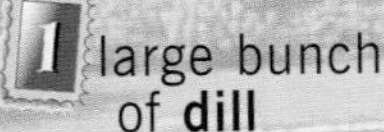

large bunch of **dill**

Topping:

puff pastry

Method:

Sweat off the **onion**, **garlic** and the chopped **leek**, cooked until soft but not coloured. Add **white wine**, reduce down to nothing, then add **white sauce**. Add **cod, salmon**, **prawns** and **mussels** and stir carefully. Roll out **puff pastry** lids and cook in hot oven. Fill individual dish with fish mixture, top with cooked lid and serve. Serves 6 people.

Wight Mouse Inn, Chale, Isle of Wight
Steak & Ale Pie

Ingredients for filling:

- 1oz/25g **plain flour**
- **salt** & **pepper**
- 2½lb/1.1kg **braising steak**, trimmed & cubed
- 1oz/25g **butter**
- 2 **garlic cloves**, skinned & crushed
- 1 large **onion**, chopped
- 6oz/175g **oyster mushrooms**
- ½ pt/275ml **beef** stock
- ½ pt/275ml **brown ale**
- 1 bottle of **light ale**
- 2 tablespoons **tomato purée**
- 2 tbls **Worcester sauce**
- sprig of fresh **thyme**
- 1 **bay leaf**

Ingredients for topping:

- 9oz/250g **plain flour**
- 5oz/150g **butter**
- 2 tablespoons cold **water**
- pinch of **salt**

Method for filling:

Season the **flour** then toss the **steak** in the flour shaking off any excess. Melt the **butter** in large saucepan and lightly fry the **garlic**, **onion** and **mushrooms** for 3 minutes, add the **steak** and remaining coating **flour** and cook for 5 minutes until lightly browned. Gradually stir in the **stock** and **ale**, then add the remaining ingredients and simmer gently for 1½ hours. Spoon the mixture into a 4 pint (2.25ltr) pie dish

Method for topping:

Put the **flour**, **butter** and **salt** into a large cold bowl and rub until it resembles fine breadcrumbs. Add the **water** and mix to form a dough. Roll out on a lightly floured surface to 2 inches wider than the pie dish, dampen dish rim and cover with **pastry** lid. Trim off excess pastry and crimp the edge, garnish with pastry leaves and brush with milk.

Cooking time and oven temp:

Gas 6/Electric (centigrade) 200 for 30-45 minutes. Serves 6 people.

Bedfordshire

BEDFORD Bedfordshire Map 04 TL04

Knife & Cleaver
BEDFORD

The Grove, Houghton Conquest MK45 3LA ☎ 01234 740387

Situated opposite the county's largest parish church, this 16th-century inn features a Jacobean oak-panelled bar, a Victorian-style conservatory, and decent wines. Expect good fresh fish, perhaps brandade of cod, monkfish and Dover sole, chicken and bacon pastry with cider sauce, and port fillet with prunes and red wine sauce among the interesting dishes.
Principal beers: Adnams Extra, Batemans XB.
Directions from A6 south of Bedford follow signs on R for Houghton Conquest. Hotel in village on L opposite the church.
Brewery/Company Free House
Open 12-2.30 7-11
Bar food 12-2.30 7-9.30 Av main course £6.25
Restaurant 12-2.30 7-11 Av 3 course à la carte £22 Av 3 course fixed price £20
Accommodation (Min) s£45 d£49

BROOM Bedfordshire Map 04 TL14

The Cock
BROOM

23 High St SG18 9NA ☎ 01767 314411

Part of a little row of 17th-century cottages, this unspoilt Victorian ale house has several, intimate, quarry-tiled rooms with latch doors, panelled walls, and where beer is dispensed straight from the cask. Homely bar food ranges from good sandwiches and ploughman's to liver and bacon and Cajun chicken.
Principal beers: Greene King - IPA, Triumph, Abbot Ale.
Directions Off B658 SW of Biggleswade
Brewery/Company Greene King
Open 12-3 6-11
Bar food 12-2.30 7-9 Av main course £4
Restaurant 12-2.30 7-9.30 Av 3 course à la carte £14

EATON BRAY Bedfordshire Map 04 SP92

The White Horse
EATON BRAY

Market Square LU6 2DG
☎ 01525 220231

Splendid 18th-century pub on the village green, with low beams, brasses and a sheltered garden for summer alfresco drinking. Straightforward bar menu offering pub favourites, and an extensive carte listing home-made duck liver paté, beef provençale, lamb with mint and rosemary, and mushroom Stroganoff.
Principal beers: Guest beers.
Directions Take A5 N of Dunstable then A5050, 1m turn L & follow signs
Brewery/Company Free House
Open 11.30-3 6.30-11
Bar food 12-2.15 7-9.15 Av main course £5
Restaurant 7-9.15 Av 3 course à la carte £17.50

KEYSOE Bedfordshire Map 04 TL06

The Chequers
KEYSOE

Pertonhall Rd, Brook End MK44 2HR
☎ 01234 708678

There is a quiet village setting for this 15th-century inn, which is characterised by beams and an open stone fireplace. Food served in the bar might include steak and ale pie, trout with Noilly Prat and almond sauce, and cashew and mushroom roast with mushroom and Madeira sauce. **Principal beers:** Hook Norton Best, Fullers London Pride.
Directions On B660 N of Bedford
Brewery/Company Free House
Open 11.30-2.30 6.30-11 (closed Tue)
Bar food 12-2 7-10 Av main course £6

LINSLADE Bedfordshire Map 04 SP92

The Globe Inn
LINSLADE

Globe Ln, Old Linslade LU7 7TA
☎ 01525 373338

The Globe stands by the Grand Union Canal, close to the River Ouzel, Linslade Wood and the Greensand Ridge. Favourite dishes include half roast duck with honey and pink peppercorn sauce, sizzling rack of lamb with port and mint gravy, and pan-fried rabbit in port and plum gravy. **Principal beers:** Theakston, Marston's Pedigree.

Directions A5 S to Dunstable, follow signs to Leighton Buzzard (A4146)
Brewery/Company Old English Inns/Hot
Open 11-3 6-11 (Sun 12-3.30, 7-10.30)
Bar food 12-2.30 Av main course £5.95
Restaurant 12-2.30 7-9.30 Av 3 course à la carte £22

MILTON BRYAN Bedfordshire Map 04 SP93

The Red Lion NEW
MILTON BRYAN
MK17 9HS ☎ 01525 210044

Nestling in a pretty village close to Woburn Abbey, this attractive, brick-built pub is festooned with colourful hanging baskets in the summer. Relaxing, neatly maintained interior, with beams, rugs on wooden floors, and well-kept Marstons ales. Wide-ranging menu offering grills, casseroles and pies, along with paella, whole plaice, and nursery puddings. **Principal beers:** Marstons Pedigree, Greene King.
Brewery/Company Free House
Open 11-3 6-11
Bar food 11-3 6-11 Av main course £6.50
Restaurant 11-3 6-11 Av 3 course à la carte £15

ODELL Bedfordshire Map 04 SP95

The Bell
ODELL
Horsefair Ln MK43 7AG
☎ 01234 720254

A large riverside garden with an aviary and picnic patio, and welcoming beamed bars are among the attractions at this 16th-century thatched village pub. An extensive menu lists snacks like sandwiches and ploughman's, alongside steak, kidney and Guinness pie, seafood pasta, omelette and chips, and beef, bacon and red wine casserole. **Principal beers:** Greene King IPA, Abbot Ale & seasonal beers.
Brewery/Company Greene King
Open 11-2.30 6-11 (Sun 12-2.30,7-10.30)
Bar food 12-2 7-9.30 Av main course £6.50

Pubs offering a good choice of seafood on the menu

RADWELL Bedfordshire Map 04 TL05

The Swan Inn
RADWELL
Felmersham Rd MK43 7HS
☎ 01234 781351

Stone and thatched listed pub in a quiet country setting overlooking the River Ouse. Good choice of starters may include smoked duck, Brixworth pate, wild mushrooms and whole smoked trout. Expect venison steak, rack of lamb, home-made fishcakes with hollandaise, and marinated herrings among the restaurant main courses. **Principal beers:** Wells Eagle.
Directions Off A6 N of Bedford
Brewery/Company Charles Wells
Open 12-2.30 6-11
Restaurant 12-2 7-9 Av 3 course à la carte £15

TURVEY Bedfordshire Map 04 SP95

The Three Cranes
TURVEY
High St Loop MK43 8EP
☎ 01234 881305

17th-century, ivy-clad stone inn set in a pretty village adjacent to the church and close to an interesting abbey. Expect a friendly atmosphere in the homely, open-plan bar and a varied menu, perhaps featuring steak and ale pie, bangers and mash, rack of lamb with mustard sauce, and fish specials.
Principal beers: Hook Norton Best, Fullers London Pride, Courage Best & Directors, Marston's Pedigree.
Directions Through Olney, R at rdbt onto A428, then R towards Bedford
Brewery/Company Old English Pub Co.
Open 11-11 (Sun 12-10.30)
Bar food 12-2 6.30-9.30 Av main course £6.50
Restaurant 12-2 6.30-9.30 Av 3 course à la carte £17
Accommodation (Min) s£35 d£45

Berkshire

ALDERMASTON Berkshire Map 04 SU56

The Hinds Head
ALDERMASTON
Wasing Ln RG7 4LX ☎ 0118 9712194

With its distinctive clock and belltower, this 16th-century inn still has the village lock-up which was last used in 1865.

contd.

Typical dishes are rack of lamb with herb crust and port and redcurrant demi-glaze, Thai crab cakes with honey and lemon grass cream sauce, and steak Dorchester flamed in brandy. **Principal beers:** Gales Best, HSB & Butser.
Directions A4 towards Newbury, then L on A340 towards Basingstoke, 2m to village
Brewery/Company Gales
Open 11-2.30 5-11 (Sat 11-2.30, 6-11; Sun 12-3, 7-10.30)
Bar food 12-2 6.30-9.30 Av main course £7.95

ALDWORTH Berkshire *Map 04 SU57*

The Bell Inn
ALDWORTH
RG8 9SE ☎ 01635 578272
Situated on the Berkshire Downs in prime walking country, the totally unspoilt Bell, a cruck-built Manor Hall, dates from 1340. People come from miles around to drink ale in the stone-floored taproom, or in the rose-filled garden. Simple food is limited to hearty soups (winter only) and hot, crusty filled rolls (Devon crab, poached salmon). **Principal beers:** Arkells 3B & Kingsdown Ale, West Berkshire ales.
Directions Just off B4009 (Newbury-Streatley rd)
Brewery/Company Free House
Open 11-3 6-11 (closed Mon ex Bhs)
Bar food 11-3 6-10.50 Av main course £3.95

ASHMORE GREEN Berkshire *Map 04 SU56*

The Sun in the Wood
ASHMORE GREEN
Stoney Ln RG18 9WF ☎ 01635 42377
True to its name, this traditional country pub is situated in delightful woodland. Bar menu offers filled baguettes, steak and kidney pudding and Stilton ploughman's. Evening fare ranges from venison and game paté and smoked salmon mousse with lemon mayonnaise, to red mullet with saffron sauce, and apple and blackberry crumble. **Principal beers:** Wadworth 6X, Farmers Glory & Henrys IPA, Badger Tanglefoot.
Directions A34 Robin Hood rndbt, L to Shaw, at mini rndbt R then 7th L into Stoney Lane, 1.5m, pub on L
Brewery/Company Wadworth
Open 12-2.30 6-11 (closed Mon)
Bar food 12-2.30 6.30-11 Av main course £7
Restaurant 12-2.30 6.30-11 Av 3 course fixed price £16

BOXFORD Berkshire *Map 04 SU47*

The Bell at Boxford NEW
BOXFORD
Lambourn Rd RG20 8DD
☎ 01488 608721
Mock-Tudor pub located at a country crossroads in the Lambourn Valley. Racing prints adorn the comfortable bar where the interesting food on offer draws a good local clientele. Dishes range from steak and Guinness pie, home-made beef burgers, and a daily roast, to cod with parsnip mash, fresh Whitstable oysters, and lobster thermidor. **Principal beers:** Flowers Original, Morrells Oxford, Badger Tanglefoot, Courage Best.
Directions A338 toward Wantage, R onto B4000, take 3rd L to Boxford
Brewery/Company Free House
Open 11-3 6-11
Bar food 12-3 7-10
Restaurant 12-3 7-10 Av 2 course fixed price £5.95
Accommodation (Min) s£40 d£55

BRAY Berkshire *Map 04 SU97*

The Fish
BRAY
Old Mill Ln SL6 2BG ☎ 01628 781111
Smartly refurbished Georgian pub set in an upmarket village close to the River Thames. A short, daily-changing menu offers imaginative, modern fish and seafood dishes, such as Cornish oysters, Malaysian fish soup, Dover sole, and swordfish with Thai dressing and coconut rice. Meat-eaters may find pheasant with red cabbage and mash on the menu. **Principal beers:** Fullers London Pride.
Directions From M4 take A308, take Bray turn-off, R opp Crown Inn, signed Monkey Island. Fish is 500yds along Old Mill Rd
Brewery/Company Free House
Open 11-3 7-11 (closed Sun eve & all Mon)
Restaurant 12-2 7-9 Av 3 course à la carte £25

BURCHETT'S GREEN Berkshire *Map 04 SU88*

The Crown
BURCHETT'S GREEN

SL6 6QZ ☎ 01628 822844

Good ales and an interesting daily-changing menu are among the attractions at this civilised village pub, close to Ashley Hill Woods. From sandwiches and Cumberland sausages with onion gravy, the short menu may list chicken with Marsala and mushroom sauce, monkfish with spring onion and smoked salmon, and scallops with bacon and cheese. **Principal beers:** Ruddles Best, Charles Wells Bombardier.

Directions From M4 take A404(M), then 3rd exit

Brewery/Company Morland

Open 12-3 6-11

Bar food 12-3

Restaurant 12-3 7-12 Av 3 course à la carte £25

CHADDLEWORTH Berkshire *Map 04 SU47*

The Ibex
CHADDLEWORTH

Main St RG20 7ER ☎ 01488 638311

Grade II listed building which was originally a bakery and then an off-licence before finally becoming a pub. Frequented by the horse-racing fraternity, with many famous stables close by. Appetising menu offers salmon and broccoli bake, home-made Ibex pie, rack of lamb with Cumberland sauce, and liver and bacon casserole.

Principal beers: Ruddles Best, Wells Bombardier.

Directions A338 towards Wantage, through Great Shefford then R, then 2nd L, pub is on R in village

Brewery/Company Morland

Open 11.30-2.30 6-11

Bar food 12-2 6.30-9.30 Av main course £5.95

Restaurant 12-2 7-9.30 Av 3 course à la carte £14

CHIEVELEY Berkshire *Map 04 SU47*

The Blue Boar Inn
CHIEVELEY

North Heath, Wantage Rd RG20 8UE
☎ 01635 248236

Oliver Cromwell stayed here before the Battle of Newbury in 1644. His troops left a statue of a wild boar from which the inn takes its name. It is an attractive thatched property, offering the likes of home-made pies, locally produced sausages, and seafood platter in the bar. **Principal beers:** Wadworth 6X, Fullers London Pride.

Directions Off B4494 S of Wantage

Brewery/Company Free House

Open 11-3 6-11

Bar food 12-1.45 7-9.30 Av main course £6.95

Restaurant 12-3 7-11 Av 3 course à la carte £23.50

Accommodation (Min) s£55 d£65

COOKHAM Berkshire *Map 04 SU88*

Bel and The Dragon
COOKHAM

High St SL6 9SQ ☎ 01628 521263

One of the oldest licensed houses in England, built of wattle and daub. The same menu is offered throughout, and ranges from sandwiches (at lunchtime) to a full a la carte selection, with dishes such as roast lamb shank and chargrilled salmon steak. **Principal beers:** Brakspear, Marston's Pedigree, Courage Best.

Brewery/Company Free House

Open 11.30-2.30 6-11 (Sun 7-9.30)

Bar food 12-2.30 7-10 Av main course £15

COOKHAM DEAN Berkshire *Map 04 SU88*

Chequers Inn Brasserie
COOKHAM DEAN

Dean Ln SL6 9BQ ☎ 01628 481232

Tucked away on the slopes of the Thames Valley, this historic pub has oak beams, open log fires and a friendly, inviting atmosphere. Blackboard menu changes daily and might offer sea bass, duck in orange and black cherry sauce, warm goat's cheese salad with hazelnut dressing, and salmon with prawns and chervil.

contd.

Principal beers: Fullers London Pride, Marstons Pedigree.
Directions From A4094 in Crookham High St take R fork after r'way bridge into Dean Lane. Pub in 1m
Brewery/Company Free House
Open 11-3 5.30-11 9.30/10
Bar food 12-3.30 6-10.30 Av main course £7

The Inn on the Green NEW
COOKHAM DEAN
The Old Cricket Common SL6 9NZ
☎ 01628 482638
Run by a young, enthusiastic team, this attractive, 300-year-old country inn offers imaginative dishes on fixed price and a la carte menus. Dinner could include brioche topped with foie gras and glazed pears, or wild boar terrine, followed by venison with blackcurrant and cassis sauce, and passion fruit cheesecake. Eclectic wine list. No bar food. **Principal beers:** Brakspear Bitter, Fullers London Pride.
Brewery/Company Free House
Open 12-11
Restaurant 12-2.30 7.30-10 Av 3 course à la carte £23
Accommodation (Min) s£55 d£90

Uncle Tom's Cabin
COOKHAM DEAN
Hills Ln SL6 9NT ☎ 01628 483339
Pretty 300-year-old cottage with a relaxing atmosphere throughout its series of old-fashioned little rooms. Attractive rear garden, and a good range of home-cooked food prepared from fresh ingredients. Dishes includes creamy seafood crêpe, warm scallop and bacon salad, hot salt beef sandwiches, and chicken balti. **Principal beers:** Benskins, Marston Pedigree.
Directions A4 towards Maidenhead, over bridge, R on to Cookham High St, through town, over r'way, past Whyteladies Ln, pub on L
Brewery/Company Carlsberg Tetley
Open 11-3 5.30-11
Bar food 12-2 7.30-10 Av main course £6.75
Restaurant 12-2 7.30-10 Av 3 course à la carte £14.50

For Pubs with AA food rosettes see page 430

CRAZIES HILL Berkshire *Map 04 SU78*

The Horns
CRAZIES HILL
RG10 8LY ☎ 0118 9401416
Formerly a Tudor hunting lodge, this neatly refurbished timbered cottage sports exposed beams, old pine tables, open fires and rugby memorabilia. Also noted for its home-cooked food, it offers lunchtime baguettes, warm salads, and ploughman's, and evening fare like calves' liver and bacon, local game, and cod with mustard crust.
Principal beers: Brakspear.
Directions Off A321 NE of Wargrave
Brewery/Company Brakspear
Open 11.30-2.30 6-11
Bar food 12-2 7-9.30 Av main course £6.50
Restaurant 12-2 7-9.30 Av 3 course à la carte £17.20 Av 3 course fixed price £18.95

CURRIDGE Berkshire *Map 04 SU47*

The Bunk Traditional Inn
CURRIDGE
RG18 9DS ☎ 01635 200400
A traditional inn dating back about 150 years, with beams, brasses and a log fire in the attractive bar. The approach to food is very flexible, the main menu can be taken in the restaurant, bar, conservatory or patio, and vice versa with the bar menu. The food is largely traditional British. **Principal beers:** Arkell's 3B, Wadworth 6X, Fullers London Pride.
Directions M4 J13/A34 S, 0.75m take 1st exit. 1m turn L, pub 400yds
Brewery/Company Free House
Open 11-11
Bar food 12-2.30 7-10 Av main course £7.50
Restaurant 12-2.30 7-10 Av 3 course à la carte £20

DORNEY Berkshire *Map 04 SU97*

The Palmer Arms
DORNEY
Village Rd SL4 6QW ☎ 01628 666612
An 18th-century pub enjoying a rural location close to Dorney Court and the River Thames. After a riverside stroll enjoy a pint of London Pride with a light snack such as mussels with garlic bread,

or something more substantial like cod with Dijon mustard sauce, or tagliatelle carbonara.
Principal beers: Fullers London Pride, Theakston Old Peculier, Courage Best.
Directions From A4 take B3026, over M4 to Dorney
Brewery/Company Old English Pub Co
Open 11-3 6-11 (Sun 11-3,7-10.30)
Bar food 12-3 6.30-11 Av main course £4.95
Restaurant 12-3 6.30-11 Av 3 course à la carte £15

EAST ILSLEY Berkshire *Map 04 SU48*

The Swan
EAST ILSLEY
RG20 7LF ☎ 01635 281238
The Swan, set in a peaceful downland village, is largely 17th century, though it may incorporate some earlier buildings. Traditional pub fare includes ploughmans', burgers, cottage pie and fish and chips. Home-made pies are a speciality, followed perhaps by treacle sponge and custard.
Principal beers: Morland Original, Wells Bombardier, Ruddles County.
Directions 5m N of J13 on A34. 18m S of Oxford on A34
Brewery/Company Morland
Open 10.30-2.30 6-11
Bar food 12-2 6-10 Av main course £7
Accommodation (Min) s£48 d£60

FRILSHAM Berkshire *Map 04 SU57*

The Pot Kiln
FRILSHAM
RG18 0XX ☎ 01635 201366
Formerly a centre for many old crafts, including brickmaking, this delightful 400-year-old pub enjoys a pleasant rural location overlooking fields. Home-brewed ales and simple wholesome food are available, including steak and kidney pudding, venison casserole, parsnip and chestnut bake, hearty soups and hot filled rolls.
Principal beers: West Berkshire Brick Kiln, Morlands Original, Arkells 3B.
Directions A34 towards Oxford, 1st L to Chieveley, then 1st R to Hermitage. 2nd L onto B4009, 2nd R to Yattendon, R on sharp L bend, on for 1m
Brewery/Company Free House
Open 12-2.30 6.30-11
Bar food 12-2 7-9.30 Av main course £5.95

GREAT SHEFFORD Berkshire *Map 04 SU37*

The Swan Inn
GREAT SHEFFORD
Newbury Rd RG17 7DS
☎ 01488 648271
A riverside coaching inn, dating from about 1818, serving a range of traditional pub snacks and more imaginative full meals. Options include a Tex-Mex Combo of deep-fried vegetables, potato skins and jalapeno peppers with a salsa dip, battered cod and chips, and 21oz stincotta, honey-roasted shank of pork.
Principal beers: Courage Best, Bass.
Directions 1.5m north of M4 J14 on A338
Brewery/Company Eldridge Pope
Open 11-3 6-11
Bar food 12-2.30 6.30-9.30 Av main course £5.25
Restaurant 12-2.30 6.30-9.30 Av 3 course à la carte £7.95

HARE HATCH Berkshire *Map 04 SU87*

The Queen Victoria
HARE HATCH
The Holt RG10 9TA ☎ 0118 9402477
A country cottage-style building dating back 300 years, this welcoming inn offers well-kept Brakspears ales and good pub food. Dishes include sweet pepper, sun-dried tomato and basil sausages, cheese and chilli beef tortillas, Chinese-style chicken kebab, and rack of lamb with rosemary and garlic. **Principal beers:** Brakspear Bitter, Old, Special & Mild.
Directions On A4 between Reading & Maidenhead
Brewery/Company Brakspear
Open 11-3 5.30-11 (Sun 12-10.30)
Bar food 12-2.30 6.30-11 Av main course £6

HURLEY Berkshire Map 04 SU88

The Rising Sun
HURLEY

High St SL6 5LT ☎ 01628 824274

Traditional style pub and restaurant with black beams and a real log fire. Fresh fish and seafood are well represented on the menu with dishes such as seafood pancakes, sole on the bone, and halibut with prawn and herb butter. Other favourites include 'mushrooms Rising Sun' and steak au poivre. **Principal beers:** Brakspears, Fullers London Pride.

Directions Off the A4130 from Maidenhead

Brewery/Company Whitbread

Open 11.30-3 5.30-11 (Sun 12-10.30, Sat 3-7)

Bar food 12-2 7-9.30 Av main course £8

Restaurant 12-2 7-9.30 Av 3 course à la carte £20

INKPEN Berkshire Map 04 SU36

The Swan Inn
INKPEN

Craven Rd, Lower Green RG17 9DX

☎ 01488 668326

Tastefully extended 17th-century village inn featuring organic meats and produce from the owners organic farm; shop attached to pub. The varied menu list fillet steak, beef Stroganoff, leek and bacon au gratin, Stilton pasta, cottage pie and fish and seafood options.

Principal beers: Butts, Hook Norton Mild & Bitter.

Directions S down Hungerford High St, L to common, R on common, pub 3m

Brewery/Company Free House

Open 11-11

Bar food 12-3 7-10 Av main course £6

Restaurant 12-3 7-12 Av 3 course à la carte £20

Accommodation (Min) d£60

KINTBURY Berkshire Map 04 SU36

The Dundas Arms
KINTBURY

53 Station Rd RG17 9UT

☎ 01488 658263

Occupying an idyllic position overlooking the Kennet and Avon Canal, this popular small hotel offers competently cooked food prepared from fresh ingredients. Dine on the attractive waterside terrace and sample the crab au gratin, shepherds pie or boiled ham hock from the bar menu, or restaurant dishes like roast partridge with bread sauce. **Principal beers:** Morlands Original, Ringwood Best, Butts Barbus Barbus, Ruddles Best.

Directions M4 J13 take A34 to Newbury, then A4 to Hungerford, L to Kintbury. Pub 1m after r'way & canal bridges

Brewery/Company Free House

Open 11-2.30 6-11 (no food all Sun, & Mon eve)

Bar food 12-2 7-9 Av main course £8

Restaurant 7.30-9 Av 3 course à la carte £25

Accommodation (Min) s£60 d£70

KNOWL HILL Berkshire Map 04 SU87

Bird In Hand Country Inn
KNOWL HILL

Bath Rd RG10 9UP

☎ 01628 826622 & 822781

Civilised, historic country inn dating from the 14th century with an oak-panelled bar featuring a huge log fire. Light meals and traditional fare (Welsh rarebit, nasi goreng, cold buffet salads) are offered in the bar, while restaurant dishes might include crispy duck pancakes, and baked sea bass with freshly-made salsa. **Principal beers:** Brakspear Bitter, Fullers London Pride.

Directions Follow A404(M) for 2m, onto A4 for 3m, pub on R
Brewery/Company Free House
Open 11-3 6-11
Bar food 12-2.30 6-10 Av main course £8.50
Restaurant 12-2.30 7-10 Av 3 course à la carte £20 Av 3 course fixed price £17.50
Accommodation (Min) s£55 d£70

LAMBOURN Berkshire *Map 04 SU37*

The Hare & Hounds NEW
LAMBOURN
Ermin St RG17 7SD ☎ 01488 71386

17th-century coaching inn in the beautiful Lambourn Valley. Notable for its individual decor and good food, the latter being favourite among the horse racing fraternity. Typical dishes include salmon fishcakes, beef and Guinness stew, scrambled eggs and smoked salmon, rack of lamb with herb marmalade, and Thai green curried chicken; sandwiches always available. **Principal beers:** Wadworth 6X, Flowers IPA, Boddingtons.
Brewery/Company Free House
Open 11-3.30 6-12
Bar food 12-3.30 7-11 Av main course £6.50
Restaurant 12-3.30 7.30-12 Av 3 course à la carte £20

LITTLEWICK GREEN Berkshire *Map 04 SU87*

The Cricketers
LITTLEWICK GREEN
Coronation Rd SL6 3RA
☎ 01628 822888

Standing in the shadow of a lovely walnut tree and overlooking the vast cricket ground spread out opposite, this late 19th-century inn has an intriguing clocking-in-clock inside, possibly once owned by the Great Western Railway. Good value, unpretentious home-cooked meals and snacks. **Principal beers:** Brakspear, Fullers London Pride.
Directions 5m W of Maidenhead on A4 toward Reading. From M4 J8/9 take A404(M) to A4 junction
Brewery/Company Free House
Open 11-11 (Sun 12-10.30/Sun only lunch in bar)
Bar food 12-2 7-9 Av main course £4.50
Accommodation (Min) d£45

MARSH BENHAM Berkshire *Map 04 SU46*

The Water Rat NEW
MARSH BENHAM
RG20 8LY ☎ 01635 582017

Attractive brick and thatch pub nestling in a small hamlet close to the Kennet and Avon Canal. Respected chef/manager (Carole Evans) offers an interesting selection of modern pub food, perhaps including broccoli and Stilton soup or crab pot, followed by seared salmon on spinach with orange balsamic dressing, or confit of duck with orange cider sauce on a bed of red cabbage. **Principal beers:** Wadworth 6X, Arkells 3B.
Directions 5m from Hungerford, 3m from Newbury & 400yds off the A4
Brewery/Company Free House
Open 11.30-3 6-11
Bar food 12-3 7-10 Av main course £8
Restaurant 12-3 7-10 Av 3 course à la carte £19 Av 3 course fixed price £15.50

NEWBURY Berkshire *Map 04 SU46*

The White Hart Inn
NEWBURY
Kintbury Rd, Hamstead Marshall
RG20 0HW ☎ 01488 658201

Very English 16th-century pub with Italian-style food that tries to use only organic and GM-free ingredients, including beef from Elm Farm opposite. The double-sided open fire is a feature in the comfortable beamed bar. Expect excellent pasta dishes, pancetta wrapped scallops with lemon butter, and warm chocolate pannetone pudding. **Principal beers:** Wadworth 6X, Hardy Country.
Directions A4, 2m after Speen, L at x-roads, cross railway & canal, L at jct, R at next jct, inn 300yds on R
Brewery/Company Free House
Open 12-2 6-11 (closed Sun, 2 wks summer)
Bar food 12-2.30 6-11
Restaurant 12-2 6-11 Av 3 course à la carte £17
Accommodation (Min) s£55 d£75

READING Berkshire *Map 04 SU77*

Fishermans Cottage
READING
224 Kennet Side RG1 3DW
☎ 0118 9571553

Situated on the tow path of the Kennet

contd.

and Avon canal, the main bar of this pub is shaped like a canal barge. There is also a conservatory, with a warm relaxed atmosphere. Daily specials might include home-made chicken and ham crumble, and aubergine, tomato and mozzarella gratin. **Principal beers:** Fullers London Pride, ESB & Chiswick Bitter.
Directions L from Kings Rd into Orts Rd then Canal Way
Brewery/Company Fullers
Open 11.30-3 5.30-11 (Fri-Sun & summer 11.30-11)
Bar food 12-2.30 6.30-9.30 Av main course £5

SONNING Berkshire *Map 04 SU77*

Bull Inn NEW
SONNING
High St RG4 6UP ☎ 01189 693901
Enjoying a picture-postcard setting opposite the village church, this 400-year-old timbered inn boasts sturdy old beams, tiled floors, winter log fires, and an attractive summer courtyard. Bar food includes sandwiches, steak and kidney pie, Thai green chicken curry, spinach and sweet pepper tart, and rack of lamb with redcurrant and port glaze.

Principal beers: Gale's HSB & Best.
Brewery/Company Gales
Open 11-3 5.30-11
Bar food 12-2 6.30-9 Av main course £9
Accommodation (Min) d£60

STANFORD DINGLEY Berkshire *Map 04 SU57*

The Bull Inn
STANFORD DINGLEY
RG7 6LS ☎ 0118 9744409
A tranquil village setting, bar food a cut above average, local miro-brewery ales, and a friendly welcome combine to make this 15th-century timbered building worth finding. Expect home-made soups (Stilton, French onion) and ploughman's, along with interesting daily specials - fish pie, beef stew, vegetable hotpot, and whole lemon sole with black butter.
Principal beers: West Berkshire Brewery Ales, Brakspear Bitter.
Directions A4/A340 to Pangbourne. 1st L to Bradfield.Thru Bradfield, 0.3m L into Back Lane. At end L, pub 0.25m on L
Brewery/Company Free House
Open 12-3 7-11
Bar food 12-3 7.30-11 Av main course £8

The Old Boot Inn
STANFORD DINGLEY
RG7 6LT ☎ 01189 744292
Located in one of Berkshire's prettiest villages, this 18th-century pub is surrounded by the unspoilt countryside of the Pang Valley. Extensive choice of bar snacks, fresh fish, including Dover sole and salmon and crab with lime and ginger, and home-cooked dishes like crispy duck, chargrilled lamb steak, and beef and venison casserole.
Principal beers: Archers Village, Brakspear, Fullers London Pride, Youngs.
Directions M4 J12, A4/A340 to Pangbourne. 1st L to Bradfield. Through Bradfield & follow signs for Stanford Dingley
Brewery/Company Free House
Open 11-3 6-11
Bar food 12-3 7-12 Av main course £7.95
Restaurant 12-3 7-12 Av 3 course à la carte £20

WALTHAM ST LAWRENCE Berkshire *Map 04 SU87*

The Bell
WALTHAM ST LAWRENCE
The Street RG10 0JJ ☎ 0118 9341788
Since 1608, when it was left to the village in trust, the rent from this 14th-century inn has been donated to the needy. Varied bar food ranges from sandwiches and filled jacket potatoes, to home-made pies, Tuscan bean bake, and evening dishes like rack of lamb, venison in red wine, and chicken tikka masala.
Principal beers: Brakspear Dark Rose, Bass, Greene King Abbot,.
Directions on B3024 E of Twyford (from A4 turn at Hare Hatch)
Brewery/Company Free House
Open 11-3 6-11

Bar food 12-2 7-9.30 Av main course £6
Restaurant 12-2 7-9.30 Av 3 course à la carte £12

WARREN ROW Berkshire *Map 04 SU88*

The Crooked Inn
WARREN ROW
RG10 8QS ☎ 01628 825861
Built in the 1920s, this attractive red-brick building with leaded windows and polished wood floors is a popular village restaurant with a modern European theme, and a small welcoming bar. Food ranges from bacon and cheese salad and Thai vegetable curry, to salmon fishcakes, dressed crab, and shoulder of lamb.
Principal beers: Brakspear.
Directions From M4 take A4 to Knowl Hill, 1st R down Warren Row Rd, inn 3m on R
Brewery/Company Free House
Open 11.30-3.30 5.30-11.30 (closed Sun eve & all Mon)
Bar food 11.30-3 Av main course £4.95
Restaurant 11-3 5.30-11.30 Av 3 course à la carte £28.95 Av 3 course fixed price £18.95

WEST ILSLEY Berkshire *Map 04 SU48*

Harrow Inn NEW
WEST ILSLEY
RG20 7AR ☎ 01635 281260
Enjoying a lovely village green setting, the historic Harrow Inn, where Morland founded their brewery in 1711, offers freshly-cooked food in its smartly rustic interior. Expect baguettes and ploughman's, or Brixham mussels, warm onion tart, or duck and lentil terrine, followed by scallops with pesto oil, lamb shank with onion jam, and lemon tart.
Principal beers: Morland Original.
Brewery/Company Morland
Open 11-3 6-11
Bar food 12-2 Av main course £10
Restaurant 12-2 7-8.55 Av 3 course à la carte £30

WINKFIELD Berkshire *Map 04 SU97*

Rose & Crown
WINKFIELD
Woodside, Windsor Forest SL4 2DP
☎ 01344 882051
A traditional country pub and restaurant on the Windsor side of Ascot Racecourse. Filled baguettes and jacket potatoes, and lasagne are among the lunchtime dishes; evening fare may include mixed game terrine, guinea fowl with bacon, shallots and red wine jus, and scallops with ginger, garlic and spring onion.
Principal beers: Adnams Broadside, Wells Bombardier, Morland Original, Ruddles Best.
Directions M3 J3 from Ascot racecourse on A332 take 2nd exit from Heatherwood Hosp r'about,then 2nd L
Brewery/Company Morland
Open 11-11 (Sun 12-10.30)
Bar food 12-2.30 7-9.30 Av main course £5.95
Restaurant 12-2.30 7-9.30 Av 3 course à la carte £17.50
Accommodation (Min) s£37.50 d£40

WINTERBOURNE Berkshire *Map 04 SU47*

The Winterbourne Arms
WINTERBOURNE
RG16 8BB ☎ 01635 248200
Black and white country pub, in an area of outstanding natural beauty, serving high quality restaurant food. Example dishes include supreme of chicken with foie gras, truffles and mushroom cream, salmon and mullet with spinach and a saffron glaze, and strawberry ganache tart with honey and ginger ice cream.

Principal beers: Bass.
Directions From M4 S on A34, 1st slip road
Brewery/Company Free House
Open 11.30-3 6-11 (closed Mon lunch ex BHs)
Bar food 12-2.30 Av main course £5.95
Restaurant 12-2.30 7-10 Av 3 course à la carte £22

Pubs offering a good choice of seafood on the menu

South & South East (& Isle of Wight)

YATTENDON Berkshire *Map 04 SU57*

The Royal Oak Hotel
YATTENDON

The Square RG18 0UG ☎ 01635 201325

Before doing battle at nearby Newbury, Oliver Cromwell and his Roundheads reportedly enjoyed a 'fynne' dinner at this handsome 16th-century coaching inn. The restaurant tends to feature roast wild duck breast, saddle of hare, and pave of caramelised sea bass. Bar meals include deep-fried plaice and ploughman's lunches. **Principal beers:** Banks Bitter, Fullers London Pride.
Directions From M4 J12, A4 to Newbury, R at 2nd rndbt to Pangbourne then 1st L. From J13, A34 N 1st L, R at T-jnct. L then 2nd R to Yattendon
Brewery/Company Regal
Open 12-3 6-11
Bar food 12-2 7-9.30
Restaurant 12-2 7-9 Av 3 course à la carte £25 Av 3 course fixed price £32.50
Accommodation (Min) s£90 d£110

Buckinghamshire

AMERSHAM Buckinghamshire *Map 04 SU99*

The Kings Arms NEW
AMERSHAM

30 The High St, Old Amersham HP7 3RL
☎ 01494 726333

Historic charm and atmosphere fill the timbered bars of this 15th-century, black and white timbered inn overlooking the High Street. Relax by the huge inglenook fireplace and tuck into a beef and horseradish baguette, lamb kebabs, warm scallop and bacon salad, or steak and kidney pie, or adjourn to the beamed restaurant for the famous seafood platter. **Principal beers:** Rebellion IPA, Burton Ale, Benskins Best, Morrells Varsity.

Brewery/Company Free House
Open 11-11 (Sun 12-10.30)
Bar food 12-2.30 Av main course £4.95
Restaurant 12-2 7-9.30 Av 3 course à la carte £13.50 Av 3 course fixed price £17

ASTON CLINTON Buckinghamshire *Map 04 SP81*

The Oak NEW
ASTON CLINTON

119 Green End St ☎ 01296 630466

Thatched, 500-year-old coaching inn with flagstone floors, inglenook fireplace and bags of old-world charm. Set in the old part of the village, it offers a good family garden and a wide-ranging menu. Expect traditional pub favourites, alongside beef Stroganoff, monkfish Provencale, and fillet steak with cream, garlic and chilli. **Principal beers:** Fullers London Pride, Fullers ESB, Fullers Chiswick.
Brewery/Company Fullers
Open 11.30-2.30 6-11
Bar food 12-2 6-10
Restaurant 12-2 6-10 Av 3 course à la carte £9.50

AYLESBURY Buckinghamshire *Map 04 SP81*

Bottle & Glass
AYLESBURY

Gibraltar, Nr Dinton HP17 8TY
☎ 01296 748488

Picture-pretty,17th century thatched pub occupying a peaceful rural setting close to the Chiltern Hills. Daily delivered fresh seafood is a speciality (tuna with cracked pepper and roast fennel sauce), while other dishes might include paella supreme, calves' liver and bacon, and beef Wellington. Decent open sandwiches and good light lunch dishes. **Principal beers:** Morrells Oxford, Varsity & Mild.
Directions On A418 between Thame & Aylesbury
Brewery/Company Morrells
Open 11-3 6-11 (closed Sun eve)
Bar food 12-2 Av main course £5.95
Restaurant 12-2 7-9.15 Av 3 course à la carte £23

Pubs offering a good choice of seafood on the menu

BEACONSFIELD Buckinghamshire *Map 04 SU99*

The Greyhound
BEACONSFIELD

33 Windsor End HP9 2JN
☎ 01494 673823

Comfortable 16th-century drovers' tavern enjoying a secluded location opposite the parish church. Traditional, home-cooked pub food is served, including smoked haddock pie, home-made burgers and open rare beef sandwiches, along with an extensive blackboard menu of specials, including fresh fish (sea bass, black bream) and pasta. **Principal beers:** Courage Best, Fullers London Pride, Wadworth 6X.

Directions Follow signs to Beaconsfield Old Town, left at central roundabout
Brewery/Company Free House
Open 11-3 5.30-11
Bar food 12-2 7-9.45 Av main course £8
Restaurant 12-2 7-9.45 Av 3 course à la carte £15

The Royal Standard of England
BEACONSFIELD

Brindle Ln, Forty Green HP9 1XT
☎ 01494 673382

Historic country inn, parts of which date from the 12th century. It has many interesting features: stained-glass windows, beams, flagstones and a large inglenook fireplace. One bar is solely candle and lamp-lit. Dishes include lime and coriander chicken, fresh salmon, and home-made curries. **Principal beers:** Marstons Pedigree, Owd Roger & Morland Old Speckled Hen, Brakspear.

Directions A40 to Beaconsfield. R at Church roundabout onto B474 towards Penn. L onto Forty Green Rd, then 1m
Brewery/Company Free House
Open 11-3 5.30-11
Bar food 12-2.15 6.30-9.30 Av main course £7

BLEDLOW Buckinghamshire *Map 04 SP70*

The Lions of Bledlow
BLEDLOW

Church End HP27 9PE ☎ 01844 343345

A favourite with Chiltern walkers, this pub has hills and lovely beechwoods right on its doorstep. A rambling, low-beamed bar adds to the charm. Apart from baguettes, salads, starters and main courses, there are usually 12 specials a day, including English lamb cutlets, duck breast, and fresh mussels. **Principal beers:** Wadworth 6X, Courage Best, Marstons Pedigree, Brakspear Bitter.

Directions M40 J6 take B4009 to Princes Risborough, through Chinnor into Bledlow
Brewery/Company Free House
Open 11.30-3 6-11
Bar food 12-2.30 7-10 Av main course £6
Restaurant 12-2.30 7-10 Av 3 course à la carte £12.50

BOLTER END Buckinghamshire *Map 04 SU79*

The Peacock
BOLTER END

HP14 3LU ☎ 01494 881417

The oldest part of this pub dates from 1620, featuring original beams and a fireplace dating from the early 1800s. It is situated on top of the Chiltern Hills overlooking the common. Popular options are steak and kidney pie, gammon hock and fresh salmon, followed by fruit crumble or pannacotta. **Principal beers:** Tetley, Brakspear Bitter, Marstons Pedigree.

Directions A40 through Stokenchurch, then B482
Brewery/Company Carlsberg Tetley
Open 11.45-2.30 6-11 (closed Sun eve)
Bar food 12-2 7-9.45 Av main course £7.25

BRILL Buckinghamshire *Map 04 SP61*

The Pheasant Inn NEW
BRILL

Windmill St HP18 9TG ☎ 01844 237104

Overlooking Brill Common and very close to a 300-year old windmill, and

contd.

from the next hill, nine counties can be seen. The late author, Roald Dahl was a regular visitor. Today's menu may include Brillburger, steak pie, pheasant in season and breast of chicken in seven different styles. **Principal beers:** Tetley, Marstons Pedigree.
Brewery/Company Free House
Open 11-3 6-11
Bar food 12-2 7-9 Av main course £6
Restaurant 12-2 7-9
Accommodation (Min) s£35 d£64

BUCKINGHAM Buckinghamshire
Map 04 SP63

The Wheatsheaf
BUCKINGHAM

Main St, Maids Moreton MK18 1QR
☎ 01280 815433
Pretty thatched and timbered 17th-century pub enjoying a peaceful village setting close to Buckingham. Sit in the relaxing bars, or in the attractive conservatory restaurant, and order home-made burger, fish and chips, moules, ribeye steak with pepper and onion sauce, or knuckle of pork with tomato and basil sauce from the short menu selection.
Principal beers: Hook Norton Best Wychwood, Flowers IPA, Wadworth 6X.
Directions From M1 J13 take A421 to Buckingham, then take A413
Brewery/Company Free House
Open 12-3 6-11
Bar food 12-2.15 7-9.30 Av main course £4.50
Restaurant 12-3 7-9.15 Av 3 course à la carte £15
Accommodation (Min) d£45

CHALFONT ST GILES Buckinghamshire
Map 04 SU99

Ivy House
CHALFONT ST GILES

London Rd HP8 4RS ☎ 01494 872184
The ghost of a young stable lad supposedly haunts this 200-year-old former coach house, turning things on and off. Superb views over the Chilterns. Specials of the day might include game pie with red wine, pan-fried veal escalopes, chargrilled swordfish steak and pan-fried ostrich with mango sauce.
Principal beers: Fullers London Pride, Brakspear Bitter, Wadworth 6X, Hook Norton Old Hooky.
Directions On A413 2m S of Amersham & 1.5m N of Chalfont St Giles
Brewery/Company Free House
Open 11.30-3.30 6-11.30 (Sat 12-11, Sun 12-10.30)
Bar food 12-2.30 6-9.30
Restaurant 12-2.30 6.30-9.30 Av 3 course à la carte £17.50

The White Hart
CHALFONT ST GILES

Three Households HP8 4LP
☎ 01494 872441
An extensive choice of food is offered at this 100-year-old pub, situated near Milton's Cottage in a pretty village. One menu covers the bar and restaurant, and may include bouillabaisse with crusty bread, haddock in beer batter, roast cod on spinach, chargrilled chicken with wild mushroom sauce, and honey marinaded pork ribs. **Principal beers:** Morland Original & Old Speckled Hen, Ruddles Best, Everard Tiger, Bass.
Directions Off A413 (Denham/Amersham)
Brewery/Company Morland
Open 11.30-2.30 (Sun 12-3) 6-11 (Sun 12-3,6-10.30)
Bar food 12-2 6.30-9.30 Av main course £6
Restaurant 12-2 6.30-9.30 Av 3 course à la carte £16
Accommodation (Min) s£48 d£62

CHENIES Buckinghamshire
Map 04 TQ09

The Red Lion
CHENIES

WD3 6ED ☎ 01923 282722
Situated near historic Chenies Manor and the River Chess. Home-made pies with short-crust pastry are a speciality, notably pork. apple and redcurrant, and their famous lamb pie. Further choices range from rare roast beef bap and filled jacket

potatoes, to oven-baked lamb with red wine and rosemary gravy. **Principal beers:** Benskins Best, Vale Notley Ale, Wadworth 6X, Rebellion Lion Pride.

Directions Between Rickmansworth & Amersham on A404
Brewery/Company Free House
Open 11-2.30 5.30-11
Bar food 12-2 7-10 Av main course £7

CHESHAM Buckinghamshire — *Map 04 SP90*

The Black Horse Inn
CHESHAM
Chesham Vale HP5 3NS
☎ 01494 784656
A 16th-century listed building constructed from ship's timbers with a huge garden pond and active ghost. The menu features a fine selection of home-made pies, while the specials board offers plenty of fresh fish and a range of sausages. There is a massive barbeque for summer weekends, weather permitting. **Principal beers:** Adnams, Black Horse Black Stallion, Morland Old Speckled Hen.
Directions A41 from Berkhamstead, A416 through Ashley Green, 0.75m before Chesham R to Vale Rd, btm of Mashleigh Hill follow rd for 1m, inn on L

Open 12-3 6-11 (summer 12-11)
Bar food 12-2 6-9.30 Av main course £6
Restaurant 12-2 6-9.30 Av 3 course à la carte £12

The Swan
CHESHAM
Ley Hill HP5 1UT ☎ 01494 783075
16th-century beamed pub overlooking the golf course, village cricket ground and common land. Rambling, character bar with wall and window seats, an old cooking range and traditional pub food. Typical menu choices include fish bake, steak and kidney pie, pork in red wine, and steaks. **Principal beers:** Marstons Pedigree, Tetley, Morland Old Speckled Hen, Youngs.
Directions E of Chesham by golf course
Brewery/Company Allied Domecq
Open 11-11 (Sun 12-10.30)
Bar food 12-3 6-10 Av main course £6
Restaurant 12-2 6-10 Av 2 course fixed price £6

CHICHELEY Buckinghamshire — *Map 04 SP94*

The Chester Arms
CHICHELEY
MK16 9JE ☎ 01234 391214
Look to the chalkboard for home-cooked dishes at this comfortable roadside pub, situated near Chicheley Hall (NT), the former home of the Chester family after whom the pub takes its name. You may find vegetable soup, chicken pie, pork casseroled in cider, and lasagne among the choice. Standard printed menu fare. **Principal beers:** Greene King & Abott Ale.
Directions On A422, 2m NE of Newport Pagnell. 4m from M1 J14
Brewery/Company Greene King
Open 11-3 6-11
Bar food 12-2 7-9 Av main course £5
Restaurant 12-2 7-9 Av 3 course à la carte £10

CHOLESBURY Buckinghamshire — *Map 04 SP90*

The Full Moon
CHOLESBURY

Hawridge Common HP5 2UH
☎ 01494 758959
A 16th-century coaching inn, known as the Half Moon in the 1800s. It has a wealth of low beams, and three real fires create a cosy atmosphere in winter. Food ranges from sandwiches and ploughman's, to daily specials such as

contd.

chargrilled lamb chops, tuna and pasta bake, and Cajun chicken. **Principal beers:** Bass, Fullers London Pride, Brakspear Special, Tetleys.
Directions At Tring on A41 take turn for Wiggington & Cholesbury
Brewery/Company Enterprise Inns
Open 12-3 (Sat open all day) 5.30-11
Bar food 12-2 6.15-9 Av main course £6
Restaurant 12-2 6.15-9 Av 3 course à la carte £10

CUDDINGTON Buckinghamshire *Map 04 SP71*

Annie Bailey's
CUDDINGTON
Upper Church St HP18 0AP
☎ 01844 291215
Ale and eating house in a pretty village setting. Originally the Red Lion, it was renamed after a former landlady circa 1850. Dishes range from fish and chips with mushy peas to fillet steak with Gruyere sauce. Tempting puddings encompass treacle sponge pudding and tarte au citron. **Principal beers:** Brakspear Bitter, Vale Wychert Ale.
Directions From M40 J8 take A418 (or from J7 take A329) towards Aylesbury, after Thame turn L after 4m
Brewery/Company Free House
Open 12-2.30 6.30-11 (closed Sun eve & all Mon)
Bar food 12-2.30 6.30-11 Av main course £8
Restaurant 12-2.30 6.30-11 Av 3 course à la carte £22 Av 3 course fixed price £13.75

FAWLEY Buckinghamshire *Map 04 SU78*

The Walnut Tree
FAWLEY
RG9 6JE ☎ 01491 638360
A 50's pub, with warm decor and comfortable seating, the Walnut Tree is located in the Chiltern Hills with wonderful views some 400ft above Henley-on-Thames. Food ranges from walkers' lunches in the bar to best end of English lamb in the restaurant, with everything prepared from fresh produce. **Principal beers:** Brakspear.
Directions From Henley on A4155 towards Marlow, L at 2nd sign for Fawley. R at village green
Brewery/Company Brakspear
Open 12-3 6-11 (Sat-Sun & Bhs 11-11)
Bar food 12-3 6-11 Av main course £5.50
Restaurant 12-3 6-11 Av 3 course à la carte £15
Accommodation (Min) s£35 d£50

FINGEST Buckinghamshire *Map 04 SU79*

The Chequers Inn
FINGEST
RG9 6QD ☎ 01491 638335
Set deep in the Chiltern Hills, opposite a splendid Norman church, the Chequers is a 15th-century redbrick pub with log fires in the winter, and a delightful sun-trap garden with rural views for summer imbibing. Good food ranges from a daily roast and a lunchtime cold buffet, to home-made pies and lasagne. **Principal beers:** Brakspear Bitter, Special & Old.
Directions From M40 L towards Ibstone, L at T junc at end of rd, stay L, pub on R
Brewery/Company Brakspear
Open 11-3 6-11
Bar food 12-2.30 7-9.45 Av main course £6
Restaurant 12-2.30 7-10 Av 3 course à la carte £25 Av 3 course fixed price £15

FORD Buckinghamshire *Map 04 SP70*

The Dinton Hermit
FORD
Water Ln HP17 8XH ☎ 01296 748379
Traditional pub with a great atmosphere. It is named after John Bigg, secretary to Simon Mayne who signed the death warrant of Charles I. He was so ashamed of his part in the execution that he became a hermit, and subsequently a local legend. **Principal beers:** Aylesbury ABC, Wadworth 6X, Adnams.
Directions Off A418 between Aylesbury & Thame
Brewery/Company Free House
Open 11-2.30 6-11 (closed all Mon, & Tue lunch)
Bar food 12-2 7-9.30
Restaurant 12-2 7-9 Av 3 course à la carte £16

FRIETH Buckinghamshire
Map 04 SU79

The Yew Tree NEW
FRIETH
☎ 01494 882330

A huge yew tree spirals majestically outside this 16th-century red-brick pub in this truly rural Chilterns village. Sit in the pretty flower garden, or in the original-beamed bar with its inglenook and tip-top ales, and enjoy a hot chicken sandwich, traditional fish and chips, smoked salmon tagliatelle, or grilled plaice. **Principal beers:** Gibbs Mew Bishops Tipple, Brakspear Bitter, Fullers London Pride.
Directions from M40 towards Stokenchurch, thru Cadmore End, L to Frieth
Brewery/Company Free House
Open 11-3 6-11
Bar food 11-3 6.30-10.30 Av main course £5
Restaurant 11-3 6.30-10.30 Av 3 course à la carte £22

GREAT BRICKHILL Buckinghamshire
Map 04 SP93

The Old Red Lion
GREAT BRICKHILL
Ivy Ln MK17 9AH ☎ 01525 261715

There are fine views over the Vale of Aylesbury at this 250-year-old pub. A house speciality is a crusty roll filled with chicken, bacon, mayonnaise and salad. Other favourites are the locally produced steaks and home-made puddings, including fruit crumbles and steamed sticky toffee. **Principal beers:** Adnams Southwold, Youngs, Flowers Original, Boddingtons.
Directions Signposted off A5, 10m S of Milton Keynes
Brewery/Company Whitbread
Open 12-2.30 (Sun 12-4) 5.30-11 (Sun 7-10.30/no food Sun & Mon Jan-Etr)
Bar food 12-2 7-9 Av main course £5
Restaurant 12-2 7-9 Av 3 course à la carte £12

GREAT HAMPDEN Buckinghamshire
Map 04 SP70

The Hampden Arms
GREAT HAMPDEN
HP16 9RQ ☎ 01494 488255

Smart, brick-built pub situated in historic Hampden, in the beech-clad Chiltern Hills bordering the Chequers Estate. Popular with walkers, it offers an extensive menu, perhaps including beer-battered cod, apple and Stilton chicken, and fillet cordon rouge - fillet steak filled with bacon - and home-made chicken and brandy paté. **Principal beers:** Wadworth 6X.
Directions From M40 take A4010, R before Princes Risborough, Great Hampden signposted
Brewery/Company Free House
Open 12-2.30 6.30-11
Bar food 12-2 6.30-9.30 Av main course £5.95
Restaurant 12-2 6.30-9.30 Av 3 course à la carte £15

GREAT MISSENDEN Buckinghamshire
Map 04 SP80

The George Inn
GREAT MISSENDEN
94 High St HP16 0BG ☎ 01494 862084

Dating back to the 15th century, this attractive coaching inn enjoys a village setting deep in the Chilterns. One menu is offered throughout, supported by daily specials. Typical dishes include seafood plattter, steaks, roast beef and home-made steak and kidney pie. **Principal beers:** Adnams Bitter, Wadworth 6X, Youngs Special.
Directions off A413 between Aylesbury & Amersham
Brewery/Company Greenalls
Open 7-11 (Sat 9-11) (Sun 9-3.30, 7-10.30)
Bar food 12-2 6.30-9 Av main course £7.95
Accommodation (Min) d£65.75

The Rising Sun
GREAT MISSENDEN
Little Hampden HP16 9PS
☎ 01494 488393 & 488360

A 250-year-old country inn nestling among beechwoods high in the Chiltern Hills. A friendly and relaxed place, with open fires and comfortable accommodation. Interesting pub food, listed on blackboard menus, may include crab and scallop pancake, warm duck and bacon salad, roast shoulder of lamb with rosemary and honey sauce, and raspberry and almond tiramisu. **Principal beers:** Adnams, Brakspear Bitter, Marstons Pedigree, Morland Old Speckled Hen.

contd.

Directions From A413 N of Gt Missenden take Rignall Rd on L (signed Princes Risborough) 2.5m turn R signed 'Little Hampden only'
Brewery/Company Free House
Open 11.30-2.30 6.30-11 (closed Sun eve & all Mon)
Bar food 12-2 7-9 Av main course £8.95
Restaurant 12-2 7-9 Av 3 course à la carte £18.80 Av 3 course fixed price £17.95
Accommodation (Min) s£30 d£58

HADDENHAM Buckinghamshire — *Map 04 SP70*

The Green Dragon
HADDENHAM
8 Churchway HP17 8AA
☎ 01844 291403
Historic coaching inn in the old part of Haddenham near the 12th-century church, village green and duck pond. Robust fare includes pan-fried pig's trotter and foie gras with confit of jalapeno peppers, ragout of squat lobster, venison and red wine pie, and braised local rabbit with Dijon mustard. **Principal beers:** Vale Notley Ale, Fullers London Pride.
Directions From M40 A329 to Thame, then A418, 1st R after entering Haddenham
Brewery/Company Whitbread
Open 11.30-3 6.30-11 (closed Sun eve)
Bar food 12-2.30 Av main course £8
Restaurant 12-2 7-11 Av 3 course à la carte £22

HAMBLEDEN Buckinghamshire — *Map 04 SP78*

The Stag & Huntsman Inn NEW
HAMBLEDEN
RG9 6RP ☎ 01491 571227
Located in an Area of Outstanding Natural Beauty, this 400-year old pub boasts three separate bars and plenty of unspoilt character. Hambleden is at the centre of numerous circular walks around the valley. Hungry walkers may sample marinated chargrilled chicken, vegetable goulash, Cajun salmon and a selection of local game. **Principal beers:** Brakspear Bitter & Special, Wadworth 6X, Old Luxters Barn Ale.
Directions 5m from Henley-on-Thames on A4155 toward Marlow, L at Mill End towards Hambleden
Brewery/Company Free House
Open 11-2.30 6-11 (Sun 12-3, 7-10.30, Sat 11-3, 6-11)
Bar food 12-2 7-9.30 Av main course £7.50

HIGH WYCOMBE Buckinghamshire — *Map 04 SU89*

The Chequers
HIGH WYCOMBE
Bullocks Farm Ln, Wheeler End HP14 3NH ☎ 01494 883070
Situated on the edge of Wheeler Common, this 300-year-old pub retains many original features. Known locally for its quality real ale and bar food, The Chequers' menu may include Cumberland sausage and mash, 'Pig in a Blanket', liver and bacon, and a variety of rolls and ploughman's. **Principal beers:** Greene King IPA, Brakspear Bitter, Adnams Broadside, Fullers London Pride.
Directions From M4 J5, B482 towards Marlow, L to Wheeler End. Or M4 J5 A40 towards H Wycombe, R to Wheeler End
Brewery/Company Free House
Open 11-11 (Sun 12-10.30)
Bar food 12-2 7-9 Av main course £4.95

LACEY GREEN Buckinghamshire — *Map 04 SP80*

Pink & Lily
LACEY GREEN
Pink Rd HP27 0RJ ☎ 01494 488308
The pub was named after a local butler (Mr Pink), who had a liaison with a chambermaid (Lily). On being dismissed from service they set themselves up as innkeepers. It is a large country establishment with several eating and drinking areas serving home-made pies, steaks, curries and pasta dishes. **Principal beers:** Brakspear Bitter, Fullers London Pride, Vale Notley Ale, Ridleys ESX.
Directions Off A4010 S of Princes Risborough
Brewery/Company Free House
Open 11-3 6-11
Bar food 12-2 7-9.30 Av main course £7

LONG CRENDON Buckinghamshire
Map 04 SP60

The Angel Inn
LONG CRENDON

47 Bicester Rd HP18 9EE
☎ 01844 208268

Lovely village setting for a 16th-century former coaching inn, with a deserved reputation for fine food. An excellent choice of fish is offered on the blackboard menu, with creative dishes such as smoked haddock on leek and mustard mash with cheese sabayon, and red snapper with vegetable stir-fry, alongside venison with port and juniper sauce. **Principal beers:** Hook Norton Best, Adnams Broadside, Ridleys Rumpus.

Directions A418 to Thame, B4011 to L Crendon, Inn on B4011
Brewery/Company Free House
Open 12-3 7-11 (Closed Sun eve)
Bar food 12-3 7-11 Av main course £9
Restaurant 12-2.30 7-11 Av 3 course à la carte £25 Av 3 course fixed price £15.95
Accommodation (Min) s£55 d£65

Mole & Chicken
LONG CRENDON

Easington Ter HP18 9EY
☎ 01844 208387

A 19th-century former village store licensed to sell only beer and cider until 1918. Rustic beamed interior with quarry-tiled floors, farmhouse tables and chairs and a splendid open fireplace. Execellent food ranges from imaginative salads and pasta dishes, to game cassoulet, shoulder of lamb with garlic and rosemary sauce, and herb-stuffed sea bass. **Principal beers:** Adnams Bitter, Morland Old Speckled Hen.
Directions Off B4011 N of Thame
Brewery/Company Free House
Open 12-3.30 6-12

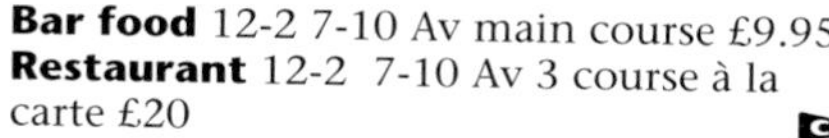

Bar food 12-2 7-10 Av main course £9.95
Restaurant 12-2 7-10 Av 3 course à la carte £20

MARLOW Buckinghamshire
Map 04 SU88

The Kings Head
MARLOW

Church Rd, Little Marlow SL7 3RZ
☎ 01628 484407

A mere 10 minutes from the Thames footpath, this 17th-century flower-adorned pub offers a varied menu within its cosy, open-plan interior. From sandwiches and filled jacket potatoes, the menu may extend to lamb's liver, bacon and onions, lamb steak with red wine, mint and garlic gravy, sea bass, and smoked haddock pasta. **Principal beers:** Brakspear Bitter, Fuller's London Pride, Wadworth 6X, Morrells Varsity.
Directions M40 J4 take A4040 S 1st A4155
Brewery/Company Whitbread
Open 11-3 5-11 (Sat 11-11, Sun 12-10.30)
Bar food 12-2 6.30-10 Av main course £6.50
Restaurant 12-2 6.30-10 Av 3 course à la carte £6.95

MOULSOE Buckinghamshire
Map 04 SP94

The Carrington Arms
MOULSOE

Cranfield Rd MK16 0HB
☎ 01908 218050

Before becoming a pub, this Grade II listed building was the home of Lord Carrington's estate manager. Orders are taken directly by the chef who cooks on a range in full view of his expectant customers. Food includes excellent steaks and fish, various Thai dishes, beef and ale cobbler and smoked chicken salad.

contd.

Principal beers: Wells Bombardier & Eagle, Boddingtons, Theakston Old Peculier, Adnams.
Directions M1 J14 take rd signed 'Cranfield & Moulsoe'.Pub 1m on R
Brewery/Company Free House
Open 11-2.30 6-11
Bar food 12-2 6.30-10 Av main course £7
Restaurant 12-2 6.30-10 Av 3 course à la carte £20
Accommodation (Min) d£44

PRINCES RISBOROUGH Buckinghamshire *Map 04 SP80*

Red Lion
PRINCES RISBOROUGH
Upper Icknield Way, Whiteleaf HP27 0LL
☎ 01844 344476
A 17th-century inn surrounded by National Trust land and old thatched cottages in the heart of the Chilterns. The pub has a nautical theme, open fires and a large collection of antiques. Traditional pub food is home cooked, perhaps featuring chilli, lasagne, ribeye steak, ocean pie, and salmon bearnaise.
Principal beers: Brakspear Bitter, Hook Norton Best, Rebellion IPA.
Directions A4010 thru Princes Risbro', then R into 'Holloway', go to end of road, R, pub on L
Brewery/Company Free House
Open 11.30-3 5.30-11
Bar food 12-2 7-9 Av main course £6.50
Restaurant 12-2 7-9 Av 3 course à la carte £11
Accommodation (Min) s£40 d£50

SKIRMETT Buckinghamshire *Map 04 SU79*

The Frog NEW
SKIRMETT
RG9 6TG ☎ 01491 638996
Among the attractions of this well-run 17th-century village inn, tucked away in a beautiful Chiltern's valley, are the lovely garden and the enterprising food served throughout the neat interior. Choose, perhaps, monkfish with fresh pasta and red pepper essence, pork with courgette confit, or seared salmon with avocado salsa and potato chive hash. Good puddings. **Principal beers:** Adnams Best, Brakspear Bitter, Fullers London Pride, guest ale.
Brewery/Company Free House

Open 11.30-3 6-11
Bar food 12-2.30 6.30-9.30 Av main course £8
Restaurant 12-2.30 6-9.30 Av 3 course à la carte £16.95
Accommodation (Min) s£48.50 d£58.50

SPEEN Buckinghamshire *Map 04 SU89*

King William IV
SPEEN
Hampden Rd HP27 0RU
☎ 01494 488329
Nestling in the Chiltern Hills, this 17th-century, family run pub and restaurant boasts log fires in winter and a popular terrace and garden ideal for summer drinking. Choose from an interesting range of blackboard specials that might include Thai green chicken curry, grilled red snapper and trio of Welsh lamb cutlets. **Principal beers:** Marstons Pedigree, Boddingtons.
Directions Through Hughenden Valley, off A4128 N of High Wycombe
Brewery/Company Free House
Open 12-3 6.30-11 (closed Mon, all Jan-Feb & Sep)
Restaurant 12-2 7-9.30 Av 3 course à la carte £25

STOKE POGES Buckinghamshire *Map 04 SU98*

Red Lion
STOKE POGES
Stoke Green Sl2 4HN ☎ 01753 213911
A 17th-century brick-built country inn set in peaceful Stoke Poges, which provides an ideal base for walks through the Chiltern Hundreds. The Red Lion is particularly hospitable to ramblers.
Principal beers: Bass.
Brewery/Company Vintage Inns
Open 11-11 (Sun 12-10.30)

TURVILLE Buckinghamshire
Map 04 SU79

The Bull & Butcher
TURVILLE

RG9 6QU ☎ 01491 638283

Lovely, timbered 16th-century pub tucked away in a secluded valley in a classic Chiltern's village. The name refers to Henry V111, who executed Anne Boleyn (born Nan Bullen), and was thus the 'Bullen butcher'. Dishes include assorted tapas, rack of lamb with herb and mustard crust, and monkfish on a bed of lightly curried lentils.
Principal beers: Brakspear Mild, Bitter, Special & Old.
Directions M40 J5 follow signs for Ibstone. Turn R T-junc. Pub 0.25m on L
Brewery/Company Brakspear
Open 11-3 6-11
Bar food 12-2 7-9.45 Av main course £9.95

WADDESDON Buckinghamshire
Map 04 SP71

The Five Arrows Hotel
WADDESDON

High St HP18 0JE ☎ 01296 651727

Built by Baron Rothschild in 1887 as part of the Waddesdon Estate (NT), this Grade II listed building originally accommodated men working on the manor house. Expect traditional English and Mediterranean dishes such as dressed Cromer crab, confit of duck with chargrilled vegetables, mustard and herb-crusted monkfish. **Principal beers:** Adnams Best, Fullers London Pride.
Directions on A41 6m NW of Aylesbury
Brewery/Company Free House
Open 11-3 5.30-11 (Sun 12-3, 7-10.30)
Bar food 12-2.30 Av main course £9
Restaurant 12-2.30 7-9.30 Av 3 course à la carte £25
Accommodation (Min) s£70 d£80

WESTON TURVILLE Buckinghamshire
Map 04 SP81

Five Bells
WESTON TURVILLE

40 Main St HP22 5RW ☎ 01296 613131

Situated on the edge of the Chiltern Hills, The Five Bells is set in very attractive Buckinghamshire countryside. It was originally built in 1854 as a private dwelling, and has retained much of its typically English character.
Principal beers: Bass.
Directions from A41 at Aston Clinton, take B4544
Brewery/Company Vintage Inns
Open 11-11 (Sun 12-10.30)

WEST WYCOMBE Buckinghamshire
Map 04 SU89

The George and Dragon Hotel
WEST WYCOMBE

High St HP14 3AB ☎ 01494 464414

Striking Tudor coaching inn set in a National Trust village beside the A40. Reputedly haunted by the 'White Lady', it features a character period bar and offers a varied menu of home-made food. Typical choices include hot crab pot, game pie, beef Wellington, and venison casserole in red wine with herb dumplings. **Principal beers:** Courage Best, Greene King Abbot Ale, Wadworth 6X, Marston's Pedigree.

Directions M40 North, J5, L onto A40, 4m into village. M40 South, J4, A4010 to T-jct, L onto A40, village 0.5m
Brewery/Company Inntrepreneur
Open 11-2.30 5.30-11
Bar food 12-2 6-9.30 Av main course £7
Accommodation (Min) s£56 d£66

WOOBURN COMMON Buckinghamshire
Map 04 SU98

Chequers Inn
WOOBURN COMMON

Kiln Ln HP10 0JQ ☎ 01628 529575

Coaching inn dating from the 17th century, now developed as a hotel with conference and meeting facilities. There is a good choice of menus, with fresh seafood available daily. Dishes might include beef Stroganoff, smoked fish platter, casserole of turbot with root

contd.

vegetables, and Thai-style chicken with wild rice. **Principal beers:** Marstons Pedigree, Fullers London Pride, Rebellion Smuggler.
Directions M40 J2 through Beaconsfield towards High Wycombe.1m turn L into Broad Lane. Inn 2.5m
Brewery/Company Free House
Open 9am-11pm
Bar food 12-2.30 7-9.30 Av main course £8
Restaurant 12-2.30 7-9.30 Av 3 course à la carte £20 Av 3 course fixed price £17.95

Greater London

COULSDON Greater London — Map 04 TQ25

The Fox
COULSDON
Coulsdon Common CR3 5QS
☎ 01883 330401
Standing above Happy Valley, - a site of special scientific interest - yet convenient for major roads into London, this Victorian pub is in a tranquil and secluded location. Traditional pub menu. **Principal beers:** Bass.
Directions Off B2030 between Caterham & Coulsdon
Brewery/Company Vintage Inns
Open 11-11 (Sun 12-10.30)

KESTON Greater London — Map 05 TQ46

The Crown
KESTON
Leaves Green BR2 6OG
☎ 01959 572920
An old pub, not far from Biggin Hill, where the food ranges from sandwiches and ploughman's to a filo basket filled with fresh mussels and white wine, garlic and bacon sauce, or fillet of halibut with tarragon mash and fresh broccoli. **Principal beers:** Shepherd Neame Master Brew, Spitfire & Best.
Directions A21 onto A232, then L onto A233, pub 4m
Brewery/Company Shepherd Neame
Open 11-2.30 5-11 (Sat-Sun, all week in summer 11-11)
Bar food 12-2 6-9 Av main course £5.95
Restaurant 12-2 6-9 Av 3 course à la carte £15

UXBRIDGE Greater London — Map 04 TQ08

The Turning Point
UXBRIDGE
Canal Cottages, Packet Boat Ln, Cowley Peachey UB8 2JF ☎ 01895 440550
This is the point on the Grand Union Canal where horsedrawn barges were able to be turned around, and the building housed employees who repaired the barges. The waterside bar and restaurant offer pleasant surroundings for a comprehensive selection of snacks and freshly cooked meals.

Directions From M4 J4 2m N on A408
Brewery/Company Free House
Open 11-11
Bar food 12-9.30 12-9.30 Av main course £5.95
Restaurant 12-2.30 7-9.30 Av 3 course à la carte £20 Av 3 course fixed price £16.95

Hampshire

ALRESFORD Hampshire — Map 04 SU53

Globe on the Lake
ALRESFORD
The Soke, Broad St SO24 9DB
☎ 01962 732294
Superbly sited on the banks of a reed-fringed lake, complete with waterside garden, this delightful old pub is the place to seek out interesting pub food. In the bar choose from salmon fishcakes, duck confit, or cod in beer batter, while evening restaurant fare may highlight lamb stuffed with apricot, and salmon with roasted spices. **Principal beers:** Courage Best, Marstons Pedigree, Wadworth 6X, John Smiths.
Brewery/Company Inntrepreneur
Open 11-3 6-11
Bar food 12-2 6.30-9.30 Av main course £6.95

Restaurant 12-2 7-9.30 Av 3 course à la carte £16 Av 2 course fixed price £9.95

BASINGSTOKE Hampshire *Map 04 SU65*

The Dean Gate Inn
BASINGSTOKE

Deane RG25 3AX ☎ 01256 780226

Formerly a tollgate on the Andover to London road, Jane Austen is believed to have stabled her horses here when her father was vicar of nearby Steventon. Representative dishes include brocolli mornay, salmon fillet with Pernod and mustard sauce, and steak and ale pie.

Principal beers: Ushers Best & Four Seasons, Courage Best.

Directions B3400 between Oakley & Overton

Brewery/Company Ushers

Open 11-3 5-11 (Sun 12-7)

Bar food 12-3 Av main course £5.95

Restaurant 12-3 7-9.45 Av 3 course à la carte £16

Accommodation (Min) d£45

BEAUWORTH Hampshire *Map 04 SU52*

The Milburys
BEAUWORTH

SO24 0PB ☎ 01962 771248

The pub is set in an area of outstanding natural beauty and has a massive treadmill, about 250 years old, drawing water from its 30ft well. Food ranges from filled baguettes and jacket potatoes to dishes such as Mediterranean beef casserole, and grilled sardines with herb and garlic butter. **Principal beers:** Hampshire King Alfred & Pride of Romsey, Burton Bridge.

Directions A272 towards Petersfield, after 6m turn R for Beauworth

Brewery/Company Free House

Open 11-3 6-11

Bar food 12-2.30 6.30-9.30 Av main course £6.95

Accommodation (Min) s£27.50 d£40

BENTLEY Hampshire *Map 04 SU74*

The Bull Inn
BENTLEY

GU10 5JH ☎ 01420 22156 & 23334

A welcome retreat for A31 travellers, the 15th-century Bull Inn offers an interesting selection of food, especially fish and seafood, in its civilised bar. Diners may well find smoked haddock risotto, confit of duck, baked lobster, liver and bacon, and fillet of John Dory, alongside sandwiches and warm salads on the menu.

Principal beers: Courage Best, Hogs Back TEA, Youngs, Marstons Pedigree.

Directions 2m out of Farnham on the A31 towards Winchester

Brewery/Company Free House

Open 11-11 (Sun 12-10.30)

Bar food 11.30-3 6.30-11 Av main course £5.95

Restaurant 11.30-3 6.30-11 Av 3 course à la carte £25 Av 3 course fixed price £20

BENTWORTH Hampshire *Map 04 SU64*

The Sun Inn
BENTWORTH

Sun Hill GU34 5JT ☎ 01420 562338

Originally two cottages, this 17th-century pub has three communicating rooms with open log fires and lots of pews, settles and scrubbed pine tables. Excellent range of tip-top real ales. Expect lamb with port and redcurrants, home-made smoked salmon pasta and giant Yorkshire pudding among the bar meals. **Principal beers:** Cheriton Pots Ale, Ringwood Best & Old Thumper, Brakspear Bitter, guest ales.

Brewery/Company Free House

Open 12-3 6-11 (Sun 12-10.30)

Bar food 12-2 7-9.30 Av main course £6.50

BROOK Hampshire *Map 04 SU21*

The Bell Inn NEW
BROOK

SO43 7HE ☎ 01703 812214

Extended 200-year-old drovers' inn on the edge of the New Forest, owned throughout its history by the same local family. Many period features remain, including inglenook fireplaces and old beams in some rooms. Popular dishes include supreme of chicken, wing of skate with capers, and peppered steak.

Principal beers: Bass, Ringwood Best.

Directions From M27 J1 (Cadnam) take B3078 signed Brook, 0.5m on R

Brewery/Company Free House

Open 11-11 (Sun 12-10.30)

Bar food 12-2.30 6.30-9.30 Av main course £7.50

Restaurant 12-2.30 7.30-9.30 Av 3 course à la carte £26.50 Av 3 course fixed price £26.50

Accommodation (Min) s£55 d£80

South & South East (& Isle of Wight)

BROUGHTON Hampshire *Map 04 SU33*

The Tally Ho!
BROUGHTON

High St SO20 8AA ☎ 01794 301280
Traditional, well restored country pub nestling in a pretty village, close to the Test Valley and popular with walkers hiking the Clarendon Way. Expect a friendly welcome, decent real ales and good-value, home-cooked food, from filled baps and ploughman's lunches, to ham and mushroom pie and beef Stroganoff. **Principal beers:** Ringwood True Glory, Cheriton Pots Ale, Adnams Broadside, Wadworth 6X.
Directions Winchester to Stockbridge rd then A30, 1st L to Broughton
Brewery/Company Free House
Open 12-2.30 6-11 (Sat & Sun 12-3 7-10.30)
Bar food 12-2 7-9 Av main course £5

BUCKLERS HARD Hampshire *Map 04 SU40*

The Master Builders House Hotel NEW
BUCKLERS HARD

SO42 7XB ☎ 01590 616253
On the banks of te Beaulieu River in the heart of the Beaulieu Manor Estate, this former house of master shipbuilder Henry Adams has undergone tasteful refurbishment. Stylish bedrooms in the original 18th-century house enjoy fine river views. Imaginative restaurant menu and decent light snacks in the welcoming Yachtsman's Bar. Expect home-made terrines, dressed crab salad, seafood stew and ploughman's on the short menu. **Principal beers:** Courage Directors, Samuel Smith.
Brewery/Company Free House
Open 11-3 6-11
Bar food 12-2.30 6.30-9 Av main course £7.50
Accommodation (Min) s£72 d£96

BURITON Hampshire *Map 04 SU71*

The Five Bells
BURITON

High St GU31 5RX ☎ 01730 263584
Named after the five bells of Buriton church, this 17th-century inn is situated on the South Downs. Fish and game dishes figure prominently on the menu, with dishes such as salmon with orange and tarragon and half a roast pheasant with blackcurrant. **Principal beers:** Ballard Best, Ringwood Best & Old Thumper, Greene King IPA, Tetley.
Directions village signposted off A3 S of Petersfield
Brewery/Company Hall & Woodhouse
Open 11-2.30 (Sat-Sun 11-3) 5.30-11
Bar food 12-2 6.30-10 Av main course £7.50

CHALTON Hampshire *Map 04 SU71*

The Red Lion
CHALTON

PO8 0BG ☎ 01705 592246
Splendid 12th-century thatched pub on the edge of the South Downs. The oldest inn in the county and originally built as a workshop for the craftsmen who built the Norman church opposite. One menu throughout offers fresh cod in beer batter, gamekeepers rabbit pie, braised duck in red wine and sea bass in coconut milk. **Principal beers:** Gales Butser, Winter Brew, GB & HSB.
Directions Just off A3 between Horndean & Petersfield.
Take exit near Queen Elizabeth Country Park
Brewery/Company Gales
Open 11-3 6-11
Bar food 12-2 6.30-9 Av main course £7.50
Restaurant 12-2 6.30-9 Av 3 course à la carte £12

CHARTER ALLEY Hampshire *Map 04 SU55*

The White Hart
CHARTER ALLEY

White Hart Ln RG26 5QA
☎ 01256 850048
Dating from 1815, but considerably extended, this beamed village pub has a good reputation for its range of well-kept real ales. On the food side, you may find steak and Stilton pie, seafood bake, braised pork with peaches, and mixed grill. **Principal beers:** Morrells Oxford, Varsity & Graduate, Fullers London Pride.
Directions From M3 J6 take A339 towards Newbury.Take turning to Ramsdell. Turn R at church, then 1st L into White Hart Lane
Brewery/Company Free House
Open 12-2.30 7-11
Bar food 12-2 7-9 Av main course £5.95
Restaurant 12-2 7-9

CHERITON Hampshire *Map 04 SU52*

The Flower Pots Inn
CHERITON
SO24 0QQ ☎ 01962 771318
Award-winning home-brewed ales, an unspoilt village pub atmosphere, and honest home cooking are among the attractions at this traditional rural inn, built as a farmhouse in the 1820s. Enjoy a pint of Diggers Gold with a giant bap filled with home-baked ham, a bowl of chilli with garlic bread, or a hearty casserole. **Principal beers:** Cheriton Pots Ale, Best Bitter & Diggers Gold.
Directions A272 toward Petersfield, L onto B3046, pub 0.75m on R
Brewery/Company Free House
Open 12-2.30 6-11 (Sun 12-3, 6-10.30)
Bar food 12-2 7-9 Av main course £4.50
Accommodation (Min) s£30 d£50

CLANVILLE Hampshire *Map 04 SU34*

The Red Lion Country Inn
CLANVILLE
SP11 9HN ☎ 01264 771007
Traditional country inn, built of brick and flint, whose facilities include a lounge bar, restaurant, conservatory function suites, a patio courtyard, large car park and heli-pad. Popular dishes include home-made steak and kidney pudding, grilled black tiger prawns, and Oxford John leg of lamb steak with Reform sauce. **Principal beers:** Fullers London Pride, Ruddles Best, Flowers Original.
Brewery/Company Free House
Open 11.30-2.30 6.30-11
Bar food 12-2.30 6.30-9 Av main course £4.95
Restaurant 12-2.30 6.30-9 Av 3 course à la carte £12.95

DAMERHAM Hampshire *Map 04 SU11*

The Compasses Inn
DAMERHAM
SP6 3HQ ☎ 01725 518231
Fresh local produce is one of the hallmarks of quality at this historic 400-year-old inn which once had its own brewery, coach house, dairy, well and butchery. The old brew tower still stands. Extensive menu choice ranges from pork Valentine and beef Stroganoff to local trout and speciality sausages.
Principal beers: Compasses Ale, Ringwood Best, Hop Back Summer Lightning, Wadworth 6X.
Directions From Fordingbridge (A338) follow signs for Sandleheath/ Damerham. Or signs from B3078
Brewery/Company Free House
Open 11-3 6-11
Bar food 12-2 7-9.30 Av main course £6.50
Restaurant 12-2 7-9.30 Av 3 course à la carte £15
Accommodation (Min) s£34.50 d£59

DUMMER Hampshire *Map 04 SU54*

The Queen Inn
DUMMER
Down St RG25 2AD ☎ 01256 397367
You can dine by candlelight at this 16th-century village pub, with its low beams and huge open log fire. Everything is home made, from the soup and light bites to the famous fish and chips with beer batter, fresh sea bass, and prime steaks. The steak and kidney pudding is only for the heartier appetite! **Principal beers:** Courage Directors, Fullers London Pride.
Directions M3 J7, turn into Dummer
Brewery/Company Courage
Open 11-3 (Sun 12-3) 5.30-11 (Sun 7-10.30)
Bar food 12-2 6-9.30 Av main course £6.95
Restaurant 12-2 6-9.30 Av 3 course à la carte £17.50

EAST END Hampshire *Map 04 SZ39*

The East End Arms
EAST END
Main Rd SO41 5SY ☎ 01590 626223
Traditional New Forest pub with an extended and refurbished lounge/bar restaurant serving modern food. The menu features warm ciabatta sandwiches, fresh fish and game in season, perhaps including grilled fish with cod cake and anchovy butter, and venison glazed with wild crab apple sauce. Good locals' bar serving Ringwood ales from the barrel.
Principal beers: Ringwood Best & Fortyniner, Hampshire Pride of Romsey.
Directions From Lymington follow signs for Isle of Wight ferry. Pass ferry terminal on R & continue for 3m
Brewery/Company Free House
Open 11.30-3 6-11 (Sun 6-10.30)
Bar food 12-3 Av main course £5

contd.

Restaurant 12-3 7-11 Av 3 course à la carte £16

EAST MEON Hampshire Map 04 SU62

Ye Olde George Inn
EAST MEON
Church St GU32 1NH ☎ 01730 823481
Originally a pair of 15th-century cottages, this country inn is situated near the River Meon. The food choice ranges from bar snacks to a full carte, and in both the bar and restaurant the emphasis is very much on fresh produce, including fish and local game. **Principal beers:** Badger Dorset Best & IPA.
Directions S of A272 (Winchester/Petersfield) turning 1.5m from Petersfield Pub on L near church
Brewery/Company Hall & Woodhouse
Open 11-3 6-11
Bar food 12-2 7-9.30 Av main course £5.50
Restaurant 12-2 7-9.30 Av 3 course à la carte £18
Accommodation (Min) s£32.50 d£60

EASTON Hampshire Map 04 SU53

The Chestnut Horse
EASTON
SO21 1EG ☎ 01962 779257
Traditional pub with a wishing well in the garden, set in a quaint village with thatched cottages and beautiful countryside. Food ranges from quality bar food to dishes such as slow-roasted half shoulder of lamb with redcurrant and wine sauce, and baked whole black bream with garlic mash. **Principal beers:** Bass, Courage Best, Chestnut Horse Special.
Directions From M3 J9 take A33 towards Basingstoke,then B3047. Take 2nd R
Brewery/Company Free House
Open 11-3 5.30-11
Bar food 12-2 7-9.30 Av main course £7
Restaurant 12-2 7-9.30 Av 3 course à la carte £18

Cricketers Inn
EASTON
EASTON SO21 1EJ ☎ 01962 779353
Genuinely a cricketers' pub (the local side is active in the county), this traditional freehouse has a lovely village setting close to the River Itchen. The menu is a constantly changing list of blackboard specials. New owners took over as we went to press. **Principal beers:** Changing guest ales.
Directions M3 J9,A33 towards Basingstoke.Turn R at Kings Worthy onto B3047.0.75m turn R
Brewery/Company Free House
Open 11.30-3 6-11
Bar food 12-2 6.45-9.15 Av main course £7
Restaurant 12-2 6.45-9.15 Av 3 course à la carte £15
Accommodation (Min) s£32 d£55

EAST TYTHERLEY Hampshire Map 04 SU22

Star Inn
EAST TYTHERLEY
SO51 0UW ☎ 01794 340225
Formerly the old coaching house for nearby Lockerley Hall, this friendly and informal pub overlooks the village cricket ground. Reliable home-made dishes, served in the homely bars and attractive restaurant, may include daily specials like curried parsnip soup, chicken, leek and Stilton pie, game pie, red bream with lemon sauce, and bread-and-butter pudding. **Principal beers:** Courage Best, Gales HSB, Ringwood Best.
Directions N of Romsey off B3084
Brewery/Company Free House
Open 8.30-3 6-11
Bar food 8.30-2 6-9 Av main course £5.95
Restaurant 12-2 7-9 Av 3 course à la carte £20 Av 3 course fixed price £15
Accommodation (Min) s£35 d£50

EMSWORTH Hampshire Map 04 SU70

The Sussex Brewery
EMSWORTH
36 Main Rd PO10 8AU ☎ 01243 371533
Popular17th-century freehouse that takes its name from the town's old brewing site. Inside, sawdust serves as a reminder of how traditional alehouses used to be. Varied choice of pub food, including fresh fish and steaks, as well as 50 different sausages containing the lean meat and freshly blended seasoning. **Principal beers:** Badger Tanglefoot, Youngs PA & Special, Taylor Landlord.
Directions On A259 (coast road), between Havant & Chichester
Brewery/Company Free House
Open 11-11

Bar food 12-2.30 7-10 Av main course £6
Restaurant 12-2.30 7-10 Av 3 course à la carte £11

FORDINGBRIDGE Hampshire — Map 04 SU11

The Augustus John
FORDINGBRIDGE

116 Station Rd SP6 1DG
☎ 01425 652098

Named after the renowned British painter who resided in the village, this neatly refurbished inn is a comfortable base for exploring the New Forest. Well-cooked and presented food ranges from steak and Guinness casserole and Thai chicken curry, to whole Poole plaice, lamb with redcurrant and mint, and interesting home-made puddings. **Principal beers:** Hardy Country, Bass, Tetley.
Brewery/Company Eldridge Pope
Open 11.30-3 6-12
Bar food 11.30-2 6.30-9 Av main course £5.95
Restaurant 11.30-2 6.30-9 Av 3 course à la carte £15
Accommodation (Min) s£25 d£50

FROXFIELD GREEN Hampshire — Map 04 SU72

The Trooper Inn NEW
FROXFIELD GREEN

Alton Rd GU32 1BD ☎ 01730 827293

Unpretentious roadside inn enjoying an isolated downland position. A relaxing, laid-back atmosphere prevails throughout the rustic, pine furnished interior; evening candlelight enhances the overall ambience. In addition to good real ales and wines, expect interesting home-cooked food, perhaps including lasagne, chicken and bacon carbonara, and cod with ginger and dill butter. **Principal beers:** Ringwood Best & Fortyniner, Bass, guest ales.
Directions E of A3 & Petersfield; follow road to Steep from town. Pub 3m.
Brewery/Company Free House
Bar food 12-2 6-10 Av main course £7

HAVANT Hampshire — Map 04 SU70

The Royal Oak NEW
HAVANT

19 Langstone High St, Langstone PO9 1RY ☎ 01705 483125

Historic 16th-century pub with stunning views over Chichester Harbour. Notable for its idyllic waterside position and for its rustic, unspoilt interior with flagstone floors, exposed beams and open fires. Front benches and secluded rear garden for summer alfresco drinking; traditional bar food and all-day snack menu.
Principal beers: Flowers Original, Wadworth 6X, Morland Old Speckled Hen, Gales HSB.
Brewery/Company Whitbread
Open 11-11 (Sun 12-10.30)
Bar food 12-2.30 6-9 Av main course £6.95
Restaurant 12-2.30 6-9 Av 3 course à la carte £10.50

HOOK Hampshire — Map 04 SU75

Crooked Billet
HOOK

London Rd RG27 9EH ☎ 01256 762118

Keep the children occupied in the play area while watching wildlife on the River Whitewater at this 1930s roadside pub. The menu is supported by daily specials, including beef in rich Stilton gravy, ham and asparagus flan, and chicken in a creamy sauce - all home-made. **Principal beers:** Courage Best & Directors.
Directions From M3 J5 follow signs for A30/Hook.Pub 1m before Hook on A30, on L by river
Brewery/Company Free House
Open 11.30-3 6-11
Bar food 12.00-2.30 7-9.30 Av main course £6

IBSLEY Hampshire — Map 04 SU10

Olde Beams Inn
IBSLEY

Salisbury Rd BH24 3PP
☎ 01425 473387

The cruck beam is clearly visible from the outside of this thatched, 14th-century building. In addition to the à la carte

contd.

restaurant, there is a popular buffet counter with freshly prepared meats, fish, seafood and home-made game pie served with a wide selection of helf-yourself salads. **Principal beers:** Ringwood.
Directions On A338 between Ringwood & Salisbury
Brewery/Company Old English Inns/Hot
Open 11-3 6-11
Bar food 12-2 7-10 Av main course £7
Restaurant 12-2 7-10 Av 3 course à la carte £15

LINWOOD Hampshire *Map 04 SU10*

Red Shoot Inn
LINWOOD
Toms Ln BH24 3QT ☎ 01425 475792
Set in the heart of the New Forest, with its own micro-brewery, the bustling Red Shoot Inn offers real ale and real food in a real country pub. From jacket potatoes and sandwiches, the menu extends to speciality sausages and steaks. There is live music on a Sunday night. **Principal beers:** Wadworth 6X, Henrys IPA, Summersault, Tom's Tipple.
Directions From M27 take A338, take Salisbury turning and follow brown signs to the Red Shoot
Brewery/Company Wadworth
Open 11-3 6-11 (wknd and summer 11-11)
Bar food 12-2 6.30-9.30 Av main course £5.25

LONGPARISH Hampshire *Map 04 SU44*

The Plough Inn
LONGPARISH
SP11 6PB ☎ 01264 720358
As it is only 100 yards away from the river this 400-year old pub is regularly visited by the local duck population. Typical menu includes scallops Mornay, lobster Thermidor, shoulder of lamb kleftico, wild boar sausage, and salmon Hollandaise. **Principal beers:** Hampshire King Alfred, Flowers, Wadworth 6X, Boddingtons.
Directions Off A303 4m S of Andover
Brewery/Company Whitbread
Open 11-4 6-11 (11-3, 6-11 in winter)
Bar food 12-3 6.30-9.30 Av main course £5.95
Restaurant 12-2.30 6.30-9.30 Av 3 course à la carte £20 Av 3 course fixed price £20
Accommodation (Min) s£25 d£40

LOWER WIELD Hampshire *Map 04 SU64*

The Yew Tree Inn
LOWER WIELD
SO24 9RX ☎ 01256 389224
Recently renovated inn, with oak beams, open fireplaces and flagstone floors, next to the 650-year-old yew tree from which it takes its name. Home-made sausage and mash and filled baguettes are staples in the bar, while the restaurant might have Angus beef with black pudding. **Principal beers:** Flowers IPA.
Directions Off A339 between Basingstoke & Alton
Brewery/Company Free House
Open 12-3 6-11 (closed Mon)
Bar food 12-3 7-11
Restaurant 12-3 7-11 Av 3 course à la carte £20

LYMINGTON Hampshire *Map 04 SZ39*

The Chequers Inn
LYMINGTON
Lower Woodside SO41 8AH
☎ 01590 673415
Dating from about 1670, this was reputedly the salt exchange (or exchequer). A warm and friendly welcome awaits along with the open fire, antique furniture and old beams. The menu is comprehensive and eclectic, offering hot chicken and Stilton salad, chargrilled tuna salad, moules mariniere and minty lamb chops. **Principal beers:** Wadworth 6X, Bass, Fullers London Pride.
Directions From Lymington take A337 towards New Milton.Turn L at White Hart PH then L into Ridgeway Lane.Pub 1m
Brewery/Company Enterprise Inns
Open 11-3 6-11 (all day Sat-Sun)
Bar food 12-2 7-10 Av main course £4.50
Restaurant 12-2 7-10 Av 3 course à la carte £16

MATTINGLEY Hampshire *Map 04 SU75*

The Leather Bottle
MATTINGLEY
Reading Rd RG27 8JU ☎ 01189 326371
Established in 1714, the Leather Bottle is heavily beamed, with big open fires all winter. A comprehensive menu includes deep-fried Camembert, lemon and peppercorn steak with honey-pink

peppercorn sauce, and raspberry ruin. **Principal beers:** Courage Best.
Directions From M3 J5 follow signs for Hook then B3349
Brewery/Company Eldridge Pope
Open 11-2.30 6-11
Bar food 12-2 6-9.30 Av main course £6.95

MEONSTOKE Hampshire *Map 04 SU53*

The Bucks Head NEW
MEONSTOKE
Bucks Head Mill SO32 3NA
☎ 01489 877313
Nestling in a quaint village in the Meon valley, close to the Saxon church, and babbling chalk stream, this former coaching inn dates from the 16th century. Two welcoming bars with open fires, beams, and a traditional menu. Choose from ploughman's, filled rolls, pork with leek and Stilton, various grills, and game in season. Lovely riverside garden. **Principal beers:** Morland Old Speckled Hen, Wells Bombardier, Ruddles Best, Morland Tanners Jack.

Directions by the jct of A32 & B2150
Brewery/Company Morland
Open 11-3 6-11
Bar food 12-2.15 7-9.15 Av main course £4
Restaurant 12-2.15 7-9.15 Av 3 course à la carte £14
Accommodation (Min) s£30 d£45

MICHELDEVER Hampshire *Map 04 SU53*

The Dever Arms
MICHELDEVER
Winchester Rd SO21 3DG
☎ 01962 774339
Wattle and daub village pub with old beams and an open fire. It has its own menagerie of animals including a pony, rabbit, guinea pig, banams, ducks, cats and a big hairy dog. Everything from the extensive menu is home-made, from bar snacks to a full carte. **Principal beers:** Greene King IPA, Marston Pedigree.
Directions Take A30 from Winchester towards Basingstoke. After Kings Worthy turn L after petrol station. Pub 0.5m on L
Brewery/Company Greene King
Open 12-3 6-11
Bar food 12-2.30 6-10 Av main course £6.50
Restaurant 12-2.30 6-10.30 Av 3 course à la carte £17

NORTH WALTHAM Hampshire *Map 04 SU54*

The Fox
NORTH WALTHAM
RG25 2BE ☎ 01256 397288
Built as three farm cottages in 1624, this peacefully situated village pub enjoys splendid views across fields and farmland. Lovely garden and a varied bar menu featuring basket meals, filled baguettes, steaks, and home-made dishes like beef in ale, and lamb and leek casserole. Game in season. **Principal beers:** Ushers.
Directions From M3 J7 take A30 towards Winchester. Village signposted
Brewery/Company Ushers
Open 11-11
Bar food 12-10

OLD BASING Hampshire *Map 04 SU65*

The Millstone
OLD BASING
Bartons Mill Ln RG24 8AE
☎ 01256 331153
Enjoying a rural location beside the River Loddon, close to a country park and Old Basing House, yet only a short drive from Basingstoke, this attractive old building is a popular lunchtime spot for summer alfresco imbibing. Bar food ranges from steak and Stilton to vegetarian specials like leek and celeriac bake. **Principal beers:** Wadworth 6X & Henrys IPA.
Directions From M3 J6 follow brown signs to Basing House
Brewery/Company Wadworth
Open 11-11
Bar food 12-2.30 6.30-9.30 Av main course £5

OVINGTON Hampshire Map 04 SU53

The Bush
OVINGTON

SO24 0RE ☎ 01962 732764

Tucked away down a winding, wooded lane off the A31 is the Bush, a delightful rose-covered pub in a charming setting by the tranquil River Itchen. Enjoy a riverside stroll then relax with a bar meal, perhaps mussel and prawn chowder or pork on mustard mash with juniper and fennel sauce. **Principal beers:** Wadworth 6X, IPA & Farmers Glory, Badger Tanglefoot.

Directions A31 from Winchester, E to Alton & Farnham, approx 6m turn L off dual carriageway to Ovington. 0.5m to pub.

Brewery/Company Wadworth

Open 11-3 6-10.30 (Sun 12-2 7-10.30)

Bar food 12-2 6.30-9.30 Av main course £9

OWSLEBURY Hampshire Map 04 SU52

The Ship Inn
OWSLEBURY

Whites Hill SO21 1LT ☎ 01962 777358

Popular 17th-century hilltop village local, close to the attractions of Marwell Zoo and Winchester. Apart from the splendid 'family' garden, it offers interesting food in the beamed bars. Daily specials range from Cajun chicken and Italian meatloaf with red wine gravy, to Irish stew, and monkfish with mild, creamy curry sauce. **Principal beers:** Bateman Mild, Marstons Best, Pedigree & Head Brewers Choice.

Directions M3 J11 take B3335 follow signs for Owslebury

Brewery/Company Marstons

Open 11-3 (Sun 12-10.30) 6-11

Bar food 12-2 6.30-9.30 Av main course £8

Restaurant 12-2 6.30-9.30

PETERSFIELD Hampshire Map 04 SU72

The White Horse Inn
PETERSFIELD

Priors Dean GU32 1DA

☎ 01420 588387

Also known as the 'Pub With No Name' as it has no sign, this splendid 17th-century farmhouse enjoys a remote downland setting. There is a new dining room in addition to the two classic bars. The menu is the same throughout except for Saturday dinner and Sunday lunch. **Principal beers:** No Name Best Strong, No Name Strong, Fullers London Pride, Bass.

Directions A3/A272 to Winchester & Petersfield. In Petersfield L to Steep, 5m then R at small X-rds to E Tisted, 2nd drive on R

Brewery/Company Gales

Open 11-2.30 6-11 (Sun 11-2.30, 6-10.30)

Bar food 12-2 7-9 Av main course £5.95

PILLEY Hampshire Map 04 SZ39

The Fleur de Lys
PILLEY

Pilley St SO41 5QB ☎ 01590 672158

Originally a pair of foresters' cottages, this delightful thatched property was established as an inn in 1096. Splendid stone-flagged hall and cosy beamed bars. Bar food specialities include fresh cod fillet in beer batter, steamed rabbit pudding, New Forest venison, and a winter broth cooked in a cauldron on the open fire.

Principal beers: Ringwood Best, Morland Old Speckled Hen, Flowers Original.

Brewery/Company Whitbread

Open 11.30-3 6-11

Bar food 12-2 6.30-9.30 Av main course £8

Restaurant 12-2 6.30-9.30 Av 3 course à la carte £15 Av 2 course fixed price £8.99

PORTSMOUTH & SOUTHSEA Hampshire *Map 04 SZ69*

The Wine Vaults
PORTSMOUTH & SOUTHSEA

43-47 Albert Rd, Southsea PO5 2SF
☎ 01705 864712

Originally several Victorian shops converted into a Victorian-style ale house with wooden floors, wood-panelled walls, interesting pictures and artefacts, and a relaxed atmosphere. Expect a good range of real ales and good-value food, including beef in ale, spinach lasagne, minted lamb stew, home-made soups, and filled jacket potatoes. **Principal beers:** Bass, Theakstons Best, Greene King, Hopback Summer Lightning.
Brewery/Company Free House
Open 12-11 (Sun 12-10.30)
Bar food 12-9.30pm Av main course £5

RINGWOOD Hampshire *Map 04 SU10*

The Struan Country Inn NEW
RINGWOOD

Horton Rd, Ashey Heath BH24 2EG ☎ 01425 473553

Built as a private house in the 1920s, this imposing inn is handy for Bournemouth, the New Forest and the Avon Valley. Food ranges from Cheddar ploughman's and bangers and mash, to jugged hare, pan-fried pheasant, sea bass with chive mash and red pepper pesto, and beef fillet with red wine sauce.
Principal beers: Badger Tanglefoot, IPA & Dorset Best.
Directions M27 to A31, at rdbt take A338 Bournemouth, R for Ashey Heath
Brewery/Company Hall & Woodhouse
Open 11-3 5.30-11 (Sun 12-3, 7-10.30)

Bar food 12-2 7-9.30 Av main course £6.95
Restaurant 12-2 7-9.30 Av 3 course à la carte £16
Accommodation (Min) s£40 d£60

ROCKBOURNE Hampshire *Map 04 SU11*

The Rose & Thistle
ROCKBOURNE

SP6 3NL ☎ 01725 518236

Delightful, long and low thatched pub enjoying a tranquil postion in one of Hampshire's most picturesque villages. A civilised atmosphere pervades the tastefully decorated interior. Diners can sample wild boar terrine, smoked salmon and scrambled eggs, fillet steak, or specials like monkfish in Oriental sauce, and venison with spring onion and chestnut sauce. **Principal beers:** Fuller's London Pride, Marstons Pedigree, Adnams Broadside, Wadworth 6X.
Directions Rockbourne is signposted from B3078 and from A354
Brewery/Company Free House
Open 11-3 6-11
Bar food 12-2.30 7-9.30 Av main course £6
Restaurant 12-2.30 7-9.30 Av 3 course à la carte £16

ROMSEY Hampshire *Map 04 SU32*

The Dukes Head
ROMSEY

Greatbridge Rd SO51 0HB
☎ 01794 514450

Festooned with flowers in summer and featuring five individually decorated rooms, this popular dining pub nestles in the Test Valley, just a stone's throw from the famous trout river. Well-prepared, adventurous food includes game terrine with Cumberland sauce, rabbit and pigeon pie, sea bass with spring onion and ginger, and chicken gumbo.
Principal beers: Romsey Pride, Hampshire King Alfred, Bass, Hardy Country.
Brewery/Company Eldridge Pope
Open 11-11
Bar food 11-3 6-10 Av main course £8.95

Old Horse & Jockey
ROMSEY
23 Maidstone SO51 8HG
☎ 01794 519515
Unassuming pub located close to the Test Way and opposite Broadlands Estate. However, the civilised interior is the perfect setting in which to savour some serious pub food, the menu listing, perhaps, roasted salmon with peppers and pesto, pheasant with glazed chestnuts, scallops with black olives and tomato, and bangers and mash with onion gravy. **Principal beers:** Courage Directors, John Smiths, Theakston Old Peculier.

Directions A36 onto A3090 (A31) to Romsey, pub 1st building on L
Brewery/Company Free House
Open 11-3 6-11
Bar food 11.30-2 6-9.30 Av main course £7.50
Restaurant 11-2 6-9.30 Av 3 course à la carte £20

ROWLANDS CASTLE Hampshire — *Map 04 SU71*

Castle Inn
ROWLANDS CASTLE
1 Finchdean Rd PO9 6DA
☎ 01705 412494
Listed mid-19th-century building located on the edge of the village opposite 500-acre Stansted Park. Traditional atmosphere with open fires, wooded floors and no music, but a modern-style menu listing, perhaps, beef and mushroom casserole, braised lamb shank with Provencal sauce, cod with ginger and coriander butter, and mussel stew with saffron sauce. **Principal beers:** Gales Butser, HSB & GB.
Directions N of Havant take B2149 to Rowlands Castle. Pass green, under rail bridge, pub 1st on L opp Stansted Park
Brewery/Company Gales
Open 11.30-3 6-11 (Fri 5-11,Sat 11.30-11,Sun 12-11)
Bar food 12-2 7-9 Av main course £4.50
Restaurant 12-2 7-9 Av 3 course à la carte £13
Accommodation (Min) s£20 d£30

ST MARY BOURNE Hampshire — *Map 04 SU45*

The George Inn
ST MARY BOURNE
SP11 6BG ☎ 01264 738340
Listed village inn in the picturesque Tarrant valley, with a bar full of cricket memorabilia, one dining room decorated with regimental battle scenes, and another one with a mural of the River Test. Food options include Desperate Dan's sausage and mash, chicken Mustique, and tournedos Rossini. **Principal beers:** Wadworth 6X, Courage Best & Directors, Morland Old Speckled Hen, Tisbury.
Directions M3 J8/A303, then A34 towards Newbury. Turn at Whitchurch & follow signs for St Mary Bourne
Brewery/Company Free House
Open 11-3 6-11
Bar food 12-2 7-9.30 Av main course £5.95
Restaurant 12-3.30 7-9.30 Av 3 course à la carte £17
Accommodation (Min) d£45

SHERFIELD ENGLISH Hampshire — *Map 04 SU22*

The Hatchet Inn
SHERFIELD ENGLISH
SO51 6FP ☎ 01794 322487
Homely 17th-century pub providing welcome refreshment to New Forest visitors and those exploring the scenic Test Valley. Good emphasis on home-cooked food, from lasagne and ploughman's platters, to pork with cream, Stilton and port, fish specials and popular Sunday roasts. **Principal beers:** Bass, Worthington Best, Tetley.
Directions A27 from Salisbury
Brewery/Company Inn Business
Open 12-11 (Sun 12-10.30)
Bar food 12-2 7-9 Av main course £4.95
Restaurant 12-2 7-9 Av 3 course à la carte £16.50

SPARSHOLT Hampshire *Map 04 SU43*

The Plough Inn
SPARSHOLT

Main Rd SO21 2NW ☎ 01962 776353

Much-extended, 200-year-old cottage, located on the village edge, featuring cosy, pine-furnished rooms, a delightful summer garden, and an imaginative range of home-cooked food. Blackboard choices may include Thai green chicken curry, cod and smoked haddock bake, halibut with pepper and parsley dressing, and beef fillet with red wine jus. **Principal beers:** Wadworth IPA, 6X, Farmers Glory & Old Timer.

Directions From Winchester take B3049(A272) W

Brewery/Company Wadworth

Open 11-3 6-11 (12-3, 6-10.30)

Bar food 12-2 6-9 Av main course £7.50

Restaurant 12-2 6-9 Av 3 course à la carte £20

STEEP Hampshire *Map 04 SU72*

Harrow Inn
STEEP

GU32 2DA ☎ 01730 262685

Tucked down a sleepy lane the Harrow is a gem of a rustic pub, still totally unspoilt and run by the same family since 1929. Simple, home-made food, served in two, flower-festooned small bars, includes a hearty bowl of pea and ham soup, smoked salmon sandwiches, various quiches and flans, Scotch eggs, and cheese and ham platters. **Principal beers:** Ringwood Best, Cheriton Diggers Gold & Pots Ale, Ballards Trotton.

Directions Off A3 to A272, L through Sheet, take road opp church (school lane) then over A3 by-pass bridge

Brewery/Company Free House

Open 12-2.30 6-11 (Sat 11-3, 6-11, Sun 12-3, 7-10.30)

Bar food 12-2 7-9 Av main course £6

STOCKBRIDGE Hampshire *Map 04 SU33*

Mayfly
STOCKBRIDGE

Testcombe SO20 6AZ ☎ 01264 860283

On fine summer days relax and eat on the terrace of this superbly situated pub, with the swiftly flowing River Test just a few feet away. The conservatory is a handy alternative in wet weather. The bar offers a hot and cold buffet, home-made quiche, chicken tandoori and a choice of about 40 cheeses. **Principal beers:** Wadworth 6X, Flowers Original, Morland Old Speckled Hen, Boddingtons.

Directions Between A303 & A30, on A3057

Brewery/Company Whitbread

Open 10-11

Bar food 11.30-9 Av main course £5.50

The Peat Spade NEW
STOCKBRIDGE

Longstock SO20 6DR ☎ 01264 810612

Striking, red-brick and gabled Victorian pub tucked away in a thatched village in the Test Valley. Worth seeking out for the imaginative blackboard menu in the neatly-furnished bar areas. Try, perhaps, pork and brandy pate, followed by pork fillet with mustard dressing, or salmon and crab fishcakes, with orange and Cointreau tart to finish. **Principal beers:** Hampshire King Alfred, Ringwood Fortyniner.

Directions village signed off A30 just W of Stockbridge

Brewery/Company Free House

Open 11.30-3 6-11 (closed Mon)

Bar food 12-2.30 7-9.30 Av main course £7.50

Accommodation (Min) d£58.75

STRATFIELD TURGIS Hampshire *Map 04 SU65*

The Wellington Arms
STRATFIELD TURGIS

RG27 0AS ☎ 01256 882214

A 17th-century former farmhouse on the Duke of Wellington's estate in rural Hampshire. The weekly restaurant menu might offer lamb Provencal, or steamed halibut steak with lime and ginger. Homely lounge bar with open fire, sofas and paintings. Bar food ranges from ploughman's to specials such as steak with green peppercorn sauce. **Principal beers:** Badger Dorset Best & Tanglefoot.

Directions on A33 between Basingstoke & Reading

Brewery/Company Woodhouse Inns

Open 11-11

Bar food 12-2.30 6-10 Av main course £11

Restaurant 12-2 6.30-9.30 Av 3 course à la carte £20

Accommodation (Min) s£50 d£60

TANGLEY Hampshire Map 04 SU35

The Fox Inn NEW
TANGLEY

SP11 0RY ☎ 01264 730276

Well worth the detour off the A343, the 300-year-old Fox is a remote brick and flint cottage with a friendly atmosphere. In the bar choose from chilli, lamb casserole and leek and pepper bake, while evening restaurant fare may include beef with pepper sauce, herb-crusted rack of lamb, and whole lemon sole with herb butter. **Principal beers:** Courage Best, Hardy Royal Oak, Theakston Best.

Directions 4m N of Andover
Brewery/Company Free House
Open 12-3 6-11
Bar food 12-3 6-11 Av main course £4.95
Restaurant 12-3 7-11 Av 3 course à la carte £18
Accommodation (Min) s£35 d£40

TICHBORNE Hampshire Map 04 SU53

The Tichborne Arms
TICHBORNE

SO24 0NA ☎ 01962 733760

Heavily thatched red-brick pub set in an idyllic rural hamlet in the Itchen Valley. Worth seeking out for the warm welcome, its splendid summer garden and traditional home-cooked pub food. Dishes range from toasted sandwiches and generously filled jacket potatoes, to decent specials like smoked salmon and scrambled eggs, chicken korma, Normandy pork, chicken in Grand Marnier, and salmon fishcakes with watercress sauce. **Principal beers:** Ringwood Best, Triple fff Moondance, Wadworth 6X.

Directions off A31 towards Alresford, after 200yds R at sign for Tichborne
Brewery/Company Free House
Open 11.30-2.30 6-11
Bar food 12-1.45 7.30-9.45 Av main course £5.50

UPPER FROYLE Hampshire Map 04 SU74

The Hen & Chicken Inn
UPPER FROYLE

GU34 4JH ☎ 01420 22115

Situated on the old Winchester to Canterbury road, this 16th-century inn was once the haunt of highwaymen. It retains its traditional atmosphere with large open fires, panelling and beams. Dishes might include tapénade of tapped cod with roast vegetables, half roast shoulder of lamb, and steaks from the char-grill. **Principal beers:** Taylor Landlord, Hook Norton Best, Courage Best, Badger Best.

Directions 6m from Farnham on A31 on R
Brewery/Company Free House
Open 11-11 (Sun 11-10.30; food all day wknds)
Bar food 12-2.30 6.30-10 Av main course £5.50
Restaurant 12-2 6.30-9 Av 3 course à la carte £21.50 Av 3 course fixed price £22

WELL Hampshire Map 04 SU74

The Chequers Inn
WELL

RG29 1TL ☎ 01256 862605

A charming 17th-century pub with a rustic, low-beamed bar and vine-covered patio, set deep in the heart of the Hampshire countryside. The changing blackboard menu may feature marinated duck breast with plum gravy, black bream stuffed with lemon and rosemary, and swordfish steak on stir-fry noodles. **Principal beers:** Badgers IPA, Dorset Best & Tanglefoot.

Directions from Odiham High St turn R into Long Lane, follow for 3m, L at T jct, pub 0.25m on top of hill
Brewery/Company Hall & Woodhouse
Open 11-3 6-11 (Sat-Sun all day)
Bar food 12-2.30 7-10 Av main course £7.50

WHERWELL Hampshire *Map 04 SU34*

The White Lion
WHERWELL

Fullerton Rd SP11 7JF ☎ 01264 860317

Set in one of the Test Valley's prettiest thatched villages, this former coaching inn is a popular watering-hole among Test Way ramblers. Traditional pub food is served, with such dishes as chicken and bacon pie, pork and cider casserole, locally smoked trout, as well as lunchtime sandwiches and special evening supper menus. **Principal beers:** Flowers Original, Adnams, Whitbread Castle Eden Ale.

Directions Off A303 onto B3048, pub on B3420

Brewery/Company Greenalls

Open 10-2.30 6-11

Bar food 12-2 7-9.30 Av main course £5.80

Restaurant 12-2 7-9.30

Accommodation (Min) s£27.50 d£40

WHITCHURCH Hampshire *Map 04 SU44*

The Red House Inn
WHITCHURCH

21 London St RG28 7LH

☎ 01256 895558

Just a short walk from the Silk Mill and the River Test, this friendly, 16th century inn offers good modern cooking. Imaginative, seasonally-changing menus and daily specials may include spicy fishcakes with coriander butter sauce, game terrine, roast poussin and chorizo sausage with saffron rice, and pan-fried scallops with bacon, pok choi and truffle oil. **Principal beers:** Cheriton Diggers Gold & Pots Ale, Itchen Valley Godfathers.

Directions From M3 or M4 take A34 to Whitchurch

Brewery/Company Free House

Open 11-3 6-11

Restaurant 12-2 6.30-9.30 Av 3 course fixed price £15.95

Watership Down Inn
WHITCHURCH

Freefolk Priors RG8 7NJ

☎ 01256 892254

Taking its name from Richard Adams' enchanting tale of rabbits, this homely 19th-century inn is situated close to the real Watership Down, an area popular with walkers. Good selection of basket meals and hot platters including Lincolnshire sausages, chilli, fish pie, and decent curries. Excellent real ales. **Principal beers:** Archers Best, Brakspear Bitter, Ringwood, Bateman XB.

Directions On B3400 between Basingstoke & Andover

Brewery/Company Free House

Open 11.30-3.30 6-11

Bar food 12-2.30 6-9.30

Restaurant 12-2.30 6-9.30 Av 3 course à la carte £12.50

WHITSBURY Hampshire *Map 04 SU11*

The Cartwheel Inn
WHITSBURY

Whitsbury Rd SP6 3PQ

☎ 01725 518362

Built at the turn of the century as a wheelwright's and shop, this listed tile and slate-roofed building has been a pub since the 1920s. Food ranges from ploughman's, salads and jacket potatoes to steaks, chicken curry and local rainbow trout. The vegetarian choice includes cashew paella. **Principal beers:** Adnams Broadside, Ringwood Best.

Directions Off A338 between Salisbury & Fordingbridge

Brewery/Company Free House

Open 11-2.30 6-11

Bar food 12-2.30 7-9.30 Av main course £6

Restaurant 12-2.30 7-9.30 Av 3 course à la carte £12.50

WINCHESTER Hampshire *Map 04 SU52*

Wykeham Arms
WINCHESTER

75 Kingsgate St SO23 9PE

☎ 01962 853834

One of the most famous city centre pubs in the country, this 250-year-old building might be difficult to find but the effort is certainly worth it. Plenty of style and

contd.

atmosphere inside, and an innovative, modern pub menu. Sample 'Wyk' cottage pie, lamb and redcurrant casserole, and creative evening fare such as rack of lamb with a port wine glaze. Impressive Burgundy-based wine list. **Principal beers:** Bass, Gales Butser, Special & HSB.
Directions Near Winchester College & Winchester Cathedral
Brewery/Company Gales
Open 11-11 (Sun 12-10.30)
Bar food 12-2.30 Av main course £5.50
Restaurant 6.30-9 Av 3 course à la carte £19
Accommodation (Min) s£45 d£79.50

WOODLANDS Hampshire *Map 04 SU31*

The Game Keeper
WOODLANDS
268 Woodlands Rd SO40 7GH
☎ 01703 293093
Backing onto open fields on the very edge of the New Forest, this 150-year-old extended cottage is the perfect resting place after a long forest walk. Comfortable modernised interior and traditional pub food, including steak and Stilton pie, shoulder of lamb with red wine and rosemary sauce, and hearty ploughman's. **Principal beers:** Wadworth 6X, IPA & Farmers Glory, Rockingham Forest Gold, Fuggles.
Directions M27 J2 follow signs for Beaulieu/Fawley(A326). At 1st rndbt after the Safeway rndbt turn R, then next L. 1m on L
Brewery/Company Wadworth
Open 11-2.30 5-11 (open all day Fri-Sun)
Bar food 12-2 6.30-9.30 Av main course £3.50
Restaurant 12-2 6.30-9.30

Hertfordshire

ALDBURY Hertfordshire *Map 04 SP91*

The Greyhound Inn
ALDBURY
19 Stocks Rd HP23 5RT
☎ 01442 851228
Historic inn overlooking the duck pond and stocks in this picturesque village, close to the Ridgeway and miles of downland walks. Bar snacks range from sandwiches to home-made salmon and prawn fishcakes or steak and ale pie. Supreme of chicken, and saddle of lamb on a pear and apple rösti are typical restaurant dishes. **Principal beers:** Aldbury Ale, Marstons Pedigree.
Brewery/Company Free House
Open 6-11
Bar food 12-2.30 6.30-9.30 Av main course £6.95
Restaurant 12-2.30 6.30-9.30 Av 3 course à la carte £20
Accommodation (Min) s£45 d£55

The Valiant Trooper NEW
ALDBURY
Trooper Rd HP23 5RW ☎ 01442 851203
With a restaurant that has been a stable, a Scout hut and a meeting place for local bikers, this 18th-century pub gets its name from a rumour that the Duke of Wellington had a tactical conference here. Among dishes available are game sausages with leek mash, smoked haddock, roasted duck and vegetable stir-fry. **Principal beers:** Fullers London Pride, Bass, John Smiths.
Directions A41 Tring jct, follow signs for railway station, go past for about 1/2m, once at village green turn R then 200yds on L
Brewery/Company Free House
Open 11-11 (Sun 10.30-10.20)
Bar food 12-2 6.30-9.15 Av main course £6
Restaurant 12-2 6.30-9.15 Av 3 course à la carte £15

ARDELEY Hertfordshire *Map 05 TL32*

The Jolly Waggoner
ARDELEY
SE2 7AH ☎ 01438 861350
Antique furniture and ancient beams typify this 500-year-old village pub. Log fires warm in the winter months whilst the well-kept garden is popular in the summer. Bar food may include Serrano ham and feta cheese, home-made burgers, vegetable and pasta bake, fillet steak, and calves' liver with Roquefort cheese and horseradish. **Principal beers:** Greene King IPA & Abbot Ale.
Brewery/Company Greene King
Open 12-2.30 6.30-11 (closed Mon & 1st wk Jan)
Bar food 12-2 6.30-9.30 Av main course £7.50
Restaurant 12.30 6.30-9.30 Av 3 course à la carte £25

AYOT ST LAWRENCE Hertfordshire *Map 04 TL11*

The Brocket Arms
AYOT ST LAWRENCE
AL6 9BT ☎ 01438 820250

Delightful 14th-century inn with many charming features inside, including oak-beamed, low ceilinged bars and restaurant. Legendary priest was tried and hanged at the inn and George Bernard Shaw lived in the village for many years. Traditional English dishes characterise the menu, with game pies, trout, sirloin steak, and Brocket pasta among many dishes. **Principal beers:** Greene King Abbot Ale & IPA, Wadworth 6X, Brakspear Bitter, Adnams Broadside.
Brewery/Company Free House
Open 11-11
Bar food 12-2.30 7.30-9.30 Av main course £5
Restaurant 12-2.30 7.30-10 Av 3 course à la carte £18.95 Av 2 course fixed price £8
Accommodation (Min) s£30 d£60

BARLEY Hertfordshire *Map 05 TL43*

The Fox & Hounds
BARLEY
High St SG8 8HU ☎ 01763 848459

Enjoying a pretty thatched village setting, this former 17th-century hunting lodge is notable for its pub sign which extends across the lane. Recent new owners are offering sardines with mustard mayonnaise, chicken with port and Stilton, fillet steak with pepper sauce, interesting fish and vegetarian dishes, and lemon tart on the varied menu.
Principal beers: Adnams Broadside, Morland Old Speckled Hen & IPA, Marston's Pedigree.
Directions A505 onto B1368 at Flint Cross, pub 4m
Brewery/Company Inn Business
Open 12-3 6-11
Bar food 12-2 6-9.30 Av main course £5
Restaurant 12-2 6-9.30 Av 3 course à la carte £13

BUNTINGFORD Hertfordshire *Map 05 TL32*

The Sword in Hand
BUNTINGFORD
Westmill SG9 9LQ ☎ 01763 271356

Early 15th-century inn, once the home of the Scottish noble family, Gregs. Pubs name taken from a motif within their family crest. The regularly changing menu might include Calvados flamed pork, brill with saffron sauce, and rump steak with port, Guinness and pickled walnuts. **Principal beers:** Greene King IPA & Abbot Ale.
Directions Off A10 1.5m S of Buntingford
Brewery/Company Free House
Open 12-3 6-11
Bar food 12-2.30 6.30-9.30 Av main course £7
Restaurant 12-2.30 6.30-9.30 Av 3 course à la carte £14

BURNHAM GREEN Hertfordshire *Map 04 TL21*

The White Horse NEW
BURNHAM GREEN
White Horse Ln AL6 0HA
☎ 01438 798416

Sympathetically restored and extended old pub situated on the village green. Civilised dining ambience within the neatly furnished beamed bar and galleried extension. Bar food ranges from traditional meals like fresh battered cod, lasagne, and home-cooked ham, to monthly specials such as beef Wellington and chargrilled calves' liver with red onion gravy. **Principal beers:** Adnams, Tetley, Theakston Old Peculier, Greene King Abbot Ale.
Brewery/Company Free House
Open 11.30-3 6-11
Bar food 12-2 6.30-9.30 Av main course £5
Restaurant 12-2 6.30-9.30 Av 3 course à la carte £14

FLAUNDEN Hertfordshire *Map 04 TL00*

The Bricklayers Arms
FLAUNDEN
Hogpits Bottom HP3 0PH
☎ 01442 833322

Listed 18th-century building, open as a pub for over a hundred years. Ploughman's, pies and giant Yorkshire puddings are offered as bar snacks. All dishes are cooked to order, and specialities include roast breast of Barbary duck marinated in orange, cloves and honey, and blackened Cajun steak.
Principal beers: Fullers London Pride, Marstons Pedigree, Chiltern Beechwood.
Directions M1 J8 through H Hempstead to Bovington then follow Flaunden sign.

contd.

M25 J18 through Chorleywood to Chenies/Latimer then Flaunden
Brewery/Company Free House
Open 11.30-2.30 6-11
Bar food 12-2 7-9 Av main course £6
Restaurant 12-2 7-9 Av 3 course à la carte £20

The Green Dragon
FLAUNDEN
HP3 0PP ☎ 01442 832269
A free house with traditional features including open fires, old beams and antique furniture. The bar menu includes snacks, light bites and 'dragon fillers' such as steak and kidney pie. A typical restaurant dish is roast pork chimera, with a curried sauce and sautéed banana.
Principal beers: Marstons Pedigree, Greene King Abbot Ale, IPA & Triumph.
Directions B4505 from Hemel Hempstead to Bovington then S to Flaunden
Brewery/Company Free House
Open 11-3 5.30-11
Bar food 12-2 7-9 Av main course £5
Restaurant 12-2 7-9 Av 3 course à la carte £20

HINXWORTH Hertfordshire *Map 04 TL24*

Three Horseshoes
HINXWORTH
High St SG7 5HQ ☎ 01462 742280
Thatched 18th-century country pub with a dining extension into the garden. The same menu is served in the bar and restaurant and might offer roast Whitby cod with horseradish mash and rich red wine sauce, or lightly spiced Barbary duck breast on stir-fried pak choi.
Principal beers: Greene King IPA Abbot Ale & Triumph.
Directions E of A1 between Biggleswade and Baldock
Brewery/Company Greene King
Open 11.30-2.30 6-11
Bar food 12-2 7-9 Av main course £10
Restaurant 12-2 7-9 Av 3 course à la carte £18

HITCHIN Hertfordshire *Map 04 TL12*

The Greyhound NEW
HITCHIN
London Rd, St Ippolyts SG4 7NL
☎ 01462 440989
Surrounded by farmland and convenient for the M1 and Luton Airport, this family-run inn offers well-appointed accommodation and good bar food. From steak and ale pie and home-made curries the menu choice extends to pork with garlic and ginger, and fresh fish like John Dory with hollandaise, and grilled red mullet. **Principal beers:** Adnams, Hook Norton Best.
Brewery/Company Free House
Open 11.30-2.30 5-11
Bar food 12-2 7-10 Av main course £7.50
Restaurant 12-2 7-10 Av 3 course à la carte £13.25
Accommodation (Min) s£40 d£50

KNEBWORTH Hertfordshire *Map 04 TL22*

The Lytton Arms
KNEBWORTH
Park Ln SG3 6QB ☎ 01438 812312
Inn designed by Sir Edwin Lutyens, brother-in-law to Lord Lytton, dating from 1877. It adjoins Knebworth estate, the Lytton family seat. Expect a fine selection of real ales, Belgian bottled beers, and whiskies, and popular pub food. Typical dishes include deep-fried whitebait, minted lamb steak and spotted dick.

Directions From A1(M)take A602.At Knebworth turn R at rail station.Follow signs 'Codicote'. Pub 1.5m on R
Brewery/Company Free House
Open 11-3 (Sun 12-10.30, Fri-Sat open all day)
Bar food 12-2 6.30-9.30 Av main course £6.75

LITTLE HADHAM Hertfordshire *Map 05 TL42*

The Nags Head
LITTLE HADHAM
The Ford SG11 2AX ☎ 01279 771555
Former brewery and coaching inn between London and Cambridge, this

cosy, 16th-century village inn is situated close to the River Ash. Interesting fish dishes highlight the daily specials board, perhaps including whole sea bass, and pan-fried monkfish with pernod. Main menu choices range from dressed crab to steak au poivre. **Principal beers:** Greene King Abbot Ale & IPA.
Directions M11 J8 take A120 towards Puckeridge & A10. At lights in Little Hadnam turn L. Pub 0.75m on R
Brewery/Company Greene King
Open 11-2.30 6-11 (Sun 12-3.30 7-10.30)
Bar food 12-2 6-9.30 Av main course £5
Restaurant 12-2 6-9.30 Av 3 course à la carte £11

MUCH HADHAM Hertfordshire *Map 05 TL41*

Jolly Waggoners
MUCH HADHAM
Widford Rd SG10 6EZ ☎ 01279 842102
The pub was built in 1840 and incorporates two older cottages. A menu of home-cooked fare is supported by daily specials, and regular theme nights, eg fish and chips Tuesday, mixed grill Wednesday, balti Thursday and steak supper Friday. Senior citizens lunches Tue-Thu provide a choice of good-value dishes. **Principal beers:** McMullen Original AK, Bass, Courage Directors.
Directions On B1004 between Bishops Stortford & Ware
Brewery/Company McMullens
Open 12-2.30 6.30-11 (Sun 12-3, 7-10.30)
Bar food 12-2 6.30-9.30 Av main course £7
Restaurant 12-3 6.30-11 Av 3 course à la carte £12

ST ALBANS Hertfordshire *Map 04 TL10*

Rose & Crown NEW
ST ALBANS
10 St Michael St AL3 4SG
☎ 01727 851903
Traditional 16th-century pub situated in a beautiful part of St Michael's 'village', opposite the entrance to Verulamium Park and Roman Museum. Classic beamed main bar with huge inglenook, a chatty atmosphere and good real ales. Lovely flower-decked summer patio. The simple choice of lunchtime food includes excellent American-style 'gourmet' sandwiches. **Principal beers:** Adnams, Tetley, Wadworth 6X, Ringwood Fortniner.
Brewery/Company Inn Partnership
Open 11.30-3 5.30-11 (Sun 12-3, 7-10.30)
Bar food 12-2 Av main course £4.75

SARRATT Hertfordshire *Map 04 TQ09*

The Cock Inn
SARRATT
Church End, Church Ln WD3 6HH
☎ 01923 282908
The pub, opposite the village church, was the resting place of the cock horse who pulled carts up the hill from the mill. Bar snacks include home-made pies, burgers and curries, while the converted barn restaurant might offer salmon en croûte, roast rack of lamb and French apple flan. **Principal beers:** Badger Tanglefoot, Dorset Best & IPA, Gribble Reg's Tipple.
Directions Between M25 J18 & A404 opposite St Clement Danes School
Brewery/Company Hall & Woodhouse
Open 11-11 (Sun 12-10.30)
Bar food 12-2.30 6-9.30 Av main course £6.50
Restaurant 12-2.30 7-10 Av 3 course fixed price £13.95

WALKERN Hertfordshire *Map 04 TL22*

The White Lion
WALKERN
31 The High St SG2 7PA
☎ 01438 861251
Late 16th-century timber-framed building, originally a coaching inn on the Nottingham to London route. Mussels marinière; ham, eggs and chips, and sausage sandwich are typical bar meals, while the restaurant offers fresh battered cod, stir-fried lamb, and fresh tortellini in tomato sauce. **Principal beers:** Greene King IPA & Abbot Ale.
Directions B1037 from Stevenage
Brewery/Company Greene King
Open 12-3 5-11 (closed Sun eve & all Mon ex BHs)
Bar food 12-3 5-11.0 Av main course £7
Restaurant 12-3 5-11.0 Av 3 course à la carte £16

For Pubs with AA food rosettes see page 430

South & South East (& Isle of Wight)

WARE Hertfordshire Map 05 TL31

The Sow & Pigs
WARE

Cambridge Rd, Thundridge SG12 0ST
☎ 01920 463281

There is predominantly porcine theme to this village pub, with piggy pictures and lots of little pigs in display cabinets (also pig roasts on Bank Holiday Mondays). Good food is served in generous portions, from USA-style salad sandwiches to Yorkshire fish with home-made chips and mushy peas. **Principal beers:** Adnams, Greenalls Shipstones, Wadworth 6X.
Directions On A10 just N of Ware turn off. Adj to entrance of Hanbury Manor
Brewery/Company Greenalls
Open 11-11
Bar food 12-2 6.30-9 Av main course £6.50
Restaurant 12-2 6.30-9 Av 3 course à la carte £17

WATTON-AT-STONE Hertfordshire Map 04 TL31

George & Dragon
WATTON-AT-STONE

82 High St SG14 3TA ☎ 01920 830285

Character village inn, furnished with antiques, dating from 1550. One interesting and varied menu is offered throughout, with options ranging from sandwiches and Corsican fish soup, to pot-roasted pheasant in red wine, and duck breast, cooked pink and served with blackberry and balsamic sauce. **Principal beers:** Greene King IPA & Abbot Ale.

Directions Off A602 between Stevenage & Hertford
Brewery/Company Greene King
Open 11-2.30 6-11
Bar food 12-2 7-11 Av main course £6.85
Restaurant 12-2 6-11 Av 3 course à la carte £17.75

WESTON Hertfordshire Map 04 TL23

The Rising Sun
WESTON

21 Halls Green SG4 7DR
☎ 01462 790487

Set in picturesque Hertfordshire countryside, The Rising Sun is especially welcoming to those with children. Play equipment, a children's menu, and tuck shop in summer are provided. Adults should enjoy the choice from a menu which may offer spicy sausage grill, shellfish platter, or steak and kidney pie. **Principal beers:** McMullen Original AK Ale & Gladstone, Bass, Courage Directors.
Directions A1(M)J9 take A6141(dual carraigeway)towards Baldock(take outside lane) & turn R towards Graveley. 100yds take 1st L
Brewery/Company McMullens
Open 11.30-2.30 6-11
Bar food 12-2 6.15-9.30 Av main course £5.95

Kent

BIDDENDEN Kent Map 05 TQ83

The Three Chimneys
BIDDENDEN

Biddenden Rd TN27 8PL
☎ 01580 291472

Unspoilt 15th-century country pub in the Kentish Weald, renowned for its hops and cherries. Low oak beams and wooden furniture add to the charm. The accent is on good, home-made food and the imaginative menu ranges from Welsh rarebit and smoked salmon to lambs' kidneys dijonnaise and pan-fried chicken livers. **Principal beers:** Harveys Best, Adnams Best, Morland Old Speckled Hen, Marstons Pedigree.
Directions on A262 W of village
Brewery/Company Free House
Open 11.30-3 6-11
Bar food 12-2 6-10 Av main course £6
Restaurant 12-2 6-10 Av 3 course à la carte £8 Av 3 course fixed price £19

BOROUGH GREEN Kent Map 05 TQ65

The Brickmakers Arms
BOROUGH GREEN

Maidstone Rd, St Mary's Platt TN15 8JJ
☎ 01732 883594

Main road pub that welcomes families and can cater for weddings. Food ranges from bar snacks to the full a la carte

selections in the restaurant. There is also a daily blackboard menu with fresh fish as a speciality. **Principal beers:** Shepherd Neame - Master Brew, Spitfire & Best.
Directions on A25 in St Mary's Platt
Brewery/Company Shepherd Neame
Open 11-11 (Sun 10.30-11)
Bar food 12-2 6.30-9 Av main course £5.50
Restaurant 12-2 6.30-9 Av 3 course à la carte £12

BOYDEN GATE Kent — *Map 05 TR26*

The Gate Inn
BOYDEN GATE
CT3 4EB ☎ 01227 860498
The setting is delightful, with ducks and geese on a pond in the pretty little garden. The pub itself is suitably rustic and totally unpretentious, with quarry-tiled floors and pine furniture, and the atmosphere chatty. Cooking is down to earth, with hearty soups, various hotpots, home-made burgers, and pasta with pesto. **Principal beers:** Shepherd Neame Master Brew, Spitfire & Bishops Finger.
Directions From Canterbury on A28 turn L at Upstreet
Brewery/Company Shepherd Neame
Open 11-2.30 6-11 (Sat 11-3,6-11/Sun 12-3,7-10.30)
Bar food 12-2.30 6-9 Av main course £4

BRABOURNE Kent — *Map 05 TR14*

The Five Bells

BRABOURNE
The Street TN25 5LP ☎ 01303 813334
Retaining many original beams and a large inglenook fireplace, this 16th-century building enjoys a quiet village setting at the base of the North Downs. An extensive menu features a range of specialities, including Wiener schnitzel, pheasant with brandy sauce, venison in port, beef bourguignon, and home-made ice creams. **Principal beers:** Courage Best, & Directors, Shepherd Neame Master Brew, Wells Bombardier.
Directions 5m E of Ashford
Brewery/Company Free House
Open 11.30-3 6.30-11
Bar food 12-2 6.30-10 Av main course £5.50
Restaurant 12-2 6.30-10

BURHAM Kent — *Map 05 TQ76*

The Golden Eagle
BURHAM
80 Church St ME1 3SD ☎ 01634 668975
Oriental food, with all the delectable flavours of China, Thailand, Malaysia and Singapore, is offered in a traditional pub setting at the Golden Eagle. Red hot chilli chicken and pork Babibangang can be enjoyed along with panoramic views of the Medway Valley and the North Downs. **Principal beers:** Wadworth 6X, Marstons Pedigree.
Directions South from M2 J3 or North M20 J6 on A229, signs to Burham
Brewery/Company Free House
Open 11-2.30 6.15-11
Bar food 12-2 7-10 Av main course £7.40
Restaurant 12-2 7-10 Av 3 course à la carte £12 Av 3 course fixed price £12

CANTERBURY Kent — *Map 05 TR15*

Old Gate Inn
CANTERBURY
160-164 New Dover Rd CT1 3EL
☎ 01227 452141
Once a Canterbury to Dover turnpike house, this timber-framed building dates from the reign of George II and has undergone a sympathetic restoration programme. Taking a step inside is like stepping back in time. **Principal beers:** Bass.
Directions From A2 turn off at Bridge exit, R to Canterbury, pub 1m on L
Brewery/Company Vintage Inns
Open 11-11 (Sun 12-10.30)

CHIDDINGSTONE Kent — *Map 05 TQ54*

Castle Inn
CHIDDINGSTONE
TN8 7AH ☎ 01892 870247
Located in a beautiful National Trust village, this striking 18th-century pub might have been where Anne Boleyn found shelter when she was stranded en route to nearby Hever. Sophisticated menu offers rack of lamb, Dover sole, local pheasant, and pancakes stuffed with prawns, as well as hearty bar snacks. Good wine list. **Principal beers:** Larkins Traditional, Harveys Sussex, Youngs Ordinary.
Directions S of B2027 between Tonbridge & Edenbridge
Brewery/Company Free House

contd.

Castle Inn

Open 10.30-11 (Sun 11-10.30, food on Sun 12-10.15)
Bar food 11-10.45 Av main course £5.75
Restaurant 12-2 7.30-9.30 Av 3 course à la carte £26.65 Av 3 course fixed price £14.50

CHILHAM Kent *Map 05 TR05*

The White Horse
CHILHAM
The Square CT4 8BY ☎ 01227 730355
Built in 1422, the White Horse is located in the picturesque Tudor square of Chilham, opposite the entrance to Chilham Castle. Home-made specials are offered from the blackboard menu, and may include quiche, curry, steak and ale pie, chops, casserole, or vegetable lasagne. **Principal beers:** Flowers Original & IPA, Fuggles.
Directions Take A28 from Canterbury then A252, 1m turn L
Brewery/Company Free House
Open 11-11 (Sun 12-10.30)
Bar food 12-2.30 7-9 Av main course £5.95

CHILLENDEN Kent *Map 05 TR25*

Griffins Head
CHILLENDEN
CT3 1PS ☎ 01304 840325
Charming, half-timbered Wealden hall house dating from 1286. Once occupied by monks who farmed the surrounding land, it features character beamed bars, fine Kentish ales and home-made food. Typical dishes include warm salads, fresh pasta dishes, various pies and stews, good steaks and fresh fish - sea bass baked with rosemary. Lovely garden.
Principal beers: Shepherd Neame.
Directions A2 from Canterbury towards Dover,then B2046.Village on R
Brewery/Company Shepherd Neame
Open 10.30am-11pm
Bar food 12-2 7-9.30 Av main course £7
Restaurant 12-2 7-9.30 Av 3 course à la carte £15

CLIFFE Kent *Map 05 TQ77*

The Black Bull
CLIFFE
186 Church St ME3 7AD
☎ 01634 220893
Overlooking bird-rich marshland, this distinctive free house is situated near the Thames estuary, and many familiar landmarks featured in Charles Dickens' Great Expectations. The restaurant specialises in authentic Malaysian, Thai and Chinese cuisine and dishes might include chilli chicken, king prawn sambal, Lohan chai and kofta curry.
Principal beers: Morland Old Speckled Hen, Black Bull Special,Theakstons Best, Flagship Ensign.
Directions On B2000 N of Rochester
Brewery/Company Free House
Open 12-2.30 7-11
Bar food 12-2.30 7-11 Av main course £5.50
Restaurant 7-11 Av 3 course à la carte £18.50

DOVER Kent

The Cliffe Tavern NEW
DOVER
High St, St Margaret's at Cliffe CT15 6AT
☎ 01304 852400
Located opposite the parish church and just half a mile from the cliffs north of Dover, this 16th-century Kentish clapboard building, formerly an 'academy for young gentleman', has two convivial bars and a delightful walled rose garden. Food ranges from sandwiches and mussels with fries, to traditional mixed grill, beef with stir-fried noodles, and rack of lamb. **Principal beers:** Adnams, Morland Old Speckled Hen, Everards Tiger Best, Tetley.
Directions 3m NE of Dover
Brewery/Company Free House
Open 12-11 (Sun 12-10.30)
Bar food 12-2.30 7-9.30 Av main course £5.50
Restaurant 12-2.30 7-9.30 Av 3 course à la carte £5.50
Accommodation (Min) s£39.95 d£49.95

EASTLING Kent *Map 05 TQ95*

Carpenters Arms
EASTLING
The Street ME13 0AZ ☎ 01795 890234
Relaxing oak-beamed pub dating from around 1380 with two inglenook fireplaces and a brick-tiled floor in the restaurant. Both the bar and restaurant are candlelit in the evening. Dishes range from home-cooked ham, egg and chips to specials like pot-roasted local pheasant. Good local downland walks. **Principal beers:** Shepherd Neame Master Brew, Bishops Finger & Spitfire.
Directions A251 towards Faversham, then A2, 1st L Brogdale Rd, 4m to Eastling
Brewery/Company Shepherd Neame
Open 11-4 6-11
Bar food 12-2.30 7-10.30 Av main course £5.95
Restaurant 12-2.30 7-10.30 Av 3 course à la carte £19.50
Accommodation (Min) s£39.50 d£47.50

EYNSFORD Kent *Map 05 TQ56*

Swallows' Malt Shovel Inn 
EYNSFORD
Station Rd DA4 0ER ☎ 01322 862164
Fresh seafood is the attraction at this timbered pub in a pretty village in the Darenth Valley. Choose oysters or lobster from tanks in the bar, or, perhaps, baked cod Portuguese, red mullet with rich tomato sauce, or Dover sole from the menu. Other dishes include venison pie, lasagne and duck with whisky and maple sauce. **Principal beers:** Brakspear Bitter, Flower Original, Wadworth 6X,Fullers London Pride.
Directions A20 to Brands Hatch, then A225, 1m to pub
Brewery/Company Free House
Open 11-3.30 7-11
Bar food 12-3.30 7-10.30 Av main course £5
Restaurant 12-3.30 7-10.30 Av 3 course à la carte £18

FAVERSHAM Kent *Map 05 TR06*

The Albion Tavern
FAVERSHAM
Front Brents, Faversham Creek ME13 7DH ☎ 01795 591411
Cottage-style pub beside Faversham Creek where the interesting and varied menu may typically feature filled baguettes (lunchtime only), fish soup, braised knuckle of lamb with garlic, tomato and rosemary, monkfish wrapped in Parma ham with white wine and cream sauce, and chargrilled steak with pepper sauce. Decent desserts include date, apple and suet pudding. **Principal beers:** Shepherd Neame Spitfire, Master Brew, Bishops Finger & Porter.
Directions From Faversham take A2 W. In Ospringe turn R just before Ship Inn, at Shepherd Neame Brewery 1m turn L over creek bridge
Brewery/Company Shepherd Neame
Open 11-3 6.30-11
Bar food 12-2 7-10 Av main course £6
Restaurant 12-2 7-10 Av 3 course à la carte £15

Shipwrights Arms 
FAVERSHAM
Hollowshore ME13 7TU
☎ 01795 590088
Step back in time at this fascinating, 300-year-old brick and clapboard building, which stands isolated across lonely marshes beside Faversham Creek. Adventurous walkers, shipwrights' and river traffic enjoy the enchanting, unspoilt interior, and the home-cooked food prepared by recent new owners. Expect, perhaps, steak pudding, 'doorstop' sandwiches and home-made soups. **Principal beers:** Shepherd Neame Master Brew & Spitfire.
Directions A2 through Ospringe then R at rdbt. Turn R at T-junct then L opp Davington School & follow signs
Brewery/Company Free House
Open 11-11 (Sun 12-10.30)
Bar food 12-3 7-9 Av main course £6
Restaurant 12-3 7-9

FORDCOMBE Kent *Map 05 TQ54*

Chafford Arms
FORDCOMBE
TN3 0SA ☎ 01892 740267
Creeper-clad village pub within easy reach of Hever Castle and Penshurst Place. Splendid cottage garden with old cider press, and homely bars and dining room offering a good range of snacks and salads, and main meals like Dover sole, wing of Skate, prawn Provencal, steaks, and lamb chops Dijonnaise. **Principal beers:** Wadworth 6X, Larkins Bitter.

contd.

Directions On B2188 (off A264) between Tunbridge Wells & E Grinstead.
Brewery/Company Whitbread.
Open 12.45-3 6.30-11
Bar food 12.30-2 7-30-9.30 Av main course £8
Restaurant 12.30-2 7.30-9.30 Av 3 course à la carte £13.50.

FORDWICH Kent — Map 05 TR15

Fordwich Arms
FORDWICH
King St CT2 0DB ☎ 01227 710444
A solid, Tudor-style village pub situated opposite the smallest English town hall, with comfortable bars and a lovely garden beside the River Stour. Lookout for the interesting, home-cooked specials such as Tuscan-style lamb, rabbit in ale with dumplings, duck with onion marmalade, and salmon on chive mash with watercress sauce. **Principal beers:** Flowers Original, Shepherd Neame Masterbrew, Wadworth 6X.
Directions From A2 take A28, on approaching Sturry turn R at 'Welsh Harp' pub into Fordwich Rd
Brewery/Company Whitbread
Open 11-11 (Sun 12-3, 7-10.30)
Bar food 12-2.30 6.30-10 Av main course £6.95
Restaurant 12-2.30 6.30-10 Av 3 course à la carte £15

GOUDHURST Kent — Map 05 TQ73

The Star & Eagle
GOUDHURST
High St TN17 1AL ☎ 01580 211512
Fine 14th-century timbered and gabled hostelry standing by the parish church, with exposed beams, vaulted stonework, and lovely views across orchards and hop gardens. The 18th-century Hawkhurst Gang of robbers and smugglers used it as their headquarters. Straightforward bar food, comfortable bedrooms; good base from which to explore the Weald.
Principal beers: Flowers Original, King & Barnes Sussex.
Directions On A262 E of Tunbridge Wells
Brewery/Company Whitbread
Open 11-11 (Sun 12-10.30)
Bar food 12-2.30 7-9.30 Av main course £9
Restaurant 12-2.30 7-9.30 Av 3 course à la carte £16
Accommodation (Min) d£55

HADLOW Kent — Map 05 TQ65

The Artichoke Inn
HADLOW
Park Rd, Hamptons TN11 9SR
☎ 01732 810763
Located in a conservation hamlet, this 15th-century timber-framed inn has oak beams, an inglenook fireplace and lots of brass and bric-a-brac. Home-made pies are a speciality and include steak and kidney and chicken and mushroom. Barnsley chop and pork loin steak are among the chargrilled dishes. **Principal beers:** Youngs, Fullers London Pride.
Directions From Tonbridge take A26. In Hadlow turn L into Carpenters Lane. L at junction, 2nd on R
Brewery/Company Free House
Open 12-3 7-11
Bar food 12-2 7-9.30 Av main course £6.95
Restaurant 7-9.30 Av 3 course à la carte £13.50

HERNHILL Kent — Map 05 TR06

Red Lion
HERNHILL
The Green NE13 9JR ☎ 01227 751207
Beams and flagstone floors are all part of the charm at this 14th-century hostelry. Freshly cooked dishes are offered from a blackboard menu and might include guinea fowl with bacon and sherry sauce, and salmon steak with orange butter, almonds and grapes. Look out, too, for the home-made pudding's. **Principal beers:** Shepherd Neame Master Brew, and 3 guest beers.
Directions S of A299 between Faversham & Whitstable
Brewery/Company Enterprise Inns
Open 11-3 6-11
Bar food 12-3 7-10 Av main course £3.95
Restaurant 11-3 6-11 Av 3 course à la carte £16.50

IDEN GREEN Kent — Map 05 TQ73

The Peacock
IDEN GREEN
Goudhurst Rd TN17 2PB
☎ 01580 211233
Grade II listed building dating from the 12th-century with low beams and inglenook fireplace. A wide range of snacks and light meals is available. Main meals include various curries, chicken

and ham pie, ocean pie, and home-made lasagne and moussaka. **Principal beers:** Shepherd Neame Master Brew, Spitfire & Best.

Directions A21 from Tunbridge Wells to Hastings, onto A262, pub 1.5m past Goudhurst
Brewery/Company Shepherd Neame
Open 12-11 (Sun in winter 12-4, 7-10.30)
Bar food 12-2 7-9 Av main course £5.50

IGHTHAM Kent *Map 05 TQ55*

George & Dragon
IGHTHAM
The Street TN15 9HH ☎ 01732 882440
The Duke of Northumberland was imprisoned here after the discovery of the Gunpowder Plot. It is a fine example of Tudor architecture in a historic village setting. A varied menu offers sizzling faitas, home-made pies, steaks, and a blackboard menu of fresh fish specialities. **Principal beers:** Shepherd Neame Master Brew, Spitfire & Seasonal Ale.
Directions From M20, A20 then A227 towards Tonbridge
Brewery/Company Shepherd Neame
Open 11.30-3 6-11 (Sun 12-3, 7-10.30)
Bar food 12-2 Av main course £5.95
Restaurant 12-2 6.30-9 Av 3 course à la carte £19

The Harrow Inn
IGHTHAM
Common Rd TN15 9EB
☎ 01732 885912
17th-century coaching inn within easy reach of the M25, Knole Park and Ightham Mote (NT). Decent food varies between chicken and tarragon pie or salmon fishcakes with citrus sauce in the bar, to grilled sea bass with tomato and olives or chargrilled lamb steak with balsamic vinegar in the restaurant. **Principal beers:** Greene King Abbot Ale & IPA, Marstons Pedigree.
Directions Off A25 between Sevenoaks & Maidstone
Brewery/Company Free House
Open 12-3 6-11 (Sun 6-10)
Bar food 12-3 6-9.30 Av main course £7
Restaurant 12-3 7-9.30 Av 3 course à la carte £18 Av 5 course fixed price £17.95

IVY HATCH Kent *Map 05 TQ55*

The Plough
IVY HATCH
High Cross Rd TN15 0NL
☎ 01732 810268
Good quality food, in particular a wide-ranging choice of fresh fish dishes, attract discerning diners to this 300-year-old village pub. From fresh rock oysters and warm potted shrimps, to grilled lobster and sauteed monkfish with sweet and sour sauce, the imaginative menu may also list broccoli soup, game casserole, and braised lamb with garlic mash. **Principal beers:** Larkins.

Directions M25 J5 take A25 towards Borough Green follow signs for Ivy Hatch
Brewery/Company Free House
Open 12-3 6-11
Bar food 12-2 7-10 Av main course £8.95
Restaurant 12-2 7-10 Av 3 course à la carte £23

LINTON Kent *Map 05 TQ75*

The Bull Inn
LINTON
Linton Hill ME17 4AW ☎ 01622 743612
Black and white 17th-century pub with a beautiful garden. Popular with walkers, it backs on to the Greensand Way. An

contd.

extensive menu ranges from Mexican fajitas to traditional lamb dishes, such as half roast shoulder with rosemary and redcurrant. Cream teas are served in summer. **Principal beers:** Shepherd Neame Master Brew, Spitfire & Bishop's Finger.
Directions A229 through Maidstone to Linton
Brewery/Company Shepherd Neame
Open 11-3 6-11 (In summer-open all day)
Bar food 11-3 6-11 Av main course £6
Restaurant 11-3 6-11 Av 3 course à la carte £15

LITTLEBOURNE Kent *Map 05 TR25*

King William IV
LITTLEBOURNE
4 High St CT3 1ST ☎ 01227 721244
Close to a bird sanctuary in the lush Kent countryside, this cosy, unassuming village inn has lots of beams and a sporting theme in the bar. Part of an original oast-house and brewery. Strong emphasis on fresh produce and local fish. Try the warm game terrine or home-made pasta. **Principal beers:** Shepherd Neame Master Brew, Bass, Harveys Best.

Directions From A2 follow signs to Howlett Zoo. After zoo & at end of road, pub is straight ahead
Brewery/Company Free House
Open 11-11
Bar food 12-2.30 Av main course £4.50
Restaurant 12-2 7-9.30 Av 3 course à la carte £15 Av 2 course fixed price £7.50
Accommodation (Min) s£28 d£40

MAIDSTONE Kent *Map 05 TQ75*

The Ringlestone Inn
MAIDSTONE
Ringlestone Hamlet, Nr Harrietsham ME17 1NX ☎ 01622 859900
Truly atmospheric 16th-century inn, an ale house since 1615, hidden away on the North Downs beside the Pilgrim's Way. Rambling series of dimly-lit rooms with open fires, excellent ales and country wines, and wide choice of food, including speciality home-made pies - fish in elderflower wine, beef in black beer and raisin wine. **Principal beers:** Shepherd Neame Bishops Finger & Spitfire, Harvey Best, Greene King Abbot Ale.

Directions Take A20 E from Maidstone/at rndbt opp Great Danes Hotel turn to Hollingbourne. Through village, R at crossroads at top of hill
Brewery/Company Free House
Open 12-3 6-11 (Sat-Sun 12-11)
Bar food 12-2 7-10 Av main course £6.95
Restaurant 12-2 7-10 Av 3 course à la carte £22 Av 3 course fixed price £24
Accommodation (Min) d£69

NEWNHAM Kent *Map 05 TQ95*

The George Inn
NEWNHAM
44 The Street ME9 0LL
☎ 01795 890237
A 16th-century property in the heart of Kent's hop fields made up of three cottages. Attractive long bar with rug-strewn boarded floor, hopbines and open fires. Freshly prepared food ranges from traditional snacks to more adventurous dishes like lamb cooked in white wine and herbs, and chargrilled tiger prawns on stir-fried noodles.
Directions 5m SW of Faversham
Brewery/Company Shepherd Neame
Open 11-3 6.30-11 (Sun 12-3 7-10.30)
Bar food 12-2.15 6.30-9.30 Av main course £6.95
Restaurant 12-2.15 6.30-9.30 Av 3 course à la carte £15 Av 3 course fixed price £12.50

PAINTERS FORSTAL Kent *Map 05 TQ95*

The Alma
PAINTERS FORSTAL
ME13 0DU ☎ 01795 533835
Typical weather-boarded Kent inn situated in the heart of apple orchard country. Good local walks and a wide range of home-cooked food. Choices range from lunchtime ploughman's and sandwiches, to traditional pub meals and daily specials such as steak and kidney pudding and seared salmon and salad. **Principal beers:** Shepherd Neame Master Brew & Spitfire.
Directions From M2 J6 take A251 towards Ashford. Turn R,through Whitehill to Painters Forstal
Brewery/Company Shepherd Neame
Open 10.30-3 6.30-11
Bar food 12-2 7-9.30 Av main course £6

PLUCKLEY Kent *Map 05 TQ94*

The Dering Arms
PLUCKLEY
Station Rd TN27 0RR ☎ 01233 840371
Originally built as a hunting lodge for the Dering estate , this unusual pub features an impressive Dutch-gabled facade. Expect home-made food, including all-day breakfast, ploughman's and pies in the bar, and decent steaks and fresh fish dishes, perhaps, monkfish with orange and bacon, and sea bass with braised cabbage and beurre blanc in the restaurant. **Principal beers:** Goacher's Ales.
Directions M20 J8 take A20 to Ashford.Then R onto B2077 at Charing to Pluckley

Brewery/Company Free House
Open 11-3 6-11
Bar food 12-2 7-9.30 Av main course £3.95
Restaurant 12-2 7-9.30 Av 3 course à la carte £20
Accommodation (Min) s£30 d£40

SELLING Kent *Map 05 TR05*

The Rose and Crown
SELLING
Perry Wood ME13 9RY
☎ 01227 752214
Real 16th-century pub, set against 150 acres of mature woodland. It is decorated with local hop garlands and a unique corn dolly collection, and has a splendid garden. On the wide-ranging menu you might find bacon and onion pudding, cod and smoked haddock mornay, and a Chinatown platter. **Principal beers:** Goachers Maidstone Ale, Harveys Best, Adnams Southwold, Taylor Landlord.
Directions A28 to Chilham R at Shottenden turning. R at Old Plough x roads, next R signed Perry Wood. Pub at top of hill
Brewery/Company Free House
Open 11-3 6.30-11
Bar food 12-2 7-9.30
Restaurant 12-2 7-9.30

SMARDEN Kent *Map 05 TQ84*

The Chequers Inn
SMARDEN
The Street TN27 8QA ☎ 01233 770217
Country inn of great character dating from 1387. It has unique rounded weatherboarding, lots of beams and open fires, and there is a lovely adjoining garden with ducks. Fish and chips and pasta are favourites in the bar, while the restaurant offers local ostrich, and pepper -crusted monkfish. **Principal beers:** Morland Old Speckled Hen, Fullers London Pride, Bass, Worthington.
Directions Through Leeds village, L to Sutton Valence/Headcorn then L for Smarden. Pub in village centre
Brewery/Company Free House
Open 11-3 6-11
Accommodation (Min) s£23 d£48

SMARTS HILL Kent *Map 05 TQ54*

The Bottle House Inn
SMARTS HILL
Coldharbour Rd TN11 8ET
☎ 01892 870306
Popular 15th-century dining pub tucked away down a remote lane in deepest Kent. Well modernised yet retaining some original charm and character, diners can expect to find duck liver paté, calves' liver with horseradish mash, ribeye steak with peppercorn sauce, fishcakes with tarragon sauce, and roasted vegetable lasagne on the extensive daily menu. **Principal beers:** Larkins Ale, Harveys Best, Youngs Bitter.
Directions From Tunbridge Wells take A264 W then B2188 N
Brewery/Company Free House
Open 11-3 6-11
Bar food 12-2 6.30-10
Restaurant 12-2 6.30-10

contd.

The Spotted Dog NEW
SMARTS HILL
TN11 8EE ☎ 01892 870253
Relax and enjoy far-reaching views over the Weald from the terraced gardens of this 15th-century weatherboarded pub. Lovely beamed bars with log fires and interesting blackboard menus. Choose, perhaps, from sweetcorn chowder, shoulder of lamb, various home-made stews and pies, and excellent fresh fish - snapper, bream, sea bass, scallop and monkfish ragout. **Principal beers:** Greene King Abbot Ale, King & Barnes Sussex, Adnams.
Brewery/Company Carlsberg Tetley
Open 11.45-3 6-11
Bar food 12-2.15 7-9.30 Av main course £7.95
Restaurant 12-2.15 7-9.30 Av 3 course à la carte £16.95

SPELDHURST Kent *Map 05 TQ54*

The George and Dragon
SPELDHURST
Speldhurst Hill TN3 0NN
☎ 01892 863125
Dating from 1213, this is one of the oldest three pubs in England. It was used as a stopping off point by knights off to the Crusades. Food includes traditional pub dishes, a fixed-price brasserie menu, and fine dining in the restaurant.
Principal beers: Harvey Best, Sussex Pale & Porter.
Brewery/Company Free House
Open 11-11
Bar food 12-3 6-9.30 Av main course £7
Restaurant 12-2.30 6-10 Av 3 course à la carte £25 Av 3 course fixed price £17

STALISFIELD GREEN Kent *Map 05 TQ95*

The Plough
STALISFIELD GREEN
ME13 0HY ☎ 01795 890256
Splendid 15th-century hall house nestling beside the village green on top of the North Downs. Choose from a comprehensive snack menu or from the varied carte, the latter featuring Italian specialities. Dishes include steak pizzaiola, chicken alla cacciatore, lasagne, gilled lemon sole, salmon en croute, and lemon brulee. Delightful summer garden with views. **Principal beers:** Adnams, Wadworth 6X, Flowers IPA.
Directions A20 to Charing, on dual carriageway turn L for Stalisfield
Brewery/Company Free House
Open 12-3 7-11
Bar food 12-3 7-11 Av main course £5.50
Restaurant 12-3 7-11 Av 3 course à la carte £15 Av 2 course fixed price £7.95

TUNBRIDGE WELLS (Royal) Kent *Map 05 TQ53*

The Beacon NEW
TUNBRIDGE WELLS (ROYAL)
Tea Garden Ln, Rusthall TN3 9JH
☎ 01892 524252
Victorian building set in 17 acres with woods, a lake and lovely views. Spacious and comfortable bar and dining areas with wooden floors and panelling. Interesting food ranges from moules mariniere and filled baguettes, to scallops with egg noodles and chive salad, monkfish with Pernod, and pork with almonds and cream. **Principal beers:** Harveys Best, Hook Norton Best, Fullers London Pride.

Directions From Tunbridge Wells take A264 towards East Grinstead. Pub 1m on L
Brewery/Company Free House
Open 11-11
Bar food 12-2.30 6.30-9.30 Av main course £5
Restaurant 12-2.30 6.30-9.30 Av 3 course à la carte £17.50

The Crown Inn
TUNBRIDGE WELLS (ROYAL)
The Green, Groombridge TN3 9QH
☎ 01892 864742
Close to Groombridge Place, a fine moated manor with lovely gardens, this beamed 16th-century inn overlooks the village green. Popular with Weald Way walkers, it features a cottagey front garden and offers home-made soups, kedgeree, red mullet with lime, local

Speldhurst sausages, and rhubarb, orange and ginger crumble, alongside pub favourites. **Principal beers:** Harveys IPA, Courage Directors.
Directions Take A264 W of Tunbridge Wells, then B2110 S
Brewery/Company Free House
Open 11-2.30 6-11 (Sun 12-10.30, Sat(summer)11-11)
Bar food 12-2 7-9.30 Av main course £5.50
Restaurant 12-2 7-9.30
Accommodation (Min) s£25 d£40

The Hare on Langton Green
TUNBRIDGE WELLS (ROYAL)
Langton Rd TN3 0JA ☎ 01892 862419
Rebuilt in 1901, this spacious Victorian pub has wooden floors and lots of old books and bric-a-brac to keep customers entertained. Good quality food and a relaxed atmosphere. Salmon and smoked haddock fishcakes, roast lamb shoulder, and deep-fried spicy Thai crab are typical examples from the wide-ranging menu. **Principal beers:** Greene King IPA & Abbot Ale.
Directions On A264 W of Tunbridge Wells
Brewery/Company Greene King
Open 11.30-11
Bar food 12-9.30 Av main course £8.95

Royal Wells Inn NEW
TUNBRIDGE WELLS (ROYAL)
Mount Ephraim TN4 8BE
☎ 01892 511188
Fine Victorian building commanding views over the common and town centre. Although more hotel than inn, the informal bar and brasserie offers real ale and an interesting menu of modern dishes. Typical choices include oysters, red lentil and bacon soup, baked cod with mustard mash, courgette and sun-dried tomato tart, and cappuccino mousse.

Principal beers: Harveys Best, Shepherd Neame Master Brew, Bishop's Finger & Spitfire.
Directions 75 yds from junction of A26 & A264
Brewery/Company Free House
Open 11-11
Bar food 11-2.15
Restaurant 12.15-2.15 6.30-10 Av 3 course à la carte £17.85
Accommodation (Min) s£55 d£70

Sankey's Cellar Wine Bar
TUNBRIDGE WELLS (ROYAL)
39 Mount Ephraim TN4 8AA
☎ 01892 511422
Built as a Victorian Gothic villa, this seafood restaurant also boasts an oyster bar and a bustling cellar wine bar. One menu is offered throughout and there's a selection of blackboard specials. Expect spider crab, poached eel, seafood paella, excellent fish and chips and salmon and cod fishcakes among the house favourites. **Principal beers:** Harveys Best, Shepherd Neame Master Brew, Larkins Ale.
Directions on A26
Brewery/Company Free House
Open 10-3.30 6-12 (closed Sun & BHs)
Bar food 12-3 7-12 Av main course £7.50
Restaurant 12.30-3 7-12 Av 3 course à la carte £25

WARREN STREET Kent *Map 05 TQ95*

The Harrow Inn
WARREN STREET
Hubbards Hill ME17 2ED
☎ 01622 858727
Isolated on top of the North Downs, this modernised inn was once the forge and rest house for travellers on the Pilgrim's Way heading for Canterbury. Typical dishes are chargrilled spicy chicken with orange yoghurt dressing, baked bream with herb butter, and good traditional bar meals. Comfortable B&B. **Principal beers:** Shepherd Neame Master Brew, Tetleys, Greene King Abbot Ale.
Directions A20 to Lenham, follow sign for Warren St on L, pub on R
Brewery/Company Free House
Open 12-2.30 7-10.30
Bar food 12-2 7-10 Av main course £7
Restaurant 12-2 7-10 Av 3 course à la carte £25 Av 3 course fixed price £12.50
Accommodation (Min) s£39.50 d£49.50

contd.

WROTHAM Kent *Map 05 TQ65*

The Green Man
WROTHAM

Hodsoll St, Ash-cum-Ridley TN15 7LE
☎ 01732 823575

An 18th-century brick and timber building with impressive floral displays in summer. The interior is warmly decorated with hops, horse brasses and local pictures. There's a large garden with a pets' corner and children's play area. Traditional, continental and Far Eastern dishes are served. **Principal beers:** Marstons Pedigree, Wadworth 6X, Boddingtons, Shepherd Neame.
Directions Off A227 between Wrotham & Meopham
Brewery/Company Whitbread
Open 11-2.30 6.30-11 (Sat 11-3, 6.30-11/Sun 12-3, 7-10.30)
Bar food 12-2 7.30-9.45 Av main course £6

LONDON

E14

The Grapes NEW
E14 Map GtL D3

76 Narrow St, Limehouse E14 8BP
☎ 0171 987 4396

Built in 1720 and frequented by Charles Dickens, this narrow riverside pub affords stunning views of the Thames, and specialises in fresh seafood. Bar food features ploughman's lunches, bangers and mash, club sandwiches, and fishcakes with caper sauce and hand-cut chips, while Dover sole, monkfish, sea bass and king scallops are specialities in the restaurant. **Principal beers:** Adnams, Burton Ale, Tetley, Marstons Pedigree.
Directions Docklands Light Railway stations: Limehouse or West Ferry
Brewery/Company Allied Domecq

Open 12-3 5.30-11 (closed Bhs)
Bar food 12-2 7-9 Av main course £5.50
Restaurant 12-2.15 7.30-9.15 Av 3 course à la carte £27.50 Av 3 course fixed price £26.95

EC1

The Eagle
EC Map E4

159 Farringdon Rd EC1R 3AL
☎ 0171 837 1353

A popular pub serving Mediterranean-style food chalked up on a blackboard menu. Interesting options are 'tagliata' (a salad of ribeye steak, potatoes, capers, tarragon, rocket and balsamic vinegar), and paella Valenciana (mussels, squid, prawns, hake, clams and chicken with broad beans, peppers, wine, rice and saffron). **Principal beers:** Flowers Original, Boddingtons, Wadworth 6X.
Directions Angel/Farringdon Stn. North end Farringdon Road
Brewery/Company Free House
Open 12-11 (Sun 12-5, closed Etr, 2wks Xmas & BHs)
Bar food 12.30-2.30 6.30-10.30 Av main course £8

The Jerusalem Tavern
EC1 Map F4

55 Britton St, Clerkenwell EC1M 5NA
☎ 0171 490 4281

Named after the Priory of St John of Jerusalem, this historic tavern dates back to the 14th century. The likes of Samuel Johnson, David Garrick and the young Handel were visitors. Sample excellent St Peter's Ales and traditional bar fare, including bangers and mash, decent sandwiches and various pies. **Principal beers:** St Peters (complete range).
Directions 100m NE of Farringdon tube, 300m N of Smithfield
Brewery/Company St Peters Brewery
Open 9-11 (closed wknds & 24 Dec-5 Jan)
Bar food 12-7 Av main course £5

The Leopard NEW
EC1 Map F5

33 Seward St EC1V 3PA
☎ 0171 253 3587

The unassuming exterior belies the civilised interior of this friendly pub near The Barbican. Splendid rear conservatory and rug-strewn, wooden-floored bar. Expect a good range of beers and an open kitchen serving such delights as Thai

green chicken curry, roast aubergine casserole, nachos with guacamole, and lamb steak with pepper sauce. **Principal beers:** Ushers Salisbury Best & Founders Ale, Greene King Abbot Ale, Batemans.
Brewery/Company Free House
Open 12-11 (wknds - private parties)
Bar food 12-9.30

The Peasant
EC1 Map D3
240 St John St EC1V 4PH
☎ 0171 336 7726
While the downstairs bar of this converted Victorian pub boasts an original mosaic floor, the upstairs restaurant is a distinctively modern venue for art exhibitions. The menu has an Italian flavour, and dishes may include scallop and rocket linguini, pizzetta with mozzarella and prosciutto, smoked halibut with caper mayonnaise, and a mezze selection.

Principal beers: Bottled beers.
Directions Angel Tube Station
Brewery/Company Free House
Open 12-11 (closed Sun & BHs)
Bar food 12.30-11 Av main course £8
Restaurant 12-3 6.30-11 Av 3 course à la carte £20

EC4

The Old Bank of England
EC4 Map E4
194 Fleet St EC4 2LT ☎ 0171 430 2255
Originally the Law Courts branch of the Bank of England, this famous pub is close to the site of the barber's shop owned by infamous Sweeney Todd. Impressive choice of home-made pies served on a traditional wooden platter, as well as beer-battered fish and chips and bangers and mash. **Principal beers:** Fullers London Pride, Chiswick Bitter & ESB.
Brewery/Company Fullers
Open 11-11 (closed wknds, BHs)

N1

The Duke of Cambridge NEW
N1 Map GtL D3
30 St Peter's St N1 8JT
☎ 0171 359 3066
Built in 1851 and recently carefully revamped, this unassuming building houses London's first organic food pub. Modern European dishes, prepared from seasonal organic or additive-free ingredients, may include spiced lentil soup, hake with chilli roast potatoes and tapenade, braised octupus in red wine with polenta, and chocolate souffle cake. Organic beers and wines too. **Principal beers:** Caledonian Golden Promise, Pitfield Singhboulton, Adnams Broadside.
Brewery/Company Free House
Open 12-11 (Mon 5-11)
Bar food 12.30-3 6.30-10.30
Restaurant 12.30-3 6.30-10.30 Av 3 course à la carte £18

NW1

The Chapel
NW1 Map B4
48 Chapel St NW1 5DP
☎ 0171 402 9220
Stripped floors and pine furniture create a relaxed atmosphere at this bright and airy pub, which offers an interesting, Anglo-Mediterranean blackboard menu. Typical dishes may include spinach and blue cheese tart, roasted sea bass with red pepper coulis, ribeye steak with thyme and red wine jus, and baked ham with smoked cheddar. **Principal beers:** Fullers London Pride, Greene King IPA.
Directions By A40 Marylebone Rd & Old Marylebone Rd junc. Off Edgware Rd by tube station
Brewery/Company Punch Taverns
Open 12-11
Bar food 12-2.30 7-10.00 Av main course £11

Crown & Goose NEW
NW1 Map GtL C3
100 Arlington Rd NW1 7HP
☎ 0171 485 2342 485 8008
Bustling pub with a distinct continental feel in the heart of Camden. Rag-washed walls and stripped floors set the scene, while the open kitchen produces some interesting pub food. Daily specials may include cauliflower and chickpea soup, smoked salmon tagliatelle, duck stir-fry, and lamb shank with root vegetables and

contd.

mash. **Principal beers:** Fullers London Pride.
Directions nearest tube: Camden Town
Brewery/Company Free House
Open 11-11
Bar food 12-3 6-10 Av main course £8
Restaurant 12-3 6-10 Av 3 course à la carte £16

The Engineer
NW1 Map GtL C3
65 Gloucester Av, Primrose Hill NW1 8JH
☎ 0171 722 0950
Designed by Isambard Kingdom Brunel in 1841, this pub is situated near a canal and Primrose Hill Park. An imaginative menu includes salmon fishcakes with coriander, ginger and chilli, organic rump steak with sweetcorn, red onion and rosemary salsa, and gorgonzola and spring green polenta with sweet plum tomato fondue.

Principal beers: Fullers London Pride, Morland Old Speckled Hen.
Directions Nearest tube: Camden Town/Chalk Farm
Brewery/Company Bass
Open 11-11
Restaurant 12-3 7-11 Av 3 course à la carte £22

The Globe
NW1 Map B4
43-47 Marylebone Rd NW1 5JY
☎ 0171 0171 935 6368
Consisting of wine bar, main bar and restaurant, this 18th-century, three storey pub, opposite Baker Street tube station, has been frequented by such luminaries as Charles Dickens and Alfred Lord Tennyson. Traditional call order restaurant menu features roast beef and sausage and mash. Bar food includes freshly-made sandwiches and fish and chips in newspaper. **Principal beers:** Courage Best & Directors, Theakston Best.
Directions Nr Baker St tube
Brewery/Company Scottish & Newcastle
Open 11-11.20 (Sun 12-10.30)
Bar food 11-3 3-11 Av main course £4

The Lansdowne
NW1 Map GtL C3
90 Gloucester Av, Primrose Hill NW1 8HX
☎ 0171 483 0409
Famous rock stars can often be spotted at this relaxed dining pub in secluded Primrose Hill. The menu changes twice a day to offer a balance of meat, fish and vegetarian dishes. Choices may include grilled ribeye of Black Mountain beef, or cod with mussels and saffron cream.
Principal beers: Woodfordes Wherry, Fullers London Pride.
Brewery/Company Bass
Open 12-11 (Mon 6-11/Sun 12-4, 7-10.30)
Bar food 12.30-2.30 7-10 Av main course £7.50

The Queens
NW1 Map GtL C3
49 Regents Park Rd, Primrose Hill NW1 8XD ☎ 0171 586 0408
With a balcony overlooking Primrose Hill, this Victorian pub is five minutes from Regents Park and the zoo. Specials may feature a tomato, garlic and okra pasta, and rainbow trout with almonds, while other main courses often include fried skate with tarragon butter, char-grilled steaks, and a zucchini and saffron risotto. **Principal beers:** Youngs.
Directions Nearest tube station - Chalk Farm
Open 11-11
Bar food 12-2.30 7-9.45 Av main course £8.95
Restaurant 12-2.30 7-9.45 Av 3 course à la carte £25

NW3

The Flask NEW
NW3 Map GtL C4
14 Flask Walk, Hampstead NW3 1HG
☎ 0171 435 4580
Atmospheric old Hampstead village pub with original Victorian panelling, conservatory and sun-trap garden; long a favourite, friendly rendezvous for comedians, artists and drinkers alike. Short selection of home-cooked food, including ham, egg and bubble and squeak, fresh fish and chips, pan-fried

lambs' liver with mash and herb gravy, and Jamaican chicken curry.
Principal beers: Young's: Special, Winter Warmer.
Directions Nearest tube: Hampstead
Brewery/Company Young & Co
Open 11-11
Bar food 12-3 6-9 Av main course £3.90

Freemasons Arms
NW3 Map GtL C4

32 Downshire Hill, Hampstead NW3 1NT
☎ 0171 433 6811

Overlooking Hampstead Heath, with the largest pub garden in central London, The Freemasons Arms has a Pell Mell pitch which was part of the original 19th-century building. Pell Mell is similar to bowls and was popularised by Charles II. **Principal beers:** Bass.
Brewery/Company Vintage Inns
Open 11-11 (Sun 12-10.30)

Spaniards Inn
NW3 Map GtL C4

Spaniards Rd, Hampstead NW3 7JJ
☎ 0181 731 6571

In its time this popular 16th-century pub has been a toll house and the home of a Spanish ambassador. Reputed to have been visited by Dick Turpin, Charles Dickens, Keats and Byron among others. Huge garden includes aviary. Ground and first floor bars. Home-cooked traditional English dishes, plus salad bar. **Principal beers:** Bass, Fullers London Pride, Hancocks HB.
Brewery/Company Bass
Open 11-11 (Sun 12-10.30)
Bar food 12-3 5-9 Av main course £6

NW8

Crocker's Folly
NW8 Map A4

24 Aberdeen Place, Maida Vale NW8 8JR
☎ 0171 286 6608

Named after its original owner, Mr Frank Crocker, who sadly jumped to his death on hearing that Marylebone station (which he thought was going to be built opposite) was actually to be built in Marylebone, this is a remarkable pub. You can enjoy home-made pies, speciality sausages, and a fine selection of British cheeses. **Principal beers:** Brakspear, Gales, Adnams.

Directions Nearest tube station - Warwick Avenue
Brewery/Company Regent Inns
Open 11-11 (Sun 12-10.30)
Bar food 12-2.30 6-9.30 (8.30 Sun) Av main course £5.50

Lord's Tavern
NW8 Map A5

Lord's Cricket Ground, St Johns Wood NW8 8QN ☎ 0171 266 5980

A popular watering-hole among test and county cricketers as well as the game's many supporters, this famous hostelry is located just outside the legendary Lord's Cricket Ground. Bar food might include ostrich steak and salmon fishcakes, while restaurant fare includes seafood tagliatelle and roast pork loin. **Principal beers:** Brakspear, Bass, Courage Directors & Best, Theakstons XB.
Brewery/Company Front Page Pubs Ltd
Open 11-11 (Sun 12-10.30)
Bar food 12-2.30 7-10 Av main course £6
Restaurant 12-2.30 7-10 Av 3 course à la carte £12 Av 312 course fixed price £12

NW10

William IV Bar & Restaurant NEW
NW10 Map GtL C3

786 Harrow Rd NW10 5JX
☎ 0181 969 5944

Modern and antique furniture fill this tastefully refurbished pub, set over three bars, a restaurant and popular heated garden. A further draw is the innovative, modern British menu on offer. Choose from curried parsnip and almond soup or parmesan and spinach risotto, followed by roast cod with polenta and herb oil, or calves' liver with mustard mash and pancetta sauce.
Principal beers: Fullers London Pride,

contd.

Badger Tanglefoot, Wells Bombardier.
Directions Nearest tube: Ladbroke Grove or Kensal Green
Brewery/Company Free House
Open 12-11 (Fri-Sat 12-12, Sun 12-10.30)
Bar food 12-4 7-8.30 Av main course £6
Restaurant 12-3 6-10.30

SE1

The Fire Station Restaurant & Bar NEW

SE1 Map D2

150 Waterloo Rd SE1 8SB
☎ 0171 620 2226

Retaining many of its original features, this listed Victorian fire station has a bright and lively atmosphere, and offers an innovative, modern British menu. Daily-changing dishes may include filled ciabattas, Rossmare oysters, smoked cod with parsley mash and tomato and chilli salsa, and Welsh lamb rump with almond and fruit couscous. **Principal beers:** Adnams Best, Brakspear, Gales, Youngs.
Brewery/Company Regent Inns
Open 11-11 (Sun 12-10.30)
Bar food 12-5.30 Av main course £6
Restaurant 12-3 5.30-11 Av 3 course à la carte £20 Av 2 course fixed price £9.95

The Market Porter NEW

SE1 Map F3

9 Stoney St, Borough Market, London Bridge SE1 9AA ☎ 0171 407 2495

Set in the middle of a fruit and veg market, this traditional tavern serves a market community that has been flourishing for about 1,000 years. Worth noting is an internal leaded bay window unique in London. Menu includes warm salad of black pudding, boozy bangers and pasta ratatouille. **Principal beers:** Harveys Best, Courage Best, Youngs, Fullers London Pride.
Directions Close to London Bridge Station
Brewery/Company Free House
Open 11-11 (Sun 12-10.30)
Bar food 12-2.30 Av main course £3.95
Restaurant 12-2.30 Av 3 course à la carte £11.75

SE16

Mayflower Inn

SE16 Map GtL D3

117 Rotherhithe St, Rotherhithe SE16 4NF ☎ 0171 237 4088

The ship The Mayflower is believed to have begun her historic voyage to the New World from the Mayflower steps by the present day inn, which was then known as the Spread Eagle. From the menu expect the likes of warm chicken and bacon salad and Aberdeen Angus steak. **Principal beers:** Greene King Abbot Ale & IPA.
Directions Exit A2 at Surrey Keys roundabout onto Brunel Rd, 3rd L onto Swan Rd, at T jct L, 200m to pub on R
Brewery/Company Greene King
Open 11-11 (Sun 12-10.30, Winter all week 12-11)
Restaurant 12-2.30 6.30-9.30 Av 3 course à la carte £15

SW1

The Albert

SW1 Map D2

52 Victoria St SW1H 0NP
☎ 0171 2225577 & 2227606

Classic Grade II listed Victorian pub containing original engraved windows and marble facia. Includes a division bell from the House of Commons and a staircase with pictures of Britain's prime ministers. Oldest building in Victoria Street and famous for its external gas lamps. Wholesome menu offers pies, baps and roasts. **Principal beers:** Courage Directors & Best, Theakston Best.
Directions Nearest tube - St James Park
Brewery/Company Scottish & Newcastle
Open 11-11 (Sun 12-10.30)
Bar food 12-11 Av main course £4.50
Restaurant 12-11 Av 3 course à la carte £14.95 Av 3 course fixed price £14.95

The Buckingham Arms NEW

SW1 Map D2

62 Petty France SW1H 9EU
☎ 0171 222 3386

Elegant and busy Young's pub situated close to the Passport Office and Buckingham Palace. Popular with tourists, business people and real ale fans alike, it offers a good range of simple pub food, including the 'mighty' Buckingham burger, nachos with chilli, shepherd's pie,

chicken ciabatta and lasagne, in its long bar with etched mirrors. **Principal beers:** Youngs Bitter, Special & Winter Warmer.
Directions nearest tube – St James's Park tube
Brewery/Company Young & Co
Open 11-11 (Sat 12-11, Sun 12-3)
Bar food 12-2.30 6-9

The Clarence
SW1 *Map D3*

55 Whitehall SW1A 2HP
☎ 0171 930 4808
Haunted pub, situated five minutes' walk from Big Ben, the Houses of Parliament, Trafalgar Square and Buckingham Palace, with leaded windows and ancient ceiling beams from a Thames pier. Traditional fare such as fish and chips, chicken and mushroom pie, and Sunday roast is served in both the bar and restaurant.
Principal beers: Greene King Abbott Ale, Theakston Old Peculier.
Directions Between Big Ben & Trafalgar Sq
Brewery/Company Scottish & Newcastle
Open 11-11
Bar food All day

The Grenadier NEW
SW1 *Map B2*

18 Wilton Row, Belgravia SW1X 7NR
☎ 0171 235 3074
Built in 1802 in a quaint cobbled mews close to Hyde Park, this busy, ivy-covered pub was originally used as a mess by the Duke of Wellington's Grenadiers. Food ranges from club sandwiches and fish and chips in the bar, to beef Wellington, game pie, herb-crusted lamb cutlets, and queen scallops in the restaurant.
Principal beers: Courage Best & Directors, Marstons Pedigree, Morland Old Speckled Hen.
Brewery/Company Scottish & Newcastle
Open 12-11 (Sun 12-10.30)
Restaurant 12-1.45 6-9.30 Av 3 course à la carte £25

The Orange Brewery
SW1 *Map C1*

37-39 Pimlico Rd SW1W 8NE
☎ 0171 730 5984
Four-storey Victorian pub with original working gas lamps. Beers and lagers are brewed on site from a full mash brew. Bar snacks include a selection of pies such as lamb and rosemary, and beef and beer. Among the types of sausages are pork and leek, Cajun, and orange and herb.
Principal beers: Orange SW1, Pimlico Passport, Pimlico Porter & Spiritual Reunion.
Directions Nr Sloane Sq or Victoria tube stations
Brewery/Company Scottish & Newcastle
Open 11-11 (Sun 12-10.30, bar food all day))

SW3

The Coopers of Flood Street NEW
SW3 *Map B1*

87 Flood St, Chelsea SW3 5TB
☎ 0171 376 3120
Lively and friendly corner pub just off the Kings Road offering good, traditional and more modern pub fare at lunchtimes. Relax in the spacious, rug-floored bar and tuck into Creole fish stew, pea and ham soup, roast cod with anchovy tapénade, or a skillet of red fish with mozzarella, tomato and fresh basil.

Principal beers: Youngs Special & Winter Warmer.
Brewery/Company Young & Co
Open 11-11 (Sun 12-10.30)
Restaurant 12-3 Av 3 course à la carte £17

The Cross Keys
SW3 *Map GtL C3*

1 Lawrence St, Chelsea SW3 5NB
☎ 0171 349 9111
Fine old Chelsea pub dating back to 1765 and just round the corner from Cheyne Walk and the Thames. Unique stylish interior includes Bohemian-style banqueting room, open-plan glass roofed conservatory, restaurant and first-floor gallery. Fresh Mediterranean food, and bar menu offering a variety of baguettes and other dishes.

contd.

Principal beers: John Smiths, Theakston Best, Courage Directors, Beamish Red.
Brewery/Company Scottish & Newcastle
Open 12-11 (Sun 12-10.30)
Bar food 12-3 6-9 Av main course £5
Restaurant 12-3 7-12 Av 3 course à la carte £20

The Front Page
SW3 *Map B1*

35 Old Church St, Chelsea SW3 5BS
☎ 0171 352 0648 352 2908

Backstreet pub nestled between the Thames and Kings Road in Chelsea. Offers a good meal, a chance to catch up on the big screen sporting action, or a quiet pint in front of the fire. Expect the likes of game casserole, roast vegetable risotto, fondue, and salmon and coriander fishcakes. **Principal beers:** Theakston XB, Front Page Bitter.
Directions Nearest tube-Sloane Square & Sth Kensington. (halfway between Albert Bridge & Battersea Bridge)
Brewery/Company Front Page Pubs Ltd
Open 11-11 (Sun 12-10.30)
Bar food 12-2.30 7-10 Av main course £7

The Phene Arms NEW
SW3 *Map B1*

Phene St, Chelsea SW3 5NY
☎ 0171 352 3294

Hidden away down a quiet Chelsea cul-de-sac, a short stroll from The Embankment, this welcoming neighbourhood pub has a charming roof terrace and large garden for summer alfesco eating. Interesting bar food ranges from chicken ciabatta, Catalan salad and beer-battered fresh cod, to lemon-peppered roast lamb, salmon fishcakes, and beef fillet with bearnaise.
Principal beers: Adnams, Courage Best & Directors, Morland Old Speckled Hen.

Directions Nearest tubes: Sloane Square & South Kensington
Brewery/Company Free House
Open 11-11 (Sun 12-10.30)
Bar food 12-3 6-10 Av main course £4
Restaurant 12-3 6-10 Av 3 course à la carte £17.50

SW4

The Windmill on the Common NEW
SW4 *Map C2*

Clapham Common South Side SW4 9DE
☎ 0181 673 4578

A pub since 1729, skilfully extended to house a bistro, lounge, wood-panelled restaurant, and hotel accommodation. Enthusiastic cooking delivers fettucini with pesto, lamb balti cod in creamy parsley sauce, marinated seafood salad, and, in the bar, sandwiches, chargrilled burgers, and home-made pies. Overlooks Clapham Common. **Principal beers:** Youngs Bitter, Special & Winter Warmer.
Directions Nearest tube: Clapham Common
Brewery/Company Young & Co
Open 11-11
Bar food 12-2.30 7-10 Av main course £6.50
Restaurant 7-10.30 Av 3 course à la carte £16.95 Av 3 course fixed price £16.95
Accommodation (Min) s£75 d£80

SW6

The White Horse NEW
SW6 *Map GtL C2*

1-3 Parson's Green, Fulham SW6 4UL
☎ 0171 736 2115

Popular pub at the apex of Parson's Green, which enjoys an enviable repuation for its food, real ales and unusual foreign bottled beers. Food options include bar snacks, a brunch menu and a carte, with dishes including Irish stew with pearl barley, herb dumplings and mashed potato, and grilled skate with salsa verde. **Principal beers:** Adnams Extra, Bass, Harveys Sussex Best, Highgate Mild.
Directions 140 mtrs from Parson's Green tube
Brewery/Company Bass
Open 11-11 (Sun 11-10.30, food all day wknds)
Bar food 12-3 5.30-10 Av main course £6.50
Restaurant 12-3 5.30-10 Av 3 course à la carte £16 Av 3 course fixed price £16

SW7

Swag and Tails NEW
SW7 Map B2

10/11 Fairholt St SW7 1EG

☎ 0171 584 6926

Flower-adorned Victorian building, just two minutes walk from Harrods, with original panelling, stripped wooden floors and a welcoming atmosphere. Interesting, freshly cooked food may include crab and spring onion fishcakes with coriander and lime dressing, followed by lamb steak with sweet potato rosti, aubergine caviar and jus, or smoked haddock with mustard mash and hollandaise. Good club sandwiches and puddings. **Principal beers:** Marstons Pedigree, Wells Bombardier.

Directions nearest tube: Knightsbridge tube

Brewery/Company Free House

Open 11-11

Bar food 12-3 6-10 Av main course £9.50

Restaurant 12-3 6-10 Av 3 course à la carte £19

SW10

The Chelsea Ram
SW10 Map GtL C2

32 Burnaby St SW10 0PL

☎ 0171 351 4008

A busy central London pub with a distinct emphasis on good, interesting food, including fresh market fish and meat from Smithfield. Modern dishes are listed on the daily-changing blackboard menu, featuring, perhaps, terrine of confit duck and foie gras with apple Cajun chutney, red snapper with lime and ginger sauce, and tempura of cod with garlic potatoes. **Principal beers:** Youngs Bitter, Special & Winter Warmer.

Directions Nearest tube - Earls Court

Brewery/Company Youngs

Open 11-3 5.30-11

Bar food 12-2.30 7-9.45 Av main course £12

Restaurant 12-2.30 7-10 Av 3 course à la carte £15

The Sporting Page
SW10 Map A1

6 Camera Place SW10 0BH

☎ 0171 376 3694

Smart Chelsea pub offering good quality food - modern British and European - with friendly service. It's the largest retail outlet in London for Bollinger Champagne, with all bottle sizes up to jeroboam. Popular features are the terrace in summer and large screen TV for major sporting events. **Principal beers:** John Smiths, Front Page Bitter, Courage Best.

Brewery/Company Front Page Pubs Ltd

Open 11-11 (Sun 12-10.30)

Bar food 12-2.30 7-10 Av main course £7.50

SW11

The Castle NEW
SW11 Map GtL C2

115 Battersea High St SW11 3JR

☎ 0171 228 8181

Ivy-covered pub tucked away in 'Battersea Village', with rugs and rustic furnishings on bare boards, open fires, an enclosed patio garden, and decent weekly-changing menus. From home-made soup and cod in beer batter, the choice extends to beef stew, salmon fishcakes, Creole fish stew, and organically-reared roast lamb. **Principal beers:** Youngs Bitter & Winter Warmer.

Directions Nearest tube - Clapham Junction

Brewery/Company Youngs

Open 12-11

Bar food 12-3 7-9.45 Av main course £5.50

Duke of Cambridge NEW
SW11 Map GtL C2

228 Battersea Bridge Rd SW11 3AA

☎ 0171 223 5662

Stylishly modernised pub offering an interesting range of traditional dishes with a modern twist. Sausages and mash come with an onion jus, chicken and mushroom pie with sweet pepper mash, and sandwiches take the ciabatta form. Venison stew, beef with red wine jus and celeriac chips, and brochette of scallops and monkfish may also feature.

Principal beers: Youngs Bitter & Special.

Brewery/Company Free House

Open 11-11

Bar food 12.30-2.30 7.30-9.45

Restaurant 12.30-2.30 7.30-9.45

For Pubs with AA food rosettes see page 430

SW18

The Alma Tavern NEW

SW18 Map GtL C2

499 Old York Rd, Wandsworth SW18 1TF
☎ 0181 870 2537

Classic Victorian pub with etched-glass windows, decorative mirrors and, surprisingly, a decidedly continental air amid the traditional surroundings. This extends to the imaginative food on offer, perhaps including chicken, pheasant and green peppercorn terrine, mussels with saffron and shallot cream, red Thai curry, and fishcakes with coriander, lemon grass and sweet chilli dip.

Principal beers: Youngs Bitter & Winter Warmer.
Brewery/Company Youngs
Open 11-11
Bar food 12-10.30 Av main course £6.95

W1

The Argyll Arms

W1 Map C4

18 Argyll St, Oxford Circus W1V 1AA
☎ 0171 734 6117

A tavern has stood on this site since 1740, but the present building is mid-Victorian and is notable for its stunning floral displays. There's a popular range of sandwiches and the hot food menu might offer vegetarian moussaka, beef and Guinness pie, chicken and leek pie, haddock and lasagne. **Principal beers:** Tetley, Marstons Pedigree, Morland Old Speckled Hen, Brakspear.

Directions Nearest tube - Oxford Circus
Brewery/Company Allied Domecq
Open 11-11
Bar food 11-7 Av main course £5.95

The Glassblower

W1 Map D3

42 Glasshouse St W1R 5RH
☎ 0171 734 8547

Ideally placed for visiting the shops and theatres, this traditional Irish-managed pub is in the heart of the West End. Specialities of the house are the national dish - fish and chips - and a comprehensive choice of sausages, from Cajun to beef and Theakston ale.

Principal beers: Theakston Best, Courage Directors, John Smiths Smooth.
Brewery/Company Scottish & Newcastle
Open 11-11 (Sun 12-10.30)
Bar food 11-11 Av main course £6

Red Lion NEW

W1 Map C3

No 1 Waverton St, Mayfair W1X 7FJ
☎ 0171 499 1307

Built in 1752, The Red Lion is one of Mayfair's most historic pubs. Originally used mainly by 18th-century builders, the clientele is now more likely to be the rich and famous of Mayfair, yet the friendly welcome remains. Menu may include beef Wellington, fish and chips or steak and kidney pie. **Principal beers:** Greene King IPA, Courage Best & Directors, Theakston IPA.

Directions Nearest tube - Green Park
Brewery/Company Scottish & Newcastle
Open 11.30-11.20 (Sat 12-3, 6-11/Sun 12-3, 6-10.30)
Bar food 12-2.30 6-9.45 Av main course £5.50
Restaurant 12-2.30 6-9.45 Av 3 course à la carte £24

W2

The Cow Saloon Bar & Dining Rooms

W2 Map GtL C3

89 Westbourne Park Rd W2 5QH
☎ 0171 221 5400 221 0021

Fresh seafood draws the crowds to this well refurbished pub in Notting Hill Gate. Enjoy Irish rock oysters and a pint of Guinness, or choose crab, mussels, langoustines or clams from the impressive shellfish display. 'Landfood' choices may include sausages and mash with red onion gravy, smoked duck with watercress and apricot compôte. Fish features in the separate upstairs restaurant. **Principal beers:** Fullers ESB & London Pride.

Directions Nearest tubes - Royal Oak & Westbourne Park
Brewery/Company Free House
Open 12-11 (Dining rooms 7-12)
Bar food 12.30-3.30 6.30-11 Av main course £8
Restaurant 12.30-3.30 7-12 Av 3 course à la carte £25

The Prince Bonaparte

W2 Map GtL C3

80 Chepstow Rd W2 5BE
☎ 0171 313 9491

A large Victorian pub, airy and open plan, offering modern British cooking with Eastern, African and Mediterranean influences. Typical dishes are Middle

Eastern vegetarian plate, with aubergine, houmous, tabouleh and feta; Cumberland sausages with roast red onions, mash and gravy, and Moroccan lamb tagine with almond couscous and harissa. **Principal beers:** Bass, Fuller London Pride.
Brewery/Company Bass
Open 12-11 (Sun 12-10.30)
Restaurant 12-3 6.30-10.30

W5

The Wheatsheaf
W5 Map GtL B3
41 Haven Ln, Ealing W5 2HZ
☎ 0181 997 5240
Large Victorian pub with rustic appearance inside. Wooden floors, panelled walls, beams from an old barn, and real fires in winter. Various Mexican and Thai specialities, plus traditional English dishes such as sausage and mash, liver and bacon, and ploughman's. Choice of four roasts on Sunday. **Principal beers:** Fullers London Pride, ESB & Chiswick.
Directions 1m from A40 junction with North Circular
Brewery/Company Fullers
Open 11-11 (Sun 12-10.30)
Bar food 12-2.30 5.30-10 Av main course £6

W6

Anglesea Arms NEW
W6 Map GtL C3
35 Wingate Rd W6 0UR
☎ 0181 749 1291
Traditional corner pub, with a Georgian facade, basic decor, real fires and a relaxed, smoky atmosphere, that positvely bustles with eager diners. The attraction is the the range of simple, robust dishes, including, perhaps, shellfish minestrone with tarragon pesto, oysters with shallot relish, John Dory with spinach and cep butter sauce, and stuffed saddle of rabbit. **Principal beers:** Courage Best & Directors, Theakstons XB, Marstons Pedigree.
Brewery/Company Free House
Open 11-11 (Sun 12-10.30)
Bar food 12.30-2.45 7.30-10.45 Av main course £8.25
Restaurant 12.30-2.45 7.30-10.45

W8

The Churchill Arms
W8 Map GtL C3
119 Kensington Church St W8 7LN
☎ 0171 727 4242
Thai food is the speciality at this traditional 200-year-old pub with strong emphasis on exotic chicken, beef and pork dishes. Try Thai rice noodles with ground peanuts, spicy sauce and a choice of pork, chicken or prawns (Kwaitiew Pad Thai), or special Thai roast duck curry served with rice (Kaeng Ped Phed Yang). **Principal beers:** Fullers London Pride, ESB & Chiswick Bitter.
Directions Off A40 (Westway). Nearest tube-Notting Hill Gate
Brewery/Company Fullers
Open 11-11
Bar food 12-2.30 6-9.30 Av main course £5.50
Restaurant 12-2.30 6-9.30 Av 3 course à la carte £7.50 Av 0 course fixed price £5.50

W14

The Havelock Tavern NEW
W14 Map GtL C3
57 Masbro Rd, Brook Green W14 0LS
☎ 0171 603 5374
Handsome Georgian corner pub just a short stroll from Olympia.Welcoming atmosphere, delightful garden, and modern menus. Interesting dishes range from game, bacon and foie gras terrine and vegetable and herb broth, to pork with parmesan and sage mash and tomato sauce, rabbit, chorizo and white bean stew, and sauternes and caramel custard. **Principal beers:** Brakspear, Marston's Pedigree, Wadworth 6X.
Directions Nearest tubes: Shepherd's Bush & Olympia
Brewery/Company Free House
Open 11-11 (Sun 12-10.30)
Restaurant 12.30-2.30 7-10 Av 3 course à la carte £19

WC1

Cittie of Yorke
WC1 Map E4
22 High Holborn WC1V 6BS
☎ 0171 242 7670
Paintings of illustrious patrons of the past adorn this 17th-century pub, including Dickens, Sir Thomas Moore and William Morris. A menu of home-

contd.

made pub food offers fish and chips, steaks and pies, plus traditional puddings such as sherry trifle, apple pie and jam roly-poly. **Principal beers:** Samuel Smith Old Brewery.
Brewery/Company Samuel Smith
Open 11.30-11 (closed Sun)
Bar food 12-9.30 Av main course £4.25

The Lamb NEW
WC1 Map E4
94 Lamb's Conduit St WC1N 3LZ
☎ 0171 4050 713
Built in the late 18th century, the flower-decked Lamb is an unspoilt Victorian gem, full of atmosphere with fine etched glass, low pillared ceilings, dark polished wood and original sepia photographs of music-hall stars. Home-cooked lunchtime bar food may include chicken and cider pie, beef in ale, ploughman's and sausage and mash. Set restaurant menu. **Principal beers:** Youngs (full range).
Directions Nearest tube: Holborn or Russell Square
Brewery/Company Young & Co
Open 11-11.20
Bar food 12-2.30 Av main course £7
Restaurant 12-2.30 6.30-9

WC2

Prince of Wales
WC2 Map E4
150-151 Drury Ln, Covent Garden WC2B 5TB ☎ 0171 836 5183 & 240 9935
Opened in 1852, this pub is a useful venue for those visiting the many theatres in London's West End. Covent Garden is close by for shopping and an abundance of street entertainment. Traditional bar food is served such as steak and mushroom pies or English fish and chips. **Principal beers:** Theakston Old Peculier & Best, Courage Best & Directors.
Brewery/Company Scottish & Newcastle
Open 11-11 (Sun 12-10.30)
Bar food 11am-10pm Av main course £4.45

Pubs offering a good choice of seafood on the menu

Surrey

ABINGER Surrey — *Map 04 TQ14*

The Volunteer
ABINGER
Water Ln, Sutton RH5 6PR
☎ 01306 730798
Enjoying a peaceful rural setting with views over the Mole Valley, this 17th-century pub is popular among walkers, who regularly fill the charming, low-ceilinged rooms. Varied bar food ranges from filled rolls, fish soup and Thai fishcakes, to monkfish and scallop kebabs, chicken supreme, local pheasant, lemon tart, and unusual South of England cheeses. **Principal beers:** Badger Tanglefoot, IPA & Best.

Directions Between Guildford & Dorking, 1m S of A25
Brewery/Company Woodhouse Inns
Open (opening times vary, ring for details)
Bar food 12-2.30 7-9.30 Av main course £9

ALBURY Surrey — *Map 04 TQ04*

The Drummond Arms Inn NEW
ALBURY
The Street GU5 9AG ☎ 01483 202039
Situated in the pretty village of Albury below the North Downs, this charming old inn has an attractive riverside garden, and offers comfortable en suite accommodation. Traditional pub food, served in the panelled bars, includes steak and kidney pie, sandwiches, sweet and sour pork, rack of lamb, and baked sea bass. **Principal beers:** Courage Best, Gales HSB, King & Barnes Broadwood, Morland Old Speckled Hen.
Brewery/Company Free House
Open 11-3 6-11

Bar food 12-2.30 7-11 Av main course £6.50
Restaurant 12-2.30 7-11 Av 3 course à la carte £25
Accommodation (Min) s£40 d£55

BETCHWORTH Surrey *Map 04 TQ25*

The Red Lion NEW
BETCHWORTH
Old Reigate Rd RH3 7DS
☎ 01737 843336
Set in 18 acres with a cricket ground and rolling countryside views, this 200-year-old pub offers an extensive menu. Beyond baguettes and ploughman's, the choice includes steaks and grills and specials like tomato and mint soup, liver and bacon, monkfish with mustard sauce, steak and ale pie, and treacle tart.

Principal beers: Wadworth 6X, King & Barnes Sussex, Fullers London Pride, Youngs.
Brewery/Company Allied Domecq
Open 11-3 6-11
Bar food 12-3 6-10 Av main course £6.95

BLACKBROOK Surrey *Map 04 TQ14*

The Plough at Blackbrook
BLACKBROOK
RH5 4DS ☎ 01306 886603
Once the haunt of highwaymen and footpads, this former coaching inn is an ideal base for country walks. Comprehensive lunchtime menu featuring ploughman's, toasted bagels and fresh salads. Grilled swordfish, spicy hot prawn curry, mussel chowder, Toulouse sausages, and lemon cream tart are typical house specialities. **Principal beers:** King & Barnes Sussex, Festive, Broadwood, Harvest & Old.
Directions A24 to Dorking, then toward Horsham, 0.75m from Deepdene rdbt L to Blackbrook
Brewery/Company King & Barnes
Open 11-2.30 6-11 (Sun 11-3, 6-10.30)
Bar food 12-2 7-9

BRAMLEY Surrey *Map 04 TQ04*

Jolly Farmer Inn
BRAMLEY
High St GU5 0HB ☎ 01483 893355
Flower-adorned, 350-year-old former coaching inn, with a restaurant housed in a 400-year-old barn. London market sourced produce features strongly on the varied menu. Dishes range from home-made beefburgers, pies and chilli, to Scotch steaks, fresh cod in beer batter, roast duck, and smoked haddock and mushroom mornay. **Principal beers:** Hogs Back TEA, Courage Theakston Best, BadgerBest.
Directions Onto A3, then A281, Bramley 3m S of Guildford

Brewery/Company Free House
Open 10-3 6-11
Bar food 12-2 6.45-10 Av main course £8.50
Restaurant 12-2 7-9.30 Av 3 course à la carte £16.50
Accommodation (Min) s£35 d£50

CAMBERLEY Surrey *Map 04 SU86*

The Bell Inn & La Bella Italia
CAMBERLEY
36 Frogmore Rd, Blackwater GU17 0NP
☎ 01252 890919
Unusual single-storey building, incorporating a lively pub and separate Italian restaurant, dating back some 200 years. Ships lamps and naval memorabilia adorn the bar, where baguettes and pizzas are available. Separate restaurant carte featuring freshly-cooked pasta and Italian specialities, notably fish and seafood. **Principal beers:** Courage Best.
Directions From M4 thru Camberley onto A30 toward Basingstoke, at 1st rdbt turn R (A3272) then 2nd R into Frogmore Rd
Brewery/Company Unique Pub Co
Open 12-2.30 6.30-11.30 (closed Sun eve & all Mon)
Bar food 12-2.30 Av main course £3.50
Restaurant 12-2.30 6.30-11.30 Av 3 course à la carte £18 Av 2 course fixed price £6.95

CHIDDINGFOLD Surrey Map 04 SU93

The Crown Inn
CHIDDINGFOLD
The Green GU8 4TX ☎ 01428 682255
Originally a guest house for pilgrims and Cistercian monks, the creeper-clad, medieval timber-framed Crown dates from 1258. Full of character featuring stained glass, Flemish tapestries and massive old beams, it offers traditional pub food, including steak and kidney pie, seafood crêpe, cod in lemon butter and darne of salmon. **Principal beers:** Badger IPA, Dorset Best & Tanglefoot.
Directions On A283 between Milford & Petworth
Brewery/Company Hall & Woodhouse
Open 8-12
Bar food 12-2.30 7-9.30 Av main course £7
Restaurant 12-2.30 7-9.30 Av 3 course à la carte £25
Accommodation (Min) s£57 d£67

COBHAM Surrey Map 04 TQ16

The Cricketers
COBHAM
Downside KT11 3NX ☎ 01932 862105
The original part of the building dates from the 16th century, and the pub retains the character of the period. Favourite bar food includes home-made pies, grilled plaice, and pear and caramel brownie, while restaurant fare may feature roast pheasant, and a mille-feuille of fresh salmon. **Principal beers:** Wadworth 6X, Websters Yorkshire Bitter, Morland Old Speckled Hen, Theakston Best.
Directions From A3 take A245 towards Cobham, 2nd r'about turn R, then 1st R opp Waitrose. Pub 1.5m
Brewery/Company Inntrepreneur
Open 11-2.30 6-11
Bar food 12-2.30 6.30-10 Av main course £6.50
Restaurant 12.15-2.30 7.15-11 Av 3 course à la carte £23

COLDHARBOUR Surrey Map 04 TQ14

The Plough Inn
COLDHARBOUR
Coldharbour Ln RH5 6HD
☎ 01306 711793
Family-run, 17th-century pub in the depths of National Trust countryside on Leith Hill. Traditional home-cooked English food accompanies a range of real ales, two of which are brewed on site. Expect smoked ham ploughman's, liver and bacon, and beer-battered fresh cod fillet.
Principal beers: Crooked Furrow, Leith Hill Tallywhacker, Shepherd Neame Best, Adnams Broadside.
Directions M25 J9 - A24 to Dorking. A25 towards Guildford. Coldharbour signposted from the one-way system
Brewery/Company Free House
Open 11.30-3 6-11 (Sat-Sun 11.30-11)
Bar food 12-2.30 7-9.30 Av main course £4.50
Restaurant 12-2.30 7-9.30 Av 3 course à la carte £13
Accommodation (Min) s£55 d£60

COMPTON Surrey Map 04 SU94

The Harrow Inn
COMPTON
The Street GU3 1EG ☎ 01483 810379
Beamed 15th-century pub tucked away in an attractive village. Varied bar food makes good use of fresh ingredients, notably fresh fish. Dishes range from hearty snacks like filled jacket potatoes and warm salads, to caramelised onion and goat's cheese tart, roast cod with red pepper sauce, calves' liver and bacon with onion jus, and chocolate-crusted lemon tart. **Principal beers:** Harvey Sussex Best, Greene King IPA & Abbot Ale.
Directions 3m S of Guildford on A3 then B3000 towards Godalming. Compton on R
Brewery/Company Allied Domecq
Open 8am-11pm (Sun 12- 4)
Bar food 12-3 6-10
Restaurant 6-10 Av 3 course à la carte £25
Accommodation (Min) s£35 d£45

DORKING Surrey Map 04 TQ14

Abinger Hatch NEW
DORKING
Abinger Ln, Abinger Common RH5 6HZ
☎ 01306 730737
Tucked away opposite the church and duck pond, this charmingly situated pub dates from the 17th century. With its flagged floors, beamed ceilings, open fires, and welcoming atmosphere, it is a popular destination for good ale and

food. Menu ranges from filled rolls, ploughman's, and pub favourites, to salmon hollandaise and various grills.

Principal beers: Badger, Harveys.
Directions A25 from Guildford, L to Abinger Common
Brewery/Company Free House
Open 11.30-11
Bar food 12-2.30 6-7.30 Av main course £5.75
Restaurant 12-2 6-9.30 Av 3 course à la carte £10

DUNSFOLD Surrey — Map 04 TQ03

The Sun Inn
DUNSFOLD

The Common GU8 4LE
☎ 01483 200242
Heavily timbered coaching inn with open fireplaces and three bar areas, opposite a cricket green. Typical dishes include steak and kidney pie, fillet of trout, venison sausages and fillet steak au poivre. **Principal beers:** Friary Meux, Marstons Pedigree, Hogs Back Hair of the Hog.
Directions A281 thru Shalford & Bramley, take B2130 to Godalming. Dunsfold on L after 2 miles
Brewery/Company Allied Domecq
Open 11-3 6-11
Bar food 12-2.15 7-10 Av main course £6.95
Restaurant 12-2.15 7-10 Av 3 course à la carte £15

EFFINGHAM Surrey — Map 04 TQ15

The Plough NEW
EFFINGHAM

Orestan Ln KT24 5SW ☎ 01372 458121
Conveniently situated for Polesden Lacey (NT), this quiet, civilised village pub, run by long-serving tenants, offers well-kept Young's ales, a good range of home-made food and an attractive garden. Typical dishes range from filled jacket potatoes and daily pasta dishes, to chicken and asparagus pie and potato and salmon rosti. **Principal beers:** Youngs Winter Warmer & Special.
Directions Between Guildford & Leatherhead on A246
Brewery/Company Youngs
Open 11-3 6-11
Bar food 12-2 7-9.30

EGHAM Surrey — Map 04 TQ07

The Fox and Hounds
EGHAM

Bishopgate Rd, Englefield Green TW20 0XU ☎ 01784 433098
A good English pub, located on the Royal Park, convenient for walkers and riders. Dishes include Cumberland sausage with mustard mash, slow-roasted split shoulder of lamb, and scallops with woodland mushrooms and wild rice. A good choice of fish is offered from the blackboard. **Principal beers:** Fullers London Pride, Brakspear, Courage Directors.
Directions From village green turn L into Castle Hill Rd, then R into Bishops Gate Rd
Brewery/Company Free House
Open 12-3 5-11 (open all day, weather permitting)
Bar food 12-3 Av main course £2.50
Restaurant 12-3 6-10 Av 3 course à la carte £25

ELSTEAD Surrey — Map 04 SU94

The Woolpack
ELSTEAD

The Green GU8 6HD ☎ 01252 703106
Plenty of wool industry memorabilia adorn this atmospheric, old fashioned pub, complete with open fire, low beams and high-backed settles. One interesting menu may offer green Thai pork curry, rich beef casserole, spinach and cottage cheese lasagne, and more unusual dishes like ostrich steak in pesto, honey and mustard. **Principal beers:** Greene King Abbot Ale, Fullers London Pride.
Directions Milford exit off A3
Brewery/Company Ind Coope
Open 11-2.30 6-11
Bar food 12-2 7-9.45 Av main course £7.50
Restaurant 12-2 7-9.45 Av 3 course à la carte £15

EWHURST Surrey Map 04 TQ04

The Windmill Inn
EWHURST

Pitch Hill GU6 7NN ☎ 01483 277566
Rebuilt after a fire in 1906, originally the haunt of 18th-century smugglers, this welcoming inn affords far-reaching views across the Weald towards the South Downs. From bar snacks like filled baguettes and jacket potatoes, the blackboard menu features local game (in season), Suffolk smoked chicken, various steaks and, perhaps, lobster thermidor. **Principal beers:** Hogs Back TEA, Courage Best, Fullers London Pride, Gales HSB.
Directions From Cranleigh take B2127, through Ewhurst. At mini rndbt take Shere road. Pub 1.5m on R
Brewery/Company Free House
Open 12-11
Bar food 12-3 7-11 Av main course £6.50
Restaurant 12-3 7-11 Av 3 course à la carte £25

HASCOMBE Surrey Map 04 TQ03

The White Horse
HASCOMBE

GU8 4JA ☎ 01483 208258
Friendly16th-century pub situated in picturesque countryside. Noted in summer for its dazzling hanging baskets and flowers. Restaurant menu and extensive blackboard specials in the bar may offer fresh tuna steak, lamb noisettes, fish pie, home-made steakburger, and sausage and mash with onion gravy. Comfortable beamed bars and rear conservatory. **Principal beers:** Adnams, Greene King IPA, Badger Tanglefoot.
Directions from Godalming take B2130. Pub on L 0.5m after Hascombe
Brewery/Company Friary Meux
Open 11-3 5.30-11 (Sat 11-11, Sun 12-10.30)
Bar food 12-3 7-11 Av main course £7.50
Restaurant 12-2 7-10 Av 3 course à la carte £30 Av 3 course fixed price £19.50

For Pubs with AA food rosettes see page 430

HASLEMERE Surrey Map 04 SU93

The Wheatsheaf Inn
HASLEMERE

Grayswood Rd, Grayswood GU27 2DE ☎ 01428 644440
Stylishly furnished Victorian village inn set beside the A286, opposite the church and green. Order a sandwich, ribeye steak, or one of the imaginative daily specials, such as rack of lamb with chargrilled vegetables, and baked mackerel with gooseberry sauce, and relax in the neatly furnished bar or in the 'Tuscan-style' restaurant. **Principal beers:** Badger Best, Wadworth 6X, Fullers London Pride & ESB.
Directions Leave A3 at Milford, A286 to Haslemere. Grayswood approx 1.5m N
Brewery/Company Free House
Open 11-3 6-11
Bar food 12-2 7-10 Av main course £7.95
Restaurant 12-2 7-10 Av 3 course à la carte £30
Accommodation (Min) s£55 d£75

HORLEY Surrey Map 04 TQ24

Ye Olde Six Bells
HORLEY

Church Rd RH6 8AD ☎ 01293 783792
With a Horsham stone roof and half-timbered walls, this pub is thought to have originally been built as a hospice by monks from Dorking monastery, around 1450. **Principal beers:** Bass.
Directions A23 to Post House rdbt, take Horley turning & L at the Nobel Clinic, pub at end of road
Brewery/Company Vintage Inns
Open 11-11 (Sun 12-10.30)

MICKLEHAM Surrey Map 04 TQ15

King William IV
MICKLEHAM

Byttom Hill RH5 6EL ☎ 01372 372590
Built as an ale house for Lord Beaverbrook's estate staff, the pub dates from 1780, though most of it is Victorian. Its hillside location provides views across the Mole Valley. Sunday roasts are popular, along with hearty snacks and home-cooked specials like seafood pie, herb-crusted rack of lamb, and steaks from the blackboard menu. No children. **Principal beers:** Hogs Back TEA & Hop Garden Gold, Badger Best, Adnams Best, Fuller's London Pride.

Directions Just off A24 (Leatherhead-Dorking), by partly green painted restaurant, just N of B2289
Brewery/Company Free House
Open 11-3 6-11 (Sun 12-3, 7-10.30)
Bar food 12-2 7-9.30 Av main course £6.75

The Running Horses
MICKLEHAM
Old London Rd RH5 6DU
☎ 01372 372279

Village inn dating back over 400 years, complete with inglenook fireplace and highwayman's hideaway. Only fresh ingredients are used in preparing such dishes as juniper roasted cod, and lamb Wellington with black pudding farcé. Bar fare includes wild boar sausage baguette, mussels and chips, and salmon fishcakes.

Principal beers: Morland Old Speckled Hen, Friary Meux, Young's, Fullers London Pride.
Directions Off A24 between Leatherhead & Dorking
Brewery/Company Vanguard
Open 11.30-3 5.30-11 (Sun 12-3.30, 7-10.30)
Bar food 12-2.30 7-9.30 Av main course £6.75
Restaurant 12-2.30 7-9.30
Accommodation (Min) s£75 d£85

NEWDIGATE Surrey *Map 04 TQ14*

The Six Bells
NEWDIGATE
Village St RH5 5HD ☎ 01306 631276

Picturesque timber-framed pub in a quiet village location and reputedly once a smugglers' haunt. Light meals and bar snacks might include the Six Bells club sandwich and a range of baguettes and filled jacket potatoes. Daily-changing blackboard menu may offer rack of lamb and poached salmon.

Principal beers: King & Barnes Sussex, Fullers London Pride, Gales HSB, Youngs.
Directions A24 S of Dorking, L at Beare Green r'about
Brewery/Company Free House
Open 11-3 6-11 (Summer Sat-Sun 11-11)
Bar food 12-3 7-11 Av main course £5.75
Restaurant 12-3 7-11 Av 3 course à la carte £15

OCKLEY Surrey *Map 04 TQ14*

Bryce's at The Old School House
OCKLEY
RH5 5TH ☎ 01306 627430

Converted 18th-century boys' school with strong emphasis on fish and seafood in the restaurant. From open sandwiches, pasta meals and fishcakes in the bar, a restaurant meal may feature ravioli of salmon, white crab and ginger, followed by plaice with a light salmon mousse, Thai-style fish stew, or steamed red snapper with bok choy, and red pepper and leek coulis, with steamed orange and ginger pudding to finish.

Principal beers: King & Barnes Sussex, Broadwood & Festive.
Directions 8m S of Dorking on A29
Brewery/Company King & Barnes

contd.

Open 11-3 6-11 (closed Sun eve)
Bar food 12-2.30 6.30-9.30 Av main course £7.50
Restaurant 12-2.30 7-9.30 Av 3 course à la carte £23.50 Av 3 course fixed price £23.50

The Kings Arms Inn
OCKLEY

Stane St RH2 5TP ☎ 01306 711224
Situated on a Roman road, this village free house dates back to the 15th century and includes old beams, a log fire and a priest hole. Examples of the daily specials board include home-made game pie, honey-roasted rack of lamb, calves' liver, bacon and onions, and a daily Thai dish. **Principal beers:** King & Barnes Sussex, Whitbread Fuggles Imperial, Flowers Original, Eldridge Pope.
Directions From M25 J9 take A24 through Dorking towards Horsham, A29 to Ockley
Brewery/Company Free House
Open 11-2.30 6-11
Bar food 12-2 7-9.30 Av main course £6.95
Restaurant 12-2 7-9.30 Av 3 course à la carte £17
Accommodation (Min) s£45 d£65

PIRBRIGHT Surrey — Map 04 SU95

The Royal Oak
PIRBRIGHT

Aldershot Rd GU24 0DQ
☎ 01483 232466
The gardens at this old Tudor cottage pub are a blaze of colour in summer and regularly win competitions. Inside the rambling bars the menu offers salads and ploughmans, hearty traditional pies, including steak and ale pie, and regular favourites like lamb balti, bangers and mash and hot chicken and bacon salad. **Principal beers:** Whitbread Fuggles Imperial, Youngs Special, Flowers Original & IPA, guest beers.
Directions M3 J3 take A322 towards Guildford, then A324 towards Aldershot
Brewery/Company Whitbread
Open 11-11 (Sun 12-10.30, food all day wknds)
Bar food 12-2 6.30-9.30 Av main course £5.95

SHALFORD Surrey — Map 04 TQ04

Seahorse
SHALFORD

The Street GU4 8BU ☎ 01483 514351
Set in historic Shalford village, once home to John Bunyan, this 17th-century listed pub is in an area of outstanding natural beauty. Nearby Shalford Mill was the first building to be purchased for the National Trust. **Principal beers:** Bass.
Directions On A281
Brewery/Company Vintage Inns
Open 11-11 (Sun 12-10.30)

SHEPPERTON Surrey — Map 04 TQ06

Thames Court
SHEPPERTON

Towpath TW17 9LJ ☎ 01932 221957
A 19th-century pub that was once a guest house and private club where artists such as Beryl Reid and Arthur Lowe performed. Its proximity to Shepperton film studios still ensures a certain amount of celebrity custom. **Principal beers:** Bass.
Directions A317 E, L at rdbt, R at T-junct, over Chertsey Bridge, R at small rdbt, R down Dockett Eddy Ln, pub on L
Brewery/Company Vintage Inns
Open 11-11 (Sun 12-10.30)

STAINES Surrey — Map 04 TQ07

The Swan Hotel
STAINES

The Hythe TW18 8HH ☎ 01784 452494
The hotel, set on the south bank of the Thames by Staines Bridge, retains its original pub atmosphere and has two large bars and a conservatory overlooking the river terrace. The same menu is offered throughout, with dishes such as Whitby scampi, and hare and pheasant pie. **Principal beers:** Fullers London Pride, Chiswick, ESB & Old Winter Ale.
Directions Just off A308, S of Staines Bridge. 12m from M25, M4 & M3. 5m from Heathrow
Brewery/Company Fullers
Open 7am-11pm (Sun & BHs 8am-10.30pm)
Bar food noon-10 Av main course £4
Restaurant noon-10
Accommodation (Min) s£41 d£59

THURSLEY Surrey Map 04 SU93

Three Horseshoes
THURSLEY
Dye House Rd GU8 6QD
☎ 01252 703268
The accent is on conversation and relaxation at this traditional establishment with panoramic countryside views. The constantly varying menu of home-cooked fare has a cosmopolitan influence. Expect the likes of leek, bacon and mushroom gratin, crab-filled mushrooms, and bread-and-butter pudding. **Principal beers:** Gales HSB & Butser.
Directions Thursley exit from A3, between Milford & Hindhead
Brewery/Company Free House
Open 12-3 6-11 (Closed Sun eve)
Bar food 12-2 7-9 Av main course £6
Restaurant 12-2 7-9 Av 3 course à la carte £15

WALLISWOOD Surrey Map 04 TQ13

The Scarlett Arms NEW
WALLISWOOD
RH5 5RD ☎ 01306 627243
Oak beams, a stone floor and a fine open fireplace give a homely feel to this unspoilt, 400-year-old rural pub. Simple country cooking is the perfect complement to the excellent King & Barnes ales on offer. Tuck into 'doorstop' sandwiches, steak and kidney pie, ham, egg and chips, or ribeye steak with pepper sauce. **Principal beers:** King & Barnes Sussex, Mild & Broadwood.
Directions S on A29 from Dorking, thru Ockley, R for Walliswood/Oakwood Hill
Brewery/Company King & Barnes
Open 11-2.30 5.30-11
Bar food 12-2 6.30-9.30 Av main course £6.25

WEST CLANDON Surrey Map 04 TQ05

Onslow Arms
WEST CLANDON
The Street GU4 7TE ☎ 01483 222447
Dating from 1623 with an inglenook fireplace and a unique traditional roasting spit, this pub is convenient for both Heathrow and Gatwick airports. Fish meals feature halibut steak, grilled Dover sole, and poached salmon with white wine and cream sauce, while other main course options include chicken with asparagus sauce, and duck in orange sauce. **Principal beers:** Courage, Whitbread, Youngs, King & Barnes.
Directions A3 then A247
Brewery/Company Free House
Open 11-11 (Sun 12-10.30)
Bar food 12-2 7-10 Av main course £6.50
Restaurant 12.30-2 7-10 Av 3 course à la carte £20 Av 3 course fixed price £18.95

WEYBRIDGE Surrey Map 04 TQ06

Badger's Rest
WEYBRIDGE
25 Oatlands Chase KT13 9RW
☎ 01932 253277
Built on land set aside by Henry VII to serve as a hunting chase in his old age, this 19th-century private residence was converted into a hotel by 1930.
Principal beers: Bass.
Directions Off A3050
Brewery/Company Vintage Inns
Open 11-11 (Sun 12-10.30)
Accommodation (Min) s£55 d£65

WINDLESHAM Surrey Map 04 SU96

Brickmakers Arms
WINDLESHAM
Chertsey Rd GU20 6HT
☎ 01276 472267 & 451914
Next door to Sunningdale golf course, this popular Victorian pub presents a good lunch menu which often features salmon and saffron fishcakes with a chive cream sauce, deep-fried Brie, and Cumberland sausages. The appealing two-course set menu may highlight salmon with mushroom and lemon sauce. **Principal beers:** Courage Best, Fullers London Pride, Brakspear.
Directions On B386 between Bagshot & Longcross
Brewery/Company Free House
Open 11.30-3 5-11
Bar food 12-2.30 6-10 Av main course £7.95
Restaurant 12-2.30 6-10 Av 3 course à la carte £25 Av 3 course fixed price £17.95

The Windmill
WINDLESHAM
London Rd GU20 6PJ ☎ 01276 450061
An early 19th-century inn three miles from Ascot, and four from Virginia Water and Wentworth. Once the scene of a famous forte between two local characters in 1866.

contd.

The Windmill

Principal beers: Bass, Caffreys.
Directions On the A30 between Sunningdale & Bagshot
Brewery/Company Vintage Inns
Open 11-11 (Sun 12-10.30)

WITLEY Surrey *Map 04 SU93*

The White Hart
WITLEY
Petworth Rd GU8 5PH ☎ 01428 683695
16th-century coaching inn with illustrious connections. George Elliot based characters in her novel Middlemarch on the clientele, the original sign is in the Victoria and Albert, and Richard II used the pub as a hunting lodge. Menu may include chicken and leek pie, breaded plaice, or liver, bacon and onions. **Principal beers:** Shepherd Neame Master Brew, Spitfire & Best.

Directions From A3 follow signs to Milford, then A283 towards Petworth. Pub 2m on L
Brewery/Company Shepherd Neame
Open 11-2.30 5.30-11 (Sun 5.30 -10.30)
Bar food 12-2 6-9.30 Av main course £5.75
Restaurant 12-2 6-9.30 Av 3 course à la carte £12

Sussex, East

ALCISTON Sussex, East *Map 05 TQ50*

Rose Cottage Inn
ALCISTON
BN26 6UW ☎ 01323 870377
A 16th-century building, with beams and an inglenook fireplace, in a peaceful village setting at the foot of the South Downs. Local produce is used where possible, including organically grown vegetables and pheasant shot by the landlord. Expect excellent fresh fish, rabbit and bacon pie, local venison braised in port and Guinness, and Thai-style tiger prawns. **Principal beers:** Harveys Best, guest ales.
Directions Off A27 between Eastbourne & Lewes
Brewery/Company Free House
Open 11.30-3 6.30-11
Bar food 12-2 7-9.30 Av main course £6.75
Restaurant 7-9.30 Av 3 course à la carte £15
Accommodation (Min) d£30

ARLINGTON Sussex, East *Map 05 TQ50*

Old Oak Inn
ARLINGTON
BN26 6SJ ☎ 01323 482072
Originally the village almshouse, dating from 1733, which became a pub in the early 1900s. Typical bar dishes are Newhaven cod in batter, home-made curries, and steak and kidney pudding. In the restaurant expect the likes of salmon en croûte, or venison with wild mushrooms. **Principal beers:** Harveys, Badger, Brakspear, Youngs.
Directions N of A27 between Polegate & Lewes
Brewery/Company Free House
Open 11-3 6-11
Bar food 12-2 7-9 Av main course £7
Restaurant 12-2 7-9 Av 3 course à la carte £12

ASHBURNHAM PLACE Sussex, East *Map 05 TQ61*

Ash Tree Inn NEW
ASHBURNHAM PLACE
Brownbread St TN33 9NX
☎ 01424 892104
The Ash Tree is a friendly old pub with three open fires, plenty of beams and a traditional local atmosphere. Bar food

includes ploughman's, salads and sandwiches, while the restaurant menu may feature duck breast in cherry sauce, cottage pie or poached salmon. **Principal beers:** Harveys Best, Fullers London Pride, Morland Old Speckled Hen, Wadworth 6X.
Brewery/Company Free House
Open 12-4 7-11 (closed Mon)
Bar food 12-11 Av main course £10

BARCOMBE Sussex, East *Map 05 TQ41*

The Anchor Inn
BARCOMBE

Anchor Ln BN8 5BS ☎ 01273 400414
18th-century smugglers' inn on the banks of the River Ouse, built to cater for bargees whose barges travelled up the river from Newhaven. Freshly prepared bar and restaurant food ranges from tomato and basil soup, baguettes and ploughman's, to skate, dressed crab, and interesting restaurant dishes like herb-crusted rack of lamb with roasted shallots. **Principal beers:** Badger Best, Badger Tanglefoot, Harvey Best, guest beers.
Directions From A26 (Lewes/ Uckfield rd)
Brewery/Company Free House
Open 10.30-11.30 (Sun 12-11)
Bar food 12-3 6-9.30 Av main course £5.50
Restaurant 12-3 7-9 Av 3 course à la carte £18
Accommodation (Min) s£32 d£55

BERWICK Sussex, East *Map 05 TQ50*

The Cricketers Arms
BERWICK

BN26 6SP ☎ 01323 870469
Originally a terrace of flint cottages dating back 400 years, the Cricketers has been an 'ale house' for 200 years, and is of special architectural interest. Traditional home-made food is served, with as much local produce, meat and fish as possible. **Principal beers:** Harveys Best, PA & seasonal ales.
Directions Off A27 between Polegate & Lewes (follow signs for Berwick Church)
Brewery/Company Harveys of Lewes
Open 11-3 6-11 (Sun 11-11, summer Sat 11-11)
Bar food 12-2.15 6.30-9.30 Av main course £5

BLACKBOYS Sussex, East *Map 05 TQ52*

The Blackboys Inn
BLACKBOYS

Lewes Rd TN22 5LG
☎ 01825 890283
Rambling, black-weatherboarded 14th-century inn set in large gardens and overlooking an iris- and lily-covered pond. Splendid, beamed and antique-furnished interior in which to sample good bar food. From ham, egg and chips and Ceylonese fish curry, the menu extends to hot seafood platter, Dover sole, chicken with wild mushroom sauce, and creme brulee. **Principal beers:** Harveys Best, Armada, Old & IPA, Knots of May Light Mild.
Directions On B2192 between Halland (on A22) and Heathfield
Brewery/Company Harveys
Open 11-3 6-11
Bar food 12-2.30 6.30-10 Av main course £6
Restaurant 12-2.30 7-10 Av 3 course à la carte £16

BRIGHTON Sussex, East *Map 04 TQ30*

The Greys
BRIGHTON

105 Southover St BN2 2UA
☎ 01273 680734
A small Brighton bar boasting original live music and a Belgian chef. Comestible delights include magret of duck with black cherries and Belgian Kriek beer sauce, roast breast of goose with fresh thyme, roasted garlic, lemon and honey, and supreme of pheasant with sloe gin and rowanberry jelly.
Principal beers: Greene King IPA, Youngs Special.
Brewery/Company Whitbread
Open 11-3 5.30-11 (wknd 11-11)
Bar food 12-2 7-9 Av main course £8.95

CHIDDINGLY Sussex, East *Map 05 TQ51*

The Six Bells
CHIDDINGLY

BN8 6HE ☎ 01825 872227
A large country freehouse, with a beer garden and fish pond, serving a good selection of pub food, including pigman's, (ham, salad and French bread) spare ribs, and butter crab. There's a choice of vegetarian fare, such as Stilton

contd.

and walnut pie, plus popular pasta, curry and chilli dishes.
Principal beers: Courage Directors, John Smiths, Harveys Best.
Directions E of A22 between Hailsham & Uckfield(turn opp Golden Cross PH)
Brewery/Company Free House
Open 11-3 6-11
Bar food 11-2.30 6-10.30 Av main course £3.50

COWBEECH Sussex, East *Map 05 TQ61*

Merrie Harriers
COWBEECH

BN27 4J ☎ 01323 833108
Coaching inn dating from the 17th century, with oak beams and an open fire. There are two restaurants, one in the old saloon bar and one (no-smoking) in an extension with glorious country views. Fresh local fish and Sunday roasts are popular, along with the home-made puddings. **Principal beers:** Harveys Best.
Directions Off A271, between Hailsham & Herstmonceux
Brewery/Company Free House
Open 11-2.30 6-11
Restaurant 12-2 6.30-9 Av 3 course à la carte £13.50 Av 2 course fixed price £6.50

DITCHLING Sussex, East *Map 05 TQ31*

The Bull NEW
DITCHLING

2 High St BN6 8TA ☎ 01273 843147
Dating from 1569, with its first known license being given in 1636, The Bull has a long history which includes a stint as a court house. Public areas are heavily beamed and furnished with antiques. Menu may include grilled tuna loin steak, roast vegetable moussaka, and battered plaice or haddock with chips and peas. **Principal beers:** Harveys Sussex, Morland Old Speckled Hen, Bass, Flowers Original.
Directions A23 N from Brighton, then A27 E towards Lewes, after 1m turn L following signs to Ditchling
Brewery/Company Free House
Open 11-11 (Sun 12-10.30)
Bar food 12-2.30 6.30-9.30
Restaurant 12-2.30 6.30-9.30
Accommodation (Min) s£35.50 d£49.50

EAST CHILTINGTON Sussex, East *Map 05 TQ31*

The Jolly Sportsman NEW
EAST CHILTINGTON

Chapel Ln BN7 3BA ☎ 01273 890400
Unpretentious, rambling Victorian building tucked down a lane with views to the South Downs. Chef/owner Bruce Wass offers quality food in stylishly rustic bars. Short menus focus on fresh produce, typical imaginative dishes may include seafood risotto, brill with pesto, duck confit with plums and ginger, guinea fowl with shiitake mushrooms, and farmhouse cheeses. **Principal beers:** Harveys Best.
Directions From Lewes take Offham/Chailey rd, L at Offham onto B2166 towards Plumpton, take Novington Ln, after approx 1m L into Chapel Ln
Brewery/Company Free House
Open 12-2.30 6.30-11 (Sun 12-4, closed Mon, BHs)
Bar food 12.30-2 7-10 Av main course £10
Restaurant 12.30-2 7-10 Av 3 course à la carte £20 Av 3 course fixed price £20

EAST DEAN Sussex, East *Map 05 TV59*

The Tiger Inn
EAST DEAN

BN20 0DA ☎ 01323 423209
Rose-covered flint-built pub on the village green, popular with walkers for its real ales and home-cooked food - from steak and ale pie to whole lobster. Quality wines are offered from a blackboard, several by the glass. In summer you can choose from 20 different ploughman's, featuring 13 English cheeses. **Principal beers:** Harvey Best, Flowers Original, Taylor Landlord, Adnams Best.
Directions Signed from A259 heading to the coast
Brewery/Company Free House
Open 11-3 6-11 (Jun-Sep & wknd all year 11-11)
Bar food 12-2.15 6.30-9 Av main course £5.75

For Pubs with AA food rosettes see page 430

EWHURST GREEN Sussex, East *Map 05 TQ72*

The White Dog Inn
EWHURST GREEN

Village St TN32 5TD ☎ 01580 830264

A 16th-century country inn enjoying a quiet village location with splendid views across the Rother Valley to Bodiam Castle. Homely bar and restaurant with polished tiled floors and inglenook fireplace. Speciality dishes include steak and kidney pudding, beef Stroganoff, pan-fried crevettes, and chicken Dijonnaise. **Principal beers:** Harveys Sussex, Fullers London Pride.

Directions Between Staplecross & Bodiam off B2165 & B2244
Brewery/Company Free House
Open 12-3.30 6.30-11 (Sun 6.30-10.30)
Bar food 12-2 7-9 Av main course £5
Restaurant 7-9 Av 3 course à la carte £15
Accommodation (Min) s£30 d£40

EXCEAT Sussex, East *Map 05 TV59*

The Golden Galleon
EXCEAT

Exceat Bridge BN25 4AB
☎ 01323 892247

Popular 18th-century inn believed to have inspired Rudyard Kipling's Song of the Smugglers. There is a pronounced Italian influence in the menu (inspired by the Italian owner), plus plenty of traditional English, Oriental and Indian dishes - something for everyone. Real ale comes from the pub's own micro-brewery. **Principal beers:** Cuckmere Haven, Harveys, Greene King.

Directions On A259, 1.5m E of Seaford
Brewery/Company Free House
Open 10.30-11 (closed Sun eve Sep-May)
Bar food 12-2 6-9 Av main course £7.25

FIRLE Sussex, East *Map 05 TQ40*

The Ram Inn
FIRLE

BN8 6NS ☎ 01273 858222

Unspoilt village coaching inn set beneath the South Downs, dating from the mid-1500s. It has a large flint-walled garden and rustic, unpretentious bars. Hearty soups with a choice of breads are popular, as are steak and mushroom or seafood pie. Quince and apple crumble is made from home-grown fruit.
Principal beers: Harvey-Best, Old, Cotleigh Harrier SPA.

Directions R off A27 3m E of Lewes
Brewery/Company Free House
Open 11.30-3, 7-11 (Sat 11.30-11, Sun 12-10.30)
Bar food 12-2 7-9 Av main course £8
Accommodation (Min) d£60

FLETCHING Sussex, East *Map 05 TQ42*

The Griffin Inn
FLETCHING

TN22 3SS ☎ 01825 722890

16th-century Grade II listed village inn with two acres of garden and fine rolling views towards Sheffield Park. Strong emphasis on quality fresh and local food with some organic influences. Modern British and Mediterranean menu offers garlic-baked barracuda steak, salmon and haddock fishcakes and confit of duck with shallot and red onion sauce.
Principal beers: Harvey Best, Badger Tanglefoot, Hardys Country.
Directions M23 J10 to East Grinstead then A22 then A275. Village signed on L. 10m from M23
Brewery/Company Free House
Open 12-3 6-11
Bar food 12-2.30 7-9.30 Av main course £8
Restaurant 12.30-2.30 7.30-9.30 Av 3 course à la carte £20 Av 3 course fixed price £17.50
Accommodation (Min) s£55 d£70

FOREST ROW Sussex, East *Map 05 TQ43*

Black Peter's Bar at Brambletye Hotel
FOREST ROW

The Square RH18 5EZ ☎ 01342 824144

Originally a private house, the hotel has been in business since 1866. Sir Arthur Conan Doyle, who was a visitor here, featured it in his legendary tales of Holmes and Watson. Main courses

contd.

include daily roasts, home-made pies, lobster with mixed seafood filling, and Dover sole stuffed with prawns and mushrooms.
Directions On A22 S of East Grinstead
Brewery/Company Free House
Open 10am-11pm
Bar food 12-2.30 6.30-10.45 Av main course £4.75
Restaurant 6.30-10.45 Av 3 course à la carte £15 Av 4 course fixed price £15.95
Accommodation (Min) s£55 d£65

GUN HILL Sussex, East *Map 05 TQ51*

The Gun Inn
GUN HILL
TN21 0JU ☎ 01825 872361
Originally a 15th-century farmhouse situated in a tiny hamlet amid rolling Sussex countryside. Resplendent in summer with its pretty gardens and flower-adorned façade, it offers fresh fish, crab in season, decent pies (lamb, apricot and rosemary, Sussex fidget), alongside smoked haddock pasta, chicken tarragon and home-made puddings. **Principal beers:** Wadworth 6X, Adnams Best, Harvey Best, Flowers Original.
Directions From A22 London-Eastbourne, Golden Cross (3m N of Hailsham) L past Esso station, 1.5m down lane on L
Brewery/Company Free House
Open 11.30-3 6-11
Bar food 12-2.30 6-10 Av main course £5.90
Restaurant 12-2.30 6-11

HARTFIELD Sussex, East *Map 05 TQ43*

Anchor Inn
HARTFIELD
Church St TN7 4AG ☎ 01892 770424
Situated in the heart of Winnie the Pooh country, on the edge of Ashdown Forest, is this 14th-century pub with stone floors and a large inglenook fireplace. Bar food ranges from ham, egg and chips and prawn and crab curry, to liver and onions, stir-fry pork, and duck with honey and almonds. **Principal beers:** Fullers London Pride, Harveys Best, Flowers IPA & Original, Bass.
Directions On B2110
Brewery/Company Free House
Open 11-11 (Sun 12-10.30)
Bar food 12-2 6-10 Av main course £5
Restaurant 12-1.30 7-9.30 Av 3 course à la carte £20
Accommodation (Min) s£35 d£50

HOOE Sussex, East *Map 05 TQ60*

Lamb Inn
HOOE
Sewerbridge TN33 9HH
☎ 01424 847891
An attractive, ancient and venerable hostelry, The Lamb is a rambling, partially thatched hotchpotch of a building overlooking the misty marshes of Pevensey Levels. Inside are low oak beams and roaring fires.
Principal beers: Bass.
Directions On A259 between Bexhill-on-Sea & Pevensey Bay
Brewery/Company Vintage Inns
Open 11-11 (Sun 12-10.30)

ICKLESHAM Sussex, East *Map 05 TQ18*

The Queen's Head
ICKLESHAM
Parsonage Ln TN36 4BL
☎ 01424 814552
Overlooking the Brede Valley and Rye, this distinctive tile-hung pub dates from 1640 and specialises in local real ales and home-cooked food. Alongside traditional snacks the daily specials list may highlight carrot and parsnip soup, chicken and asparagus pie, lentil and courgette gratin, fresh cod and chips, and Bakewell tart. **Principal beers:** Old Forge Brothers Best, Rother Valley Level Best, Courage Directors, Greene King Abbot Ale.
Directions Between Hastings & Rye on A259
Brewery/Company Free House
Open 11-11 (Sun 12-5, 7-10.30)
Bar food 12-2.45 6.15-9.45 Av main course £6.50

KINGSTON (Near Lewes) Sussex, East *Map 05 TQ30*

The Juggs
KINGSTON (NEAR LEWES)
The Street BN7 3NT ☎ 01273 472523
Named after the women who walked from Brighton with baskets of fish for sale, this rambling 15th-century inn offers an interesting selection of freshly cooked food, including a hearty steak and kidney pudding, daily specials and tempting desserts such as home-made

chocolate brownie with chocolate fudge sauce. **Principal beers:** Harveys Best, King & Barnes Festive.
Directions E of Brighton on A27
Brewery/Company Free House
Open 11-3 6-11 (11-11 summer)
Bar food 12-2 6-9.30 Av main course £6
Restaurant 12-2 6-9.30 Av 3 course à la carte £12

LITLINGTON Sussex, East *Map 05 TQ50*

Plough & Harrow
LITLINGTON
BN26 5RE ☎ 01323 870632
Old country pub, nestling in the picturesque Cuckmere Valley, close to the South Downs Way, adorned with plenty of railway paraphernalia reflecting the landlord's interest. Home-made soups and pies are popular in the bar, as are the crab and seafood salads. In the restaurant, expect roast duckling, steaks and various fish dishes. **Principal beers:** Harveys Best, Old Forge Pett Progress, Badger IPA, Dorset Best & Tanglefoot.
Directions S of A27 between Lewes & Polegate
Brewery/Company Free House
Open 11-3 6.30-11
Bar food 12-2.30 7-10 Av main course £6
Restaurant 12-2.30 7-10 Av 3 course à la carte £12

MAYFIELD Sussex, East *Map 05 TQ52*

The Middle House
MAYFIELD
High St TN20 6AB ☎ 01435 872146
Grade 1 listed property, dating from 1575, renowned as one of the finest timber-framed buildings in Sussex. A snack menu is served in the bar, while the oak-panelled restaurant offers an extensive carte supported by daily specials, including several fish dishes, perhaps monkfish with chargrilled peppers and garlic and lime butter.
Principal beers: Harvey Best, Wadworth 6X, Greene King Abbot Ale, Fullers ESB.
Directions E of A267, S of Tunbridge Wells
Brewery/Company Free House
Open 11-11
Bar food 12-2.30 7-9.30 Av main course £8.50
Restaurant 12-2 7-9.30 Av 3 course à la carte £20 Av 3 course fixed price £16.95
Accommodation (Min) s£45 d£55

Rose & Crown Inn NEW
MAYFIELD
Fletching St TN20 6TE ☎ 01435 872200
Attractive 16th-century village inn with splendid front patio and a rambling interior with low beams, open fires and an unspoilt atmosphere. Consult the blackboard for the day's specials, perhaps crab mousse, lamb shank with haricot beans, garlic and herbs, or beef in red wine. For a snack try the seafood chowder or a toasted ciabatta sandwich.
Principal beers: Harveys Sussex Best, Greene King Abbot Ale, Morland Old Speckled Hen.
Brewery/Company Enterprise Inns
Open 11-3 5.30-11
Bar food 12-2.30 Av main course £6.25
Restaurant 12-2.30 7-9.30 Av 3 course à la carte £15
Accommodation (Min) s£38 d£48

OLD HEATHFIELD Sussex, East *Map 05 TQ52*

Star Inn
OLD HEATHFIELD
Church St TN21 9AH ☎ 01435 863570
Creeper-clad pub built for the stonemasons who constructed the church in the 14th century. Of particular note are the wonderful summer garden and the beamed main bar with inglenook fireplace. Good bar food includes steak and kidney pie, Hastings cod and chips, knuckle of gammon with onion sauce, and halibut in garlic. **Principal beers:** Harvey Best, Greene King IPA
Directions E of Heathfield (A265), r onto B2096, then r into Old Heathfield.
Brewery/Company Free House
Open 11.30-3 5.30-11
Bar food 12-2.15 7-9.30 Av main course £7.50
Restaurant 12-2.15 7-9.30

POYNINGS Sussex, East

Royal Oak Inn NEW
POYNINGS
The Street BN45 7AQ ☎ 01273 857389
Nestling at the foot of the South Downs, close to the Devil's Dyke, this white-painted village pub is popular on summer weekends for its excellent barbecue facilities. Also busy with walkers, it offers a good ales and a varied menu, including ploughman's platters, sandwiches, chicken, leek and mushroom pie, and freshly battered haddock and chips.
Principal beers: Harveys Best, Bass, Courage Directors, Morland Old Speckled Hen.
Directions N on the A23 just outside Brighton, take the A281 (signed for Henfield & Poynings), then follow signs into Poynings village
Brewery/Company Free House
Open 11-11 (Sun 12-10.30)
Bar food 12-2.30 6.30-10 Av main course £6

RINGMER Sussex, East *Map 05 TQ41*

The Cock NEW
RINGMER
Uckfield Rd BN8 5EX ☎ 01273 812040
Enjoying lovely views over the South Downs, this 15th-century coaching inn has original oak beams and an inglenook fireplace. Local legend has it that Cromwell mustered troops here before the seige of Arundel. Hungry diners may find grilled whole plaice, pork Dijonnaise, brazil nut roast, or swordfish provençale on the menu. **Principal beers:** Harveys Best, Ruddles County, Fullers London Pride.
Directions On A26 approx 2m N of Lewes(not in Ringmer village)
Brewery/Company Free House
Open 11-3 6-11
Bar food 12-2 6.30-9.30
Restaurant 12-2 6.30-9.30 Av 3 course à la carte £14.50

RUSHLAKE GREEN Sussex, East *Map 05 TQ61*

Horse & Groom NEW
RUSHLAKE GREEN
TN21 9QE ☎ 01435 830320
Enjoying an idyllic village green setting, this rustic, Grade II listed building is run by the owners of the Star Inn at Old Heathfield. Blackboard menus in the cosy, traditional bars highlight excellent fresh fish, perhaps sea bass, Hastings cod and chips, and lemon sole, alongside hearty fare like rabbit pie and guinea fowl in mustard and cider.
Principal beers: Harveys Sussex, Greene King IPA.
Brewery/Company Free House
Open 11.30-3 6-11
Bar food 12-2.30 7-9.30 Av main course £6
Restaurant 12-2.30 7-9.30 Av 3 course à la carte £20

RYE Sussex, East *Map 05 TQ92*

The Ypres Inn NEW
RYE
Gun Garden TN31 7HH
☎ 01797 223248
Named after Sir John of Ypres, this 18th-century inn was once something of a smuggling centre. The menu features an original picture by artist John Ryan, showing his famous TV pirate Captain Pugwash, sitting outside the pub. Inside the menu you may find scallops, monkfish, guinea fowl and squid.
Principal beers: Harveys Best, Youngs, Adnams Broadside, Bass.
Brewery/Company Free House
Open 12-12
Bar food 12-2.30 7-10.30
Restaurant 12-2.30 7-10.30 Av 3 course à la carte £12.50 Av 3 course fixed price £12.50

THREE LEGGED CROSS Sussex, East *Map 05 TQ63*

The Bull
THREE LEGGED CROSS
Dunster Mill Ln TN5 7HH
☎ 01580 200586
Based around a Wealden hall house built around 1385, The Bull is a real country pub, with oak beams and large open fires, in a peaceful hamlet setting. Food choice ranges from filled baguettes and home-made soups, to Thai fishcakes, rabbit casserole, game pudding, and fresh whole Dover sole. Charming summer garden.
Principal beers: Harvey-Best, Old, Morland Old Speckled Hen, Bull Best.
Directions From M5 exit at Sevenoaks toward Hastings, R at X-rds onto B2087, R onto B2099 through Ticehurst, R for Three Legged Cross

Brewery/Company Free House
Open 12-3 6-11
Bar food 12-2.30 7-9.30 Av main course £5.50
Restaurant 12-2.30 7-9.30 Av 3 course à la carte £12

UPPER DICKER Sussex, East *Map 05 TQ50*

The Plough
UPPER DICKER
Coldharbour Rd BN27 3QJ
☎ 01323 844859
A 17th-century former farmhouse, which has been a pub since the late 18th century. It is popular with walkers and has a large beer garden with a play area for children. A menu of home-cooked food is on offer, along with a range of bar snacks and daily specials. **Principal beers:** Shepherd Neame Master Brew, Best & Bishop's Finger.
Directions Off A22, W of Hailsham
Brewery/Company Shepherd Neame
Open 11-3 6-11 (Sun 12-3, 7-10.30, Summer wknd 11-11)
Bar food 12-2.30 6-9.30 Av main course £6.95
Restaurant 12-2.30 6-9.30 Av 3 course à la carte £15

WARBLETON Sussex, East *Map 05 TQ61*

The Warbill in Tun Inn
WARBLETON
Church Hill TN21 9BD ☎ 01435 830636
An attractive and peacefully situated 15th-century village inn about which many stories are told: tales of contraband, priest holes and ghosts. Modernised interior with red plush furnishings and inglenook fireplace. The extensive menu runs from sandwiches, seafood salads and cold meat platters, to curries, grills and specials like minted lamb casserole. **Principal beers:** Harveys Best.
Brewery/Company Free House
Open 11-3 6.15-11
Bar food 12-1.45 7-9.30 Av main course £3.50
Restaurant 12-1.45 7-9.30 Av 3 course à la carte £10.50 Av 3 course fixed price £9.25

WITHYHAM Sussex, East *Map 05 TQ43*

The Dorset Arms
WITHYHAM
TN7 4BD ☎ 01892 770278
Former farmhouse dating from the mid-15th century with many period features, notably the Sussex oak floor and magnificent log fire in the bar. Food is mostly home made from local produce, ranging from ham, egg and chips and decent ploughman's, to halibut with lemon mayonnaise and venison with port and redcurrant sauce. Lovely front terrace. **Principal beers:** Harveys Best, PA, Mild & seasonal beers.

Directions on B2110 between Hartfield & Groombridge
Brewery/Company Harveys of Lewes
Open 11.30-3 5.30-11
Bar food 12-2 7.30-11 Av main course £6
Restaurant 12-3 7.30-11

Sussex, West

AMBERLEY Sussex, West *Map 04 TQ01*

The Bridge Inn
AMBERLEY
Houghton Bridge BN18 9LR
☎ 01798 831619
The original structure of the inn dates from 1420, and the building has a Grade II listing. Special features are the open fires and display of original oil and watercolour paintings. The menu offers a comprehensive fish choice plus dishes such as pheasant casserole Normandy or traditional roast beef. **Principal beers:** Gales GB, Flowers Original, Morlands Speckled Old Hen, Harveys Sussex.
Directions 5m N of Arundel on B2139
Brewery/Company Free House
Open 11-3 6-11
Bar food 12-2.30 7-9.30 Av main course £7.50

contd.

Restaurant 12-2.30 7-9.30 Av 3 course à la carte £15 Av 3 course fixed price £15

ASHURST Sussex, West *Map 04 TQ11*

The Fountain Inn
ASHURST
BN44 3AP ☎ 01403 710219
Authentic 16th-century country pub with original flagstone floors, two inglenook fireplaces and low beams. A varied menu features traditional lasagne, goat's cheese salad, steak, mushroom and ale pie, rack of lamb, baked salmon fillet, and a good range of chargrilled dishes. Lovely garden and scenic local walks. **Principal beers:** Harveys Best, John Smiths, Fullers London Pride.
Directions On B2135 N of Steyning
Brewery/Company Free House
Open 11.30-2.30 6-11
Bar food 12-2 6-9.30 Av main course £6.95
Restaurant 12-2 6-9.30

BILLINGSHURST Sussex, West *Map 04 TQ02*

Ye Olde Six Bells
BILLINGSHURST
76 High St RH14 9QS ☎ 01403 782124
Attractive timbered town pub dating back to 1436 and featuring flagstone floors, an inglenook fireplace, and a legend of a cursed tunnel to the nearby church. Good King and Barnes ales, a pretty roadside garden, and traditional pub food, including steak and kidney pie and lasagne.
Principal beers: King & Barnes.
Directions On the A29 between London & Bognor, 17m from Bognor
Brewery/Company King & Barnes
Open 11-2.30 5.30-11 (Sun 12-3, 7-10.30)
Bar food 12-2 7-9 Av main course £3.75

BURPHAM Sussex, West *Map 04 TQ00*

George & Dragon
BURPHAM
BN18 9RR ☎ 01903 883131
Impressive 17th-century pub within easy reach of the South Downs Way and plenty of good local walks. Quality menu features an imaginative range of bar meals, including steak and Stilton pie, and lamb, mint and apricot casserole. Expect risotto of local game and rump of Southdown lamb among the restaurant main courses. **Principal beers:** Harvey Best, Arundel ASB, Courage Directors, Brewery-on-Sea Spinnaker Bitter.
Directions Off A27 1m E of Arundel, signed Burpham, 2.5m pub on L
Brewery/Company Free House
Open 11-2.30 6-11
Bar food 12-2 7-9.45 Av main course £6.50
Restaurant 12.15-2 7.15-9.30 Av 3 course à la carte £21

CHILGROVE Sussex, West *Map 04 SU81*

The White Horse at Chilgrove
CHILGROVE
High St PO18 9HX ☎ 01243 535219
Inviting 18th-century pub with low exposed beams and a high standard of English cooking, situated on the South Downs. Noted for its fine wine list. Fishcakes, dressed Selsey crab, lobster, scallops and game in season (roast quail with pigeon mousse and port wine sauce) might feature on the monthly-changing menu.
Directions On B2141 between Chichester & Petersfield
Brewery/Company Free House
Open 11-2.30 6-10.30 (closed Mon & Feb)

Bar food 12-2 7-9.30 Av main course £7
Restaurant 12-2 7-9.45 Av 3 course à la carte £24.50

COMPTON Sussex, West *Map 04 SU71*

Coach & Horses
COMPTON

The Square PO18 9HA ☎ 01705 631228

White-painted 15th-century coaching inn located in the village square. Expect a lively atmosphere and hearty snacks such as chicken mushroom and tarragon pie in the pine-furnished Village Bar, and baked sea bass, Spanish fish soup and duck breast with caramelised onion and peach wine sauce in the charming beamed lounge and dining room. **Principal beers:** Fullers ESB, Ballard's Best,Cheriton Diggers Gold.
Directions On B2146 S of Petersfield
Brewery/Company Free House
Open 11-3 6-11
Bar food 12-1.30 6-9 Av main course £5.50
Restaurant 12-1.30 6.30-9 Av 3 course à la carte £17

COPTHORNE Sussex, West *Map 04 TQ33*

Hunters Moon Inn
COPTHORNE

Copthorne Bank RH10 3JF
☎ 01342 713309

Once associated with poachers and smugglers, this comfortable village pub offers good snacks and light lunches, including Egyptian lamb, Creole stew. Evening fare may highlight seafood mixed grill, dressed crab, ribeye steak with thyme and shallot sauce, and pork with plum sauce and stir-fried vegetables. **Principal beers:** Badger Best, Fullers London Pride.
Directions M23, J10 Copthorne Way to roundabout, 1st L, then R into Copthorne Bank
Brewery/Company Free House
Open 11-3 (12-3 Sun) 5.30-11 (Sun 12-3, 7-10.30)
Bar food 12-2 Av main course £6
Restaurant 7-9.30 Av 3 course à la carte £19.50
Accommodation (Min) d£55

EARTHAM Sussex, West *Map 04 SU90*

The George Inn
EARTHAM

PO18 0LT ☎ 01243 814340

Built in the 18th century as an ale house for local estate workers, the pub has a candlelit restaurant with an open fire, exposed ships' beams and patio doors leading to a delightful garden. Hearty bar food ranges from traditional fish and chips to supreme of red mullet with citrus sauce. **Principal beers:** Gales HSB, GB & Eartham Ale.
Directions From A27 at Tangmere r'about follow signs for Crockerhill/Eartham
Brewery/Company Gales
Open 11-3 6.30-11 (open all day during summer)
Bar food 12-2 6-9 Av main course £6.95
Restaurant 12-2 6-9 Av 3 course à la carte £16.50

ELSTED Sussex, West *Map 04 SU81*

The Elsted Inn
ELSTED

Elsted Marsh GU29 0JT
☎ 01730 813662

Quality local produce, notably venison, free-range eggs, hand-made sausages and bread, are used to create the hearty range f interesting dishes on offer at the homely Victorian roadside pub. Booking is essential and the menu offers good English cooking (Sussex bacon pudding) with the odd exotic item, notably excellent curries in winter. **Principal beers:** Ballard Trotton, Best & Wassail, Fullers London Pride, Hopback Summer Lightning.
Directions From Midhurst take A272 W. After 4m L signed 'Elsted & Harting'(NB Elsted Marsh also known as Lower Elsted)
Brewery/Company Free House
Open 11.30-3 5.30-11
Bar food 12-2.00 7-9.30 Av main course £4.95
Restaurant 12-2 7-9.30 Av 3 course à la carte £16
Accommodation (Min) s£35 d£50

The Three Horseshoes NEW
ELSTED

GU29 0JY ☎ 01730 825746

Built as a drovers' ale house in 1540, this pretty tiled cottage is full of rural charm, with bowed walls, tiled floors, log fires

contd.

and ale tapped from the cask. Home-cooked dishes highlight the blackboard menu, including steak, kidney and ale pie, rabbit and prune casserole, unusual ploughman's, and fish in summer. Splendid garden with South Downs views. **Principal beers:** Cheriton Pots Ale, Ballards Best, Fullers London Pride, Ringwood Fortyniner.
Directions A272 from Midhurst to Petersfield, after 2m L to Harting & Elsted, after 3m pub on L
Brewery/Company Free House
Open 11-2.30 6-11 (Sun 12-3, 7-10.30)

FERNHURST Sussex, West *Map 04 SU82*

The King's Arms NEW
FERNHURST
Midhurst Rd GU27 3HA
☎ 01428 652005
Former 14th-century farmhouse surrounded by 22 acres of rolling fields. Expect a cosy, civilised interior and imaginative modern cooking. Dishes range from lunchtime ploughman's and salmon fishcakes, to courgette and garlic soup, crab ravioli with lobster and tarragon sauce, and salmon and sea bass fillets on herb rôsti with tomato and lime salsa. **Principal beers:** Taylor Landlord, Otter Bright, Fullers London Pride, Gales HSB.
Directions On A286 between Haslemere and Midhurst, in S of Fernhurst

Brewery/Company Free House
Open 11.30-3 5.30-11 (closed Sunday eves)

Bar food 12-2.30 7-10 Av main course £6.75
Restaurant 12-2 7-10 Av 3 course à la carte £21

The Red Lion
FERNHURST
The Green GU27 3HY ☎ 01428 653304
Reputedly the oldest pub in the village, this 500-year-old building overlooks the village green and has a striking sandstone exterior, old oak beams and open fires. Good varied menu may list smoked pork fillet, Tuscan chicken and salmon en croûte. Interesting range of fish dishes. **Principal beers:** King & Barnes Best, Marstons Pedigree, Morland Old Speckled Hen,Hogs Back TEA.
Directions From A3 at Hindhead take A287 to Haslemere, then A286 to Fernhurst
Brewery/Company Free House
Open 10-3.20 5-11.20
Bar food 12-3 6-11
Restaurant 12-3 6-11 Av 3 course à la carte £15

HALNAKER Sussex, West *Map 04 SU90*

Anglesey Arms
HALNAKER
PO18 0NQ ☎ 01243 773474
Situated in the village of Halnaker, famous for its windmill immortalised in a poem by Hilaire Belloc, this traditional village inn, one mile from Goodwood House, offers a wide-ranging menu, including various seafood dishes and salads. Expect to find macaroni cheese, nut roast, fresh cod, and beef curry among the blackboard main courses. **Principal beers:** Friary Meux, Greene King IPA, Burton Ale.
Directions 4m E from centre of Chichester on A285 (Petworth Road)
Brewery/Company Pubmaster
Open 11-3 6-11
Bar food 12-2 7.30-10 Av main course £65
Restaurant 12-2 7.30-10 Av 3 course à la carte £15

HORSHAM Sussex, West *Map 04 TQ02*

The Black Jug NEW
HORSHAM
31 North St RH12 1RJ ☎ 01403 253526
Relaxed, light and airy town pub with stripped wood floors, darkwood furnishings, and a spacious rear conservatory. Changing blackboard menu listing an interesting range of dishes, including seafood risotto, tagliatelle with mushroom and garlic sauce, ribeye steak with peppercorn

sauce, lemon sole, and an extensive tapas selection. **Principal beers:** Morland Old Speckled Hen, Courage Directors, Marstons Pedigree, Wadworth 6X.
Directions 100yrds from Horsham railway station, almost straight opp Horsham Art Centre
Brewery/Company Scottish & Newcastle
Open 11-11 (Sun 12-10.30)
Bar food 12-2.30 6-10 Av main course £7.85
Restaurant 12-2.30 6-10 Av 3 course à la carte £15.50

KIRDFORD Sussex, West *Map 04 TQ02*

The Half Moon Inn
KIRDFORD
RH14 0LT ☎ 01403 820223
Attractive, tile-hung village pub dating from 1640 and renowned locally for the excellent choice of fresh fish, served in the neat, quarry-tiled lounge bar. Expect to find tuna with Cajun spices, crab cakes with red pepper jam, scabbard fish, and exotic mahi mahi, alongside filled baguettes and steak and kidney pie. **Principal beers:** Arundel, Wadworth 6X, Greene King Abbot Ale, King & Barnes Sussex.
Directions Off A272 between Billingshurst & Petworth. At Wisborough Green follow signs 'Kirdford'
Brewery/Company Whitbread
Open 11-3 7-11 (Sun 12-3 7-10.30)

Bar food 12-2.30 7-9.30 Av main course £5
Restaurant 12-2.30 7-9.30 Av 3 course à la carte £20
Accommodation (Min) d£45

Pubs offering a good choice of seafood on the menu

LICKFOLD Sussex, West *Map 04 SU92*

Lickfold Inn
LICKFOLD
GU28 9EY ☎ 01798 861285
Splendid timber-framed coaching inn dating from around 1460, situated in unspoilt countryside close to Petworth. Noted for its attractive gardens and imaginative food. From curried parsnip soup and wild boar sausages with mustard mash, the eclectic choice may include chargrilled ostrich with horseradish jam, and lamb with kumara and thyme galette. **Principal beers:** Ballard Best, Shepherd Neame Master Brew, Gales HSB, Ringwood Fortyniner.
Directions From A3 take A283, through Chiddingfold, 2m on R signed 'Lurgashall Winery', pub in 1m
Brewery/Company Free House
Open 11-11 (closed Mon in winter)
Bar food 12-2.30 7-9.30 Av main course £9.50
Restaurant 12-4 7-12

LOWER BEEDING Sussex, West *Map 04 TQ22*

Jeremy's at the Crabtree
LOWER BEEDING
Brighton Rd RH13 6PT ☎ 01403 891257
Writer Hilaire Belloc was a visitor to this inn which has a Georgian dining room and an original 16th-century beamed bar. Marinated pigeon and caramelised pear salad, seared tuna on egg noodles, or cod fillet with watercress and basil butter may be on today's menu. **Principal beers:** King & Barnes Sussex.
Directions On A281, 4m SE of Horsham
Brewery/Company King & Barnes
Open 11-3 6-11 (Closed Sun eve)
Bar food 12.30-2 7.30-9.45
Restaurant 12.30-2 7.30-9.30 Av 3 course à la carte £25

LURGASHALL Sussex, West *Map 04 SU92*

The Noah's Ark
LURGASHALL
The Green GU28 9ET ☎ 01428 707346
Built in 1537, this pub overlooks the village green where cricket is the summer highlight. Starters feature mussels in garlic butter and watercress soup. The main course menu includes home-made

contd.

curries, steaks and various omelettes, plus moussaka, calves' liver and bacon, and vegetable Cumberland pie.
Principal beers: Greene King - IPA, Abbot Ale & seasonal ales.
Directions Off A283 N of Petworth
Brewery/Company Greene King
Open 11.30-3.30 6.30-11
Bar food 12-2 7-9 Av main course £5.95
Restaurant 12-2 7-9 Av 3 course à la carte £16.05

MIDHURST Sussex, West *Map 04 SO82*

The Angel Hotel NEW
MIDHURST
North St GU29 9DN ☎ 01730 812421
16th-century former coaching inn with Georgian façade, 'country-house' comfort and style in the lounge, and a rustic feel to the bar and brasserie. Soup, sandwiches and ploughman's can be ordered in the bar, while imaginative brasserie fare includes oysters, monkfish with orange and anchovy sauce, lamb with tarragon mousse, and hot banana tart. Period charm extends to the stylish bedrooms. **Principal beers:** Gales HSB, Butser Bitter.
Brewery/Company Free House
Open 12-2.30 6.30-10
Bar food 12-2.30 6.30-10 Av main course £7
Restaurant 12-2.30 7-10 Av 3 course à la carte £30
Accommodation (Min) s£75 d£85

OFFHAM Sussex, West *Map 04 TQ00*

Black Rabbit
OFFHAM
Mill Ln BN18 9PB ☎ 01903 882828
This popular inn, though uniquely named, is located on a sheltered stretch of the River Arun enjoying unspoiled views of Arundel Castle. All tastes and appetites are catered for from bar food to restaurant dishes such as scallops, bacon and pepper bruschetta followed by orange and cranberry duck.
Principal beers: Badger Dorset Best, Tanglefoot & IPA.
Directions From Arundel Bridge take Mill Road past the Wildfowl Trust & straight on for 300yds
Brewery/Company Hall & Woodhouse
Open 11-11 (Sun 12-10)
Bar food 12-3 6.30-10.30 Av main course £5
Restaurant 12-3.30 7-11 Av 3 course à la carte £20 Av 3 course fixed price £11.95

OVING Sussex, West *Map 04 SU90*

The Gribble Inn
OVING
PO20 6BP ☎ 01243 786893
A fine thatched 16th-century inn with secluded garden, and two enormous log fires, low wooden beams, and settle seating in the character main bar. Beers are brewed on the premises, with seven on the bar at the last count. Dishes include home-made bacon and onion roly-poly, fresh fish, mixed grills and garlic chicken. **Principal beers:** Gribble.
Directions From A27 take A259. After 1m L at roundabout, 1st R, 1st L to Oving
Brewery/Company Hall & Woodhouse
Open 11-3 5.30-11 (Sun 12-3, 7-10.30)
Bar food 12-2.30 6.30-9.30 Av main course £6.50
Restaurant 12-2.30 6.30-9.30 Av 3 course à la carte £14

PETWORTH Sussex, West *Map 04 SU92*

The Halfway Bridge Inn
PETWORTH
Halfway Bridge GU2 9BP
☎ 01798 861281
Set midway between Midhurst and Petworth, this rambling, upmarket 18th-century coaching inn provides good real ale and interesting food. Freshly prepared dishes may include spinach and rocket Caesar salad, pan-fried cod with watercress and warm potato salad, and raspberry crème brûlée. **Principal beers:** Gales HSB, Cheriton Pots Ale, Fullers London Pride.
Directions On A272
Brewery/Company Free House
Open 11-3 6-11 (Closed Sun eve in winter)
Bar food 12-2 7-10 Av main course £7.95
Restaurant 12-2 7-10 Av 3 course à la carte £15

Welldiggers Arms NEW
PETWORTH
Polborough Rd ☎ 01798 342287
Welldiggers once occupied this rustic, 300-year-old roadside pub which boasts low-beamed bars with open log fires and huge oak tables. Casseroles, local game

and properly-hung steaks feature on the blackboard menu, along with fish soup, oysters, salmon and dill quiche, and excellent fresh fish like whole Dover sole or sea bass. **Principal beers:** Youngs.
Directions 1m E of Petworth on the A283
Brewery/Company Free House
Bar food 12-3 6.30-10 Av main course £5.50
Restaurant 12-2 6.30-10 Av 3 course à la carte £13.50

ROWHOOK Sussex, West *Map 04 TQ13*

The Chequers Inn
ROWHOOK
RH12 3PY ☎ 01403 790480
16th-century inn with beams, flagstones and open fires, named after the chequer tree in the garden. Interesting food choice may include butternut squash and pea soup, game terrine, lamb shank with truffled polenta and redcurrant jus, and red mullet with chilli and ginger salsa. Ciabatta rolls and simple bar snacks are also available. **Principal beers:** Wadworth 6X, Flowers Original, King & Barnes Sussex, Fullers London Pride.
Directions Off A29 NW of Horsham
Brewery/Company Sussex Inns
Open 11-3 6-11
Bar food 12-2.30 Av main course £5.95
Restaurant 12-2.30 7-9.15 Av 3 course à la carte £18

SIDLESHAM Sussex, West *Map 04 SZ89*

Crab & Lobster NEW
SIDLESHAM
Mill Ln PO20 7NB ☎ 01243 61233
Lookout for Selsey crab and lobster and the home-cooked specials (fish pie, soups) at this well-kept pub situated close to the shores of Pagham Harbour, a noted nature reserve. Popular with walkers and twitchers who fill the cosy bars (open fires) in winter, and the pretty rear garden with mudflat views in summer.
Principal beers: Gale's, Badger, Arundel.
Directions Off B2145 between Chichester & Selsey
Brewery/Company Free House
Open 11-3 6-11
Bar food 12-2.30 7-9.45 Av main course £6.50

SINGLETON Sussex, West *Map 04 SU81*

The Fox Goes Free NEW
SINGLETON
Charlton PO18 0HU ☎ 01243 811461
Close to Goodwood, Singleton Open Air Museum and downland walks, this 400-year-old village inn enjoys a peaceful South Downs setting. Full of old-world charm, it offers excellent ales and decent pub food, including spicy lamb couscous, rabbit in mustard and cream, venison in juniper and red wine, and crab and sherry bake. **Principal beers:** Ringwood Best, Ballards Best, Marston Pedigree.
Directions A286 6m from Chichester, towards Midhurst, 1m from Goodwood racecourse
Brewery/Company Free House
Open 11-3 5.30-11
Bar food 11.30-2.30 6-10.30 Av main course £5.50
Restaurant 11.30-2.30 6-10.30 Av 3 course à la carte £13 Av 3 course fixed price £13
Accommodation (Min) s£30 d£45

SOUTH HARTING Sussex, West *Map 04 SU71*

The Ship Inn
SOUTH HARTING
GU31 5PZ ☎ 01730 825302
17th-century inn constructed from a ships timbers, hence its name. Home-made pies are a feature, and other popular dishes include Sussex hotpot, lemon sole, moussaka, venison steaks and a choice of vegetarian options. A range of bar snacks is also available.
Principal beers: Palmers IPA.
Directions From Petersfield take B2146 towards Chichester
Brewery/Company Free House
Open 11-11 (Winter,Tue-Thu closed 3-6)
Bar food 12-2.30 7-9.30 Av main course £6

STEDHAM Sussex, West *Map 04 SU82*

Hamilton Arms/Nava Thai Restaurant
STEDHAM
Hamilton Arms School Ln GU29 0NZ
☎ 01730 812555
Situated in a picturesque village, it is the choice of Thai cuisine that distinguishes this straightforward pub from other local inns. Traditional English bar meals are available, while the Thai restaurant

contd.

menu, offered by waitresses in Thai costume, features red and green curries, numerous fried dishes, salads and hot and sour soups. **Principal beers:** Ballards Best, Fullers London Pride, Courage Directors, Morland Old Speckled Hen.
Directions Off A272 between Midhurst & Petersfield
Brewery/Company Free House
Open 11-3 6-11 (closed Mon)
Bar food 12-2.30 6-10.30 Av main course £5.50
Restaurant 12-2.30 6-10.30 Av 3 course à la carte £16 Av 4 course fixed price £18

SUTTON Sussex, West *Map 04 SU91*

White Horse Inn
SUTTON
The Street RH20 1PS ☎ 01798 869221
Pretty Georgian inn tucked away in a sleepy village at the base of the South Downs. Neat bars and dining room, and comfortable en suite accommodation. Expect imaginative food, the daily-changing choice featuring, perhaps, Stilton and broccoli soup and carpaccio of tuna, followed by confit of duck, lamb shank with tomatoes and red wine, and French lemon tart. **Principal beers:** Wadworth 6X, Youngs PA, Brewery-on-Sea Rain Dance, Courage Best.
Directions Turn off A29 at foot of Bury Hill. After 2m pass Roman Villa on R. 1m to Sutton
Brewery/Company Free House
Open 11-3 6-11

Bar food 12-2 7-10 Av main course £6.40
Restaurant 12-2 7-10 Av 3 course à la carte £20
Accommodation (Min) s£48 d£58

TILLINGTON Sussex, West *Map 04 SU92*

The Horse Guards Inn
TILLINGTON
GU28 9AF ☎ 01798 342332
Originally three cottages, this charming, part 16th-century village inn offers imaginative home-cooked food and comfortable en suite accommodation. Local game and fresh fish highlight the daily-changing menus. Dishes range from parsnip and ginger soup and steak and kidney pie, to pheasant casserole, grilled turbot, and duck with redcurrant and port gravy. Good puddings. **Principal beers:** Wadworth 6X, Badger Best.
Directions On A272 1m W of Petworth. Inn next to church
Brewery/Company Free House
Open 11-3 6-11
Bar food 12-2 7-10 Av main course £8
Restaurant 12-2 7-10
Accommodation (Min) d£60

WARNHAM Sussex, West *Map 04 TQ13*

The Greets Inn
WARNHAM
47 Friday St RH12 3QY
☎ 01403 265047
Fine Sussex hall house dating from about 1350, featuring low beams, inglenook fireplaces and a flagstone bar. Favourite dishes include sea bass with hollandaise, venison and cumberland sausage, petit chocolate pot with Grand Marnier and treacle suet pudding. Summer weekend barbeques. **Principal beers:** Flowers Original, Fullers London Pride, King & Barnes Sussex.
Directions Off A24 N of Horsham
Brewery/Company Whitbread
Open 11-2.30 6-11
Bar food 12-3 7-11 Av main course £11
Restaurant 12-3 7-11 Av 3 course à la carte £18

WALBERTON Sussex, West *Map 04 SU90*

The Royal Oak & Rendezvous Restaurant
WALBERTON
Yapton Ln BN18 OLS ☎ 01243 552865
Featuring artefacts designed by the landlord for James Bond and Superman films, and a bar created from a church pulpit, this well refurbished village pub

offers an interesting range of food. Choices include ploughman's lunches, steak, kidney and Guinness pie, monkfish with red onion and coriander dressing, and beef medallions with wild mushroom ragout. **Principal beers:** Arundel Gold.
Directions on A27 between Arundel & Fontwell
Brewery/Company Free House
Open 11-3 6-12
Bar food 12-3 6.30-12.30 Av main course £10
Restaurant 12-3 6.30-12.30 Av 3 course à la carte £19.50 Av 3 course fixed price £19.50

Wight, Isle of

BEMBRIDGE Wight, Isle of — Map 04 SZ68

The Crab & Lobster Inn
BEMBRIDGE
32 Foreland Fields Rd PO35 5TR
☎ 01983 872244
Well-established clifftop inn affording magnificent views across the Solent and English Channel. Locals and tourists alike seek out the friendly atmosphere in the inviting, nautically-themed bars, and the seafood specialities (lobster, crab, shell-on prawns, lemon sole) on the menu. Traditional bar snacks are also available. **Principal beers:** Flowers Original, Castle Eden Ale, Goddards Fuggle-Dee-Dum.
Brewery/Company Whitbread
Open 11-3 6-11
Bar food 12-2.30 6.30-9 Av main course £6
Restaurant 12-2.30 7-9 Av 3 course à la carte £16

BONCHURCH Wight, Isle of — Map 04 SZ57

The Bonchurch Inn
BONCHURCH
Bonchurch Shute PO38 1NU
☎ 01938 852611
Italian-owned 19th-century coaching inn with sheltered cobbled courtyard and homely bars. Menus have a distinct Italian flavour featuring such dishes as Milanese risotto, tagliatelle carbonara and chicken in tomato, mushroom and white wine sauce. Whole lemon sole, fillet steak and traditional pub snacks are also available.
Principal beers: Courage Best & Directors
Brewery/Company Free House
Open 11-3.30 6.30-11
Bar food 11-2.30 6.30-10.00 Av main course £5
Restaurant 6.30-9 Av 3 course à la carte £17

CHALE Wight, Isle of — Map 04 SZ47

Clarendon Hotel & Wight Mouse Inn
CHALE
PO38 2HA ☎ 01983 730431
Popular 17th-century coaching inn overlooking Chale Bay. The oak beams originally came from the Clarendon which was shipwrecked nearby in 1836. Seafood specialities and an amazing selection of over 300 whiskies. Expect Mexican hot chilli and lasagne among the chef's specials, alongside favourites like steak and ale pie and local crab mornay. **Principal beers:** Boddingtons, Wadworth 6X, Gales HSB, Morland Old Speckled Hen.

Directions On B3099 (main coast rd)
Brewery/Company Free House
Open 11-midnight (Sun 12-10.30)
Bar food 12-10 Av main course £5
Restaurant 12-2.30 6-10 Av 3 course à la carte £12 Av 2 course fixed price £5
Accommodation (Min) s£25 d£50

FRESHWATER Wight, Isle of — Map 04 SZ38

The Red Lion
FRESHWATER
Church Place PO40 9BP
☎ 01983 754925
Built in the 12th-century and situated next to the church. The River Yar and causeway are nearby. Starters include crab and Stilton stuffed mushrooms. Main

contd.

menu features duck breast with cranberry and orange sauce, and marinated trout wrapped in bacon. Also a choice of home-made ice creams. **Principal beers:** Flowers Original, Fullers London Pride, Wadworth 6X, Goddards.
Directions In Freshwater follow signs for parish church
Brewery/Company Whitbread
Open 11.30-3 (Sun 12-3) 5.30-11 (Sun 7-10.30)
Bar food 12-2 6.30-9 Av main course £9

GODSHILL Wight, Isle of *Map 04 SZ58*

Cask & Taverners NEW
GODSHILL
High St PO38 3HZ ☎ 01983 840707
Interesting restaurant fare and daily home-made specials in the bar are among the attractions of this popular 17th-century inn set in the heart of pretty Godshill. Beyond traditional pub favourites look for noisettes of lamb with redcurrant sauce, roast pheasant with mushrooms and bacon, venison with red wine jus, and baked herb-crusted haddock. **Principal beers:** Burts Nipper, Ushers Founders Ale, Mansfield Four Seasons.
Brewery/Company Ushers
Open 11-3 7-11
Bar food 12-2.30 7-9.30 Av main course £6
Restaurant 12-2.30 7-9.30 Av 3 course à la carte £15.95 Av 4 course fixed price £15.75

NITON Wight, Isle of *Map 04 SZ57*

Buddle Inn
NITON
St Catherines Rd PO38 2NE
☎ 01983 730243
Friendly cliff-top pub, popular with walkers who might come to sample favourites such as home-cooked ham,

chilli con carne, fresh crab and lobster in season. There are also light snacks during the day such as garlic mushrooms, country pâté and deep-fried vegetables. **Principal beers:** Flowers Original, Bass, Greene King Abbot Ale, Wadworth 6X.
Directions Take A3055 from Ventnor. In Niton take 1st L signed 'to the lighthouse'
Brewery/Company Whitbread
Open 11-11 (Sun 12-10.30)
Bar food 11.30-2.45 6-9.30 Av main course £4.95

SEAVIEW Wight, Isle of *Map 04 SZ69*

Seaview Hotel & Restaurant
SEAVIEW
High St PO34 5EX ☎ 01983 612711
There is a strong nautical theme to this small Victorian hotel. The main bar is a naval wardroom, decked with numerous models and pictures warships and liners. Try smoked haddock with mash and mustard sauce from the excellent bar menu, or duck with apricot and ginger chutney in the restaurant. Extensive wine list. **Principal beers:** Goddards, Flowers IPA.
Directions B3330 Ryde-Seaview rd, turn L via Puckpool along seafront road, hotel is situated on left hand side adjacent to the sea
Brewery/Company Free House
Open 10.30-2.30 6-11
Bar food 12-2.15 7-9.30 Av main course £8.95
Restaurant 12-2 7.30-9.30 Av 3 course à la carte £21.50
Accommodation (Min) s£55 d£70

SHORWELL Wight, Isle of *Map 04 SZ48*

The Crown Inn NEW
SHORWELL
Walkers Ln PO30 3JZ ☎ 01983 740293
Standing opposite the church in the centre of pretty Shorwell, the 17th-century Crown boasts a fine garden, complete with trout stream and resident ducks. Traditional pub fare is enhanced by decent specials, such as sea bream with crab sauce, liver and bacon casserole, fisherman's pie, and trout with spring onions and ginger butter.
Principal beers: Whitbread Boddingtons, Wadworth 6X, Flowers Original, Badger Tanglefoot.
Directions From Newport to

Carisbrooke High St, then L at rdbt at top of hill, take B3323 to Shorwell
Brewery/Company Whitbread
Open 10.30-3.30 6-11
Bar food 12-3 6-10 Av main course £5.50

VENTNOR Wight, Isle of *Map 04 SZ57*

The Spyglass Inn
VENTNOR

The Esplanade PO38 1JX
☎ 01983 855338

Peruse the fascinating collection of seafaring memorabilia at this 19th-century pub which sits at the western end of Ventnor Esplanade, overlooking the sea. Typical daily specials might feature several starters, including soup or crab and lobster bisque, followed by chicken curry, seafood pasta, beef cooked in ale and lamb chops.

Principal beers: Badger Dorset Best & Tanglefoot, Ventnor Golden.
Directions Town centre
Brewery/Company Free House
Open 10.30-3 6.30-11 (May-Oct 10.30-11, food all day)
Bar food 12-2.15 7-9.30 Av main course £4
Restaurant 12-2.15 7-9.30
Accommodation (Min) d£45

Pubs offering a good choice of seafood on the menu

Red Lion Hotel, East Haddon, Northamptonshire

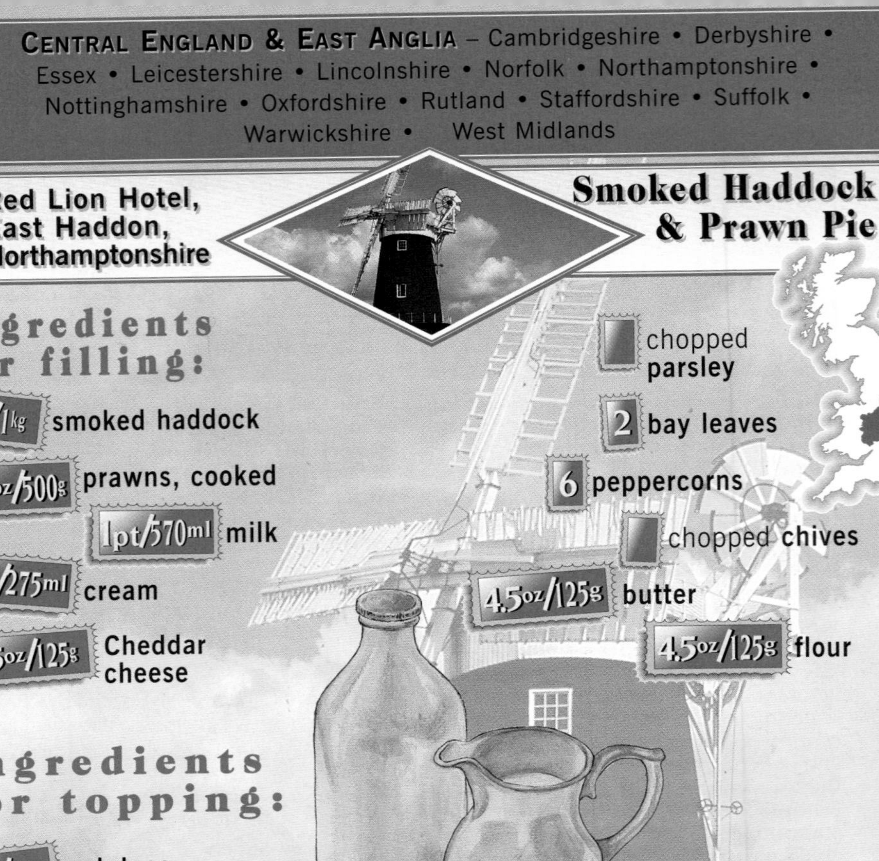

Smoked Haddock & Prawn Pie

Ingredients for filling:

- 2.2lb/1kg **smoked haddock**
- 1lb2oz/500g **prawns, cooked**
- 1pt/570ml **milk**
- 1/2pt/275ml **cream**
- 4.5oz/125g **Cheddar cheese**
- chopped **parsley**
- 2 **bay leaves**
- 6 **peppercorns**
- chopped **chives**
- 4.5oz/125g **butter**
- 4.5oz/125g **flour**

Ingredients for topping:

- 2.2lb/1kg **potatoes**
- 1 large **onion**
- 1 **egg white**
- **seasoning**
- **oil** for frying

Method for filling:

Poach the **smoked haddock** in the **milk** with **bay leaves** and **peppercorns**. Strain **milk** into a jug. Skin and flake the **fish** into a pie dish and toss with **prawns**, **chives** and chopped **parsley**. Melt **butter** in a pan, add **flour** and cook it out. Add the **milk** and bring to the boil. Simmer, adding the **cream**, grated **cheese** and seasoning.Divide the **fish** into 6 individual pie dishes and pour the sauce over the fish.

Method for topping:

Grate the **potato** into a tea towel, wring out excess water and empty into a large bowl.Grate the **onion,** add it to the **potato** and **seasoning**.

Lightly beat **egg** white and use it to bind the **potato** and **onion**.

Make into 6 individual **potato** rösti, coat in **flour** and shallow fry.

Top each pie with a rösti.

Cooking time and oven temp:

Gas Mark 5 for 15 minutes
Electric (Centigrade) 190.
Serves 6 people.

Cambridgeshire

BYTHORN Cambridgeshire Map 04 TL07

The White Hart
BYTHORN

PE18 0QN ☎ 01832 710226

A meal at Bennett's, the restaurant at this Cambridgeshire pub, could feature spicy fish gumbo or celeriac salad with remoulade sauce for starters, an entrée of calves' liver, saddle of hare, or veal sweetbreads, followed by burnt Cambridgeshire cream or praline parfait for dessert. **Principal beers:** Greene King IPA & Abbot Ale.

Directions 0.5m off A14 (Kettering/Huntingdon rd)

Brewery/Company Free House

Open 11-2 (closed Sun eve, Mon) 6-10

Bar food 11-2 7-10 Av main course £7.50

Restaurant 11-2 7-10 Av 3 course à la carte £26

CAMBRIDGE Cambridgeshire Map 05 TL45

The Eagle
CAMBRIDGE

Benet St CB2 3QN ☎ 01223 505020

Splendidly atmospheric city-centre pub with a fascinating history, first recorded in 1667, and retaining many original features - mullioned windows, fireplaces, wall paintings and pine panelling. Good Greene King ales and a wide-ranging pub menu, favourite dishes include beef and ale pie, deep-fried spicy prawns, and 'English fish & chips'.

Principal beers: Greene IPA & Abbot Ale.

Brewery/Company Greene King

Open 11-11 (Sun 12-10.30)

Bar food 12-2.30 5.30-8.45 Av main course £4.50

Free Press
CAMBRIDGE

Prospect Row CB1 1DU
☎ 01223 368337

A small, highly atmospheric pub in a picturesque street near the city centre. Rowing and cricketing memorabilia adorn the bars, where out ahead among the snacks are home-made soups (carrot and orange) and delicious pies. Also available are pork and cider casserole, Persian lamb, and lemon cheesecake. Totally non-smoking. **Principal beers:** Greene King - IPA, Abbot Ale, Dark Mild.

Brewery/Company Greene King

Open 12-2.30 6-11 (Sat-Sun 12-3, Sun 7-10.30)

Bar food 12-2 6-9

CASTOR Cambridgeshire Map 04 TL19

The Fitzwilliam Arms
CASTOR

34 Peterborough Rd PE5 7AX
☎ 01733 380251

Pretty thatched pub with a serious approach to food. Bar meals include Thai dishes, vegetarian options and salads, but the main feature is the impressive display of fish and meat that the customers select from. Sea bass, venison and steaks are cooked in front of you on the huge chargrill cooker in the restaurant.
Principal beers: Adnams, Theakstons, Fuller's London Pride, Wadworth 6X.

Directions Off A47 Leicester to Peterborough rd, take Castor/ Ailsworth turning (5m from A1)

Brewery/Company Free House

Open 11-2.30 6-11

Bar food 12-2 6.30-10 Av main course £7

Restaurant 12-2 6.30-10 Av 3 course à la carte £20

COTTENHAM Cambridgeshire Map 05 TL46

The White Horse
COTTENHAM

215 High St CB4 8QP ☎ 01954 250257

Friendly old family-run pub with large open bar areas and a restaurant. Bar food includes home-made lasagne, ploughman's and a carvery option offering a fresh joint or dish of the day. In the restaurant you might find tournedos Rossini or oven-baked salmon in lemon sauce.

Principal beers: Fullers London Pride.
Directions Exit A14 at Histon, on to Cottenham
Brewery/Company Free House
Open 11.30-2.30 6.30-11 (closed Mon)
Bar food 11.30-2.30 Av main course £4.95
Restaurant 7-11 Av 3 course à la carte £17

DRY DRAYTON Cambridgeshire
Map 05 TL36

The Black Horse
DRY DRAYTON

Park St CB3 8DA ☎ 01954 781055

Characterised by exposed wooden beams and open fires, this 350-year-old village pub offers a warm welcome and an extensive menu of traditional pub dishes. Typical examples include short-crust pies (beef and Guinness), freshly-made sandwiches, ploughman's platters, chilli and lasagne. **Principal beers:** Greene King IPA, Morland Old Speckled Hen, Adnams, Everards Tiger.
Directions Just outside Cambridge between A14 & A428
Brewery/Company Free House
Open 11-2.30 6.30-11 (Sun 12-3 only)
Bar food 12-2 7-9 Av main course £6
Restaurant 12-2 7-9 Av 3 course à la carte £17.50

DUXFORD Cambridgeshire
Map 05 TL44

The John Barleycorn
DUXFORD

3 Moorfield Rd CB2 4PP
☎ 01223 832699

Traditional thatched and beamed English country pub situated close to Cambridge. The same menu is served throughout and ranges from a cheese sandwich to tournedos Rossini. Typical dishes are large leg of lamb in mint gravy and chicken breast with garlic and herbs. **Principal beers:** Greene King IPA & Abbot Ale.
Directions Turn off A505 into Duxford
Brewery/Company Greene King
Open 11-11 (Sun 12-10.30)
Bar food 12-2.30 6.30-11 Av main course £7.50

Pubs offering a good choice of seafood on the menu

ELSWORTH Cambridgeshire
Map 05 TL36

The George & Dragon
ELSWORTH

41 Boxworth Rd CB3 8JQ
☎ 01954 267236

Set in a pretty village just outside Cambridge, this pub has one menu and three separate dining areas, each with its own appeal. Dishes feature fresh fish from Lowestoft and prime Scottish steaks. Tempting sweets include treacle tart and bread-and-butter pudding. **Principal beers:** Greene King IPA, Ruddles County.
Directions SE of A14 between Cambridge & Huntingdon
Brewery/Company Free House
Open 11-3 6-11 (Sun 12-3 only)
Bar food 12-2.30 6-9

ELTISLEY Cambridgeshire
Map 04 TL25

The Leeds Arms
ELTISLEY

The Green PE19 4TG ☎ 01480 880283

Named after local landowners, the Leeds Arms is located opposite the village green where the local cricket team play in season. Sizzling dishes are a speciality, including Cajun chicken, or fillet steak and tiger prawn kebabs. Scampi Thermidor and steak Rossini are favourites along with fish and chips on Friday. **Principal beers:** Greene King, Websters Yorkshire Bitter.
Directions On A428 between Cambridge & St Neots
Brewery/Company Free House
Open 11.30-2.30 6.30-11 (closed one week Xmas)
Bar food 12-2 7-9.45 Av main course £7.50
Restaurant 12-2 7-9.45 Av 3 course à la carte £12.50

ELTON Cambridgeshire
Map 04 TL09

The Black Horse NEW
ELTON

14 Overend PE5 6RU ☎ 01832 280240

Enjoying a picturesque village setting close to Elton Hall, this 17th-century inn draws a good dining clientele for the civilised atmosphere and the imaginative food on offer. From lunchtime only sandwiches and salads, the blackboard menu extends to smoked haddock risotto, duck with cinnamon and baby fig

contd.

sauce, and mackerel with rosemary and lime. **Principal beers:** Bass, Nethergate, Marstons Pedigree, Youngs Special.
Directions Off A605 (Peterborough to Northampton rd)
Brewery/Company Free House
Open 11-3 6-11 (Sun 12-3, 6-11)
Bar food 12-3 6-11 Av main course £4.50

ELY Cambridgeshire — Map 05 TL58

The Anchor Inn
ELY
Bury Ln, Sutton Gault CB6 2BD ☎ 01353 778537
Lit by gas lights and furnished with antiques, this 350-year-old riverside inn is situated on the edge of the Ouse washes. Expect tip-top East Anglian ales, imaginative food and comfortable B&B. Typical dishes include venison in red wine with celeriac mash, chicken, leek and bacon crumble, and home-made puddings. **Principal beers:** Nethergate IPA, Adnams, Hobson, Wolf.
Directions From A14, B1050 to Earith, take B1381 to Sutton. Sutton Gault on L
Brewery/Company Free House
Open 12-3 7-11
Restaurant 12-2 7-9 Av 3 course à la carte £24 Av 2 course fixed price £7.50
Accommodation (Min) s£50 d£62

FEN DITTON Cambridgeshire — Map 05 TL46

Ancient Shepherds
FEN DITTON
High St CB5 8ST ☎ 01223 293280
Named after the ancient order of Shepherders who used to meet here, this pretty, 16th-century pub offers a friendly atmosphere and freshly-cooked food. As well as filled baguettes, you can enjoy mussels in white wine and garlic, nut Wellington, ribeye steak, and lambs' liver with red wine and bacon. **Principal beers:** Benskins, Flowers Original.
Directions From A14 take B1047 signed Cambridge/Airport
Brewery/Company Pubmaster
Open 11-3 6-11 (Fri-Sat 11-3, 6.30-11)
Bar food 12-2.15 7-9.15 Av main course £8.95
Restaurant 12-2.15 7-9.15 Av 3 course à la carte £17

FENSTANTON Cambridgeshire — Map 05 TL36

King William IV
FENSTANTON
High St PE18 9JF ☎ 01480 462467
Charming 17th-century pub with beams and inglenooks. Most appetites are catered for, with a snack menu at lunchtime in addition to the main menu and daily specials board which offers a variety of fresh fish. Steak and kidney pudding and home-made sweets are popular options. Live music every Wednesday. **Principal beers:** Greene King Abbot Ale & IPA.
Directions Off A14 between Cambridge & Huntingdon
Brewery/Company Greene King
Open 11-3 6-11 (Sun 12-11)
Restaurant 12-2.15 7-10 Av 3 course à la carte £18

FOWLMERE Cambridgeshire — Map 05 TL44

The Chequers
FOWLMERE
High St SG8 7SR ☎ 01763 208369
Restored 16th-century coaching inn with a galleried restaurant featuring imaginative dishes using local produce. Fresh mussels with shallots, white wine and cream might be followed by lamb shank, slowly braised in balsamic vinegar and herbs. To finish, perhaps try the hot date sponge with toffee sauce. **Principal beers:** Adnams Bitter.
Directions From M11 A505, 2nd R to Fowlmere
Brewery/Company Free House
Open 12-2.30 6-11 10
Bar food 12-2 7-10
Restaurant 12-2 7-10

GODMANCHESTER Cambridgeshire — Map 04 TL27

Black Bull
GODMANCHESTER
32 Post St PE18 8AQ ☎ 01480 453310
Just yards from the Great River Ouse and the parish church, this 17th-century coaching inn sports beams and a large inglenook fireplace. Beyond a standard bar menu, the interesting daily specials may feature seared king scallops, duck with ginger and limes, beef fillet with Madeira sauce, and raspberry brûlée. **Principal beers:** Black Bull.

Directions Off A1198 S of Huntington
Brewery/Company Inn Business
Open 11-3 6-11 (Sun 12-10.30, food all day)
Bar food 12-2 6-9.30 Av main course £6.95
Accommodation (Min) s£20 d£35

GOREFIELD Cambridgeshire
Map 09 TF41

Woodmans Cottage
GOREFIELD
90 High Rd PE13 4NB ☎ 01945 870669
Expect a lively pub atmosphere where the Australian landlady is a former jazz singer. The premises are a popular venue for birthday parties and special occasions. Bar menu includes omelettes and mixed grills, while main courses feature traditional favourites like roast beef and rainbow trout. Vegetarian selection, and a large sweet trolley. **Principal beers:** Greene King IPA, Bass, Shephard Neame Bishop's Finger, Ruddles Best.
Directions A47 to Peterborough, ring road to A1M
Brewery/Company Free House
Open 11-2.30 7-11
Bar food 12-2 7-10 Av main course £4.50
Restaurant 12-2 7-10 Av 3 course à la carte £15 Av 0 course fixed price £10

HILDERSHAM Cambridgeshire
Map 05 TL54

The Pear Tree
HILDERSHAM
CB1 6BU ☎ 01223 891680
Facing the village green and enjoying a good local trade, this friendly turn of the century pub offers home-cooked food, including interesting vegetarian dishes. Beyond traditional grills and beef in Guinness, the short menu may list celery and apple soup, butterfish with mango sauce, cashew nut, vegetable and fruit crumble, and syrup sponge. **Principal beers:** Greene King IPA & Abbot Ale.
Directions Just off A1307
Brewery/Company Greene King
Open 11.45-2 6.30-11
Bar food 12-2 6.30-9.30 Av main course £5.95

HINXTON Cambridgeshire
Map 05 TL44

The Red Lion
HINXTON
High St CB10 1QY ☎ 01799 530601
Tastefully extended and modernised 16th-century inn with lots of clocks and other memorabilia. Chefs specials change daily and typically feature chicken Jalfrezi, honey and rosemary glazed lamb shank, lemon sole with roast red pepper butter, and apricot bread-and-butter pudding. **Principal beers:** Adnams, Greene King IPA, Woodforde's Wherry.
Directions 1m from M11 J9, 2m from M11 J10
Brewery/Company Free House
Open 11-2.30 6-11 (Sun 12-2.30,7-10.30)
Bar food 12-2 7-9.30

HOLYWELL Cambridgeshire
Map 05 TL37

The Old Ferryboat Inn
HOLYWELL
PE17 3TG ☎ 01480 463227
Thatched riverside inn, which claims to be England's oldest. It is haunted by a 17-year-old girl who killed herself for the love of a local woodcutter in 1050. Fresh produce is used in a range of dishes, including boozy beef pie, spiced coconut cod, and a 17oz mixed grill. **Principal beers:** Marstons Pedigree, Greene King Abbot Ale, Taylor Landlord.
Directions A14 then R onto A1096 then A1123 R to Holywell
Brewery/Company Marstons
Open 12-3 6-11 (Sun 12-3, 7-11)
Bar food 12-2 6.30-9.30 Av main course £7
Accommodation (Min) s£49.50 d£65

HORNINGSEA Cambridgeshire
Map 05 TL46

The Plough & Fleece
HORNINGSEA
High St CB5 9JG ☎ 01223 860795
Extended late 18th-century building, built in the Dutch style so popular at the time, with an unspoilt bar featuring ancient settles, tiled floor and unusual open fire. Menus feature good regional cooking, including comforting hotpots (Suffolk ham), Welsh fish pie, hot garlic cockles, Romany rabbit, beef Wellington

contd.

with Madeira sauce, and Norfolk treacle tart. **Principal beers:** Greene King IPA & Abbott Ale.
Directions E from A14 take B1047. Top of slip rd turn L. Pub opp garden centre
Brewery/Company Greene King
Open 11.30-2.30 7-11
Bar food 12-2 7-9.30 Av main course £6
Restaurant 12-2 7-9.30 Av 3 course à la carte £12

HUNTINGDON Cambridgeshire *Map 04 TL27*

The Old Bridge House
HUNTINGDON
1 High St PE18 6TQ ☎ 01480 452681
An 18th-century ivy-clad building with two restaurants and a busy bar. One innovative and modern menu is served throughout, along with an award-winning wine list. Expect carpaccio of beef, herb-and spice-crusted tuna with aubergine salad, roast chump of lamb with caper mash, and baked sea bass with saffron. **Principal beers:** Adnams Best, Hobsons Choice, Bateman XXXB.
Directions Signposted from A1 & A14
Brewery/Company Huntsbridge Inns
Open 12-2.30 6.30-10.30
Bar food 12-2.30 6.30-10.30 Av main course £7.95
Restaurant 12-2.30 6.30-10.30 Av 3 course à la carte £24
Accommodation (Min) s£79.50 d£89.50

KEYSTON Cambridgeshire *Map 04 TL07*

The Pheasant Inn
KEYSTON
Village Loop Rd PE18 0RE
☎ 01832 710241
Attractive thatched pub characterised by oak beams, open fires and simple wooden furniture. One eclectic modern menu is offered throughout and may include parsnip and ginger soup, turbot with tarragon and mustard sauce, sirloin steak with green beans and pesto, venison with pink peppercorn sauce, and pear and almond tart. **Principal beers:** Adnams, Fullers Best & London Pride, Hobsons Choice, Bass.
Directions Signposted from A14, W of Huntingdon
Brewery/Company Huntsbridge Inns
Open 12-2 6.30-11
Restaurant 12-2 6-10 Av 3 course à la carte £25

KIMBOLTON Cambridgeshire *Map 04 TL16*

The New Sun Inn
KIMBOLTON
20-22 High St PE18 0HA
☎ 01480 860052
An impressive display of flowers greets the visitor to this 16th-century inn near Kimbolton Castle. Enjoy a pint of Bombardier with a decent bar meal, the extensive and interesting choice featuring, perhaps, cod and chips, tagliatelle carbonara, pork with mustard mash and red onion stew, and herb-crusted salmon with lemon sauce.
Principal beers: Wells.

Directions From A1 N, B645 for 7m, From A1 S B661 for 7m, From A14 B660 for 5m
Brewery/Company Charles Wells
Open 11-2.30 6-11 (all day Sun)
Bar food 12-2.15 7-9.30 Av main course £5
Restaurant 12-2 7-9.30 Av 3 course à la carte £15

KIRTLING Cambridgeshire *Map 05 TL65*

The Queen's Head
KIRTLING
Newmarket Rd CB8 9PA
☎ 01638 731737
Charming 16th-century inn, with open fires, rug-strewn quarry-tiled floors and evening candlelight, hidden away down rural lanes close to the Suffolk border. Worth seeking out for the interesting food on offer, in particular steak and kidney pudding, duck with apple and cinnamon sauce, lobster with lemon and garlic butter, and home-made soups.

Principal beers: Greene King IPA.
Directions From M11 J9 take A11, then A1304 to Newmarket. At clock tower in Newmarket take B1063, then straight over X-roads to Kirtling
Brewery/Company Free House
Open 12-3 7-11.30
Bar food 12-3 7-11.30 Av main course £7.50
Restaurant 12-3 7-11.30 Av 3 course à la carte £16

MADINGLEY Cambridgeshire Map 05 TL36

The Three Horseshoes
MADINGLEY

High St CB3 8AB ☎ 01954 210221

Vibrant and cosmopolitan Mediterranean style of cooking draws discerning diners to this neat thatched country pub, with a pretty garden for summer alfresco imbibing. The interesting menu may list spinach, pancetta and Dolcelatte tart, turbot with black olive sauce, and venison with mustard and tarragon sauce, with caramelised lemon tart, or unpasteurised cheeses among the desserts. **Principal beers:** Fullers London Pride, Adnams Southwold, Everards Tiger, Wadworth 6X.
Directions M11 J13. 1.5m from A14
Brewery/Company Huntsbridge Inns
Open 11.30-2.30 6-11
Bar food 12-2 6.30-10
Restaurant 12-2 7-9.30 Av 3 course à la carte £23

NEWTON Cambridgeshire Map 05 TL44

The Queen's Head
NEWTON

CB2 5PG ☎ 01223 870436

Genuine country pub with beer tapped from the barrel. A record of previous landlords dating back to 1729 hangs in the crooked-beamed bar. Baked potato, hot toast with beef dripping and an extensive choice of sandwiches make up the lunchtime menu. Plates of beef, ham, pâté, and mixed cheeses are served in the evening. **Principal beers:** Adnams Southwold, Broadside & Old (winter only).
Directions 6m S of Cambridge on B1368, 1.5m off A10 at Harston, 4m from A505
Brewery/Company Free House
Open 11.30-2.30 6-11 (Sun 12-2.30, 7-10.30)
Bar food 12-2.15 7-10 Av main course £4

PETERBOROUGH Cambridgeshire Map 04 TL19

Charters Café Bar
PETERBOROUGH

Town Bridge PE1 1DG ☎ 01733 315700

Charters is a floating barge on the River Nene right in the centre of Peterborough - reputedly the biggest converted barge in Great Britain. The bistro-style menu offers the likes of chargrilled rump steak, pan-fried tuna with lime butter, and leek and Roquefort cannelloni. **Principal beers:** Fullers London Pride, Oakham JHB.
Directions A1/A47 Wisbech, 2m for city centre & town bridge (River Nene). Barge is moored at Town Bridge
Brewery/Company Free House
Open 12-11.30
Bar food 12-2.30 Av main course £3.95
Restaurant 12-3.30 7-12 Av 3 course à la carte £15

STILTON Cambridgeshire Map 04 TL18

The Bell Inn
STILTON

Great North Rd PE7 3RA
☎ 01733 241066

16th-century former coaching inn in the birthplace of Stilton cheese, featuring beams and open fires. Bar food features, naturally, Stilton and celery soup, followed by venison with liquorice, and home-made ice cream. Restaurant dishes may include scallops with garlic mash and sauce vierge, and duck with prune and shallot compôte and jasmine tea sauce.

contd.

Principal beers: Marstons Pedigree, Greene King Abbot Ale, Oakham JHB, Hop Back Summer Lightning.
Directions from A1 follow signs for Stilton, hotel is situated on the main road in the centre of the village.
Brewery/Company Free House
Open 12-2 6.30-9.30 (Sun 12-2, 6.30-9)
Bar food 12-2 6.30-9.30 Av main course £8
Restaurant 12-2 7-9.30 Av 3 course fixed price £19.95
Accommodation (Min) s£49 d£64

Derbyshire

ALFRETON Derbyshire *Map 08 SK45*

White Horse Inn
ALFRETON
Badger Ln, Woolley Moor DE55 6FG
☎ 01246 590319
Situated on an old toll road, close to Ogston Reservoir, this 18th-century inn enjoys outstanding views over the Amber valley. Typical examples of the wide-ranging specials are roast loin of pork, fresh salmon and asparagus fricassée, and chicken, leek and wild mushroom pie. Good sandwiches and cold dishes also feature. **Principal beers:** Bass.
Directions From A632 (Matlock/Chesterfield rd) take B6036. Pub 1m after Ashover. From A61 take B6036 to Woolley Moor
Brewery/Company Free House
Open 11.30-2.30 6-11 (Sun 11.30-11), food 11.30-8.30)
Bar food 11.30-2 6-9 Av main course £4.50
Restaurant 11.30-2 6-9 Av 3 course à la carte £11.50

ASHBOURNE Derbyshire *Map 07 SK14*

The Green Man
ASHBOURNE
St Johns St DE6 1GH ☎ 01335 345783
Located in the heart of Ashbourne, this 17th-century coaching inn has two bars, the Johnson and the Boswell. On the specials board you'll find fresh fish and shellfish, and local game in dishes such as trio of venison - sausage, haunch and liver - set on a spring onion mash.
Principal beers: Marstons Pedigree, Bass.
Directions In town centre off A52
Brewery/Company Free House
Open 11-11 (Sun 12-10.30)
Bar food 12-2.30 6-8.30 Av main course £5
Accommodation (Min) s£32 d£52

BAKEWELL Derbyshire *Map 08 SK26*

The Lathkil Hotel
BAKEWELL
Over Haddon DE45 1JE
☎ 01629 812501
19th-century inn situated in the Peak District National Park high above Lathkil Dale, offering stunning views. Hearty dishes like steak and kidney pie and venison casserole are served in the bar, and the monthly restaurant menu might offer baked trout wrapped in bacon, or roast goose with Cumberland sauce.
Principal beers: Wards, Whim Hartington, Taylor Landlord.
Brewery/Company
Open 11.30-3 7-11
Bar food 12-2 Av main course £5.75
Restaurant 7-9 Av 3 course à la carte £16.50
Accommodation (Min) s£37.50 d£55

The Monsal Head Hotel
BAKEWELL
Monsal Head DE45 1NL
☎ 01629 640250
With its views over scenic Monsal Dale, this superbly situated hotel is one of the Peak District's most famous landmarks. Horses used to pull guests and their luggage up from the railway station. Rabbit pie and decent sandwiches feature on the bar menu. Expect pot roasts and casseroles on the restaurant menu.
Principal beers: Monsal Best, Theakston Best & Old Peculier, Courage Directors, Black Sheep.
Directions A6 from Bakewell towards Buxton. 1.5m to Ashford. Follow Monsal Head signs, B6465 for 1m
Brewery/Company Free House
Open 10.30-11.30
Bar food 12-9.30 Av main course £5.50
Accommodation (Min) d£45

The Rutland Arms Hotel NEW
BAKEWELL
The Square DE45 1BT ☎ 01629 812812
Historic 18th-century former coaching inn, famous for being where Jane Austen wrote ' Pride and Prejudice' . Popular food is served in both the Tavern Bar and Four Seasons restaurant, the latter offering starters like black pudding with

roasted shallots and smoked bacon, and glazed goat's cheese on toasted brioche. **Principal beers:** Theakstons.
Directions Town centre
Brewery/Company Free House
Open 11-11 12-10.30
Bar food 12-2.15 6.30-9 Av main course £5.95
Restaurant 12-2.15 7-9 Av 3 course à la carte £15.95 Av 2 course fixed price £15.95
Accommodation (Min) s£54 d£84

BAMFORD Derbyshire *Map 08 SK28*

Yorkshire Bridge Inn

BAMFORD

Ashopton Rd S33 0AZ ☎ 01433 651361

The inn dates from 1846 and is named after the nearby stone bridge which marks the crossing point over the River Derwent from Cheshire/Derbyshire to Yorkshire. Specialities of the house are a giant prawn cocktail, freshly battered cod, pot-roasted lamb, and hot sponge of the day with custard. **Principal beers:** Theakston Best & Old Peculiar, Stones, Bass.

Directions A57 from M1, L onto A6013, pub 1m on R
Brewery/Company Free House
Open 8-11
Bar food 12-2 6-9.30 Av main course £6.50
Restaurant 12-2 6-9.30 Av 3 course à la carte £15
Accommodation (Min) s£38 d£54

BEELEY Derbyshire *Map 08 SK26*

The Devonshire Arms

BEELEY

The Square DE4 2NR ☎ 01629 733259

Converted from three stone cottages in 1747, this civilised village inn features open fires, oak beams, and flagged floors. The menu features venison in red wine,

Barnsley chop, fish on Friday (fresh seafood platter), and a Victorian breakfast complete with Bucks Fizz and the papers on Sunday. Close to Chatsworth Estate and Haddon Hall.
Principal beers: Black Sheep Best & Special, Theakston Old Peculier & XB.
Directions From A6 onto B6012 at Rowsley
Brewery/Company Free House
Open 11-11
Bar food 11-9.30 Av main course £5.95

BIRCHOVER Derbyshire *Map 08 SK26*

The Druid Inn

BIRCHOVER

Main St DE4 2BL ☎ 01629 650302

Ivy-covered 18th-century stone inn situated above Darley Dale in a quiet rural village. Visitors and locals flock to this rambling pub for the enterprising and eclectic range of dishes available. Stilton and port pate, Thai fishcakes, steak and mussel pie, Gascony fish stew, and Turkish lamb casserole give an indication of the global choice.
Principal beers: Mansfield Bitter, Morland Old Speckled Hen, Marstons Pedigree.
Directions From A6 between Matlock & Bakewell take B5056, signed Ashbourne.Take 2nd L to Birchover
Brewery/Company Free House
Open 12-3 7-11
Bar food 12-2 7-9.30 Av main course £8.80
Restaurant 12-2 7-9.30 Av 3 course à la carte £14.50

Pubs offering a good choice of seafood on the menu

BIRCH VALE Derbyshire *Map 07 SK08*

The Waltzing Weasel Inn
BIRCH VALE
New Mills Rd SK22 1BT
☎ 01663 743402
Set in the heart of the Peak District with stunning views of Kinder Scout, this traditional country inn is a favoured retreat among 'tired businessmen, hardy walkers and confirmed slouches'. The varied clientele can enjoy some good food, perhaps including seafood tart, roast garlic lamb, pan-fried sardines, and game in season. **Principal beers:** Marstons Best & Pedigree.
Directions W from M1 at Chesterfield
Brewery/Company Free House
Open 12-3 5.30-11
Bar food 12-2 7-9.30 Av main course £9.50
Restaurant 12-2 7-9 Av 3 course à la carte £25.50 Av 3 course fixed price £25.50
Accommodation (Min) s£38 d£68

BRADWELL Derbyshire *Map 07 SK18*

The Bowling Green NEW
BRADWELL
Smalldale S33 9SQ ☎ 01433 620450
The Bowling Green is an attractive 16th-century, white village inn decorated with colourful hanging baskets. Specialising in seafood, the menu may include Seafood Extravanganza, haddock, cod, scampi, garlic prawns and salmon. Steaks are also available. **Principal beers:** Stones, Bass.
Brewery/Company Free House
Open 12-3 7-11
Bar food 12-2 7-9 Av main course £6.95
Restaurant 12-2 7-9 Av 3 course à la carte £10
Accommodation (Min) s£35 d£50

BRASSINGTON Derbyshire *Map 08 SK25*

Ye Olde Gate Inne
BRASSINGTON
Well St DE4 4HJ ☎ 01629 540448
The inn has plenty of historic character, it was built in 1616 of local stone and salvaged Armada timbers exchanged for locally mined lead. The same menu is offered throughout the neat interior, with dishes such as lamb balti, chicken with Stilton and leeks, cheese bake, and black pudding hotpot.
Principal beers: Marstons Pedigree & Head Brewer's Choice.
Directions 3m NW of Carsington Water
Brewery/Company W'hampton & Dudley
Open 12-2.30 6-11
Bar food 12-1.45 7-8.45 Av main course £8.95

CASTLETON Derbyshire *Map 07 SK18*

The Castle
CASTLETON
Castle St S30 2WG ☎ 01433 620578
Set in the heart of the Peak District in lovely countryside, The Castle has been a coaching inn since the reign of Charles II, when the landlord was fined for brewing beer without a license. Also resident to four ghosts. **Principal beers:** Bass, Stones, Worthington.
Directions On the A625 between Sheffield & Chapel-en-le-Firth
Brewery/Company Vintage Inns
Open 11-11 (Sun 12-10.30)

DARLEY ABBEY Derbyshire *Map 08 SK33*

The Abbey
DARLEY ABBEY
Darley St DE22 1DX ☎ 01332 558297
Dating from 1147, this simple medieval hall house is the only remaining building of an Augustian Abbey and makes a striking pub. With splendid oak beams and doors and massive stone remnants, it is worth the riverside walk from the city centre. Standard pub food. **Principal beers:** Samuel Smith Old Brewery Bitter.
Directions A38 onto A6 to Duffield Rd
Brewery/Company Samuel Smith
Open 11.30-2.30 6-11
Bar food 12-2 Av main course £4.50

DOE LEA Derbyshire *Map 08 SK46*

Hardwick Inn
DOE LEA
Hardwick Park S44 5QJ
☎ 01246 850245
Dating from 1607 and built of locally quarried sandstone, this historic inn was originally the lodge to the National Trust's Hardwick Hall. Home-made pies feature prominently on the menu and daily specials may include venison pie in red wine, sausage, liver and bacon casserole, braised steak and onion and various fresh fish dishes.

Principal beers: Theakston Old Peculier & XB, Morland Old Speckled Hen, Ruddles County, Courage Directors.
Directions M1 J29 take A6175. 0.5m L (signed Stainsby/Hardwick Hall). After Stainsby, 2m L at staggered jnctn
Brewery/Company Free House
Open 11.30-11 (Sun 12-10.30, food 12-9)
Bar food 11.30-9.30 Av main course £5.50
Restaurant 12-1.45 7-9 Av 3 course à la carte £10.95 Av 3 course fixed price £10.95

DRONFIELD Derbyshire *Map 08 SK37*

The Old Sidings NEW
DRONFIELD
91 Chesterfield Rd S18 2XE
☎ 01246 410023

Unpretentious, stone-built tavern, situated just 30 feet from the main Sheffield railway line. A must for railway buffs, it's full of railway paraphernalia, and even the menu features 'signalman's starters' and 'chef's Inter-City specials'. Hearty South Yorkshire fare includes home-made meat and potato pie, liver and bacon casserole and 'Bill's' giant grill. **Principal beers:** Burton Ale, Stones, Bass.
Brewery/Company Free House
Open 12-11 (Sun 12-10.30)
Restaurant 12-5 5.30-11 Av 3 course à la carte £9 Av 3 course fixed price £12.95

EYAM Derbyshire *Map 08 SK27*

Miners Arms
EYAM
Water Ln S32 5RG ☎ 01433 630853

Historic 17th-century pub situated in the famous plague village of Eyam. Good reputation for food which is freshly prepared using local produce where possible. Style is traditional English with some French influences. Restaurant evening menu may feature baked lemon sole, pot-roast guinea fowl and blanquette of lamb. **Principal beers:** Tetley, John Smiths.
Directions Off B6521, 5m S of Bakewell
Brewery/Company Free House
Open 12-3 7-11 (closed 1st 2wks Jan, Sun eve & Mon lunch)
Bar food 12-2 Av main course £6.50
Restaurant 12-2 7-9 Av 3 course à la carte £17
Accommodation (Min) s£27.50 d£55

FOOLOW Derbyshire *Map 08 SK17*

The Bulls Head Inn NEW
FOOLOW
S32 5QR ☎ 01433 630873

Open fires, oak beams, good views and home-cooked food are among the attractions of this family-run inn, located in a scenic village high up in the Peak District. Sample, perhaps, marinated monkfish with red pepper and coriander coulis, fresh grilled plaice, Irish stew, deep-fried black pudding, followed by apple pie. **Principal beers:** Black Sheep Bitter, Wards.
Directions Just off A623, N of Stoney Middleton
Brewery/Company Free House
Open 12-2.30 7-11 (closed Mon)
Bar food 12-2 7-9 Av main course £7.50
Restaurant 12-2 7-9 Av 3 course à la carte £15
Accommodation (Min) s£50 d£60

GRINDLEFORD Derbyshire *Map 08 SK27*

The Maynard Arms
GRINDLEFORD
Main Rd S32 2HE ☎ 01433 630321

Handy for walks in the Peak National Park, this turn-of-the-century inn offers fine views of the Derbyshire hills. Hearty bar meals may feature rabbit and leek pie and steamed suet pudding, while the Padley Restaurant offers an interesting choice of dishes that might include poached Orkney salmon. **Principal beers:** Boddingtons, Morland Old Speckled Hen, Marston's Pedigree.
Directions On B6001 from Sheffield take A625 towards Castleton. Turn into Grindleford. Hotel is approx 2m on L
Open 11-3 5.30-11

contd.

Bar food 12-2 6-9.30
Restaurant 12-2 7-9.30 Av 3 course à la carte £19 Av 4 course fixed price £19
Accommodation (Min) s£67 d£77

HASSOP Derbyshire *Map 08 SK27*

Eyre Arms
HASSOP
DE45 1NS ☎ 01629 640390
Dating back to the Civil War and boasting its own resident Cavalier ghost, this quaint, ivy-clad inn is furnished with old pictures and horse brasses, stuffed birds in glass cases and a grandfather clock. The wide-ranging menu features many fish and steak dishes, as well as Barnsley chop, rabbit pie and spiced chicken.
Principal beers: Marston's Pedigree, John Smiths, Black Sheep Bitter.
Directions A6 then A619 toward Sheffield, 0.5m take B6001 to Hathersage & Hassop
Brewery/Company Free House
Open 11.30-3 6.30-11
Bar food 12-2 6.30-9 Av main course £6

HAYFIELD Derbyshire *Map 07 SK08*

The Sportsman NEW
HAYFIELD
Kinder Rd SK22 2LE ☎ 01663 741565
Well placed for famished walkers tackling the Kinder Trail to Kinder Scout (Derbyshire's highest peak) and the Pennine Way, this comfortable, family-run inn offers hearty, home-cooked meals. From ploughman's and hot sandwiches, the short blackboard menu may list bean, pasta and vegetable soup, lamb with port and redcurrant, and apple tart.
Principal beers: Thwaites.
Directions Hayfield is 5m S of Glossop on A624
Brewery/Company Thwaites
Open 12-3 7-11
Bar food 12-2 7-10 Av main course £7.95

HOGNASTON Derbyshire *Map 08 SK25*

The Red Lion Inn
HOGNASTON
Main St DE6 1PR ☎ 01335 370396
A relaxed, welcoming atmosphere greets customers at this traditional style 17th-century inn which features beamed ceilings and open fires. Close to Carsington Water, Britain's newest reservoir. Home-cooked fare served in the bar includes thick rib of beef, natural smoked haddock, glazed duck breast and three cheese lasagne.
Principal beers: Marstons Pedigree, Morland Old Speckled Hen.
Directions M1 J25 take A52 towards Derby & Ashbourne. Hognaston on B5035
Brewery/Company Free House
Open 12-3 6-11 (closed Mon eve)
Bar food 12-2 6.30-9 Av main course £10
Restaurant 12-2 6.30-9 Av 3 course à la carte £17
Accommodation (Min) s£45 d£70

HOPE Derbyshire *Map 07 SK18*

Cheshire Cheese Inn
HOPE
Edale Rd S33 6ZF ☎ 01433 620381
Tiny 400-year-old village inn, built of mellow stone and overflowing with flowers. It's on the old Cheshire cheese route, where a bed for the night was paid for in cheese. Food is freshly cooked and the beer hand-pulled. Dishes include rabbit pie, fresh cod, and pheasant casserole.
Principal beers: Wards, Coach House Innkeeper's Special Reserve, Vaux Moonlight Mouse, Ward's Boxing Hare.
Directions On A625 between Sheffield & Chapel-en-le-Frith
Brewery/Company Free House
Open 12-3 6.30-11
Bar food 12-2 6.30-8.30 Av main course £6.95
Restaurant 12-2 6.30-8.30
Accommodation (Min) d£50

LITTON Derbyshire *Map 07 SK17*

Red Lion Inn
LITTON
SK17 8QU ☎ 01298 871458
Largely unspoilt by modernisation, this village pub was once part of a 300-year old farm, and sits opposite a village green that comes complete with stocks! Typical menu features Barnsley chop, braised ham hock with lentils, cheese, leek and potato pie, and poached salmon with watercress sauce.
Principal beers: Tetley, Black Sheep, Theakston Old Peculier.
Directions just off the A623 Chesterfield to Stockport rd 1m E of Tideswell

Brewery/Company Free House
Open 11-11
Bar food 11.30-2 6-8.30 Av main course £5.80
Restaurant 11.30-2 6-8.30 Av 3 course à la carte £15

MATLOCK Derbyshire *Map 08 SK35*

The White Lion Inn NEW
MATLOCK

195 Starkholmes Rd DE4 5JA
☎ 01629 582511

With spectacular views over Matlock Bath, and its proximity to many beautiful dales and valleys, this 18th-century inn is the ideal place for a relaxing break. The daily-changing menu may include Gressingham duck with caramelised pineapple, chicken cordon bleu with ham and cheese, and baked chocolate ganache with kumquats for dessert.
Principal beers: Marstons Pedigree, Courage Directors, Ruddles County, Tiger.
Brewery/Company Scottish & Newcastle
Open 12-2.30 6-11 (closed Mon lunch)
Bar food 12-2 6-9 Av main course £5
Restaurant 12-2.30 7-9.30 Av 3 course à la carte £18.50
Accommodation (Min) s£30 d£40

SHARDLOW Derbyshire *Map 08 SK43*

The Old Crown
SHARDLOW

Cavendish Bridge DE72 2HL
☎ 01332 792392 799292

Bustling 17th-century village pub situated next to the River Trent in the heart of the Derbyshire countryside. Besides an impressive choice of real ales, visitors can tuck into home-made beef and kidney pie, roast lamb shank, smoked haddock pot, calves' liver with smoked bacon and onions, or hot-filled baguettes.
Principal beers: Marston's Pedigree, Bass, Whim Hartington IPA, Exmoor Gold.
Directions M1 J24 take A6 towards Derby turn L before river bridge into Shardlow
Brewery/Company Free House
Open 11.30-3 5-11 (Sun 12-10.30)
Bar food 12-2.30 Av main course £5
Accommodation (Min) s£20 d£30

STANTON BY DALE Derbyshire *Map 08 SK21*

The Chequers Inn
STANTON BY DALE

Dale Rd DE7 4QF ☎ 0115 944 2774

In 1846 The Chequers was established as a grocer's shop and beer house. It is now a typical country pub offering a good pint of beer and ploughman's, toasties and daily specials in the bar. The 'Dish of the Day' varies from traditional roasts and pies, to curries, pizzas and chilli.
Principal beers: Bass.
Directions From M1 J25 take A52 towards Derby. Follow signs for Sandiacre then Stanton by Dale
Brewery/Company Punch Taverns
Open 11-2.30 6-11 (Sat-Sun 11-11)
Bar food 12-2 Av main course £4

TISSINGTON Derbyshire *Map 07 SK15*

Bluebell Inn
TISSINGTON

DE6 1NH ☎ 01335 350317

A 17th-century farmhouse/public house set in rural surroundings on the edge of the Peak District. Outbuildings have been converted into a restaurant, with the same menu as the bar. A good variety of food includes a vegetarian choice, tipsy pie, local trout, and baked whisky and peppercorn ham. **Principal beers:** Bass.
Directions 3m N of Ashbourne on A515
Brewery/Company Free House
Open 12-3 6.30-11.30
Bar food 12-2.30 6.30-9.30 Av main course £7.50

WARDLOW Derbyshire *Map 08 SK35*

The Bull's Head at Wardlow
WARDLOW

SK17 8RP ☎ 01298 871431

The inn is situated in the heart of the Peak District National Park, close to Monsal Head. Unaltered for many years, it is adorned with antique pictures, clocks, coach lamps, brass and copperware. Dishes include rump steaks, chicken supreme, and fillet of plaice with prawn and mushroom sauce. **Principal beers:** Wards, John Smiths.
Brewery/Company Free House
Open 11.30-3 6.30-11
Bar food 11.30-3 6.30-9.30 Av main course £4.95
Restaurant 11.30-3 6.30-9.30 Av 3 course à la carte £12

contd.

Essex

ARKESDEN Essex Map 05 TL43

Axe & Compasses
ARKESDEN
CB11 4EX ☎ 01799 550272

Nestling in a pretty village with an occasional stream running through it, this extended brick and thatch pub is adorned with colourful hanging baskets in summer. Freshly cooked food ranges from bar snacks to steak and kidney pie, monkfish with roasted pepper sauce, chargrilled steaks, and beef casserole with dumplings. **Principal beers:** Greene King IPA & King Abbot Ale.

Directions From Buntingford B1038 towards Newport.Then L for Arkesden
Brewery/Company Greene King
Open 11.30-2.30 6-11
Bar food 12-2 6.45-9.30 Av main course £8
Restaurant 12-2 6.45-9.30 Av 3 course à la carte £20

BLACKMORE END Essex Map 05 TL73

The Bull Inn
BLACKMORE END
CM7 4DD ☎ 01371 851037

Listed building in a quiet village location. Typical dishes include rack of lamb with braised shallots and a redcurrant and rosemary jus, and guinea fowl with herb mash on wild mushroom and tomato concasse. Restaurant food is also available in the bar along with a range of snacks.
Principal beers: Greene King IPA, Adnams.
Brewery/Company Free House
Open 12-3 6.30-11 (closed Mon, ex BHs)
Bar food 12-1.45 7-9.45 Av main course £10.50
Restaurant 12-1.45 7-9.45 Av 3 course à la carte £20

BRADWELL Essex Map 05 TL82

The Swan Inn
BRADWELL
CM7 ☎ 01376 562111

Sympathically extended and refurbished old pub, with exposed beams and brickwork, open fires, and cricketing memorabilia in the character bars. Freshly-cooked dishes, listed on blackboards, may feature avocado and bacon salad, spinach and cheese tart, chargrilled steaks, and cod and chips.
Principal beers: Greene King IPA & Abbot Ale.
Directions On A120 between Braintree & Coggeshall
Brewery/Company Greene King
Open 11-2.30 6-11 (Sun all day)
Bar food 12-2 7-9.30 Av main course £8
Restaurant 12-2 7-9.30 Av 3 course à la carte £16

BRAINTREE Essex Map 05 TL73

The Green Dragon at Young's End
BRAINTREE
Upper London Rd, Young's End
CM7 8QN ☎ 01245 361030

Originally a house and stables, now a popular dining pub with restaurants in a barn and a recently converted hayloft. Old beams are a particular feature. Seafood is a speciality, including oysters, monkfish, and, perhaps, sea bass with oranges and coriander, along with seasonal meat dishes and a changing curry board. **Principal beers:** Greene King IPA & Abbot Ale.
Directions M11 J8 take A120 towards Colchester. At Braintree b'pass take A131 S towards Chelmsford
Brewery/Company Greene King
Open 11.30-3 6-11 9.30
Bar food 12-2.15 6-9.30 Av main course £5.50

Restaurant 12-3 6-9.30 Av 3 course à la carte £15 Av 3 course fixed price £10.50

BURNHAM-ON-CROUCH Essex *Map 05 TQ99*

Ye Olde White Harte Hotel
BURNHAM-ON-CROUCH

The Quay CM0 8AS ☎ 01621 782106

The hotel dates from the 1600s and retains many original features. It overlooks the River Crouch and has its own jetty on the quay. There is a choice of menus, with a daily roast in the bar and restaurant dishes such as lobster thermidor, fillet steaks, and Dover sole meunière.

Principal beers: Tolly Cobbold, Adnams, Crouch Vale.

Brewery/Company Free House
Open 11-11
Bar food 12-2 7-9 Av main course £4.50
Restaurant 12-2 7-9 Av 3 course à la carte £15 Av 3 course fixed price £12.50
Accommodation (Min) s£20 d£38

CASTLE HEDINGHAM Essex *Map 05 TL73*

The Bell Inn
CASTLE HEDINGHAM

St James St CO9 3EJ ☎ 01787 460350

15th-century coaching inn with a large function room where Disraeli once made a speech. A nearby Norman keep was used for the BBCs production of Ivanhoe. Seafood includes New Zealand green lipped-mussels and rainbow trout. Other options might be Thai chicken curry, and home-made toffee and banana pie.
Principal beers: Shepherd Neame Spitfire, Greene King IPA & Abbot Ale.
Directions On A1124(A604) N of Halstead, R to Castle Hedingham
Brewery/Company Grays
Open 11.30-3 (Sun, 12-3) 6-11 (Sun,7-10.30)
Bar food 12-2 7-10 Av main course £6

CLAVERING Essex *Map 05 TL43*

The Cricketers
CLAVERING

CB11 4QT ☎ 01799 550442

Located near the cricket green in a beautiful unspoilt village, this attractive 16th-century freehouse offers an imaginative choice of dishes with a strong emphasis on seafood; fillet of hake, lobster thermidor and crab are typical examples. Rack of lamb and home-made steak and kidney pie may feature on the restaurant menu.
Principal beers: Flowers IPA & Flowers Original, Adnams, Boddingtons, Wethereds.

Directions From M11 J10 take A505 E. Then A1301, B1383. At Newport take B1038
Brewery/Company Free House
Open 12-3 6-11
Bar food 12-3 7-11 Av main course £8
Restaurant 12-3 7-12 Av 3 course à la carte £23 Av 3 course fixed price £23
Accommodation (Min) s£60 d£80

COLCHESTER Essex *Map 05 TL92*

Rose & Crown Hotel
COLCHESTER

East St CO1 2TZ ☎ 01206 866677

Situated in the heart of Britain's oldest town, this splendid 14th-century posting house retains much its Tudor character. With ancient timbers, smartly decorated bedrooms, and wide-ranging meus, it is a popular destination. Typical dishes may include calves liver with bacon and sage, rack of lamb, seared venison fillet, and salmon with hollandaise.
Principal beers: Tetley, Rose & Crown Bitter.

contd.

Directions From M25 J28 take A12 N & follow signs for Colchester
Brewery/Company Free House
Open 12-2 7-11
Bar food 12-2 7-11 Av main course £7.50
Restaurant 12-2 7-11 Av 3 course à la carte £25 Av 3 course fixed price £16.45
Accommodation (Min) s£65 d£65

DEDHAM Essex *Map 05 TM03*

Marlborough Head Hotel
DEDHAM

Mill Ln CO7 6DH ☎ 01206 323250
Set in glorious Constable country, close to Flatford Mill and peaceful walks, this former wool merchants house dates from 1455. Full of heavy beams and open fireplaces it has been an inn since 1704, offering character accommodation and straightforward bar food. Choice includes seafood carbonara, paella, aga-roasted bacon steak, and chicken dijonnaise.
Principal beers: Adnams Southwold, Greene King IPA.
Directions E of A12, N of Colchester
Brewery/Company Old English Inns/Hot
Open 11-3 6-11 (Sat 11-11, Sun 12-10.30)
Bar food 12-2.30 7-9.30 Av main course £7.50
Restaurant 12-2.30 7-9.30 Av 3 course à la carte £15
Accommodation (Min) s£45.50 d£55

ELSENHAM Essex *Map 05 TL52*

The Crown
ELSENHAM

The Cross, High St CM22 6DG
☎ 01279 812827
A pub for over 300 years, with oak beams, open fireplaces, and Essex pargeting at the front. The menu, which has a large selection of fresh fish, might offer seafood mixed grill, or pork fillet with Calvados. All the sweets are home made, including 15 ice creams. **Principal beers:** Shepherd Neame Spitfire, Wolf Granny Wouldn't Like It, Youngs, Marston's Pedigree.
Directions M11 J8 towards Takeley L at traffic lights
Brewery/Company Allied Domecq
Open 11-2.30 6-11
Bar food 12-2.30 7-9.30 Av main course £6
Restaurant 12-2.30 7-9.30 Av 3 course à la carte £14

FEERING Essex *Map 05 TL82*

The Sun Inn
FEERING

Feering Hill CO5 9NH ☎ 01376 570442
Thought to date from 1525 and originally part of a gentleman's residence, this welcoming pub has two log fires in winter and a seemingly endless choice of home-cooked dishes. Typical examples include traditional cottage pie, jugged hare, spiced lamb and Kentish cassoulet. Extensive range of soups, vegetarian dishes and puddings. **Principal beers:** 5 guest beers.
Directions On A12 between Colchester and Witham
Brewery/Company Free House
Open 11-3 6-11
Bar food 12-2 6-10 Av main course £4.50
Restaurant 12-2 6-10 Av 3 course à la carte £11.50 Av 3 course fixed price £12.60

GOSFIELD Essex *Map 05 TL72*

The Green Man
GOSFIELD

The Street CO9 1TP ☎ 01787 472746
Smart yet traditional village dining pub with old beams, named after a pagan symbol of fertility. Popular for the relaxing atmosphere, Greene King ales and decent bar food. Blackboard menus may list steak and kidney pudding, pheasant in red wine, sweet and sour pork, and good fresh fish. Lunchtime cold carvery table, sandwiches and ploughman's.
Principal beers: Greene King IPA & Abbot Ale.
Directions Braintree A131 then A1017
Brewery/Company Greene King
Open 11-3 6-11 (Sun 12-3, 7-10.30)
Bar food 12-2 6.30-9 Av main course £7.50
Restaurant 12-2 6.30-9 Av 3 course à la carte £14

GREAT BRAXTED Essex *Map 05 TL81*

Du Cane Arms
GREAT BRAXTED

The Village CM8 3EJ ☎ 01621 891697
The Du Cane family's original property was demolished and rebuilt in 1936, about half a mile away. Enjoying a quiet village setting, this homely pub offers a variety of dishes, many using fresh herbs

from the garden. Typical choices include steak and kidney pie, cod in Adnams beer batter, and rack of lamb.
Principal beers: Adnams, Courage, Greene King IPA, Mauldons.
Directions Great Braxted signed between Witham and Kelvedon on A12
Brewery/Company Free House
Open 11.30-3 6.30-11
Bar food 12-2.30 7-9.30 Av main course £7.95
Restaurant 12-2.30 7-9.30 Av 3 course à la carte £15

GREAT YELDHAM Essex *Map 05 TL73*

The White Hart
GREAT YELDHAM

Poole St CO9 4HJ ☎ 01787 237250
Set in four acres and dating from 1505, this elegantly restored, black and white timbered inn offers some of the best pub food in the country. Innovative, modern menus have a distinct Mediterranean flavour, including, perhaps, duck liver parfait with brioche and shallot confit, seared salmon with courgette tagliatelle and tomato and olive sauce, lamb with potato and aubergine moussaka, fine bean salad and garlic dressing, and lunchtime ploughman's and home-made pasta.
Principal beers: Guest ales.
Directions On A1017 between Haverhill & Halstead
Brewery/Company Huntsbridge Inns
Open 11-3 6-11
Bar food 12-2 6.30-10 Av main course £6.50
Restaurant 12-2 6.30-10 Av 3 course à la carte £18.50 Av 2 course fixed price £8.50

HARLOW Essex *Map 05 TL41*

Rainbow & Dove
HARLOW

Hastingwood Rd CM17 9JX
☎ 01279 415419
Quaint listed inn with many charming features, originally a farmhouse and staging post. Became a pub when Oliver Cromwell stationed his new model army on the common here in 1645. Relaxed atmosphere inside and good quality bar food including hot sandwiches and a selection of fried and pasta dishes on the specials board. **Principal beers:** Morland Old Speckled Hen, Courage Directors, Friary Meux.
Directions M11 J7 take A414 towards Chipping Ongar. Then L into Hastingwood Rd
Brewery/Company Inn Business
Open 11.30-3 6-11
Bar food 11.30-2.30 7-9.30 Av main course £4.75

HORNDON ON THE HILL Essex *Map 05 TQ68*

Bell Inn & Hill House
HORNDON ON THE HILL

High Rd SS17 8LD ☎ 01375 642463
Historic 500-year-old coaching inn offering interesting, twice daily-changing menus in both the beamed and flagstone-floored bar and intimate restaurant. Competently cooked dishes may include lamb shank with garlic and rosemary, beetroot and sweet potato tart with goat's cheese, and peppered skate wing with lemon and parsley. Comfortable bedrooms. **Principal beers:** Greene King IPA, Fullers London Pride, Bass, Youngs Special.
Directions Off M25 J30/31 signed Thurrock. Lakeside A13 then B1007 to Horndon
Brewery/Company Free House
Open 11-2.30 (Sat 11-3) 6-11 (Sun 12-3, 7-10.30)
Bar food 12-1.45 6.45-9.45 Av main course £7.50
Restaurant 12-1.45 6.45-9.45 Av 3 course à la carte £20
Accommodation (Min) d£45

LANGHAM Essex — Map 05 TM03

The Shepherd and Dog
LANGHAM
Moor Rd CO4 5NR ☎ 01206 272711
Popular village pub in the Dedham Vale, where the blackboard menu offers lasagne, steak and kidney pudding, home-made curries, Aberdeen Angus steaks, and braised pheasant in red wine. Seafood dishes include Torbay sole with caviar butter, Dublin Bay prawns and, perhaps, fresh cod and skate. **Principal beers:** Greene King IPA & Abbot Ale, Nethergate Old Growler.
Directions A12 toward Ipswich, 1st turning on L out of Colchester, marked Langham
Brewery/Company Free House
Open 11-3.30 5.30-11.30
Bar food 12-3 6-11 Av main course £6.95
Restaurant 12-3 6-11 Av 3 course à la carte £15

LEIGH-ON-SEA Essex — Map 05 TQ88

Crooked Billet
LEIGH-ON-SEA
51 High St, Old Town SS9 2EP
☎ 01702 714854
Fine 16th-century timbered ale house, with open fires, original beams and local fishing pictures, set in the picturesque fishing village of Old Leigh. Enjoy views of cockle boats and the estuary from the terrace, and straightforward bar food, including seafood platter, battered cod, and ploughman's.
Principal beers: Adnams, Burton, Marstons Pedigree, Youngs.
Directions A13 towards Southend, follow signs for Old Leigh
Brewery/Company Allied Domecq
Open 12-11 (Sun 12-10.30)
Bar food 12-2.30 Av main course £4.95

LITTLE CANFIELD Essex — Map 05 TL52

The Lion & Lamb
LITTLE CANFIELD
CM6 1SR ☎ 01279 870257
Comfortable bric-a-brac filled pub where the conservatory overlooks surrounding countryside. Extensive menus run from ploughman's, sandwiches and Sunday lunches, to chicken liver pâté with Cumberland sauce, sea bass with tomato and herb broth, medallions of lamb with cardamon and vanilla sauce, and fresh cream desserts. **Principal beers:** Ridleys IPA & ESX Best.
Directions M11 J8 A120 towards Braintree
Brewery/Company Ridley & Sons
Open 11-2.30 6-11
Bar food 12-2 6.30-10 Av main course £7.50
Restaurant 12-2 6.30-10 Av 3 course à la carte £18

LITTLE DUNMOW Essex — Map 05 TL62

Flitch of Bacon
LITTLE DUNMOW
The Street CM6 3HT ☎ 01371 820323
The name of this 15th-century country inn refers to the ancient award of a flitch of bacon to a married couple who could describe a harmonious first year of marriage. Expect bacon and onion pudding, sausage hotpot, and smoked salmon and scrambled eggs on the menu, and fresh fish on Friday. **Principal beers:** Greene King IPA.
Directions A120 to Braintree for 10m, turn off at Little Dunmow, 1/2m pub on R
Brewery/Company Free House
Open 12-3 6-11
Bar food 12-2.30 6.30-9 Av main course £6.50
Restaurant 12-2 6-9 Av 3 course à la carte £15 Av 3 course fixed price £10.50
Accommodation (Min) s£29.60 d£49.60

NORTH FAMBRIDGE Essex — Map 05 TQ89

The Ferry Boat Inn
NORTH FAMBRIDGE
Ferry Ln CM3 6LR ☎ 01621 740208
500-year-old Essex boarded pub next to the sea wall of the River Crouch. It has low beams, open fires and a duck pond, and is adjacent to the newly opened Essex Wildlife Trust 600-acre sanctuary. Simple food includes the usual pub grub plus fresh fish and steaks. **Principal beers:** Morland Old Speckled Hen, Flowers IPA, Wadworth 6X.
Directions From Chelmsford take A130 S then A132 to South Woodham Ferrers, then B1012. R to village
Brewery/Company Free House
Bar food 12-2 7-9 Av main course £4.50
Restaurant 12-2 7-9.30 Av 3 course à la carte £6.50
Accommodation (Min) d£40

NORTH WEALD BASSETT Essex *Map 05 TL40*

Kings Head
NORTH WEALD BASSETT

High Rd CM16 6BU ☎ 01992 522204

This ancient half-timbered pub is nearly 450 years old, and was originally built of old ships timbers. It was targeted by the Luftwaffe during WWII, as it was often frequented by personnel and crews from nearby North Weald airbase. **Principal beers:** Bass.

Directions A414 to Chelmsford, R at rdbt to North Weald
Brewery/Company Vintage Inns
Open 11-11 (Sun 12-10.30)

SAFFRON WALDEN Essex *Map 05 TL53*

The Cricketers' Arms
SAFFRON WALDEN

Rickling Green CB11 3YG
☎ 01799 543210

Said to take its name from the village's one-time London society cricket ground, this historic inn was originally built as a terrace of three 'one up, one down' Elizabethan timber-framed cottages. Balti curries are a firm favourite, while the inn's main speciality dish is mussels.

Principal beers: Flowers IPA, Fullers ESB.
Directions exit B1383 at Quendon. Pub 300yds on L opp cricket ground
Brewery/Company Free House
Open 11-11
Bar food 12-2 7-9.30 Av main course £6.85
Restaurant 12-2 7-9.30 Av 3 course à la carte £19.50
Accommodation (Min) s£50 d£60

STOCK Essex *Map 05 TQ69*

The Hoop
STOCK

21 High St CM4 9BD ☎ 01277 841137

Former 15th-century weavers' cottages, situated near Hanningfield reservoir. Unpretentious little bar serving a decent range of real ales and a good selection of snacks and light meals. Expect sandwiches, filled jacket potatoes, steak and kidney pie, Lancashire hotpot, and specials like braised leg of lamb and fresh fish (cod, skate and reservoir trout).
Principal beers: Fullers, Hop Back, Nethergate, Crouch Vale.

Directions On B1007 between Chelmsford & Billericay
Brewery/Company Free House
Open 11-11 (Sun 12-10.30)
Bar food 11-11 Av main course £5

TILLINGHAM Essex *Map 05 TL90*

Cap & Feathers Inn
TILLINGHAM

South St CM0 7TH ☎ 01621 779212

Traditional white weatherboard inn, reputedly an ale house since 1427, that changed its name from the King's Head to the Cap & Feathers during the Civil War. Classic unspoilt bars and appetising bar food, including home-made Tillingham pie, Lincolnshire sausages, fresh fish and chips, and Thai vegetarian schnitzel and rice.
Principal beers: Crouch Vale Best, Woodham IPA, Woodfordes Wherry, Fuller's London Pride.

Directions From Chelmsford take A414, follow signs for Burnham-on-Crouch, then for Tillingham
Brewery/Company Crouch Vale
Open 11.30-3 6-11 (Sun 12-4,7-10.30)
Bar food 12-2 7-9.30 Av main course £5.50
Restaurant 12-2 7-9.30 Av 3 course à la carte £14
Accommodation (Min) s£25 d£35

WENDENS AMBO Essex *Map 05 TL53*

The Bell
WENDENS AMBO

Royston Rd CB11 4JY ☎ 01799 540382

Formerly a farm, this 16th-century timber-framed building nestles in a picturesque village close to Audley End House. Complete with extensive and attractive gardens, and cottagey low-ceilinged rooms, it offers traditional home-made pub food, including beef and

contd.

Guinness pie, Cajun chicken, mixed grill and syrup sponge pudding.
Principal beers: Adnams, Ansells Mild, Marstons, Crouch Vale.
Directions Near Audley End train station
Brewery/Company Free House
Open 11.30-2.30 6-11 (Sun 12-3 7-10.30)
Bar food 12-2 7-9 Av main course £6.50
Restaurant 12-2 7-9 Av 3 course à la carte £15

WICKHAM BISHOPS Essex *Map 05 TL81*

The Mitre
WICKHAM BISHOPS
2 The Street CM8 3NN ☎ 01621 891378
The Bishops of London used to stay at this 19th-century pub - hence the name. Noted for its friendly atmosphere and character. Favourite dishes include steak and kidney pie, steaks, fresh cod in beer batter, vegetarian Wellington and pasta dishes. **Principal beers:** Ridleys Rumpus & IPA.
Directions Off B1018 between Witham and Maldon
Brewery/Company Ridley & Sons
Open 11.30-11
Bar food 12-3 7-9.30 Av main course £5
Restaurant 12-3 7-9.30 Av 3 course à la carte £18

WIVENHOE Essex *Map 05 TM02*

The Black Buoy Inn
WIVENHOE
Black Buoy Hill CO7 9BS
☎ 01206 822425
Formerly three 16th-century cottages near the Colne estuary, Wivenhoe's oldest inn offers river views and varied menus, including good sandwiches and local fish. Choose from mussels in white wine, cream and garlic, steak and kidney pudding, Spanish omelette, and specials like liver and bacon or lamb steak with rosemary and garlic.
Principal beers: Flowers IPA, Greene King IPA & Abbot Ale.
Directions From Colchester take A133 towards Clacton, then B1027, B1028. In Wivenhoe turn L after church into East St
Brewery/Company Pubmaster
Open 11.30-2.30 6.30-11 (Sun 12-3.30 7-10.30)

Bar food 12-2 Av main course £3.75
Restaurant 12-2 7-9.30 Av 3 course à la carte £12

Leicestershire

CASTLE DONINGTON Leicestershire *Map 08 SK42*

The Nag's Head
CASTLE DONINGTON
Hilltop DE74 2PR ☎ 01332 850652
Small country pub with low-beamed ceilings and open coal fires, close to Castle Donington motor-racing circuit. Two no-smoking restaurants in French country style with colour washed walls and mixed pine tables. Interesting food ranges from ciabatta sandwiches to blackened swordfish with crème fraîche, and lamb with saffron and tomato mash.
Principal beers: Banks, Marstons Pedigree.
Brewery/Company Marstons
Open 11.30-2.30 5.30-11
Bar food 12-2 5.30-7 Av main course £4.50
Restaurant 12-2 6-9.15 Av 3 course à la carte £20

CROXTON KERRIAL Leicestershire *Map 08 SK82*

Peacock Inn
CROXTON KERRIAL
1 School Ln NG32 5JX ☎ 01476 870324
Stone-built 300-year-old inn with a large garden, set in the Vale of Belvoir within walking distance of Belvoir Castle. Lambs' liver and onions and local sausage and mash are traditional favourites in the bar, while the restaurant might offer monkfish and scallops in green peppercorn sauce.
Principal beers: Bass, John Smiths, Courage Directors, Batemans XXXB.
Brewery/Company Free House

Open 11.30-11
Bar food 11.30-10 Av main course £5.50
Accommodation (Min) s£30 d£35

EAST LANGTON Leicestershire Map 04 SP79

The Bell Inn NEW
EAST LANGTON
Main St LE16 7TW ☎ 01858 545278
Attractive, creeper-clad, 16th-century village pub with a long, pine-furnished bar, open fire and head-crackingly low beams. Visitors are guaranteed a warm welcome and homely bar food. Choose from lemon chicken, lamb Madras, game and port casserole, pigeon with apple and gooseberry sauce, and hand-cut chips. Good-value B&B.

Principal beers: Greene King IPA & Abbot Ale, Jennings Cumberland, Marstons Pedigree, Grainstore.
Brewery/Company Free House
Open 10-2.30 7-11
Bar food 11.30-2 7-10 Av main course £9
Restaurant 11.30-2 7-10 Av 3 course à la carte £15
Accommodation (Min) s£37.50 d£49.50

GLOOSTON Leicestershire Map 04 SP79

The Old Barn Inn & Restaurant
GLOOSTON
Andrew's Ln LE16 7ST ☎ 01858 545215
The same menu is served throughout this 16th-century country inn tucked away in an isolated rural hamlet. Intertesting, monthly-changing menus may list chicken liver parfait with home-made chutney, Moroccan chicken, beef topped with 'devil on horseback', red cabbage potato cake and elderberry port sauce, and lemon sole with marinaded salmon and Martini Rosso sauce.
Principal beers: Theakston, Fullers, Woodfordes, Adnams.
Directions A6 from Market Harborough. At Kibworth follow signs to Langtons/Hallaton. Glooston signposted
Brewery/Company Free House
Open 12-2.30 (Sat-Sun only) 7-11 (Mon-Sat)
Bar food 12-1.30 7-9.30 Av main course £8
Restaurant 12-1.30 7-9.30 Av 3 course à la carte £20 Av 3 course fixed price £13.95
Accommodation (Min) s£37.50 d£49.50

HALLATON Leicestershire Map 04 SP49

The Bewicke Arms
HALLATON
1 Eastgate LE16 8UB ☎ 01858 555217
400-year-old thatched inn with low beamed bars and roaring log fires making it an authentic country local. Hallaton is the venue for two exuberant pagan customs - hare pie scrambling and bottle kicking. Good choice of weekly-changing blackboard specials might include Bewicke banger, creamy seafood pancakes, stuffed courgettes, and beery beef casserole. **Principal beers:** Ruddles Best & County, Marstons Pedigree.
Directions S of A47 between Leicester & junction of A47/A6003
Brewery/Company Free House
Open 12-3 7-11
Bar food 12-2 7-11 Av main course £5.50
Restaurant 12-2 7-9.45 Av 3 course à la carte £12

HOSE Leicestershire Map 08 SK72

Rose & Crown
HOSE
43 Bolton Ln LE14 4SE
☎ 01949 860424
Pub converted from 19th-century cottages, with a patio and paddock. Renowned for its eight regularly changing hand-pumped guest ales, and its hearty food. Dishes range from a generous seafood salad to stew and dumplings in winter, and include steaks and home-made pies.
Principal beers: 8 guest beers.
Directions Off A606 N of Melton Mowbray

contd.

Brewery/Company Free House
Open 12-3 7-11 (Sun 7-10.30)
Bar food 12-2 7-9.30 Av main course £7.95

KEGWORTH Leicestershire *Map 08 SK42*

Cap & Stocking
KEGWORTH
20 Borough St DE74 2FF
☎ 01509 674814

Traditional and genuinely unspoilt pub, affectionately known as the 'Cap', that serves Bass straight from the jug and home-cooked meals in the comfortable yet old-fashioned rooms. Choose from filled rolls, ploughman's lunches, Hungarian goulash, beef in red wine and spicy Thai curries. Well-placed for M1 travellers (J24).
Principal beers: Hancocks HB, Bass.
Directions Village centre (chemist on LHS. Turn L, left & left again to Borough St)
Brewery/Company Punch Taverns
Open 11.30-2.30 (Sat-Sun 11.30-3) 6.30-11 (Sun 7-10.30)
Bar food 11.30-2.30 6.30-9 Av main course £5.75

LEICESTER Leicestershire *Map 04 SK50*

Welford Place
LEICESTER
9 Welford Place LE1 6ZH
☎ 0116 247 0758

Busy city centre pub with high ceilings and huge windows, offering food all day and popular live jazz and classical events. Home-cooked light meals or starters might feature smoked salmon, chilli, and ratatouille, while panaché of seafood, pan-fried fillet steak, and baked guinea fowl wrapped in Parma ham feature among the imaginative main dishes.
Principal beers: Adnams, Marstons Pedigree.
Directions Town centre
Brewery/Company Free House
Open 8am-12 midnight
Bar food 8am-12 midnight Av main course £7.25
Restaurant 8am-12 midnight Av 3 course à la carte £20 Av 3 course fixed price £12.50

LOUGHBOROUGH Leicestershire *Map 08 SK51*

The Swan in the Rushes
LOUGHBOROUGH
21 The Rushes LE11 5BE
☎ 01509 217014

A 30s tile-fronted real ale pub with two drinking rooms, a cosmopolitan atmosphere and no frills. Healthy home-cooked food is served (no chips), including ploughman's lunches, beef and mushrooms in Guinness, pork and potato balti, and Stilton and broccoli quiche.
Principal beers: Archers Golden, Bateman XXXB, Tetley, Marstons Pedigree.
Directions Town centre
Brewery/Company Tynemill Ltd
Open 11-11 (Sun 12-10.30)
Bar food 12-2.30 6-8.30 Av main course £5
Restaurant 12-2.30 6-8.30 Av 3 course à la carte £12 Av 3 course fixed price £12
Accommodation (Min) s£20 d£30

MARKET HARBOROUGH Leicestershire *Map 04 SP78*

The Queens Head Inn
MARKET HARBOROUGH
Main St, Sutton Bassett LE16 8HP
☎ 01858 463530

Traditional English pub with real ale and bar meals including Sunday lunch, with an upstairs restaurant specialising in regional Italian cuisine. The Italian influence ranges from a pizza and pasta selection to petto di pollo maiori, chicken breast stuffed with asparagus and wrapped in Parma ham. Well-kept real ales. **Principal beers:** Adnams, Taylor Landlord, Marston Pedigree, Greene King Abbot Ale.
Brewery/Company Free House
Open 11-3 6.30-11
Bar food 11.30-2 7-10 Av main course £6.95
Restaurant 7-11 Av 3 course à la carte £14.50

The Sun Inn
MARKET HARBOROUGH
Main St, Marston Trussel LE16 9TY
☎ 01858 465531

Successfully combining historic charm and modern comfort, this late 17th-century village inn is noted for its imaginative food. Using fresh produce,

dishes range from liver and bacon with red wine, and salmon with lemon butter sauce, in the bar, to trout and sea bass terrine with sauce vierge, and duck with rich port jus, in the restaurant.
Principal beers: Bass, Hook Norton Best, Everards Tiger.
Directions S of A4304 between Market Harborough & Lutterworth
Brewery/Company Free House
Open 11-3 6-11.30
Bar food 12-2 6.30-10 Av main course £8
Restaurant 12-2 7-9.30 Av 3 course à la carte £20 Av 5 course fixed price £22.50
Accommodation (Min) s£47.50 d£60

MEDBOURNE Leicestershire — *Map 04 SP89*

The Nevill Arms
MEDBOURNE
12 Waterfall Way LE6 8EE
☎ 01858 565288
Attractive stone-built pub set by a stream and on the village green, with a beamed bar, large open fire and attractive gardens. Home-made soups, spicy lamb with apricots, beef in Guinness casserole, and pork with honey and ginger are typical blackboard specials; filled jacket potatoes and open sandwiches are also available. **Principal beers:** Ruddles Best & County, Adnams.
Directions From Northampton take A508 to Market Harborough then B664 for 5m.L for Medbourne
Brewery/Company Free House
Open 12-2.30 (Sun 12-3) 6-11
Bar food 12-2 7-9.45 Av main course £5.25
Accommodation (Min) s£32.50 d£39.95

MOUNTSORREL Leicestershire — *Map 08 SK51*

The Swan Inn
MOUNTSORREL
10 Loughborough Rd LE12 7AT
☎ 0116 2302340
Traditional 17th-century coaching inn, with exposed beams and open fires, set on the banks of the River Soar. The weekly menu offers a range of snacks and international dishes. Home-made enchiladas, and beef and onions casseroled in Old Peculiar are specialities of the house.
Principal beers: Theakston Best, XB, Old Peculier, Morland Old Speckled Hen.
Directions On main road between Leicester & Loughborough
Brewery/Company Free House
Open 12-2.30 5.30-11
Bar food 12-1.45 6.30-9.30 Av main course £5
Restaurant 12-1.45 6.30-9.30 Av 3 course à la carte £12
Accommodation (Min) s£20 d£32

OLD DALBY Leicestershire — *Map 08 SK62*

The Crown Inn
OLD DALBY
Debdale Hill LE14 3LF ☎ 01664 823134
300-year-old converted farmhouse in a small village in the Vale of Belvoir. Series of rambling and cosy, antique-furnished bar, where fine ales and imaginative, freshly cooked food can be sampled. Expect, perhaps, black pudding with apple mustard cream sauce, salmon baked in filo with chive beurre blanc, and banana, pear and toffee crumble.
Principal beers: Black Sheep Bitter, Taylor Landlord, Marstons Pedigree, Greene King Abbot Ale.
Directions Newark A46 R at Upper Broughton
Brewery/Company Free House
Open 12-3 6-11
Bar food 12-2 6-10 Av main course £10.95
Restaurant 12-3 7-9 Av 3 course à la carte £20

REDMILE Leicestershire — *Map 08 SK73*

Peacock Inn
REDMILE
Church Corner NG13 0GA
☎ 01949 842554
Located close to Belvoir Castle, this stone-built, 18th-century village pub draws a discerning dining clientele into its beamed and comfortably furnished bar. Interesting, freshly prepared dishes might include local asparagus with butter and lemon sauce, roast monkfish wrapped in smoked salmon with celeriac mash and pesto sauce. **Principal beers:** Boddingtons, Wadworth 6X, Greene King Abbot Ale, Mansfield.
Directions From A1 take A52 towards Nottingham
Brewery/Company Free House
Open 11.30-11

contd.

Bar food 12-2.30 6.30-9.30 Av main course £7
Restaurant 12.30-2 7-10 Av 3 course à la carte £20
Accommodation (Min) d£75

SADDINGTON Leicestershire — Map 04 SP69

The Queens Head NEW
SADDINGTON
Main St LE8 0QH ☎ 0116 240 2536
Traditional village inn with a continental-style conservatory overlooking Saddington Reservoir and the Laughton Hills. Traditional pub food is served in the bar. The restaurant menu is supplemented by specials, and includes grills, seafood and local lamb.

Principal beers: Greene King Abbot Ale, Morlands Old Speckled Hen, Everards Tiger, Adnams.
Directions Between A50 & A6 S of Leicester, NW of Market Harborough
Brewery/Company Everards Brewery
Open 11-3 5.30-11
Bar food 11.30-2.30 6.30-10 Av main course £5
Restaurant 12-2 6.30-10 Av 3 course à la carte £15

SIBSON Leicestershire — Map 04 SK30

The Cock Inn
SIBSON
Twycross Rd CV13 6LB ☎ 01827 880357
Low heavy beams, exposed wattle and daub walls and ancient timbers testify to the age of this quaint thatched and half timbered inn. Built in 1250 it has a cosy atmosphere in which to enjoy steak and kidney pie, ham, egg and chips, rabbit casserole, beef Wellington, and various salads and sandwiches from the wide-ranging menus.
Principal beers: Bass, M&B Brew XI.
Directions On A444 between Nuneaton & M42 J11
Brewery/Company Punch Taverns
Open 11.30-2.30 6.30-11 (Sun 12-3, 7-10.30)
Bar food 11.30-2 6.30-9.45 Av main course £6.95
Restaurant 11.30-2 6.30-9.45 Av 3 course à la carte £18.50 Av 4 course fixed price £11.50

SILEBY Leicestershire — Map 08 SK61

The White Swan
SILEBY
Swan St LE12 7NW ☎ 01509 814832
Proud of its repuation for good-value home-cooked food, this homely pub offers bar snacks and a good menu selection in the book-lined restaurant. Typical choices include tomato and basil soup, fish pie, lamb with apricot and nut stuffing, baked tuna with roasted vegetables and tomato and garlic sauce, and treacle tart.
Principal beers: Marstons Pedigree, Shipstones, Ansells.
Brewery/Company Free House
Open 11.45-3 7-11 (Closed Sun eve & 1-7 Jan)
Bar food 12-2 7-11 Av main course £7.50
Restaurant 12-2 7-11 Av 3 course à la carte £16

THORPE LANGTON Leicestershire — Map 04 SP79

The Bakers Arms
THORPE LANGTON
Main St LE16 7TS ☎ 01858 545201
Imaginative modern pub food attracts diners from miles around to this cosy thatched pub set in a pretty village. Rug-strewn quarry-tiled floors, open fires and an informal atmosphere set the scene in which to enjoy scallops with chive butter sauce, sea bass with chargrilled vegetables, cod on pesto mash, and shank of lamb with colcannon.
Principal beers: Tetley.
Directions Take A6 S from Leicester then L signed 'The Langtons'
Brewery/Company Free House
Open 12-3 6.30-11 (closed Mon)
Bar food 12-2 6.30-9.30 Av main course £11

WOODHOUSE EAVES Leicestershire *Map 08 SK51*

The Pear Tree Inn
WOODHOUSE EAVES
Church Hill LE12 8RT ☎ 01509 890243
Family-run inn at the centre of a lovely village in the beauty spot known as Charnwood Forest. The food is freshly cooked and favourite dishes include home-made salmon and tuna fishcakes, beefburgers made to the inn's own recipe, and prime Aberdeen Angus steaks.

Principal beers: Tetley, Marston's Pedigree, Greene King Abbot Ale, Burton Ale.
Directions Village centre
Brewery/Company Free House
Open 12-3 6-11 (Sun 6-10.30)
Bar food 12-2 7-10 Av main course £6.50
Restaurant 12-2 7-10 Av 3 course à la carte £6.50

Lincolnshire

ALLINGTON Lincolnshire *Map 08 SK84*

The Welby Arms
ALLINGTON
The Green NG23 2EA ☎ 01400 281361
A 17th-century former farmhouse, licensed in the 19th century while still a working farm, offering a welcome retreat for A1 travellers. Enjoy regularly-changing guest ales and some honest home cooking, including Jim's special fish pie, Grimsby haddock in beer batter, Brie and bacon chicken, mixed grill, and treacle sponge pudding. **Principal beers:** John Smiths, Bass, Taylor Landlord.
Directions From Grantham take either A1 north, or A52 west. Allington is 1.5m
Brewery/Company Free House
Open 12-2.30 6-11
Restaurant 12-2.30 6.30-10 Av 3 course à la carte £12
Accommodation (Min) s£40 d£50

ASWARBY Lincolnshire *Map 08 TF03*

The Tally Ho Inn
ASWARBY
NG34 8SA ☎ 01529 455205
Originally a farmhouse, this 17th-century inn is surrounded by parkland on which sheep graze contentedly. Exposed beams, stone walls and log fires create a warm ambience. Dishes include hot smoked salmon tartlets, beef and horseradish casserole, and date and walnut pudding.
Principal beers: Batemans, Bass.
Directions From A1 take Grantham exit onto A52 towards Boston. Take A15 towards Sleaford.
Brewery/Company Free House
Open 12-3 6-11
Bar food 12-2.30 6.30-10
Restaurant 12-2.30 7-10 Av 3 course à la carte £15
Accommodation (Min) s£33 d£45

BARNOLDBY LE BECK Lincolnshire *Map 08 TA20*

The Ship Inn
BARNOLDBY LE BECK
Main Rd DN37 0BG
☎ 01472 822308
Situated on the edge of the Lincolnshire Wolds, this 200-year-old inn is filled with interesting bric-a-brac, fresh flowers and vines. Home cooking with bistro flair is offered, with specials such as lobster thermidor, pan-fried lamb steak and parfait of duckling with smoked bacon in a cherry brandy sauce.
Principal beers: Courage Directors, Whitbread Castle Eden Ale.
Directions Off A46/A18 SW of Grimsby
Brewery/Company Free House
Open 11-3 6.30-11
Bar food 11-2 6.30-9.30 Av main course £3.95
Restaurant 12-2 6.30-9.30 Av 3 course à la carte £17.50

BOURNE Lincolnshire *Map 08 TF02*

The Black Horse Inn NEW
BOURNE
Grimsthorpe PE10 0LY
☎ 01778 591247
Expect a warm welcome and some interesting food at this stone-built, 18th-century coaching inn situated opposite Grimsthorpe Castle. Quality local produce is used in preparing such dishes as game terrine with cranberry confit,

contd.

tuna with coriander butter sauce, ravioli of smoked fish, and pot-roast lamb shank with mixed bean and vegetable broth. **Principal beers:** Black Horse Bitter, Batemans XXXB.

Brewery/Company Free House
Open 11.30-2.30 6-11

Black Horse Inn

Bar food 12-2 7-9.30 Av main course £6.50
Restaurant 12-2 7-9 Av 3 course à la carte £23.50 Av 3 course fixed price £12.50
Accommodation (Min) s£45 d£65

The Wishing Well Inn
BOURNE

Main St, Dyke PE10 0AF
☎ 01778 422970

A country inn named after the wishing well in the restaurant, this attractive building is adorned with old oak beams, stone and brass and roaring inglenook fires in winter. The varied menus include lemon sole, village grill, chicken supreme, steak and Guinness pie, Lincolnshire sausages and choices from the sweet table.
Principal beers: Greene King Abbot Ale, Everards Tiger, Ward's Waggle Dance.

Directions Inn 1.5m from the A15, 12m from A1 Colsterworth rdbt
Brewery/Company Free House
Open 11-2.30 6-11
Bar food 11.30-2.30 6.30-9.30 Av main course £6
Restaurant 12-2.30 7-11 Av 3 course à la carte £18
Accommodation (Min) s£25 d£49

CONINGSBY Lincolnshire *Map 08 TF25*

The Old Lea Gate Inn
CONINGSBY

Leagate Rd LN4 4RS ☎ 01526 342370

Last of the once numerous Fen Guide Houses, places of safety on the treacherous eastern marshes, built in 1542. Heavy beams, high-backed settles and roaring open fires characterise the period interior. Straightforward bar food includes sandwiches, lasagne, steak and kidney pie, ham platter and steak au poivre. **Principal beers:** Batemans XB, Marstons Pedigree.
Directions Off B1192 just outside Coningsby
Brewery/Company Free House
Open 11.30-3 6.30-11
Bar food 11.30-2 7-9.30 Av main course £5.50

CORBY GLEN Lincolnshire *Map 08 TF02*

The Woodhouse Inn
CORBY GLEN

NG33 4NS ☎ 01476 550316 & 550006

Late Georgian country inn with an imaginative range of dishes, including a number of Sardinian specialities; it has a Sardinian brick-built oven in the garden, and holds regular authentic Sardinian banquets. **Principal beers:** Theakston - Best, XB.
Directions 4m E of A1 Colsterworth roundabout on the A151
Brewery/Company Free House
Open 12-2.30 7-12
Bar food 12-2.30 7-12 Av main course £6.50

Restaurant 12-2.30 7-12 Av 3 course à la carte £15
Accommodation (Min) s£32.50 d£42.50

DONINGTON ON BAIN Lincolnshire *Map 08 TF28*

The Black Horse
DONINGTON ON BAIN

Main Rd LN11 9TJ ☎ 01507 343640
Ideal for walkers, this old-fashioned country pub is set in the heart of the Lincolnshire Wolds on the Viking Way. It is also popular with visitors to nearby Cadwell Park race track. A sample menu includes Black Horse grill, duck in orange and Grimsby haddock. **Principal beers:** John Smiths, Ruddles, Theakston Mild.
Brewery/Company Free House
Open 11.30-3 6.30-11
Bar food 12-2 7-10 Av main course £5.95
Restaurant 12-2 7-10 Av 3 course à la carte £12
Accommodation (Min) s£25 d£40

EWERBY Lincolnshire *Map 08 TF14*

Finch Hatton Arms
EWERBY

43 Main St NG34 9PH ☎ 01529 460363
Family-run hotel, pub and restaurant with a friendly atmosphere and value-for-money prices. Typical bar fare includes haddock and chips, steak pie and sweet and sour chicken. The restaurant has a full range of steaks, salmon, and dishes such as duck with orange sauce.
Principal beers: Everards Tiger & Beacon, Morland Old Speckled Hen, Greene King Abbot Ale, Bateman XXXB.
Directions from A17 to Kirkby-la-Thorne, then 2m NE. Also 2m E of A153 between Sleaford & Anwick
Brewery/Company Free House
Open 11.30-3 6.30-11
Bar food 12-3 6.30-11 Av main course £6
Restaurant 12-3 6.30-11 Av 3 course à la carte £17.50
Accommodation (Min) s£36 d£54

FREISTON Lincolnshire *Map 08 TF34*

Kings Head
FREISTON

Church Rd PE22 0NT ☎ 01205 760368
Originally two 14th-century cottages, this village pub is a riot of colour in summer with overflowing hanging baskets and tubs adorning the façade. In the low-beamed bar you can enjoy one of the speciality home-made pies (steak and ale), served with hand-cut chips, or a prime steak from the local butcher.
Principal beers: Batemans.
Directions from Boston take A52 towards Skegness. 3m turn R at Haltoft End to Freiston
Brewery/Company Batemans
Open 11-2.30 7-11
Bar food 12-2 7-9.30 Av main course £4.50
Restaurant 12-2 7-9.30 Av 3 course à la carte £15 Av 1 course fixed price £7.95

FROGNALL Lincolnshire *Map 08 TF11*

The Goat
FROGNALL

155 Spalding Rd PE6 8SA
☎ 01778 347629
Renovation work and new extensions have given this welcoming country pub a fresh look in recent years. Part of the building dates back to the 16th century. Straightforward but comprehensive menu with an emphasis on healthy eating, includes a fish selection, grills, pies, curry and chilli.
Principal beers: Adnams Southwold.

Directions A1 to Peterborough, A15 to Market Deeping, old A16 to Spalding, pub about 1.5m from jct of A15 & A16

Brewery/Company Free House
Open 11-2.30 6-11 (Sun 12-3, 7-10.30)
Bar food 12-2 6.30-9.30 Av main course £6.25
Restaurant 12-2 6.30-9.30 Av 3 course à la carte £15 Av 3 course fixed price £9.25

Pubs offering a good choice of seafood on the menu

GEDNEY DYKE Lincolnshire *Map 09 TF42*

The Chequers
GEDNEY DYKE

PE12 0AJ ☎ 01406 362666

An 18th-century country inn located in a remote Fenland village close to The Wash wildfowl sanctuaries. Gressingham duck and locally-reared beef might feature among the interesting meat dishes, while excellent fresh fish, delivered from Grimsby, may include Cajun-spiced monkfish with red berry dressing and spiced sea bass with red wine sauce.
Principal beers: Adnams, Bass, Elgoods Pageant, Morland Old Speckled Hen.
Directions From King's Lynn take A17, 1st roundabout after Long Sutton take B1359
Brewery/Company Free House
Open 12-3 7-11 (Sun 7-10.30)
Bar food 12-2 7-9.30 Av main course £6.50
Restaurant 12-2 7-9.30 Av 3 course à la carte £15.50 Av 2 course fixed price £7.50

GRANTHAM Lincolnshire *Map 08 SK93*

The Beehive Inn
GRANTHAM

10/11 Castlegate NG31 6SE
☎ 01476 404554

Grantham's oldest inn (1550) is notable for having England's only living pub sign - a working beehive high up in a lime tree. Otherwise, this simple town hostelry offers a good pint of Batemans XB and good-value, yet basic bar food. Home-cooked dishes include soups and steak and ale pie.
Principal beers: Batemans XB.
Directions A52 to town centre, L at Finkin st, pub at end
Brewery/Company Free House
Open 11-11
Bar food 11.30-2.30 Av main course £3.25

HOLDINGHAM Lincolnshire *Map 08 TF04*

Jolly Scotchman
HOLDINGHAM

NG34 8NP ☎ 01529 304864

With an indoor play room and a garden featuring an adventure playground, aviary and pets' corner, this friendly old pub is the perfect family destination. Victorian-style conservatory restaurant and homely bars where traditional pub food, such as beef in stout, seafood platter and peppered pork can be enjoyed. **Principal beers:** Flowers IPA, Courage Directors, Marstons Pedigree.
Directions 200yds S of A15/A17 rdbt, 1m from Sleaford
Brewery/Company Free House
Open 11-2.30 6.30-11 (11-3, 5.30-11 summer)
Bar food 12-2.30 6.30-10 Av main course £5
Restaurant 12-2.30 5.30-10 Av 3 course à la carte £15

LINCOLN Lincolnshire *Map 08 SK97*

Pyewipe Inn
LINCOLN

Fossebank, Saxilby Rd LN1 2BG
☎ 01522 528708

Barging inn on the Fossedyke Canal dating from 1750, standing in four acres of trees with its own moorings. Pyewipe chicken, with Stilton and bacon, and game casserole with herby dumplings are typical bar dishes. The restaurant offers duck with blackcurrant sauce, and Chateaubriand.
Principal beers: Wadworth 6X, Greene King IPA, Fullers London Pride, Tetley.
Directions Out of Lincoln on A57 past Lincoln Bypass, pub signed after 0.5m
Brewery/Company Free House
Open 11-11 (Mon-Sat) 12-10.30 (Sun)
Bar food 11.30-9.30 Av main course £7
Restaurant 7-9.30 Av 3 course à la carte £16

Wig & Mitre
LINCOLN

30 Steep Hill LN2 1TL ☎ 01522 535190

Located in medieval Lincoln, on a picturesque street close to the city's cathedral, this historic 14th-century pub offers a comprehensive menu including a cooked English breakfast, sandwiches and toasted Lincolnshire plum bread. Expect fillet of sea bass, rack of lamb and chargrilled fillet steak among the appetising home-cooked main courses.
Principal beers: Taylor Landlord, Marston's Pedigree.
Directions Adjacent to Lincoln Cathedral

Brewery/Company Free House
Open 8am-midnight
Bar food 8am-midnight Av main course £7

LONG BENNINGTON Lincolnshire *Map 08 SK84*

The Reindeer
LONG BENNINGTON
Main Rd NG23 5EH ☎ 01400 281382
A small, welcoming pub with exposed beams and cosy fireplaces set in a pretty, bustling village within easy reach of the main A1. A typical menu includes liver bacon and champ, poached salmon, grilled plaice fillet and haddock in beer batter. **Principal beers:** John Smiths, Ruddles County, Morland Old Speckled Hen, Theakston XB.
Directions 7m North of Grantham on the A1
Brewery/Company Free House
Open 11-3 7-11
Bar food 11.30-2 7-10 Av main course £8
Restaurant 11.30-2 7-10 Av 3 course à la carte £18

MARSTON Lincolnshire *Map 08 SK84*

Thorold Arms
MARSTON
Main St NG32 2HH ☎ 01400 250899
A typical country pub, this large Victorian building is situated in the centre of the village on the Viking Way. A range of snacks, along with grills and curries are served in the bar, while the restaurant carte offers a good choice of fish, rack of lamb, and steaks.
Principal beers: Bass, Marston's, Ward's, Worthington.
Directions Off A1 N of Grantham
Brewery/Company Free House
Open 12-3.30 7-11.30
Bar food 12.15-2.15 7-10.50 Av main course £4
Restaurant 12.15-2.15 7-11 Av 3 course à la carte £10.50 Av 3 course fixed price £6.50

NEWTON Lincolnshire *Map 08 TF03*

The Red Lion
NEWTON
NG34 0EE ☎ 01529 497256
Civilised, neartly-kept pub tucked away in a peaceful hamlet off the A52. Good home-produced food with a cold buffet offering cooked meats, fish and up to 15 fresh salads, and a popular hot carvery (Sat evening/Sun lunch) with four roast joints. Good puddings like Bakewell tart. Lovely rear garden for summer drinking.
Principal beers: Bateman XXXB, Bass.
Directions 10m E of Grantham on A52
Brewery/Company Free House
Open 12-3 6-11
Bar food 12-3 7-9.30 Av main course £8
Restaurant 12-3 7-9.30 Av 3 course à la carte £14.95

OLD SOMERBY Lincolnshire *Map 08 SK93*

Fox & Hounds
OLD SOMERBY
NG33 4AB ☎ 01476 564121
Nestling in a rural village in the Lincolnshire Wolds, this rambling, traditional country pub offers a wide ranges of snacks and meals to suit all palates. From fresh Grimsby haddock and seafood platter, the menu may feature home-made steak pie, liver and bacon, and steak with mushroom, cream and brandy sauce.
Principal beers: Marston's Pedigree, Fuller's London Pride, Batemans XB.
Directions From A1 take A52 E, after 3m take B1176, then 1m to Old Somerby
Brewery/Company Free House
Open 11.30-3 6.30-11 (closed Mon)
Bar food 12-2 7-9.30 Av main course £6
Restaurant 12-2 7-9.30 Av 3 course à la carte £15

PARTNEY Lincolnshire *Map 08 TF46*

Red Lion Inn
PARTNEY
PE23 4PG ☎ 01790 752271
Parts of this Lincolnshire inn may date back 400 years, but reports of a ghost seem to be unsubstantiated. Home-made dishes include beef, mushroom and Stilton pie, vegetable lasagne, pheasant pie, pork in cheese and cream, sugar baked gammon and peaches, and barbecued spare ribs.
Principal beers: Bass, Bateman.
Directions On A16 from Boston, or A158 from Horncastle
Brewery/Company Free House
Open 11-2.30 7-11 (Sun 12-2.30, 7-10.30, closed Mon & Tue)
Bar food 12-2 7-9.30 Av main course £6
Accommodation (Min) s£25 d£35

RAITHBY Lincolnshire Map 08 TF36

Red Lion Inn
RAITHBY

PE23 4DS ☎ 01790 753727

Set in the attractive village of Raithby, this Tudor-style listed inn has a varied international menu. Dishes include chicken Marengo, cannelloni, and a range of curries such as tikka masala, lamb balti and beef Madras.

Principal beers: John Smiths, Tom Wood.

Directions Take A158 from Horncastle, R at Sausthorpe, keep L into Raithby

Brewery/Company Free House

Open 12-2.30 7-11(closed Mon-Wed lunchtime)

Bar food 12-2 7-10 Av main course £4.75

Restaurant 12-2 7-10 Av 3 course à la carte £8.35

Accommodation (Min) s£26 d£38

ROTHWELL Lincolnshire Map 08 TF19

The Nickerson Arms
ROTHWELL

Hill Rise LN7 6AZ ☎ 01472 371300

Originally the village forge, and said to be haunted by an old cellarman, this village inn dates back to the 16th century. Dishes on offer might include roast lamb shank with cream and mint sauce, chicken with mild curry sauce, grilled Dover sole, salmon with lemon dill butter, and home-made steak and Guinness pie.

Principal beers: Batemans XB & XXXB, Courage Directors, Fullers London Pride.

Directions 3m off the A46 between Grimsby and Caistor

Brewery/Company Free House

Open 12-3.30 7-11.30

Bar food 12-2 7-9 Av main course £4.90

Restaurant 12-2 7-9 Av 3 course à la carte £20

SAXILBY Lincolnshire Map 08 SK87

The Bridge Inn
SAXILBY

Gainsborough Rd LN1 2LX
☎ 01522 702266

Traditional Sunday lunch goes down well at this canalside pub near Lincoln. Day to day food ranges from bar snacks to specials such as sirloin with cream and a seafood platter with fish and shellfish. Traditional sweets follow, including sticky toffee pudding and syrup sponge.

Principal beers: John Smiths

Directions On A57 W of Lincoln

Open 11.30-2.30 5.30-11 (open all day Sun, closed Mon)

Bar food 11.30-2 7-various Av main course £5.95

Restaurant 11.30-2 7-Various

SPALDING Lincolnshire Map 08 TF22

The Ship Inn
SPALDING

15A Reservoir Rd, Surfleet-Seas-End
PE11 4DH ☎ 01775 680384

A 17th-century pub with old beams and open fires, situated on the village edge at the confluence of three rivers. Hearty traditional food is freshly prepared, the blackboard menu may list rabbit and prune casserole, steak and kidney pudding, bouillabaisse, monkfish provençale, and skate in black butter.

Principal beers: Marstons Best & Pedigree.

Directions Off A16 (Spalding to Boston)

Brewery/Company Free House

Open 12-3 7-11

Bar food 12-3 Av main course £4.95

Restaurant 12-3 7-11 Av 3 course à la carte £15

Accommodation (Min) s£17.50 d£35

STAMFORD Lincolnshire Map 04 TF00

The George at Stamford
STAMFORD

71 St Martins PE9 2LB ☎ 01780 750750

Handsome 16th-century coaching inn with log fires, a walled monastery garden and cobbled courtyard. Expect Brittany seafood platter and sirloin of beef on the traditional yet imaginative menu, along with game terrine, pan-fried sea bass, lamb shank, calves' liver, and pheasant flamed in brandy. Very extensive wine list.

Principal beers: Adnams Broadside, Fullers London Pride.
Directions take A1 N from Peterborough. From A1 roundabout signposted B1081 Stamford, down hill to lights. Hotel on L
Open 7am-11pm
Bar food 7am-11pm Av main course £9.50
Restaurant 12.30-2.30 7.30-10.30 Av 3 course à la carte £30 Av 2 course fixed price £14.50
Accommodation (Min) s£78 d£103

St Peter's Inn and The Bistro
STAMFORD
11 St Peter's St PE9 2DQ
☎ 01780 763298
Thai style dishes are among the specialities at this 18th-century pub and bistro in the conservation area of Stamford, where the television adaption of Middlemarch was filmed. Imaginative home-cooked meals include feta cheese omelette, pasta carbonara and fillet steak Royale. Expect a good vegetarian selection. **Principal beers:** Marstons Best & Pedigree.
Directions From A1 take A6121 to Stamford.Pub 1m on R
Brewery/Company Free House
Open 12-2.30 (Tue-Thu) 12-11 (Fri-Sun)
Bar food 12-2 Av main course £5.95
Restaurant 12-2 6.30-9 Av 3 course à la carte £12

TETFORD Lincolnshire Map 09 TF37

The White Hart Inn
TETFORD
East Rd LN9 6UU ☎ 01507 533255
Built around 1520, this three-bar country pub in the heart of the Lincolnshire Wolds was frequented by Dr Johnson and Tennyson - though not at the same time! There's a frequently changing menu of home-cooked food. Items from the specials board include steak and kidney pie, pork in cider and cream, game pie, amd liver and bacon casserole. **Principal beers:** Adnams Best, Fullers London Pride, Greene King Abbot Ale.
Directions From Louth take A16 S Tetford signed on R
Brewery/Company Free House
Open 12-3 7-11 (closed Mon)
Bar food 12-3 7-11 Av main course £5
Restaurant 12-3 7-11 Av 3 course à la carte £10 Av 4 course fixed price £7.95
Accommodation (Min) s£12 d£24

WADDINGHAM Lincolnshire Map 08 SK99

Brandy Wharf Cider Centre
WADDINGHAM
Brandy Wharf DN21 4RJ
☎ 01652 678364
Riverside walks, nature trails and a fascinating cider museum add to the enjoyment of a visit to this unusual cider tavern on the River Ancholme. Simple food includes speciality sausages, steak and vegetable pie, hearty sandwiches and home-made burgers. Up to 15 ciders on draught. **Principal beers:** Cider Only.
Directions On B1205 between S Kelsey & Waddingham
Brewery/Company Free House
Open 12-3 (closed Mon lunch Nov-Apr) 7-11 (Sun 7-10.30, closed Xmas wk)
Bar food 12-2 7-9.45 Av main course £5

WOOLSTHORPE Lincolnshire Map 08 SK83

Rutland Arms
WOOLSTHORPE
NG32 1NY ☎ 01476 870111
Better known to locals as the 'Dirty Duck', this family pub sits at the side of the Grantham canal, in the shadow of Belvoir Castle. Specialities include Bobby T's freshly-caught cod and haddock, grilled pork cutlet, roast beef and Yorkshire pudding, and rainbow trout with almond butter. **Principal beers:** Castle Eden Ale, Bass, John Smith.
Brewery/Company Free House
Open 11-3 6-11 (Sat-Sun open all day)
Bar food 11-3 6-9.30 Av main course £5
Restaurant 11-3 6-9.30 Av 3 course à la carte £11

Norfolk

BAWBURGH Norfolk Map 05 TG10

Kings Head
BAWBURGH
Harts Ln NR9 3LS ☎ 01603 744977
Named after King Edward VII, a renowned sportsman and bon viveur, this popular pub uses fresh local produce and offers a varied selection of starters and main courses, as well as snacks, baguettes and sandwiches. Bar meals might include steak and kidney pudding, bangers and mash, and honey and lime chicken.

contd.

Kings Head

Principal beers: Adnams, Boddingtons, Woodforde's Wherry, Green King IPA.
Directions From A47 W of Norwich take B1108 W
Brewery/Company Free House
Open 11-11
Bar food 12-2 7-10 Av main course £6.95
Restaurant 12-2 7-10 Av 3 course à la carte £15.25

BINHAM Norfolk — Map 09 TF93

Chequers Inn
BINHAM

Front St NR21 0AL ☎ 01328 830297
Grade 11 listed 17th-century inn, left in trust to the village of Binham to provide financial support to the elderly of the parish. Local game and fresh fish feature strongly, and one noteworthy dish is grunt gobble and zoom coo pie prepared from wild boar, turkey, hare and pigeon.
Principal beers: Greene King Abbot Ale, & IPA, Woodforde's Wherry, Adnams.
Directions On B1388 between Wells next the Sea & Walsingham
Brewery/Company Free House
Open 11.30-3 5.30-11
Bar food 12-2 6-9 Av main course £6
Restaurant 12-2 6-9
Accommodation (Min) s£25 d£45

BLAKENEY Norfolk — Map 09 TG04

White Horse Hotel
BLAKENEY

4 High St NR25 7AL ☎ 01263 740574
Located on the cobbled high street that runs down to Blakeney Harbour, this 17th-century coaching inn is ideally placed for coastal walks and visiting nearby bird sanctuaries. Monthly-changing menu featuring local seasonal produce, perhaps including cockle chowder, fresh mussels, beef fillet and salmon with crab sauce.
Principal beers: Adnams, Boddingtons.
Directions From A148 (Cromer to King's Lynn rd) turn onto A149 signed to Blakeney.
Brewery/Company Free House
Open 11-3 6-11
Bar food 12-2 6-9 Av main course £6.25
Restaurant 7-9 Av 3 course à la carte £17.50
Accommodation (Min) s£25 d£60

BLICKLING Norfolk — Map 09 TG12

The Buckinghamshire Arms
BLICKLING

Blickling Rd NR11 6NF
☎ 01263 732133
Dating from 1693, this coaching inn was originally built for guests and servants of nearby Blickling Hall. Favourite dishes include pan-fried monkfish with warm vinaigrette, pasta with green pesto, walnut and onions, and real Norfolk treacle tart. Fresh fish is a speciality.
Principal beers: Reepham, Adnams, Woodforde's Blickling.
Directions From Cromer (A140) take exit at Aylsham onto B1354
Brewery/Company Free House
Open 12-3 6-11 (sometimes open all day in summer)
Bar food 12-2.30 7-9 Av main course £6.50
Restaurant 12-2.30 7-9 Av 3 course à la carte £14

BURNHAM MARKET Norfolk — Map 09 TF84

The Hoste Arms
BURNHAM MARKET

The Green PE31 8HD ☎ 01328 738777
Handsome 17th-century inn overlooking the green and parish church in a delightful village close to the coast. Quality food draws on fresh local and seasonal produce, the interesting menus listing, perhaps, Burnham Creek oysters, red mullet and scallops poached in chilli with tomato broth, turbot with tarragon cream, and chargrilled beef with red wine jus. First-class accommodation, tip-top East Anglian ales, and well-chosen wines. **Principal beers:** Woodforde's Wherry, Greene King Abbot Ale, & IPA, Adnams Broadside.
Directions Signposted off B1155, 5m w of Wells-next-the-Sea
Brewery/Company Free House
Open 11-11

Restaurant 12-2 7-9 Av 3 course à la carte £17.50
Accommodation (Min) s£52 d£68

BURNHAM THORPE Norfolk — Map 09 TF84

The Lord Nelson
BURNHAM THORPE
Walsingham Rd PE31 8HN
☎ 01328 738241
An unspoilt gem tucked away in a sleepy village and named after England's most famous seafarer, who was born in the rectory. Step inside this 350-year-old cottage, with its huge settles, old brick floor and Nelson memorabilia, and sample ale tapped from the cask and enjoyable bar food such as red mullet with pesto, chicken liver pâté, pork with rosemary, garlic and sweet chilli sauce, or a more traditional bar snack.
Principal beers: Greene King Abbot Ale, & IPA, Dark Mild, Woodforde's Nelsons Revenge.
Brewery/Company Greene King
Open 11-3 6-11 (Sun 12-3,7-10.30)
Bar food 12-2 7-9 Av main course £7

CLEY NEXT THE SEA Norfolk — Map 09 TG04

George & Dragon Hotel
CLEY NEXT THE SEA
High St NR25 7RN ☎ 01263 740652
Classic Edwardian inn, with high ceilings and polished parquet floors, overlooking Cley Marshes and popular with birdwatchers and walkers. Local cod in prawn sauce and fresh dressed crab salad are favoured choices on the bar menu, while restaurant dishes include pork tenderloin stuffed with nuts and mushrooms. **Principal beers:** Greene King-IPA, Abbot Ale.
Directions On coast road (A149). Centre of village
Brewery/Company Free House
Open 11-3 6-11 (Winter 11.30-2.30 6.30-11)
Bar food 12-2 7-8.45 Av main course £5.50
Restaurant 12-2 7-8.45 Av 3 course à la carte £13.50
Accommodation (Min) s£35 d£40

COLKIRK Norfolk — Map 09 TF92

The Crown
COLKIRK
Crown Rd NR21 7AA ☎ 01328 862172
Comfortable country pub with open fires and a relaxed atmosphere. Garden, suntrap terrace and pleasant non-smoking dining room. Strong emphasis on good food. Bar fare tends to feature ploughman's, fried brunch, gammon and egg, and specials such as fresh haddock, steak and kidney pie, and fillet of chicken in leek and Stilton sauce. **Principal beers:** Greene King - IPA, Abbot Ale, Mild, Triumph.
Directions 2m from B1146 Fakenham-Dereham rd
Brewery/Company Greene King
Open 11-2.30 6-11 (Sun 12-2.30, 7-10.30)
Bar food 12-1.45 7-9.30 Av main course £6.50
Restaurant 12-1.45 7-9.30 Av 3 course à la carte £14

COLTISHALL Norfolk — Map 09 TG21

Kings Head
COLTISHALL
26 Wroxham Rd NR12 7EA
☎ 01603 737426
Homely 17th-century beamed inn, located on the banks of the River Bure, in the heart of the Norfolk Broads. Food ranges from ploughman's and Thai green curry, to stir-fried beef with noodles, whole lemon sole, sea bass with herb and tomato vinaigrette, and scallops with chardonnay sauce. **Principal beers:** Adnams, Woodforde's Wherry.
Directions A47 Norwich ring road onto B1150 to North Walsham at Coltishall. R at petrol station, follow rd to R past church, on R next to car park
Brewery/Company Free House
Open 11-3 6-11
Bar food 12-2 Av main course £4.95

contd.

Restaurant 12-2 7-9 Av 3 course à la carte £16.50 Av 3 course fixed price £16.50
Accommodation (Min) s£20 d£40

DITCHINGHAM Norfolk *Map 05 TM39*

Duke of York
DITCHINGHAM
8 Norwich Rd NR35 2JL
☎ 01986 895558

Cosy traditional pub fronted by two large bay windows. The blackboard menu changes daily and may feature lamb Kleftico, salmon steak with vegetable compote, sirloin steak with mushroom, red wine and butter sauce, and Burmese chicken and vegetables. Vegetarians might like to try the mushroom Stroganoff or vegetable balti curry.
Principal beers: Adnams, Tetley.
Directions L off A143 at Bungay/Ditchingham rdbt 200yrds on R
Brewery/Company Free House
Open 11-3.30 6-11 (closed Tue, 1wk Feb & 2wks Nov)
Bar food 12-2 7-9 Av main course £5

DOCKING Norfolk *Map 09 TF73*

Pilgrims Reach
DOCKING
High St PE31 8NH ☎ 01485 518383

A 16th-century inn, originally a barn, with Tudor beams and inglenook fireplaces. A house speciality is the crab menu in summer, with six different crab dishes, and a similar mussels menu in winter. Other options include duo of sea trout, smoked duck breast, and pork steaks with Stilton glaze. **Principal beers:** Boddingtons, Shepherd Neame Spitfire.
Directions From Hunstanton take A1495 then B1454 or A149 E then B1153
Brewery/Company Free House
Open 12-3 6-11.30 (closed Tue)
Bar food 12-2 6-9.30 Av main course £7
Restaurant 12-2.30 6-10.30 Av 3 course à la carte £18

EASTGATE Norfolk *Map 09 TG12*

Ratcatchers Inn
EASTGATE
Easton Way NR10 4HA ☎ 01603 871430

Rat catchers used to meet to collect 'a penny a tail' at this 200-year-old pub. Steak and kidney pie is a stalwart of the menu, while specials might include local duck breast with caramelised orange and brandy sauce. A favourite to finish is the icky sticky toffee pudding.
Principal beers: Bass, Adnams.
Directions Off A140, past Norwich Airport take B1149 to Holt, thru Horsford, 6m then pub signed
Brewery/Company Free House
Open 11.45-3 6-11 (Sun 12-3, 6.45-11)
Bar food 12-2 6-10 Av main course £7
Restaurant 12-2 6-10 Av 3 course à la carte £15

EATON Norfolk *Map 05 TG20*

Red Lion
EATON
Eaton St ☎ 01603 454787

Former 17th-century coaching inn located just off the A11 south-west of Norwich. Neat and comfortable panelled bar and carvery offering fresh fish from Lowestoft (sea bass, skate), steaks and a limited choice of quality blackboard specials.
Principal beers: Theakston, Courage Best, Greene King IPA.
Directions off the A11
Brewery/Company Free House

Open 11-11
Bar food 12-2 7-9
Restaurant 12-2 7-9 Av 3 course à la carte £15
Accommodation (Min) s£29 d£38

ERPINGHAM Norfolk *Map 09 TG13*

Saracen's Head
ERPINGHAM
Wolterton NR11 7LX ☎ 01263 768909

Built by Lord Walpole as a coaching inn for his estate, this early 19th-century pub, designed like a Tuscan farmhouse, offers decent snacks as well as an eclectic and highly imaginative menu. Expect

monkfish with orange and ginger, venison with wild mushrooms and Madeira, or lamb with herb and cream sauce, followed by boosey trifle. **Principal beers:** Adnams, Woodforde's.
Directions A140 2.5m N of Aylsham, L through Erpingham, signs 'Calthorpe'.Through Calthorpe 1m on R (in field)
Brewery/Company Free House
Open 11.30-3 6-11
Bar food 12.15-2.15 7.15-9.30 Av main course £8
Accommodation (Min) s£35 d£40

GREAT BIRCHAM Norfolk *Map 09 TF73*

King's Head Hotel
GREAT BIRCHAM
PE31 6RJ ☎ 01485 578265
A friendly village hotel serving bar food of fresh fish and seafood, including crab and lobster, from the Norfolk coast, with alternatives such as steak and kidney pudding. The hotel's restaurant offers Italian specialities - chicken, veal and pork in creamy sauces, along with grilled steaks and fish dishes.
Principal beers: Worthington Best, Bass, Adnams.
Brewery/Company Free House
Open 11-2.30 7-11
Bar food 12-2 7-9.30 Av main course £6.50
Restaurant 12-2.30 7-9.30 Av 3 course à la carte £18
Accommodation (Min) s£38 d£59

GREAT RYBURGH Norfolk *Map 09 TF92*

The Boar Inn
GREAT RYBURGH
NR21 0DX ☎ 01328 829212
Nestling in the heart of rural Norfolk, just a few yards from the River Wensum, this 300-year-old village inn is opposite the village's round-towered Saxon church. Expect mushroom Royale, smoked mackerel and tandoori chicken tikka among the snacks and starters. Daily specials might feature beef and ale casserole and tuna steak.
Principal beers: Adnams.
Directions Off A1067 4m S of Fakenham
Brewery/Company Free House
Open 11-2.30 6.30-11
Bar food 12-2 7-9.30 Av main course £6
Restaurant 12-2 7-9.30 Av 3 course à la carte £14
Accommodation (Min) s£20 d£35

HEMPSTEAD Norfolk *Map 09 TG13*

Hare and Hounds
HEMPSTEAD
Baconsthorpe Rd NR25 6LD
☎ 01263 712340
Flint-built in dating from 1620, recently extended to provide better kitchen and cellar space. Food choice consists of four menus: snack, country, fish and game. The fish menu offers fresh fish and seafood from Lowestoft, while game dishes include game medley with brandy, garlic and cream sauce. **Principal beers:** Woodeforde's Nelsons Revenge, Woodforde Wherry, Wolf Golden Jackal, & Granny Wouldn't Like It.
Directions From Holt follow signs for Baconsthorpe. Pub 1.5m from Holt (pub not actually in Hempstead)
Brewery/Company Free House
Open 9.30am-11.30pm
Restaurant 12-3 6-10 Av 3 course à la carte £17

HETHERSETT Norfolk *Map 05 TG10*

Kings Head
HETHERSETT
36 Norwich Rd NR9 3DD
☎ 01603 810206
An attractive 17th-century roadside inn with a beamed snug and a comfortable lounge with a wood-burning stove in the inglenook fireplace. Wide range of pub food, from granary baps and ploughman's, to standard pub meals and home-made specials like chicken balti, freshly battered cod, and pork in Dijon mustard sauce. **Principal beers:** Woodforde's Wherry, Marstons Pedigree, Greene King Abbot Ale, John Smiths.
Directions Old Norwich Road just off B1172 Cringleford to Wymondham road. 5m SW of Norwich
Brewery/Company Free House
Open 11-2.30 5.30-11 (Sun 7-10.30)
Bar food 12-2.15 6.30-9.30 Av main course £5.95
Restaurant 12-2.15 6.30-9.30

For Pubs with AA food rosettes see page 430

Central & East Anglia

HORSEY Norfolk Map 09 TG42

Nelson Head
HORSEY
The Street NR29 4AD
☎ 01493 393378 01692 581016
Convenient for the coast path and local bird reserves, this homely 16th-century pub offers snacks, light lunches and Austrian specialities. Dishes include various steaks, pork fricassée, venison casserole, cottage pie, roast Norfolk duckling, mixed vegetable platter with garlic mayonnaise, and vegetarian tagliatelle. **Principal beers:** Woodforde's Wherry, Nelsons Revenge.
Directions On coast rd (B1159) between West Somerton & Sea Palling
Brewery/Company Free House
Open 11-2.30 7-11
Bar food 11-2.30 7-11 Av main course £6.50
Restaurant 11-2 7-11 Av 3 course à la carte £12

HORSTEAD Norfolk Map 09 TG21

Recruiting Sergeant
HORSTEAD
Norwich Rd NR12 7EE ☎ 01603 737077
A warm country pub, dating from the Domesday Book, with a large inglenook fireplace. The same menu is served in both the bar and restaurant, offering dishes like fresh wing of Norfolk skate, steak and mushroom pie, and baked venison with redcurrant and mushroom sauce. **Principal beers:** John Smiths, Wadworth 6X, Boddingtons, Greene King Abbot Ale.
Directions on the B1150 between Norwich & North Walsham
Brewery/Company Free House
Open 11-11
Bar food 12-2 6.30-9.30
Restaurant 12-2 6.30-9.30 Av 3 course à la carte £12

KING'S LYNN Norfolk Map 09 TF62

The Tudor Rose Hotel
KING'S LYNN
St Nicholas St PE30 1LR
☎ 01553 762824
Family-run hotel in the heart of the Old Town, opposite St Nicholas' Chapel. It is a timber-framed building, dating from about 1500, with a jettied street frontage. Dishes range from hot chicken sandwich or chilli, in the bar, to seafood medley and Mediterranean lamb in the restaurant.
Principal beers: Batemans XB, Woodforde's Wherry, Bass.
Directions Hotel is of Tuesday Market Place in the centre of Kings Lynn
Brewery/Company Free House
Open 11-11 (Sun 7-10.30)
Bar food 12-2 7-9 Av main course £5
Restaurant 7-9 Av 3 course à la carte £15.50
Accommodation (Min) s£30 d£50

LARLING Norfolk Map 05 TL98

Angel Inn NEW
LARLING
NR16 2QU ☎ 01953 717963
Run by the same family since 1913, this unassuming and neatly kept roadside pub offers a friendly welcome, locally-brewed ales, and traditional pub meals within its comfortable bars. Home-cooked dishes include ploughman's, steak and kidney pie, fresh cod in beer batter, lasagne, and daily fish specials, perhaps Dover sole.
Principal beers: Adnams.
Brewery/Company Free House
Open 10-11
Bar food 12-2 6.30-9.30 Av main course £6.95
Restaurant 12-2 6.30-9.30 Av 3 course à la carte £12.50 Av 3 course fixed price £12.50
Accommodation (Min) s£30 d£50

MARSHAM Norfolk Map 09 TG12

Flags Free House
MARSHAM
Old Norwich Rd NR10 5PS
☎ 01263 735000
Smart, traditional style pub and restaurant close to the historic town of Aylsham and ideally placed for the Norfolk Broads. Good base for fishing and walking. Expect standard bar snacks and weekly specials like beef in red wine, carrot and coriander soup, and Stilton cobbler.
Principal beers: Adnams.
Brewery/Company Free House
Open 11-3 6-11
Bar food 12-2 6-9.30 Av main course £6
Restaurant 12-2 6-9.30 Av 3 course à la carte £15 Av 3 course fixed price £13
Accommodation (Min) s£40 d£50

MUNDFORD Norfolk *Map 05 TL89*

Crown Hotel
MUNDFORD
Crown Rd IP26 5HQ ☎ 01842 878233
Traditional inn on the edge of Thetford Forest, dating back to 1652. It is built on a hill so, unusually, the garden is on the first floor. Dishes might include braised beef in local ale with mushrooms, peppercorns and cream, and roasted monkfish tail with home-made lobster ravioli. **Principal beers:** Woodforde's Wherry, Courage Directors, Marstons Pedigree, Theakston Best.
Directions Take A11 until Barton Mills interception, then A1065 to Brandon & thru to Mundford
Brewery/Company Free House
Open 11-11
Bar food 12-3 7-10 Av main course £5.95
Restaurant 12-3 7-10 Av 3 course à la carte £20
Accommodation (Min) s£32.50 d£49.50

NORWICH Norfolk *Map 05 TG20*

Adam & Eve
NORWICH
Bishopsgate NR2 2RZ ☎ 01603 667423
Norwichs oldest pub, built around a Saxon well which still exists beneath the Lower Bar floor. Originally a brewhouse for the workmen building the city's Cathedral. Menu features beef and mushroom pie, prawn curry, and vegetable bake. Salads, ploughman's and granary baps, with daily specials listed on chalk boards. **Principal beers:** Adnams Best, John Smiths, Theakston Best & Old Peculier, Greene King IPA.
Brewery/Company Free House
Open 11-11 (Sun 12-10.30 – food 12-2.30)
Bar food 12-7 Av main course £4.50

Ribs of Beef
NORWICH
24 Wensum St NR3 1HY
☎ 01603 619517
Welcoming riverside pub incorporating remnants of the original 14th-century building destroyed in the Great Fire in 1507. Once used by the wherry skippers, it is still popular among boat owners cruising the Broads. Simple bar food includes baked ham, egg and chips, toasted pitta breads, salads, and fish and chips.
Principal beers: Woodforde's, Adnams, Courage, Whitbread.
Brewery/Company Free House
Open 10.30am-11pm (Sun 12-10.30, bar food 12-5.30 wknds)
Bar food 12-2.30 Av main course £4.65

REEDHAM Norfolk *Map 05 TG40*

The Reedham Ferry Inn

REEDHAM
Ferry Rd NR13 3HA ☎ 01493 700429
Quaint 17th-century inn situated in superb Norfolk Broads countryside and associated with the last working chain ferry in East Anglia. Typical bar food includes ploughman's, prawn submarine and smoked salmon salad. In the restaurant you might find game pie, braised pheasant, and skate wings with caper and prawn butter. **Principal beers:** Woodforde's Wherry, Adnams - Best & Broadside, Greene King Abbot Ale.

Directions 6m S of Acle on B1140 (Acle to Beccles rd)
Brewery/Company Free House
Open 11-3 6.30-11 (Sun 12-3,7-10.30)
Bar food 12-2.30 7-9.30 Av main course £4.75
Restaurant 12-2.30 7-9.30 Av 3 course à la carte £12

SNETTISHAM Norfolk *Map 09 TF63*

The Rose & Crown
SNETTISHAM
Old Church Rd PE31 7LX
☎ 01485 541382
Built to accommodate the workmen who constructed Snettisham church in 1396, this popular pub is also handy for some splendid beaches and local walks. Daily-changing menus may list game pate with onion compote, baked sea bass with chive and balsamic vinegar dressing, Cromer crab, lamb steak with green peppercorn sauce, and cod and chips.

contd.

Principal beers: Adnams, Bass, Fullers London pride, Wolf Granny Wouldn't Like It.
Directions Head N from Kings Lynn on A149 signed to Hunstanton. Inn in centre of Snettisham between market square and the church
Brewery/Company Free House
Open 11-11
Bar food 12-2 6-9 Av main course £8.50
Restaurant 12-2 6-9 Av 3 course à la carte £15
Accommodation (Min) s£40 d£60

STIFFKEY Norfolk — *Map 09 TF94*

Stiffkey Red Lion
STIFFKEY
44 Wells Rd NR23 1AJ ☎ 01328 830552
Fresh fish from King's Lynn, crab from Cromer, and tip-top East Anglian ales draws coast path walkers, holidaymakers and devoted fish fanciers to this rustic 16th-century pub overlooking the Stiffkey Valley. Expect hearty home-cooking, including fish pie, mussels, grilled sea bass, locally-smoked sea trout and game (pheasant, rabbit) in season. **Principal beers:** Woodforde's Wherry, Adnams, Greene King Abbot Ale.
Directions Take A149 from Wells toward Sheringham, 4m onL
Brewery/Company Free House
Open 11-3 5.30-11
Bar food 12-1.45 7-9 Av main course £6
Accommodation (Min) s£30 d£50

STOKE HOLY CROSS Norfolk — *Map 05 TG20*

The Wildebeest Arms NEW
STOKE HOLY CROSS
82-86 Norwich Rd NR14 8QJ
☎ 01598 492497
Vibrant and robust Mediterranean/British style of cooking and a buzzy, unpretentious atmosphere characterise this upbeat foodie pub with its distinctive African decor. Expect real ales on tap, decent wines and an eclectic menu offering, perhaps, confit of duck salad, wild pigeon terrine, seared salmon with vegetable and spinach risotto, and sirloin steak with spring onion mash and mustard and redcurrant sauce. **Principal beers:** Adnams.
Brewery/Company Free House
Open 12-3 6-11
Restaurant 12-2 7-9.30 Av 3 course à la carte £25 Av 3 course fixed price £15

STOW BARDOLPH Norfolk — *Map 05 TF60*

The Hare Arms
STOW BARDOLPH
PE34 3HT ☎ 01366 382229
Popular country pub in a delightful estate village with a good reputation for its food. Expect traditional fare in the bar, from home-made curries, lasagne and pies, to specials like plaice with salmon mousse, and a range of international dishes in the restaurant, perhaps Thai green chicken curry, or sea bass with Chinese spices. **Principal beers:** Greene King - Abbot Ale, IPA, Triumph.
Directions From King's Lynn take A10 to Downham Market.After 9m village signed on L
Brewery/Company Greene King
Open 11-3 6-11.30
Bar food 12-2 7-10 Av main course £10
Restaurant 12-2 7-9.30 Av 3 course à la carte £20 Av 3 course fixed price £17.50

SWANTON MORLEY Norfolk — *Map 09 TG01*

Darbys Freehouse
SWANTON MORLEY
1&2 Elsing Rd NR20 4NY
☎ 01362 637647
Popular pub converted from two cottages, furnished with old pine tables and farming memorabilia. Close to the Wensum valley, Norwich and The Broads. Offers Thai and English cuisine, with a range of dishes including chicken and mushroom pie, tuna steak, duck with orange sauce, and Thai chilli beef, prawns and cashews. **Principal beers:** Woodforde's Wherry, Badger Tanglefoot, Adnams - Broadside, Best.
Directions From A47 (Norwich/King's Lynn) take B1147 to Dereham
Brewery/Company Free House
Open 11-2.30 6-11 (Sat 11-11, Sun 12-3,7-10.30)
Bar food 12-2 7-10 Av main course £6.50
Restaurant 12-2 7-10
Accommodation (Min) s£25 d£45

Pubs offering a good choice of seafood on the menu

THOMPSON Norfolk *Map 05 TL99*

Chequers Inn
THOMPSON
Griston Rd IP24 1PX ☎ 01953 483360
Splendid, long and low, thatched 14th-century inn with wonky wall timbers, low doorways and log fires throughout its charming interconnecting rooms. Extensive main menu and interesting blackboard specials, perhaps featuring mushroom soup, mussels in wine, garlic and cream, pheasant in red wine, seafood tagliatelle and grilled plaice. Tranquil setting; excellent walks. **Principal beers:** Fullers London Pride, Adnams Best, Wolf Best, Greene King IPA.

Directions From A11 at Thetford, L to Watton at main rdbt, after 10m 2nd L to Thompson, pub 1m on R
Brewery/Company Free House
Open 11.30-2.30 6.30-11
Bar food 12-2 7-9.30 Av main course £6.50
Restaurant 12-2 7-9.30 Av 3 course à la carte £15 Av 3 course fixed price £8.95

THORNHAM Norfolk *Map 09 TF74*

Lifeboat Inn
THORNHAM
Ship Ln PE36 6LT ☎ 01485 512236
Extended former 16th-century smugglers' ale house overlooking unspoilt salt marsh to the sea. Enjoy smoked trout mousseline, Cromer crab, fish pie, char-grilled lamb cutlets, or date and ginger pudding in the character bars, vine-covered conservatory, or on the sun-trap rear patio. Separate, more elaborate restaurant menu. **Principal beers:** Adnams, Woodforde's Wherry, Greene King Abbot Ale.

Directions A149 to Hunstanton, follow coast rd to Thornham, pub 1st L
Brewery/Company Free House
Open 8am-11.30pm
Bar food 12-3 6.30-10 Av main course £6.95
Restaurant 12-3 7-10 Av 3 course à la carte £18 Av 3 course fixed price £18
Accommodation (Min) s£48 d£65

THORPE MARKET Norfolk *Map 09 TG23*

Green Farm Restaurant & Hotel
THORPE MARKET
North Walsham Rd NR11 8TH
☎ 01263 833602
Conveniently situated for exploring the Norfolk Broads, or the historic houses at Blickling, Felbrigg and Sandringham, this 16th-century former farmhouse features a pubby bar and an interesting menu. Typical dishes may include crispy duck leg salad, skate with caper sauce, beef and walnut casserole, Cromer crab, local lobster, and Holkham venison. **Principal beers:** Greene King IPA, Wolf - Best, Granny Wouldn't Like It.
Directions Situated on A149
Brewery/Company Free House
Open 11-2 6.30-11
Bar food 12-2 6.45-9 Av main course £7.50
Restaurant 12-2 6.45-9 Av 3 course à la carte £18.95 Av 5 course fixed price £18.95
Accommodation (Min) s£40 d£50

TITCHWELL Norfolk *Map 09 TF74*

Titchwell Manor Hotel
TITCHWELL
PE31 8BB ☎ 01485 210221
Originally a farmhouse, the hotel has lovely old walled gardens and offers magnificent views of the RSPB reserve and golden beaches. Local seafood is a speciality, with crab salads and lobster thermidor in the bar, and modern, competently cooked dishes like seared king scallops and pesto, or baby brill with mussels, in the restaurant. **Principal beers:** Greene King IPA & Abbot Ale.
Directions A149 (coast rd) between Brancaster & Thornham
Brewery/Company Free House
Open 12-2 6-9.30 (closed 2 wks end Jan)

contd.

Titchwell Manor Hotel

Bar food 12-2 6.30-9.30 Av main course £12.50
Restaurant 12-2 6.30-9.30 Av 3 course fixed price £24
Accommodation (Min) s£35 d£70

TIVETSHALL ST MARY Norfolk *Map 05 TM18*

The Old Ram Coaching Inn
TIVETSHALL ST MARY

Ipswich Rd NR15 2DE ☎ 01379 676794

Grade 11 listed property, originally a farmhouse and then a popular coaching inn between Norwich and London. The same menu is served throughout the rambling, beamed and antique-furnished rooms. Expect such dishes as seafood chowder, roast hock of lamb with red wine and rosemary sauce, beef Wellington, and pan-fried monkfish. **Principal beers:** Boddingtons, Adnams, Woodforde's.
Directions On A140 approx 15m S of Norwich
Brewery/Company Free House
Open 7.30am-11pm
Bar food 7.30am-10pm Av main course £8.95
Accommodation (Min) s£45 d£57

TOFT MONKS Norfolk *Map 05 TM49*

Toft Lion
TOFT MONKS

NR34 0EP ☎ 01502 677702

The pub dates from 1650 and was originally the White Lion, but by Norfolk tradition is referred to by the name of its village - to avoid confusion. It features an inglenook fireplace, beams, and a large single bar where a daily roast and other popular dishes are served. **Principal beers:** Adnams - Best, Broadside.
Directions Take A146 from Beccles, then A143
Brewery/Company Free House
Open 11.30-2.30 5-11.20
Bar food 12-2 7-9 Av main course £4.75
Restaurant 12-2 7-9 Av 3 course à la carte £10
Accommodation (Min) s£25 d£35

UPPER SHERINGHAM Norfolk *Map 09 TG14*

The Red Lion Inn
UPPER SHERINGHAM

The Street NR26 8AD ☎ 01263 825408

17th-century cottage inn situated in small village close to a steam railway and North Norfolk's splendidly isolated coast. Imaginative menu with good choice of fish dishes, including, perhaps, roast cod on bacon and cabbage cooked in beer, plaice baked in herb butter, spicy baked crab salad, and various game pies.
Principal beers: Woodfordes Wherry, Greene King IPA.
Directions A140(Norwich to Cromer) then A148 to Sheringham/Upper Sheringham
Brewery/Company Free House
Open 11.30-11 (Winter 11.30-3, 7-11)
Bar food 12-2.30 6.30-8.45 Av main course £6.50
Restaurant 12-2.30 6.30-8.45
Accommodation (Min) s£25 d£36

WARHAM ALL SAINTS Norfolk *Map 09 TF94*

Three Horseshoes
WARHAM ALL SAINTS

NR23 1NL ☎ 01328 710547

Timeless 18th-century village pub within easy reach of the coast. Unspoilt bars, real ale from the cask, and hearty Norfolk cooking using fresh local ingredients. Typical dishes include game pie, cheese baked crab, smoke-house mackerel pot, ham and lentil soup, cider mussels, chicken and rabbit pie and, for pudding, golden syrup sponge. **Principal beers:** Greene King IPA, Woodforde's Wherry.
Directions From Wells A149 to Cromer, then R onto B1105 to Warham
Brewery/Company Free House
Open 11.30-2.30 6-11
Bar food 12-2 6.30-8.30 Av main course £6.80
Accommodation (Min) s£22 d£48

WEST BECKHAM Norfolk *Map 09 TG13*

The Wheatsheaf NEW
WEST BECKHAM
Manor Farm, Church Rd NR25 6NX
☎ 01263 822110
Brick and flint 18th-century farmhouse converted to a pub in 1984. Traditional pub food (deep-fried Brie, ham and egg, sandwiches) is offered throughout the beamed bar and dining rooms. More imaginative specials may include haddock with prawns glazed in white wine sauce, stuffed quail with whisky cream sauce, tournedos Rossini, and Bakewell tart. **Principal beers:** Woodforde's: Wherry, Nelsons Revenge, Norfolk Nog, Headcracker.
Directions off the A148 (between Holt & Cromer) opp Sheringham Park, signed Baconsthorpe Castle, L at village triangle after 1m
Brewery/Company Free House
Open 10-3 6.30-11
Bar food 12-2 7-9 Av main course £5.50
Accommodation (Min) d£25

WINTERTON-ON-SEA Norfolk *Map 09 TG41*

Fishermans Return
WINTERTON-ON-SEA
The Lane NR29 4BN ☎ 01493 393305
300-year-old brick and flint pub in a village location, just a short stroll from the beach. The regular menu includes ploughman's, steaks and burgers, and a tempting choice of daily specials from the blackboard might offer moules marinière, and venison sausage with mash and onion gravy. **Principal beers:** Woodforde's Wherry, Great Eastern, & Norfolk Nog.
Directions N of Gt Yarmouth on B1159
Brewery/Company Free House
Open 11-2.30 6.30-11 (weekend open 11-11)
Bar food 12-2 6.30-9.30 Av main course £7
Accommodation (Min) s£30 d£50

WIVETON Norfolk *Map 09 TG04*

Wiveton Bell
WIVETON
Blakeney Rd NR25 7TL ☎ 01263 740101
Also known as the 'Ultimate Classic Car Pub', the open-plan bar of the 17th-century Bell is adorned with Jaguar and other motoring memorabilia. A good pit stop for home-brewed 'Jaguar' ales, traditional snacks, and hearty specials like beef and mushroom pie, chicken and asparagus crumble and duck with ginger and plum sauce. **Principal beers:** Cambridge Brewery, Jaguar Ales.
Brewery/Company Free House
Open 11-3 6-11
Bar food 12-2.30 6-9 Av main course £6.50

WOODBASTWICK Norfolk *Map 09 TG31*

The Fur & Feather
WOODBASTWICK
Slad Ln NR13 6HQ ☎ 01603 720003
Woodforde's Brewery flagship, converted from two cottages once used as brewery offices, with a thatched roof and a splendid rural location close to the Norfolk Broads. Sample their full range of ales and some traditional pub food, the printed menu listing sandwiches and salads, sausage casserole, lasagne, beef Stroganoff, hot spicy chilli, and scampi. **Principal beers:** Woodforde's Broadsman, Wherry, Great Eastern, Norfolk Nog.
Directions 1.5m N of B1140, 8m NE of Norwich
Brewery/Company Woodforde's
Open 12-3 6-11
Bar food 12-2 6.30-9.30 Av main course £6.95
Restaurant 12-2 7-9 Av 3 course à la carte £14.20

WRENINGHAM Norfolk *Map 05 TM19*

Bird in Hand
WRENINGHAM
Church Rd NR16 1BH ☎ 01508 489438
Interesting pub food is offered in a choice of restaurants at this refurbished redbrick pub, one in elegant Victorian style, the other traditional farmhouse. Meals are also available in the neat bar and the beamed and tiled snug. Options range from filled baguettes and home-made pies, to honey and mustard chicken, and chargrilled monkfish.
Principal beers: Adnams, Woodforde's Wherry, Fullers London Pride, Greene King IPA.
Directions 6m S of Norwich on the B1113

Brewery/Company Free House
Open 11.30-3 6-11

contd.

Bar food 12-2 6-9.30 Av main course £6.50
Restaurant 12-2 6-9.30 Av 3 course à la carte £15 Av 3 course fixed price £15

Northamptonshire

BADBY Map 04 SP55 Northamptonshire

The Windmill Inn
BADBY
Main St NN11 3AN ☎ 01327 702363
A 17th-century thatched inn, with a log fire and flagstone floor, set in a pretty village at the edge of Badby Woods. Varied menu and daily specials are offered in both the character bar and cosy restaurant. Dishes might include crab salad, Stilton chicken, venison burgers, and sea bass with garlic, ginger and coriander. **Principal beers:** Bass , Flowers, Boddingtons, Wadworth 6X.
Directions M1 J16 take A45 to Daventry then A361 S. Village 2m
Brewery/Company Free House
Open 11.30-3.30 5.30-11
Bar food 12-3 7-10.30 Av main course £6.50
Restaurant 12-3 7-10.30 Av 3 course à la carte £13
Accommodation (Min) s£50 d£65

BULWICK Map 04 SP99 Northamptonshire

The Queen's Head NEW
BULWICK
High St NN17 3DY ☎ 01780 450272
Built in 1678 and restored in 1998, this stone village inn features antiques, old beams and open fires. Relaxing atmosphere in which to enjoy interesting food, perhaps roast salmon with saffron and thyme sauce, baked cod with black olive crust, lamb rump with rosemary and garlic sauce, or Irish seafood platter. Good sandwiches and ploughman's.
Principal beers: Bass, Taylor Landlord, Nethergate, Adnams.
Directions Just off the A43 nr Corby, 12m from Peterborough, 2m from Dene Hall
Brewery/Company Free House
Open 12-2.30 6-11
Bar food 12-2 6-11 Av main course £5
Restaurant 12-2 6-11 Av 3 course à la carte £20

CASTLE ASHBY Map 04 SP85 Northamptonshire

Falcon Hotel
CASTLE ASHBY
NN7 1LF ☎ 01604 696200
Claimed to be the prettiest hotel in the county, the 400-year-old Falcon stands in the centre of a privately owned village. Restaurant fare includes salmon marinated with garlic, white wine and citrus fruit, and confit of leg and pink breast of duck on roquette with beetroot dressing. **Principal beers:** Courage Best, Theakstons, John Smiths.
Directions S of A45 between Northampton & Wellingborough, Opposite War Memorial
Brewery/Company Old English Inns/Hot
Open 12-3 6.30-11
Bar food 12-2 7-9.30 Av main course £6.50
Restaurant 12-2 7-10 Av 3 course à la carte £27 Av 3 course fixed price £22.50
Accommodation (Min) s£69.50 d£87.50

CHACOMBE Map 04 SP44 Northamptonshire

George and Dragon
CHACOMBE
Silver St OX17 2JR ☎ 01295 711500
Situated in a conservation village, this honey-stoned 16th-century inn is characterised by log fires and beams. The interesting blackboard menus may list seafood pasta carbonara, lamb with honey and thyme, chicken in whisky sauce, and good seafood dishes such as sea bream on a bed of spinach and peppers, and sea bass with stir-fry vegetables. **Principal beers:** Theakston-Best, XB, Marston Pedigree, Courage Directors.
Directions From M40 take A361 to Daventry, 1st R to Chacombe, 2nd L in village
Brewery/Company Free House
Open 12-11
Bar food 12-9.30 Av main course £8
Accommodation (Min) s£38.50 d£55

CLIPSTON Northamptonshire *Map 04 SP78*

The Bulls Head
CLIPSTON

Harborough Rd LE16 9RT
☎ 01858 525268

The beams at this 17th-century village pub are studded with coins which US airmen wedged there during World War Two, while waiting for their next pint. Varied menu ranges from drunken Bull pie and chicken Kiev, to giant haddock and whole plaice filled with prawns and mushrooms. **Principal beers:** Bateman's, Taylor Landlord, Flowers, Black Sheep.
Directions On B4036 S of Market Harborough
Brewery/Company Free House
Open 11.30-2.30 6.15-11
Bar food 11.30-2.30 6.15-11 Av main course £5.95
Restaurant 11.30-2.30 6.15-11 Av 3 course à la carte £11.95
Accommodation (Min) s£29.50 d£39.50

COSGROVE Northamptonshire *Map 04 SP74*

The Navigation Inn
COSGROVE

Thrupp Wharf, Castlethorpe Rd MK19 7BE ☎ 01908 543156

Built 200 years ago at the same time as the Grand Union Canal beside which it stands. The menu offers steaks, cod amd scampi, while home-made specials might include venison and red wine sausages with bubble and squeak, spaghetti Bolognaise and mushroom and chestnut Stroganoff.
Principal beers: Greene King Abbot Ale & IPA, Marston Pedigree, guest beers.
Directions From A5 W of Milton Keynes take A508 N.Take 2nd R, 1st L.Inn 0.5m
Brewery/Company Free House
Open 11-3.30 6-11 (Sat, Sun & BHs 11-11)
Bar food 12-2.30 6.30-9.30
Restaurant 12-2.30 6.30-9.30

CRICK Northamptonshire *Map 04 SP57*

The Red Lion Inn
CRICK

52 Main St NN6 7TX ☎ 01788 822342

Fine 17th-century coaching inn situated near a canal. Lunchtime fare features chicken and mushroom pie, liver and bacon casserole, and moussaka. Lookout for sirloin steak, roast duckling with apple sauce, and rainbow trout on the evening menu. Vegetarian options include mushroom and spinach lasagne, vegetable samosas, and creamy pasta bake. **Principal beers:** Websters, Marstons Pedigree, Theakston Best, Morland Old Speckled Hen.
Directions M1 J18 0.75m E on A428
Brewery/Company Wellington Pub Co
Open 11-2.30 6.15-11 (Sun 12-3,7-10.30)
Bar food 12-2 7-9 Av main course £7

EASTCOTE Northamptonshire *Map 04 SP65*

Eastcote Arms NEW
EASTCOTE

6 Gayton Rd NN12 8NG
☎ 01327 830731

Brick and stone village inn dating from 1670 with inglenook fireplaces, original beams, a welcoming atmosphere, and a splendid south-facing garden. Good value lunchtime snacks include filled baguettes, old favourites like ham, egg and chips, and fish and chips, while evening fare features steak with pepper sauce and steak and ale pie. **Principal beers:** Adnams, Hook Norton, Fullers London Pride.
Brewery/Company Free House
Open 12-2.30 6-11 (Sun 12-3, 7-10.30, closed Mon eve)
Bar food 12-2 Av main course £4
Restaurant 12-2 7.30-9.30 Av 3 course à la carte £20

EAST HADDON Northamptonshire *Map 04 SP66*

Red Lion Hotel NEW
EAST HADDON

NN6 8BU ☎ 01604 770223

Enjoying a peaceful village location, yet handy for the M1 (J18), this neat 17th-century inn of golden stone and thatch offers a convivial atmosphere and home-cooked food. From carrot and coriander soup, ham platter and fish and chips in the bar, the daily-changing restaurant menu offers wild mushroom terrine, pheasant casserole, and lemon sole. **Principal beers:** Morland Old Speckled Hen, Wells Eagle IPA, & Bombardier, Adnams Broadside.

contd.

Directions 7m NW of Northampton on A428, 8m from J18 of M1. Midway between Northampton & Rugby.
Brewery/Company Charles Wells
Open 11-2.30 6-11
Bar food 12.15-2 7-10.30 Av main course £8.95
Restaurant 12.15-2 7-10.30 Av 3 course à la carte £24 Av 3 course fixed price £17.95
Accommodation (Min) s£60 d£75

EASTON-ON-THE-HILL Northamptonshire
Map 04 TF00

The Exeter Arms NEW
EASTON-ON-THE-HILL
Stamford Rd PE9 3NS ☎ 01780 757503
Old village pub now converted to a restaurant. Typical menu includes pan fried Maigret duck breast with raspberry vinaigrette and Seville orange sauce, baked cod with a basil crust, duo of salmon and red snapper, and lamb fillet wrapped in Prosciutto ham with rosemary roasted vegetables. **Principal beers:** Theakstons.
Directions A43 & A1 junct
Brewery/Company Free House
Open 12-3 7-11 (closed Mon)
Bar food 12-3 Av main course £5.25
Restaurant 12-3 7-12 Av 3 course à la carte £19

FARTHINGSTONE Northamptonshire
Map 04 SP65

The Kings Arms
FARTHINGSTONE
Main St NN12 8EZ ☎ 01327 361604
Tucked away in unspoilt countryside near Canons Ashby (NT), this cosy, 18th-century Grade II listed inn is adorned by a collection of stone gargoyles. Interesting weekend menus feature home-made dishes, including spiced lamb tagine, game casserole, mustard and bacon pork steak, and vegetable and bean pie. Excellent real ales. **Principal beers:** Adnams Broadside, Jennings Cumberland, Shepherd Neame Spitfire, Batemans XB.
Directions from M1 take A45 W, at Weedon join A5 then R on road signed Farthingstone
Brewery/Company Free House
Open 12-3 7-11
Bar food 12-2 Av main course £6.35

FOTHERINGHAY Northamptonshire
Map 04 TL09

The Falcon Inn
FOTHERINGHAY
PE8 5HZ ☎ 01832 226254
Innovative modern cooking attracts discerning diners to this attractive 18th-century stone pub, located near the site of Fotheringhay Castle. Expect seared tuna with spiced lentil salsa, pigeon with white onion tart, spinach and roast garlic, and herb-crusted halibut with tomato and fennel stew, with warm chocolate tart among the interesting puddings. **Principal beers:** Elgoods Cambridge, Adnams, Ruddles County, Bass.

Directions N of A605 between Peterborough & Oundle
Brewery/Company Free House
Open 10.30-3 6-11 (Sun 12-3,7-11)
Bar food 12.15-2 6.45-9.45 Av main course £5
Restaurant 12.15-2 6.45-9.45

GRAFTON REGIS Northamptonshire
Map 04 SP74

The White Hart
GRAFTON REGIS
Northampton Rd NN12 7SR
☎ 01908 542123
18th-century stone-built thatched pub tucked away in a pretty thatched village. Expect a warm welcome at this family-run establishment, with its open fires and big summer garden, and a wide range of food prepared from fresh produce. Local game, prime steaks, home-made pies and battered cod feature on the menu. **Principal beers:** Greene King Abbot Ale & IPA.
Directions M1 J15 on A508 between Northampton & Milton Keynes
Brewery/Company Free House
Open 12-2 6-11 (closed Mon)

Bar food 12-2 6.30-9.30 Av main course £6.25
Restaurant 12-1.30 6-9 Av 3 course à la carte £16.50

HARRINGTON Map 04 SP78
Northamptonshire

The Tollemache Arms
HARRINGTON
High St NN6 9NU ☎ 01536 710469
Village inn dating from 1547, situated near to Harrington Airfield and Museums. On the bar menu you could find home-made venison and cranberry pie, while the restaurant might offer medallions of monkfish marinated with lime, honey and garlic. **Principal beers:** Wells Eagle IPA & Bombardier.
Directions E of A508 S towards Market Harborough(take turning at Kelmarsh)
Brewery/Company Charles Wells
Open 12-2.30 6-11
Bar food 12-2 6.45-9.15 Av main course £7.95
Restaurant 12-2 6.45-9.15 Av 3 course à la carte £17

HARRINGWORTH Map 04 SP99
Northamptonshire

The White Swan
HARRINGWORTH
Seaton Rd NN17 3AF ☎ 01572 747543
Memorabilia from the nearby USAF wartime airfield, local pictures and old trades' tools are displayed at this stone-built 15th-century coaching inn. Chicken Harringworth is a favourite dish, stuffed with mushroom and onion and grilled with Stilton cheese, and poached salmon fillet with lime and herb butter.
Principal beers: Greene King IPA, Abbot Ale, Marstons Pedigree.
Directions Off B672 NE of Corby
Brewery/Company Free House
Open 11.30-2.30 6.30-11
Bar food 12-2 7-10 Av main course £7.50
Restaurant 12-2 7-10 Av 3 course à la carte £13.50
Accommodation (Min) s£38.50 d£52

For Pubs with AA food rosettes see page 430

KETTERING Map 04 SP87
Northamptonshire

The Overstone Arms
KETTERING
Stringers Hill, Pytchley NN14 1EU ☎ 01536 790215
An 18th-century coaching inn, with its own orchard and country garden, in the village of Pytchley. There is a varied menu with favourites such as Guinness pie (with steak and mushrooms), fish dishes, grills, pasta and vegetarian options. This is supported by a list of daily specials. **Principal beers:** Greene King, Theakston, Bass, Adnams.
Directions village situated 1m from Kettering, 5m from Wellingborough
Brewery/Company Free House
Open 12-2.30 7-11
Bar food 12-2.30 7-11
Restaurant 12-2.30 7-11

LITTLE ADDINGTON Map 04 SP97
Northamptonshire

The Bell Inn
LITTLE ADDINGTON
High St NN14 4BD ☎ 01933 651700
Tastefully modernised country pub with open fires, oak beams and interesting blackboard menus. The kitchen makes good use of fresh local produce, creating such dishes as salmon fishcakes, decent sausage and mash, caramelised duck breast with Oriental sauce, and baked cod with wild mushroom tagliatelle.
Principal beers: Greene King IPA, Adnams, Fullers London Pride, Nethergate IPA.
Directions From A14, S of Kettering, follow signs for The Addingtons
Brewery/Company Free House
Open 11-3 6-11
Bar food 12-2 6-10 Av main course £7.50
Restaurant 12-2 6-10 Av 3 course à la carte £22

LITTLE HARROWDEN Map 04 SP87
Northamptonshire

The Lamb
LITTLE HARROWDEN
Orlingbury Rd NN9 5BH
☎ 01933 673300
Tucked away in a delightful village, this neatly refurbished 17th-century pub offers a friendly welcome within its comfortable lounge bar and adjoining

contd.

public bar with games area. Home-cooked food includes game (in season), steak and kidney pie, beef bourguignon, lasagne, and good Sunday roasts.
Principal beers: Wells-Eagle IPA, Bombardier, Adnams Broadside, Morland Old Speckled Hen.
Brewery/Company Charles Wells
Open 11-2.30 7-11
Bar food 12-2 7-9.30 Av main course £5.95
Restaurant 12-2 7-9.30 Av 3 course à la carte £11.75

LOWICK Northamptonshire *Map 04 SP98*

The Snooty Fox
LOWICK

NN14 3BS ☎ 01832 733434
Exquisite Italian artisan carved beams are among the more unusual features at this pretty 16th-century pub, originally the manor house. Supposedly haunted by ghosts of a horse and its rider killed at the Battle of Naseby. Varied bar food including steaks, chicken and pork. Fresh fish delivered daily from Devon. Good vegetarian selection.
Principal beers: Banks, Morrells, Adnams, Marstons.
Directions off the A14 5 m E of Kettering on A6116. Straight over at 1st roundabout and L into Lowick
Open 12-3 6.30-11
Bar food 12-2 7-10 Av main course £5.95
Restaurant 12-2 7-10 Av 3 course à la carte £13

MARSTON ST LAWRENCE Northamptonshire *Map 04 SP54*

The Marston Inn
MARSTON ST LAWRENCE

OX17 2DB ☎ 01295 711906
Originally three cottages, this 15th-century inn was seized by Cromwell prior to the Battle of Edgehill and sold to raise money for his army. Used to be known as 'The Case is Altered'. Traditional in style, typical dishes include halibut steak, sea bass, mustard-glazed lamb cutlets, and rabbit casserole.
Principal beers: Hook Norton.
Directions 4m from M40 J11
Brewery/Company Hook Norton
Open 12-3 7-11 (closed Mon lunch)
Restaurant 12-2 7.30-9.30 Av 3 course à la carte £14

OUNDLE Northamptonshire *Map 04 TL08*

The Mill at Oundle
OUNDLE

Barnwell Hill PE8 5PB ☎ 01832 272621
At this converted watermill you can see the River Nene flow under the bar, dine by the water and watch the boats go by. Dishes range from Mexican specialities to steak and kidney pie. To finish there is a tempting choice of hot and cold home-made desserts. **Principal beers:** 3-6 regularly changing guest ales.
Directions A14 Thrapston exit, A605 toward Peterborough, 8m Oundle turning, 1m to pub
Brewery/Company Free House
Open 11-3 6.30-11 (Fri-Sun 11-11 in summer)
Bar food 11-2 6.30-9 Av main course £8.95

SIBBERTOFT Northamptonshire *Map 04 SP68*

The Red Lion
SIBBERTOFT

43 Welland Rise LE16 9UD
☎ 01858 880011
Friendly and civilised village pub with beamed restaurant and comfortably furnished bar. The same menu is offered in both, the chalkboard listing such specials as steak and Stilton pie, lasagne, chicken Mississippi, green-lipped mussels, freshly battered cod, and monkfish. **Principal beers:** Everards Tiger, Ruddles Best, Greene King IPA.
Directions From Market Harborough take A4304, then A50. After 1m turn L
Brewery/Company Free House
Open 12-2 6.30-11 (closed Mon & Tue lunch)
Bar food 12-2 7-10 Av main course £8.50
Restaurant 12-2 7-10 Av 3 course à la carte £12

STOKE BRUERNE Northamptonshire *Map 04 SP74*

The Boat Inn
STOKE BRUERNE

NN12 7SB ☎ 01604 862428
Thatched canalside inn by working locks and opposite the canal museum. Narrowboat trips on the 40-seater Indian Chief are a feature. Bar snacks range from sandwiches to barbecue ribs, while

restaurant dishes include stuffed red mullet, and Barbary duck with rosemary and juniper sauce. **Principal beers:** Marstons-Bitter, Pedigree, Fullers London Pride, Morland Old Speckled Hen.
Directions just off A508
Brewery/Company Free House
Open 9am-11pm (3-6 closed Mon-Thu in winter)
Bar food 9.30-9 Av main course £5
Restaurant 12-2 7-9 Av 3 course à la carte £15 Av 3 course fixed price £15

SULGRAVE Northamptonshire

Map 04 SP54

The Star Inn

SULGRAVE

Manor Rd OX17 2SA ☎ 01295 760389

Immaculately maintained 300-year-old village inn situated on the Oxfordshire and Northamptonshire border close to Sulgrave Manor. Civilised bar and dining room serving spinach and ricotta tart, steak, mushroom and ale pie, venison and red wine suet pudding, halibut on garlic mash, and traditional, home-battered cod with chips and mushy peas. **Principal beers:** Hook Norton Best, Old Hooky, Generation, & Haymaker.
Directions M1 J15A follow signs for Silverstone race circuit then M40 J11 follow brown signs for golf course, then for Sulgrave Manor
Brewery/Company Hook Norton
Open 11-2.30 6-11
Bar food 12-2 7-9.30 Av main course £9
Restaurant 12-2 7-9.30 Av 3 course à la carte £16
Accommodation (Min) s£30 d£50

Pubs offering a good choice of seafood on the menu

UPPER BENEFIELD Northamptonshire

Map 04 SP98

Benefield Wheatsheaf Hotel

UPPER BENEFIELD

PE8 5AN ☎ 01832 205254

Memorabilia of the 401st Bomber Squadron USAF is a feature of this relaxing country hotel. The Garden Bistro overlooks the gardens, and there is a candlelit restaurant. Home-smoked chicken salad, and Jacobean steak stuffed with ham and cheese are typical bistro dishes.
Principal beers: Tetleys.
Directions take A605 from Peterborough to Oundle, then A427 to Benefield
Brewery/Company Free House
Open All day
Bar food 12-2 7-9.30 Av main course £5.95
Restaurant 12-2 7-9.30 Av 3 course à la carte £18
Accommodation (Min) s£39.95 d£39.95

WADENHOE Northamptonshire

Map 04 TL08

The King's Head

WADENHOE

Church St PE8 5ST ☎ 01832 720024

Oak beams, quarry-tiled floors and open fires characterise this welcoming and sympatheticly refurbished 17th-century stone village inn. Good summer garden on the banks of the River Nene. Home-made food ranges from ploughman's and pasta al forno, to steak and kidney casserole, pheasant with Madeira jus, and bread and butter pudding. **Principal beers:** Adnams Southwold & Broadside, Marston's Pedigree,.
Brewery/Company Free House
Open 12-3 6-11 (closed Sun eve, Mon lunch)
Bar food 12-2 Av main course £8
Restaurant 7-9 Av 3 course à la carte £14
Accommodation (Min) s£35 d£50

WOODNEWTON Northamptonshire

Map 04 TL09

The White Swan

WOODNEWTON

22 Main St PE8 5EB ☎ 01780 470381

Welcoming village local with a simple, single oblong room, one end focusing on the bar and wood-burning stove, the

contd.

other set up as a dining area. The regularly-changing blackboard may list venison with tarragon, cream and Madeira sauce, rack of lamb with basil and garlic, and lemon mousse **Principal beers:** Badger Tanglefoot, Oakham, Fullers London Pride.
Brewery/Company Free House
Open 12-11
Bar food 12-2.30 7-9.30 Av main course £7.50
Restaurant 12-2.30 7-9.30 Av 3 course à la carte £17.95

Nottinghamshire

BEESTON Nottinghamshire
Map 08 SK53

Victoria Hotel
BEESTON
Dovecote Ln NG9 1JG ☎ 0115 925 4049
Converted Victorian railway hotel, specialising in traditional ales and fine whiskies, and known for its stained glass and acid-etched windows. Menu may include baked red snapper, Lincolnshire sausages with champ, and chicken supreme Andalusian with tomatoes, peppers, olives and white wine.
Principal beers: Twelve changing guest beers.
Directions M1 J25 take A52 E. R at Nursuryman PH & R opp Rockaway Hotel into Barton St 1st L
Brewery/Company Tynemill Ltd
Open 11-11
Bar food 12-9 Av main course £5.95

CAUNTON Nottinghamshire
Map 08 SK76

Caunton Beck
CAUNTON
NG23 6AB ☎ 01636 636793
Dating back to 1820, Caunton Beck invites its customers to use the inn as a meeting place, an eating house, a reading room or a watering hole. Herb gardens and a rose arbour create a dazzling picture outside. Wide-ranging, ever changing menus may list baked plaice, braised lamb and mixed tagliatelle. **Principal beers:** Adnams, Taylor Landlord.
Directions 5m NW of Newark on A616
Brewery/Company Free House
Open 8am-midnight
Bar food 8am-midnight Av main course £7

COLSTON BASSETT Nottinghamshire
Map 08 SK73

The Martins Arms Inn
COLSTON BASSETT
School Ln NG12 3FN ☎ 01949 81361
Dating from around 1690, this Grade II listed former farmhouse is situated in a conservation village. Speciality sandwiches on ciabatta bread (smoked chicken with tarragon mayonnaise), pasta dishes and warm salads on the imaginative snack menu, while for more formal dining expect game casserole, salmon with chervil cream sauce, and beef with confit of garlic and Madeira jus.
Principal beers: Marstons Pedigree, Bass, Greene King Abbot Ale, Black Sheep.
Directions M1 J22, Take A50 then A46 North towards Newark. Colston Bassett is situated east of Cotgrave.
Brewery/Company Free House
Open 12-3 6-11
Bar food 12-2 6-10 Av main course £10.95
Restaurant 12-3 7-11 Av 3 course à la carte £25.95

ELKESLEY Nottinghamshire
Map 08 SK67

Robin Hood Inn
ELKESLEY
High St DN22 8AJ ☎ 01777 838259
Unassuming village local just off the A1, providing an excellent stop-off point for an interesting, home-made bar meal. From decent snacks like filled baguettes and ploughman's, look to the chalkboard for dishes like mussels in white wine, cod on herb mash with provençale dressing, seafood casserole, and chargrilled chicken with roasted vegetables.
Principal beers: Wadworths 6X, Boddingtons.
Brewery/Company Whitbread
Open 11.30-3 6.30-11
Bar food 12-2 7-9.30 Av main course £8

NORMANTON ON TRENT Nottinghamshire
Map 08 SK75

The Square & Compass
NORMANTON ON TRENT
Eastgate NG23 6RN ☎ 01636 821439
The building is over 400 years old, and was originally three cottages, though the main bar area has always been a pub. There is plenty of character, with an open

fire and low beamed ceilings. Favourite dishes include gingered beef, and hare casserole with apples and blackberries. **Principal beers:** Stones, Mansfield, Adnams.
Directions Off A1 & B1164 N of Newark-on-Trent
Brewery/Company Free House
Open 12-3 6-11 (Sat 12-11, Sun 12-4,7-10.30)
Bar food 12-2.30 7-9.30 Av main course £5
Restaurant 12-2.30 7-9.30 Av 3 course à la carte £12
Accommodation (Min) d£20

NOTTINGHAM Nottinghamshire
Map 08 SK54

Fellows Morton & Clayton

NOTTINGHAM
54 Canal St NG1 7EH ☎ 0115 950 6795
Unusual and atmospheric city centre pub with cobbled courtyard overlooking the canal. Originally a warehouse belonging to the brewers Samuel Fellows and Matthew Claytons. Apart from an award-winning flower display, it offers a range of snacks, including lasagne, steak and kidney pie and Moby Dick haddock.
Principal beers: Castle Eden Ale, Boddingtons, Taylor Landlord, Fellows Bitter.
Brewery/Company Free House
Open 11-11 (Sun 12-10.30/bar food to 6pm at wknds)
Bar food 11.30-2.30 Av main course £3.50
Restaurant 11.30-2.30 Av 3 course à la carte £9 Av 2 course fixed price £4.95

Lincolnshire Poacher

NOTTINGHAM
161-163 Mansfield Rd TG1 3FR
☎ 0115 941 1584
Traditional pub with up to ten real ales and seventy whiskies on display. Regular brewery evenings are held, with food and live music. Typical dishes include Lincolnshire sausages, smoked mackerel and prawn fishcakes, and a vegetarian harvester's pie. **Principal beers:** Bateman XB, XXXB, & Victory, Marstons Pedigree.
Directions M1 J26.Town centre
Brewery/Company Tynemill Ltd
Open 11-11 (Sun 12-10.30, bar food 12-8) (bar food Mon 12-3, Fri-Sun 12-4)
Bar food 12-8 Av main course £4.95

Ye Olde Trip to Jerusalem
NOTTINGHAM
1 Brewhouse Yard, Castle Rd NG1 6AD
☎ 0115 947 3171
Thought to be the oldest inn in England, dating from 1070 and associated with Richard the Lionheart's crusaders. In addition to its range of sandwiches and snacks, the pub is known for its giant filled Yorkshire puddings, and Chicken Jerusalem, with melted Stilton and celery.
Principal beers: Kimberley, Marstons.
Brewery/Company Hardys & Hansons
Open 11-11 (Sun 12-10.30)
Bar food 12-4 Av main course £5.99

THURGARTON Nottinghamshire
Map 08 SK64

The Red Lion

THURGARTON
Southwell Rd NG14 7GP
☎ 01636 830351
Try not to be put off your meal by the 1936 Nottingham Guardian cutting on the wall which tells of the murder of Sarah Ellen Clarke, dispatched by her own. An extensive menu includes Whitby scampi, mushroom Stroganoff, duck with wildberry, and sea bass Provencal. **Principal beers:** Mansfield.
Directions On A612 between Nottingham & Southwell
Brewery/Company Free House
Open 11-2 6.30-11.30 (Sat & Sun 11-11.30)
Bar food 12-2 7-10 Av main course £7
Restaurant 12-2 7-10 Av 3 course à la carte £12.50

WALKERINGHAM Nottinghamshire
Map 08 SK78

The Three Horse Shoes

WALKERINGHAM
High St DN10 4HR ☎ 01427 890959
A quiet village pub festooned with hanging baskets and some 10,000 bedding plants, all grown and tended by the owner. There's also an aviary. Home made steak pie, mushroom, cheese, leek and nut pie, roast stuffed breast of lamb, or chicken Ceylon may be on today's menu. **Principal beers:** Stones, Bass, Worthington.
Brewery/Company Free House
Open 11.30-3 7-11
Bar food 12-2 7-9.30 Av main course £5.95

contd.

Restaurant 12-2 7-9.30 Av 3 course à la carte £12.50

WEST LEAKE Nottinghamshire Map 08 SK52

Star Inn
WEST LEAKE

Melton Ln LE12 5RQ ☎ 01509 852233

Homely 18th-century inn with a traditional beamed and quarry-tiled bar, log fires and peaceful village views. Expect straightforward pub food on the printed lunch and dinner menus; specials may feature daily roasts, beef stew and dumplings, and chicken and leek pie.
Principal beers: Bass, Adnams, Courage Directors, Wadworth 6X.
Directions A6 toward Loughborough, 0.33m L to Kingston, over canal, R to Sutt Bonn, over crossroad, 1m Star on L
Brewery/Company Enterprise Inns
Open 11-2.30 6-11 (Sun 12-3, 6-10.30)
Bar food 12.15-2.15 6.30-8.30 Av main course £4.25
Restaurant 12.15-2.15 6.30-8.30 Av 3 course à la carte £9

Oxfordshire

ABINGDON Oxfordshire Map 04 SU49

The Merry Miller NEW
ABINGDON

Cothill OX13 6JW ☎ 01865 390390

Former 17th-century granary situated in a quiet village close to Oxford. Beams, flagstones, log fires and pine furnishings characterise the tastefully refurbished bar and restaurant. Contemporary English cooking may include tomato and fennel soup, game pie with roasted root vegetables, duck with grapefruit and ginger sauce, and chocolate truffle terrine. **Principal beers:** Taylor Landlord, Marstons Pedigree, Wadworth 6X.
Directions 1m from the Marcham interchange on the A34
Brewery/Company Marstons
Open 12-3 5-11 (wknd open all day)
Restaurant 12-3 5-11 Av 3 course à la carte £17

ARDINGTON Oxfordshire Map 04 SU48

The Boars Head
ARDINGTON

Church St OX12 8QA ☎ 01235 833254

200-year-old pub situated on a privately owned estate in the Vale of the White Horse. Starters include smoked chicken with mango and jalapenos. Typical main dishes are roast venison with red wine and juniper pancakes, honeyed duck on a parsnip purée, and pork in orange and mustard sauce.
Principal beers: Morland & guest beers.
Directions Off A417 W of Wantage
Brewery/Company Free House
Open 11.30-3 6.30-11 (closed Mon)
Bar food 12-2 7-9 Av main course £6
Restaurant 12-2 7-9 Av 3 course à la carte £25

ASTHALL Oxfordshire Map 04 SP21

The Maytime Inn
ASTHALL

OX18 4HW ☎ 01993 822068

Traditional Cotswold inn, close to the river, with log fires and flagstone floors. The atmosphere is friendly and relaxed and children are made welcome. There is one menu throughout, with dishes such as steak and kidney pie, seafood thermidor, and king prawn extravaganza.
Principal beers: Bass, Fullers London Pride.
Directions A361 from Swindon, R onto A40 then onto B4047 to Asthall
Brewery/Company Free House
Open 11-3 6-11
Bar food 12-2.15 7-9.15 Av main course £5
Restaurant 12-2.15 7-9.15 Av 3 course à la carte £13.95 Av 3 course fixed price £13.95
Accommodation (Min) s£47.50 d£57.50

BANBURY Oxfordshire Map 04 SP44

Ye Olde Reine Deer Inn
BANBURY

47 Parsons St OX16 8NB
☎ 01295 264031

Historic town centre pub dating from 1570, where Oliver Cromwell once held court in the oak-panelled Globe Room. Noted for its atmosphere, tip-top Hook

Norton ales, Irish whiskey, and popular lunchtime bar food. Look to the specials board for cheese and leek pie, steak and kidney cobbler, and prawn and pesto pasta. **Principal beers:** Hook Norton.
Brewery/Company Hook Norton
Open 11-11 (closed Sun & BHs)
Bar food 11-2 Av main course £4

BARNARD GATE Oxfordshire *Map 04 SP41*

The Boot Inn
BARNARD GATE
OX8 6XE ☎ 01865 881231

Civilised Cotswold stone-built pub set back from the A40, noted for its fascinating collection of celebrity 'boots', brasserie-style atmosphere and interesting freshly-cooked food. From olives and french bread on the bar, the menu extends to ciabatta sandwiches, steak and kidney pudding, Dover sole, seafood pasta, and bhuna chicken curry. Good wines. **Principal beers:** Hook Norton.
Directions off the A40 between Witney & Eynsham
Brewery/Company Free House
Open 11-2.30 6-11
Bar food 11-2.30 6-10
Restaurant 11-2.30 6-10

BINFIELD HEATH Oxfordshire *Map 04 SU77*

Bottle & Glass
BINFIELD HEATH
RG9 4JT ☎ 01491 575755

A thatched 15th-century inn situated on an old drovers' route on the edge of the Chilterns. Traditional English fare is offered from the regularly changing blackboard menu, with dishes like beef casserole, loin of pork, lemon sole, potted shrimps, and mussels with garlic butter. Good local walks.

Principal beers: Brakspear.
Directions N of B4155 between Reading & Henley
Brewery/Company Brakspear
Open 11-3 6-11
Bar food 11-1.45 7-9.30 Av main course £5.95

BLEWBURY Oxfordshire *Map 04 SU58*

Blewbury Inn NEW
BLEWBURY
London Rd OX11 9PD ☎ 01235 850496

White-painted 200-year-old pub set in a downland village close to the Ridgeway. Friendly newish owners offer superior pub food in comfortably furnished surroundings. Begin with goat's cheese and chorizo tart with onion marmalade, followed by beef fillet with spinach fondue, shallot confit and Stilton crust, or herb-crusted cod on grain mustard mash, and walnut nougatine parfait.

Principal beers: Hook Norton: Best, Old Hooky & Generation; Wadworth 6X.
Directions At the junction of the A417 & B4016 below Didcot
Brewery/Company Free House
Open 12-3 6-11 (no food Sun eve & all Mon)
Bar food 12-2 Av main course £5
Restaurant 12-3 6.30-11 Av 3 course à la carte £22
Accommodation (Min) s£40 d£50

BRITWELL SALOME Oxfordshire *Map 04 SU69*

The Goose NEW
BRITWELL SALOME
OX9 5LG ☎ 01491 612304

Short and imaginative daily-changing menus make good use of fresh local ingredients at this 17th-century brick and flint village pub. Begin with Tuscan bean soup, or ragout of mussels, gnocci and wild mushrooms, followed by monkfish

contd.

with saffron rice and gazpacho sauce, or roast partridge with bubble and squeak. Finish with warm pear tart or crème brûlée. **Principal beers:** Brakspears.
Directions 1.5 from Watlington on B4009 towards Benson & Wallingford
Brewery/Company Free House
Open 12-3 6-11 (closed Sun eve & all Mon)
Restaurant 12-3 7-11 Av 3 course à la carte £25 Av 3 course fixed price £25

BURCOT Oxfordshire Map 04 SU59

The Chequers
BURCOT
OX14 3DP ☎ 01865 407771

Partly dating back to the 16th century and originally a staging post for barges on the Thames, this inn has been managed by the same team for the last twenty years. Various imaginatively themed food events have included a French evening, an Italian evening, and a Valentine's chocolate fondue evening!
Principal beers: Wadworth 6X, Brakspear.
Directions On A415 (Dorchester/Abingdon rd)
Brewery/Company Phoenix Inns
Open 11-2.30 6-11
Bar food 12-2 6.30-9.30 Av main course £5.50
Restaurant 12-2 6.30-9.30 Av 3 course à la carte £11.50

BURFORD Oxfordshire Map 04 SP21

Golden Pheasant
BURFORD
91 High St OX18 4QA ☎ 01993 823223

Attractive, honey-coloured, 15th-century stone inn situated in the centre of unspoilt Burford. Expect an informal atmosphere, comfortable bedrooms, and freshly prepared food in both the inviting bar or restaurant. Typical dishes include steamed mussels, braised lamb knuckle, salmon and spinach fishcakes, and venison with peppercorn and port sauce. **Principal beers:** Theakston, Courage Directors.
Directions Leave M40 at junction 8 and follow signs A40 Cheltenham into Burford
Brewery/Company Old English Inns/Hot
Open 9-11
Bar food 12-2.30 7-9.30 Av main course £6.95
Restaurant 12-2 7-9.30 Av 3 course à la carte £25.30
Accommodation (Min) d£75

The Inn for All Seasons
BURFORD
The Barringtons OX18 4TN
☎ 01451 844324

Expect a warm welcome and enjoyable food at this 16th-century coaching inn. Retaining the original charm of open fireplaces, oak beams and period furniture, it offers interesting fish dishes (red mullet with rosemary and tomato butter sauce), alongside duck confit with hoisin sauce, beef with shallot sauce, and pear and almond cake with honey ice cream.

Principal beers: Wadworth 6X, Bass, Wychwood, Badger.
Directions 3 miles W on A40
Brewery/Company Free House
Open 11-2.30 6-11
Bar food 11-2.20 6-9.30 Av main course £8
Restaurant 11-2.30 6-9.30 Av 3 course à la carte £17.50 Av 4 course fixed price £17.50
Accommodation (Min) s£33 d£65

The Lamb Inn
BURFORD
Sheep St OX18 4LR ☎ 01993 823155

Built of mellow Cotswold stone and set in a pretty village, this wonderful, vine-clad old inn boasts antique furnishings, flagged floors and log fires. Food is of a

high standard, the daily menus listing, perhaps, Cornish crab and scallop tart, jugged hare, venison and cranberry casserole, sea bass with egg noodles and pesto, and pear tart tatin. **Principal beers:** Wadworth 6X, Hook Norton Best, Adnams Best.
Directions from M40 J8 follow signs for A40 & Burford, off High Street
Brewery/Company Free House
Open 11-2.30 6-11

Bar food 12-2 Av main course £7.50
Restaurant 12.30-1.45 7-9 Av 3 course à la carte £25 Av 3 course fixed price £25
Accommodation (Min) s£55 d£95

CHADLINGTON Oxfordshire — *Map 04 SP32*

The Tite Inn
CHADLINGTON
Mill End OX7 3NY ☎ 01608 676475

Pretty 17th-century Cotswold pub, adorned with roses in summer, named after the constantly flowing stream (tite) running beneath it. Expect home-cooked food prepared from fresh ingredients, including local vegetables and game, and an unusual choice of cheeses. Lunchtime bar menu features salads, pâtés and a range of soups. **Principal beers:** Archers, Fullers, Greene King.
Directions 3m S of Chipping Norton
Brewery/Company Free House
Open 12-2.30 6.30-11 (closed Mon)
Bar food 12-2.30 6.30-9.30 Av main course £5.95
Restaurant 12-2.30 7-11 Av 3 course à la carte £12.85

CHALGROVE Oxfordshire — *Map 04 SU69*

The Red Lion Inn

CHALGROVE
The High St OX44 7SS ☎ 01865 890625

Owned by Chalgrove Parish Church since 1637, parts of this lovely cream-painted pub date back to the 11th century. Expect above average pub food, the imaginative daily specials menu listing, perhaps, herb-crusted rack of lamb with garlic and rosemary jus, game casserole, roast cod with saffron bouillabaisse, and cappuccino mousse for pudding.
Principal beers: Brakspear, Fullers London Pride & ESB.
Directions B480 from Oxford Ring rd, thru Stadhampton, L then R at mini-rdbt, at Chalgrove Airfield R fork into village
Brewery/Company Free House
Open 12-3 6-11 (Sun 7-10.30)
Bar food 12-3 7-11 Av main course £4.50
Restaurant 12-3 7-11 Av 3 course à la carte £15 Av 0 course fixed price £5.95

CHARLBURY Oxfordshire — *Map 04 SP31*

The Bell House
CHARLBURY
Church St OX7 3PP ☎ 01608 810278

On the banks of the River Evenlode, this 17th-century inn offers an ideal base for cycling, walking, or touring holidays. Whole grilled plaice or chicken supreme stuffed with crab set on a cream and wine sauce may be on the menu. Sandwiches, baguettes, cottage pie and fish and chips are among the bar snacks and meals.
Principal beers: Hook Norton.
Directions From Oxford take A34 to Woodstock, L onto B4437 to Charlbury. In village, 2nd road on L, Hotel opposite St Mary's church
Brewery/Company Old English Inns/Hot
Open 11-11
Accommodation (Min) s£55 d£55

The Bull Inn
CHARLBURY
Sheep St OX7 3RR ☎ 01608 810689

Beautiful old beamed pub, dating from the 16th century, restored and renovated to retain its features, including three inglenook fireplaces. A fine choice of food is available, including salmon and dill fishcakes with fresh tarragon

contd.

hollandaise, Mediterranean fish stew, Thai green chicken curry with jasmine rice, and apricot and Amaretto crème brûlée. **Principal beers:** Greene King-IPA, Abbot Ale.
Directions On A40 at Oxford R to Woodstock, thru Woodstock & after 1.5m L to Charlbury
Brewery/Company Free House
Open 12-2.30 7-11.30 (closed Mon ex BH lunch)
Bar food 12-2.30 7-11 Av main course £6.95
Restaurant 12-2.30 7-11 Av 3 course à la carte £18
Accommodation (Min) d£50

CHECKENDON Oxfordshire Map 04 SU68

The Highwayman NEW
CHECKENDON
Exlade St RG8 0UA ☎ 01491 682020
Rambling 16th-century inn on the edge of the wooded Chiltern Hills and the Thames Valley. Civilised bar and dining room, decent ales and wines, and interesting food. Expect bacon and rabbit terrine or Thai-style mussels, followed by fish grill, roast sea bass, rack of lamb with parsley mash, or calves' liver and bacon. **Principal beers:** Brakspears, Fullers London Pride, Adnams, Gibbs Mew Bishops Tipple.
Directions On A4074 Reading to Wallingford Rd
Brewery/Company Free House
Open 11-3 6-11
Bar food 11-3 6-11 Av main course £8.95
Restaurant 11-3 6-11 Av 3 course à la carte £21
Accommodation (Min) s£50 d£60

CHINNOR Oxfordshire Map 04 SP70

Sir Charles Napier
CHINNOR
Spriggs Alley OX9 4BX
☎ 01494 483011
Situated high in the Chiltern Hills amomg beechwoods, this casual country inn attracts discerning diners from far afield for the serious cooking and fine wines on offer. Daily-changing menus may list noodles with crab, chilli and ginger, and parfait of foie gras with truffle butter, followed by confit of rabbit, roast partridge with braised lentils, and lime and ginger brûlée. **Principal beers:** Wadworth 6X.
Directions M40 J6 to Chinnor. Turn R at rdbt into Spriggs Alley
Brewery/Company Free House
Open 12-2.15 6.30-10 (closed Mon)
Bar food 12-2 Av main course £9.50
Restaurant 12-2 6.30-10 Av 3 course à la carte £26 Av 2 course fixed price £15

CHIPPING NORTON Oxfordshire Map 04 SP32

Chequers
CHIPPING NORTON
Goddards Ln OX7 5NP
☎ 01608 644717
Low beams, open fires and a new, airy, courtyard dining area are popular features of this town-centre pub. Enjoy the full range of Fullers ales and some interesting bar food, typically duck and cashew nut stir-fry, smoked haddock and mussel chowder, crispy-fried cod with ginger and garlic, and Thai vegetable curry. **Principal beers:** Fullers - Chiswick Bitter, London Pride, ESB.

Directions Town centre, next to theatre
Brewery/Company Fullers
Open 11-11
Bar food 12-2.30 6-9 Av main course £5.95
Restaurant 12-2.30 6-9 Av 3 course à la carte £15

The Falkland Arms
CHIPPING NORTON
Great Tew OX7 4DB ☎ 01608 683653
500-year-old stone-built inn with flagstone floors, oak panelling and high-backed settles. Named after Viscount Falkland who lived nearby and was Secretary of State to Charles I. Extensive range of fresh, home-cooked food, with beef and ale pie and shoulder of lamb basted in honey among the choices. **Principal beers:** Wadworth 6X & Somersault.

Directions Off A361 1.25m, signposted Great Tew
Brewery/Company Wadworth
Open 11.30-2.30 6-11 (Sat 11-11, Sun 12-10.30)
Bar food 12-2 Av main course £6.95
Restaurant 12-2 7-8 Av 3 course à la carte £12.95

CHURCH ENSTONE Oxfordshire *Map 04 SP32*

Crown Inn
CHURCH ENSTONE

Mill Ln OX7 4NN ☎ 01608 677262

A 17th-century free house in a village setting on the edge of the Cotswolds. All dishes are home cooked. Ranging from Thai chicken curry or Welsh rarebit in the bar to fillet of black bream or tenderloin of pork in the restaurant. **Principal beers:** Hook Norton, Hampshire.
Brewery/Company Free House
Open 12-3 7-11
Bar food 12-2 7-9.30 Av main course £5.50
Restaurant 7-9.30
Accommodation (Min) s£32 d£45

CLANFIELD Oxfordshire *Map 04 SP20*

Plough Hotel NEW
CLANFIELD

Bourton Rd OX18 2RB ☎ 01367 810222

Well-preserved 16th-century manor house situated in a sleepy Cotswold village. Personally-run and full of historic charm, it offers comfortable accommodation and a light luncheon menu in the bar. Dishes include leek and potato soup, broccoli and Stilton quiche, tuna and caper tagliatelle and ploughman's. More elaborate restaurant menu.
Directions Clanfield is at the jct of the A4095 & B4020 between Witney & Faringdon, 15m W of Oxford
Brewery/Company Free House
Bar food 12.15-2 Av main course £6
Restaurant 12-2 7-9.30 Av 3 course à la carte £27 Av 3 course fixed price £27
Accommodation (Min) s£65 d£95

CLIFTON Oxfordshire *Map 04 SP43*

Duke of Cumberland's Head
CLIFTON

OX15 0PE ☎ 01869 338534

Close to Edge Hill in quiet open countryside, this 16th century listed building preserves a peaceful atmosphere in which to enjoy steak and stout pie and chicken supreme dijonnaise in the bar and, perhaps, fish soup, pork with sherry and mushroom sauce, and calves' liver with Madeira and mustard sauce in the restaurant. **Principal beers:** Hook Norton, Adnams, Hampshire King Alfred, Wadworth 6x.

Directions A4260 from Banbury, then B4031 from Deddington
Brewery/Company Free House
Open 12-2.30 6.30-11
Bar food 12-2.30 7-11 Av main course £8
Restaurant 12-2 7-11 Av 3 course à la carte £18 Av 3 course fixed price £18
Accommodation (Min) s£30 d£60

CLIFTON HAMPDEN Oxfordshire *Map 04 SU59*

The Plough Hotel & Restaurant NEW
CLIFTON HAMPDEN

Abingdon Rd OX14 3EG
☎ 01865 407811

Lovingly renovated, 16th-century thatched and timbered gem of a building offering a genuine warm welcome, comfortable and tastefully decorated bedrooms, and good food served all day. Expect excellent sandwiches, warm salads, goat's cheese soufflé with pesto

contd.

dressing, and main meals like confit of duck, and herb-crusted rack of lamb with redcurrant and rosemary sauce. **Principal beers:** John Smiths, Courage Best, Directors.
Brewery/Company Free House
Open 11-11
Bar food 11-11
Accommodation (Min) s£62.50 d£82.50

CUMNOR Oxfordshire Map 04 SP40

Bear & Ragged Staff
CUMNOR
Appleton Rd OX2 9QH
☎ 01865 862329
When Richard Cromwell stayed here in 1650, the inn was already over three centuries old. The best of local produce is used in modern English dishes, which might include sea bass with bacon and onion hash, rump of lamb with roasted ratatouille, and steamed treacle sponge with pears in caramel. **Principal beers:** Morrells Varsity & Graduate.
Directions A420 from Oxford, R to Cumnor on B4017
Brewery/Company Morrells
Open 11-11
Bar food 12-2.30 6.30-10 Av main course £10
Restaurant 12-2.30 6.30-10 Av 3 course à la carte £22 Av 3 course fixed price £20

The Vine Inn
CUMNOR
11 Abingdon Rd OX2 9QN
☎ 01865 862567
Country village inn/restaurant, dating from 1743, with a strong emphasis on good modern pub food. Specials change almost daily and may incude gazpacho soup, calves' liver with lime sauce, haddock casserole, pan-fried duck breast, and braised fillet of pork. Extensive choice of starters, alongside interesting stir-fry and pasta dishes. **Principal beers:** Wadworth 6X, Adnams, Morland Old Speckled Hen.
Directions A420 from Oxford, R onto B4017
Brewery/Company Free House
Open 11-2.30 6-11
Bar food 12.30-2.15 6.30-9.15 Av main course £8
Restaurant 12.30-2.15 6.30-9.15 Av 3 course à la carte £15

DEDDINGTON Oxfordshire Map 04 SP43

Deddington Arms
DEDDINGTON
Horsefair OX15 0SM ☎ 01869 338364
Customers have been offered hospitality at this traditional village inn for the last 400 years. Character bar with timbers, open log fires, and village views. Fresh ingredients are used and the innovative menu may offer dressed crab, fillet steak Diane, pot-roasted duck, monkfish with tomato, basil and cream, and good home-made puddings. **Principal beers:** Tetleys, Greene King, Marstons Pedigree.
Directions A43 to Northampton, B4100 to Aynho, B4031 to Deddington
Brewery/Company Free House
Open 7am-11pm
Bar food 12-2 6.30-9.30 Av main course £6.50
Restaurant 12-2 6.30-9.30 Av 3 course à la carte £15
Accommodation (Min) s£55 d£65

DORCHESTER-ON-THAMES Oxfordshire Map 04 SU59

The George
DORCHESTER-ON-THAMES
25 High St OX10 7HH ☎ 01865 340404
Historic 15th-century coaching inn standing opposite a medieval abbey close to the Thames. Civilised interior with comfortable accommodation, beamed restaurant and character bar. Interesting modern menus offering lamb cutlets with lyonnaise potatoes, sea bream with spicy tomato confit, lamb shank with red wine and lentil jus, and créme brûlée.
Principal beers: Brakspear.
Directions From M40 J7 take A329 S to A4074 at Shillingford. Follow signs to Dorchester.From M4 J13 take A34 to Abingdon then A415 E to Dorchester
Brewery/Company Free House
Open 11-11
Bar food 12-2.15 7-9.30 Av main course £8.95
Restaurant 12-2.15 7-9.30 Av 3 course à la carte £20
Accommodation (Min) s£65.50 d£80

DUNS TEW Oxfordshire *Map 04 SP42*

The White Horse Inn
DUNS TEW
OX6 4JS ☎ 01869 340272
Dating back to the 17th century, this Cotswold coaching inn has a wealth of charming features, including log fires, oak panelling and flagstone floors. Bar food ranges from baguettes and jacket potatoes, to pheasant casserole, rabbit in prune gravy, and steak and kidney pudding. **Principal beers:** Hook Norton, Wadworth 6X, Theakston XB.
Directions M40 J11, A4260, follow signs to Deddington and then onto Duns Tew
Brewery/Company Old English Inns/Hot
Open 12-11 (Sun 12-10.30)
Bar food 12-2 7-9 Av main course £5.95
Restaurant 12-2 7-9 Av 3 course à la carte £14
Accommodation (Min) s£45 d£55

FARINGDON Oxfordshire *Map 04 SU29*

The Lamb at Buckland
FARINGDON
Lamb Ln, Buckland SN7 8QN
☎ 01367 870484
An 18th-century inn in the tranquil village of Buckland on the edge of the Cotswolds, offering en suite accommodation and an imaginative range of home-cooked food. Typical blackboard dishes may include fish soup, rabbit and guinea fowl terrine, baked sea bass with Pernod sauce, roast saddle of lamb with couscous and, for pudding, orange and cardamon tart. **Principal beers:** Hook Norton.
Directions Just off A420 3m E of Faringdon
Brewery/Company Free House
Open 8-3 5.15-11
Bar food 12-2 6.30-9.30 Av main course £10
Restaurant 12-2 6.30-9.30 Av 3 course à la carte £20 Av 3 course fixed price £19.75
Accommodation (Min) s£37.50 d£37.50

The Trout at Tadpole Bridge NEW
FARINGDON
Buckland Marsh SN7 8RF
☎ 01367 870382
Originally a coal storage house, this 17th-century building was converted into cottages and then into a pub in the 19th century. Chargrilled mojo chicken ciabetta sandwich is typical of the imaginative bar fare, while the restaurant might offer Thai-style red snapper, or honey roast duck breast. **Principal beers:** Archers Village & Golden, Fullers London Pride, Hook Norton Old Hooky, Wychwood Special.
Directions Halfway between Oxford & Swindon on the A420, take rd signed Bampton, pub is approx 2m down it.
Brewery/Company Free House
Open 11.30-3 6-11
Bar food 12-2 7-9 Av main course £5
Restaurant 12-2 7-9

FERNHAM Oxfordshire *Map 04 SU29*

Woodman Inn NEW
FERNHAM
YN7 7NX ☎ 01367 820643
Stone walls, heavy beams and real ale straight from the barrel are features of this traditional 17th-century village local in the Vale of the White Horse. The long-serving landlord offers a good range of bar food, from filled baguettes to specialities like herb-crusted rack of lamb with mint jus, Woodman pie and steak au poivre. **Principal beers:** Morland Original, Tanners Jack, Old Speckled Hen, & Ruddles County.

Brewery/Company Free House
Open 12-2.30 6.30-11
Bar food 12-3 7-11 Av main course £9
Restaurant 12-2.30 7-9.30 Av 3 course à la carte £12

FYFIELD Oxfordshire *Map 04 SU49*

The White Hart
FYFIELD

Main Rd OX13 5LW ☎ 01865 390585
Former 15th-century priest's chantry house with original oak beams and inglenook fireplaces. Offers a good

contd.

selection of snacks and light lunches, plus favourites like steak, mushroom and Guinness pie, and chicken Strasbourg. House specials include Stilton steak, venison casserole, and duck with black cherry and orange sauce. **Principal beers:** Hook Norton, Wadworth 6X, Theakston Old Peculier, Boddingtons.
Directions Just off A420, 8m SW of Oxford
Brewery/Company Free House
Open 11-3 6-11
Bar food 12-2 7-10 Av main course £8
Restaurant 12-2 7-10 Av 3 course à la carte £12

GORING Oxfordshire — *Map 04 SU68*

Miller of Mansfield
GORING

High St RG8 9AW ☎ 01491 872829
Situated in the Goring Gap, an area of outstanding natural beauty, and handy for the Thames Path (just 200 yards away) and the Ridgeway, this ivy-clad village inn is a welcome watering-hole. Bar food ranges from lasagne to grilled whole plaice and peppered steak.
Principal beers: Courage Best, Youngs Special, Marstons Pedigree.
Directions From Pangbourne A329 to Streatley, then R on B4009, 0.5m to Goring
Brewery/Company Free House
Open 11-11 (Sun 12-10.30, food all day wknds)
Bar food 12-2 6.30-10 Av main course £5.95
Restaurant 12-2 7-10 Av 3 course à la carte £16 Av 2 course fixed price £6.95
Accommodation (Min) s£47.50 d£62.50

HAILEY Oxfordshire — *Map 04 SP31*

Bird in Hand
HAILEY

Whiteoak Green OX8 5XP
☎ 01993 868321
Fine 17th-century country inn ideally placed for visiting Oxford, Stratford and the Cotswolds. Imaginative menu featuring mainly English cooking with a Mediterranean influence, and a strong emphasis on fresh seafood. Begin with lemon and basil risotto or Thai-style fishcakes, following on, perhaps, with beef and suet pudding or red mullet roasted with peppers and garlic.
Principal beers: Wadworth 6X, Boddingtons, Marstons Pedigree.
Directions Leave A40 for Witney town centre, onto B4022, through Hailey, inn 1m N
Brewery/Company Heavitree
Open 11-11
Bar food 12-2 7-9.30 Av main course £8.50
Restaurant 12-2 7-9.30 Av 3 course à la carte £20
Accommodation (Min) s£55 d£60

HENLEY-ON-THAMES Oxfordshire — *Map 04 SU78*

The Five Horseshoes
HENLEY-ON-THAMES

Maidensgrove RG9 6EX
☎ 01491 641282
Overlooking the Chiltern hills and the Warburg Nature Reserve, with its woodland trails, this 17th-century country pub has many attractive features. Good range of imaginative, well presented food includes salmon and crab cakes with fresh tomato sauce, braised knuckle of Parma ham with herbs and honey, and chicken with home-made spicy fruit chutney. **Principal beers:** Brakspear - Ordinary, Special, Dark Rose.

Directions A4130 from Henley, onto B480
Brewery/Company Brakspear
Open 11-2.30 6-11
Bar food 12-2 7-10 Av main course £7.50
Restaurant 12-3.30 6-11 Av 3 course à la carte £19.95 Av 3 course fixed price £19.95

The Golden Ball
HENLEY-ON-THAMES

Lower Assendon RG9 6AH
☎ 01491 574157
Dick Turpin hid in the priest hole at this 400-year-old building tucked away in the

Assendon Valley close to Henley. Traditional pub food includes lasagne, baked avocado, smoked fish pie and whole Dover sole. Large, children-friendly garden with climbing frame and pot-bellied pigs. **Principal beers:** Brakspear-Bitter, Special.
Directions A4130, R onto B480, pub 300yrds on L
Brewery/Company Brakspear
Open 11-3 6-11
Bar food 11.45-2.15 7-9.30 Av main course £7.50

The Little Angel
HENLEY-ON-THAMES
Remenham Ln RG9 2LS
☎ 01491 574165
Just over the bridge from Henley, this Grade II-listed, 17th-century building with brasserie and conservatory overlooks the cricket pitch, and has recently become something of a celebrity watering-hole. Menu may include sausage and mash, cod with linguini, roast guinea fowl, or cheese and nut terrine. **Principal beers:** Brakspear.
Directions from M4, pub is on the R at bottom of hill as you arrive in Henley
Brewery/Company Brakspear
Open 11-3 5-11
Bar food 12-2.30 6-10 Av main course £7.95
Restaurant 12.30-2.30 7-10 Av 3 course à la carte £22.50

HOOK NORTON Oxfordshire *Map 04 SP33*

The Gate Hangs High
HOOK NORTON
Whichford Rd OX15 5DF
☎ 01608 737387
'The gate hangs high and hinders none/refresh and pay and travel on.' The rhyme reflects the pub's former role as a tollgate en route to Banbury Market. Traditional home cooking ranges from steak and kidney pudding, honey-baked ham, and chicken curry, to beef Wellington with Madeira sauce, venison with port and Stilton sauce, and fresh grey mullet with limes.
Principal beers: Hook Norton - Best, Old Hooky, Haymaker & Generation.
Directions Off A361 SW of Banbury
Brewery/Company Hook Norton
Open 11.30-3 6.30-11

Bar food 12-2 6.30-9.30 Av main course £6
Restaurant 12-2 6.30-9.30 Av 3 course à la carte £15

KELMSCOT Oxfordshire *Map 04 SU29*

The Plough Inn NEW
KELMSCOT
GL7 3HG ☎ 01367 253543
Peacefully situated in an unspoilt village close to Kelmscot Manor and the Thames, the 17th-century Plough is a favoured refreshment stop among the walking and boating fraternity. Good home-made food includes traditional snacks and decent specials like venison casserole, beef stew and dumplings, grilled sea bass, bouillabaisse, and game pie. **Principal beers:** Morland Original, Bass, Wadworth 6X, Marston Pedigree.

Directions From M4 onto A419 then A361 to Lechlade & A416 to Faringdon, pick up signs to Kelmscot
Brewery/Company Free House
Open 11-11
Bar food 12-2 7-9.30 Av main course £6
Accommodation (Min) s£30 d£50

Pubs offering a good choice of seafood on the menu

KINGSTON LISLE Oxfordshire
Map 04 SU38

The Blowing Stone Inn
KINGSTON LISLE

OX12 9QL ☎ 01367 820288

Situated in an area rich in ancient history, this inn is named after a nearby sarsen stone pierced with holes which, legend has it, King Alfred used to summon his troops. Fresh fish and shell fish figure prominently, along with local game dressed by the landlord himself.

Principal beers: Morland Original, Bass, Wadworth 6X.

Directions B4507 from Wantage toward Ashbury/Swindon, after 6m R to Kingston Lisle

Brewery/Company Free House

Open 11-2.30 6.30-11

Bar food 11-2.30 6.30-11 Av main course £6.50

Restaurant 11-2.30 6.30-11 Av 3 course à la carte £16

Accommodation (Min) s£20 d£40

LOWER WOLVERCOTE Oxfordshire
Map 04 SP41

The Trout Inn
LOWER WOLVERCOTE

195 Godstow Rd OX2 8PN

☎ 01865 302071

Originally constructed in the 17th century using stones from the ruined Godstow Abbey, this charming inn is the local of Colin Dexter's Inspector Morse, and has a bar dedicated to this popular character. The pub has a rich history which includes its torching by Parliamentarian troops in the 1640s, and connections with Matthew Arnold and Lewis Carroll.

Principal beers: Bass, Worthington.

Directions From A40 at Wolvercote rdbt (N of Oxford) follow signs for Wolvercote

Brewery/Company Vintage Inns

Open 11-11

MARSTON Oxfordshire
Map 04 SP50

Victoria Arms
MARSTON

Mill Ln OX3 0PZ ☎ 01865 241382

Friendly country pub situated on the banks of the River Cherwell, only 10 minutes from the centre of Oxford, and accessible by punt. Dishes on the daily-changing blackboard may feature sweet and sour pork, home-made steak and Stilton pie, spinach lasagne, and lemon brulee among the list of puddings.

Principal beers: Wadworth 6X, Henrys IPA & Summersault, Badger Tanglefoot.

Directions From A40 follow signs to Old Marston, sharp R into Mill Lane, pub lane 500yrds on L

Brewery/Company Wadworth

Open 11-11

Bar food 12-2.30 6.30-9.30 Av main course £4.95

MIDDLETON STONEY Oxfordshire
Map 04 SP52

The Jersey Arms NEW
MIDDLETON STONEY

OX6 8SE ☎ 01869 343234

Charming family-run hotel, formerly a coaching inn with the original courtyard housing comfortable bedrooms. Extensive menu supplemented by interesting blackboard specials, offering a good choice of starters/light meals including soup and pate, a pasta selection and main courses such as baked trout stuffed with mussels, basil and orange.

Principal beers: Courage, John Smiths.

Brewery/Company Free House

Open 7am-11pm

Bar food 12-2.15 6.30-9.30 Av main course £7.50

Restaurant 12-2.15 6.30-9.30 Av 3 course à la carte £20

Accommodation (Min) s£75 d£89

MINSTER LOVELL Oxfordshire
Map 04 SP31

The Mill & Old Swan
MINSTER LOVELL

OX8 5RN ☎ 01993 774441

An inn and conference centre, set in 60 acres of Cotswold countryside. this former coaching inn dates back over 600 years. In the bar you can relax in front of the open fire with traditional pub food such as ploughman's, sandwiches and steak and kidney pie.

Principal beers: Worthington, Bass.
Directions On A4095 W of Witney
Brewery/Company Free House
Open 12.15-3 6.30-11.30
Bar food 12.15-3 7-9 Av main course £10

MOULSFORD Oxfordshire *Map 04 SU58*

The Beetle & Wedge Hotel
MOULSFORD
Ferry Ln OX14 2HY ☎ 01491 651381
Nestling on the banks of the Thames, this hotel sits by the stretch of river immortalized in 'Wind in the Willows' and 'Three Men in a Boat.' Diners can enjoy pleasant views of the river as they tuck into dishes such as squid and bacon with salad, gratin of aubergines and mozzarella, and escalope of salmon hollandaise. **Principal beers:** Adnams Best, Badger Tanglefoot, Wadworth 6X.

Directions Off A329 between Reading & Oxford
Brewery/Company Free House
Open 12.30-3 7.30-11
Bar food 12.30-2 7.30-10 Av main course £10
Restaurant 12.30-2 7.30-10 Av 3 course fixed price £35
Accommodation (Min) s£90 d£120

MURCOTT Oxfordshire *Map 04 SP51*

The Nut Tree
MURCOTT
Main St OX5 2RE ☎ 01865 331253
Quaint white thatched pub with a duck pond, set in a peaceful hamlet. Steaks are a popular choice, and fresh fish according to availability, along with calves' liver and bacon, Cajun chicken and mushroom Stroganoff. To finish there is a wide choice of sweets, including gateaux and giant meringues.

Principal beers: Morrells, Wychwood, Hook Norton, Wadworth 6X.
Brewery/Company Free House
Open 11-3 6.30-11
Bar food 12-3 6.30-11
Restaurant 12-3 6.30-11

NORTH MORETON Oxfordshire *Map 04 SU58*

The Bear
NORTH MORETON
High St OX11 9AT ☎ 01235 813236
15th-century inn with exposed beams, open fireplaces and a cosy, relaxed atmosphere. Strong emphasis on fresh fish on the single menu, which offers appetising dishes such as sizzling seafood, Mediterranean king prawn salad, Loch Fyne smoked salmon, and roast Barbary duck with cranberry gravy.
Principal beers: Hook Norton.
Directions Off A4130 between Didcot & Wallingford
Brewery/Company Free House
Open 12-3 6.30-11
Bar food 12-2.30 6.30-10 Av main course £8
Restaurant 12-2.30 6.30-10 Av 3 course à la carte £16.50

NUFFIELD Oxfordshire *Map 04 SU68*

The Crown
NUFFIELD
RG9 5SJ ☎ 01491 641335
A heavily beamed, traditional pub set in a village on the edge of the Chilterns on the Ridgeway Path, the Crown offers English and continental dishes with full restaurant facilities and bar meals. There is a large garden at the rear with a play area for children.
Principal beers: Brakspear.
Directions Follow Henley signs, then Wallingford rd on L past turning for village
Brewery/Company Brakspear
Open 11-2.30 6-11 (Sat 11-3,6-11 Sun 12-3,7-10.30)
Bar food 12-2 6.30-9 Av main course £7.50
Restaurant 12-2 6.30-9 Av 3 course à la carte £15.50

For Pubs with AA food rosettes see page 430

OXFORD Oxfordshire Map 04 SP50

Anchor
OXFORD

2 Hayfield Rd, Walton Manor OX2 6TT
☎ 01865 510282

A friendly 1930s pub, once frequented by local resident Lawrence of Arabia. Generous portions of home-style cooking are served, with dishes such as a half roast chicken, baked potatoes and other pub fare. In summer there are barbecues and pig roasts in the garden. **Principal beers:** Wadworth 6X & Henrys IPA.
Directions A34 Oxford Ring Road(N), exit Peartree Roundabout, 1.5m then R at Polstead Rd, follow rd to bottom, pub on R
Brewery/Company Wadworth
Open 12-11
Bar food 12-2.30 6-8.30 Av main course £3.50

The White House
OXFORD

2 Botley Rd OX2 0AB ☎ 01865 242823

Set back from a busy road, this pub was once a tollhouse where people crossed the river to enter Oxford. The menu may include loin of pork and apple sauce, sauteed calves' liver with onion sauce, tagliatelle with seafood and tarragon, or wild mushroom ravioli. **Principal beers:** Wadworth 6X, Greene King Abbot Ale, Tetley, Morland Old Speckled Hen.
Directions 2 minutes walk from rail station
Brewery/Company Free House
Open 11-11
Bar food 12.30-2 6-9.30 Av main course £4.50
Restaurant 12.30-2 6-9.30 Av 3 course à la carte £16

PISHILL Oxfordshire Map 04 SU78

The Crown Inn
PISHILL

RG9 6HH ☎ 01491 638364

Brick and flint coaching inn situated amid glorious Chiltern hills and beechwoods, and close to the magnificent parkland of Stonor House. Among the popular dishes expect to find venison steak, pork and sage sausage and mash and a choice of fresh fish specials, including halibut, tuna and John Dory. **Principal beers:** Brakspear, Fullers.

Directions On B480 off A4130, NW of Henley-on-Thames
Brewery/Company Free House
Open 11.30-2.30 6-11
Bar food 12-2 7-10 Av main course £8
Restaurant 12-2 7-10 Av 3 course à la carte £15
Accommodation (Min) d£75

RAMSDEN Oxfordshire Map 04 SP31

The Royal Oak NEW
RAMSDEN

High St OX7 3AU ☎ 01993 868213

Listed 17th-century Cotswold stone inn, formerly a coaching inn, situated opposite the church in a peaceful village. Expect good real ales and interesting home-cooked meals in the welcoming beamed bar. From ploughman's, chilli and chargrilled burgers, the menu choice includes oysters, game casserole, lamb steak with port and redcurrant, and ribeye steak. **Principal beers:** Hook Norton, Fullers ESB, Adnams Broadside, Archers Golden.
Directions From Witney take B4022 toward Charlbury, then turn R before Hailey, and go through Poffley End.
Brewery/Company Free House
Open 11.30-3 6.30-11
Bar food 12-2 7-10 Av main course £6
Restaurant 12-2 7-10 Av 3 course à la carte £21
Accommodation (Min) s£35 d£50

ROKE Oxfordshire Map 04 SU69

Home Sweet Home
ROKE

OX10 6JD ☎ 01491 838249

Situated in a quiet road in the tiny hamlet of Roke, this 15th-century inn was converted from four cottages, by a local brewer. Typical dishes include smoked haddock and egg pancakes, cheesy vegetable pie, chicken and stilton

roulade with bacon, and a variety of ploughman's, salads, sandwiches and jacket potatoes. **Principal beers:** Hardy Popes Ale & Royal Oak.
Directions Just off the B4009 from Benson to Watlington, signed on B4009
Brewery/Company Free House
Open 11-3 6-11 (closed Sun eve)
Bar food 12-2 6-9.30 Av main course £5.95
Restaurant 12-2 7-9.30 Av 3 course à la carte £15

SHENINGTON Oxfordshire *Map 04 SP34*

The Bell
SHENINGTON
OX15 6NQ ☎ 01295 670274
Overlooking the pretty village green, this 18th-century inn offers good home-cooked food and lots of specialities. Dishes range from steak and kidney pie and salmon and tuna quiche, to pork casserole and pan-fried fillet steak. The inn is renowned for its home-made puddings, including sticky toffee pudding and banoffee pie. **Principal beers:** Hook Norton, Boddingtons.
Directions M40 J11 take A422 towards Stratford. Village is signposted 3m N of Wroxton
Brewery/Company Free House
Open 12-2.30 7-11
Bar food 12-2.30 7-11 Av main course £10
Restaurant 12-2.30 7-11 Av 3 course à la carte £10
Accommodation (Min) s£20 d£40

SHIPTON-UNDER-WYCHWOOD Oxfordshire *Map 04 SP21*

The Lamb Inn
SHIPTON-UNDER-WYCHWOOD
High St OX7 6DQ ☎ 01993 830465
A delightful old Cotswold-stone inn, in which the rustic beamed bar with its stone walls, wooden floor and sturdy furniture make a fine setting for enjoying a wholesome meal. Interesting dishes on the blackboard menu may include game terrine, calves' liver in Pernod, poached salmon, chargrilled tuna with Mediterranean vegetables, and chocolate truffle torte. **Principal beers:** Hook Norton.
Directions 4m N of Burford on the A361
Brewery/Company Old English Inns/Hot
Open 11-3 6-11 (Sun 12-3 7-10.30)
Bar food 12-2 7-9.30 Av main course £10
Restaurant 12-2 7-9.30 Av 3 course à la carte £25
Accommodation (Min) s£65 d£75

The Shaven Crown Hotel
SHIPTON-UNDER-WYCHWOOD
High St OX7 6BA ☎ 01993 830330
Originally a 14th-century hospice for the monks of nearby Bruern Abbey, this is one of the oldest inns in the country. Medieval hall, mullioned windows and central courtyard garden. Impressive menu includes salmon and crab fishcakes, pork goulash and 'Shiptons' chicken curry. Home-made soups and pies are particular favourites. **Principal beers:** Hook Norton, Youngs Special, Morland Old Speckled Hen, Wychwood Hobgoblin.
Directions On A361, halfway between Burford and Chipping Norton opposite village green and church
Brewery/Company Free House
Open 12-2.30 5-11
Bar food 12-2 5-10 Av main course £6.95
Restaurant 12-2 7-9 Av 3 course à la carte £21.50 Av 3 course fixed price £21.50
Accommodation (Min) s£40 d£85

SOUTH MORETON Oxfordshire *Map 04 SU58*

The Crown Inn
SOUTH MORETON
High St OX11 9AG ☎ 01235 812262
Good food, ale and a friendly atmosphere prevail at this rambling local which dates from 1850 and enjoys a pretty village location. Diners can expect to find fresh haddock in beer batter, home-made salmon fishcakes, half shoulder of lamb, and steak, kidney and Stilton pie on the menu. **Principal beers:** Badger Tanglefoot, Adnams, Wadworth 6X, & Henrys IPA.
Directions From Didcot take A4130 towards Wallingford. Village on R

Brewery/Company Wadworth
Open 11-3 5.30-11

contd.

Bar food 12-2 6.30-9.30 Av main course £7.50
Restaurant 12-2 6.30-9.30 Av 3 course à la carte £11.95

SOUTH STOKE Oxfordshire *Map 04 SU58*

The Perch and Pike
SOUTH STOKE
RG8 0JS ☎ 01491 872415
At this quiet, 17th-century pub/restaurant, furnished principally with antiques, all food is cooked to order. Have a drink on the patio or by the fire while anticipating dishes such as chargrilled lamb chop, or whole lemon sole with prawn and pink peppercorn butter.
Principal beers: Brakspear PA.
Directions Between Goring and Wallingford just off B4009
Brewery/Company Brakspear
Open 12-2.30 6-11 (Closed Sun evening)
Bar food 12-2 7-9 Av main course £9.95

STADHAMPTON Oxfordshire *Map 04 SU69*

The Crazy Bear
STADHAMPTON
Bear Ln OX44 7UR ☎ 01865 890714
Comfortably refurbished 16th-century inn featuring a two AA rosette restaurant and a Thai brasserie with authentic Thai chefs. Bar and brasserie food includes champagne and oysters, foie gras sandwich on brioche, Red duck curry, and seafood with chilli oil and lemon grass. In the restaurant expect partridge with garlic confit and port jus and fresh lobster. **Principal beers:** Bass, Adnams Broadside, Wadworth 6X.
Directions M40 J7 L on A329
Brewery/Company Free House
Open 12-11
Bar food 12-3 7-10 Av main course £7.95
Restaurant 12-3 7-10 Av 3 course à la carte £23 Av 3 course fixed price £12.95
Accommodation (Min) s£50 d£60

STANDLAKE Oxfordshire *Map 04 SP30*

The Bell at Standlake
STANDLAKE
21 High St OX8 7RH ☎ 01865 300784
Early 17th-century half-timbered village pub renowned locally for its fine food and good wines. An extensive blackboard menu choice ranges from lunchtime doorstep sandwiches, Malaysian-style chicken curry and game pie in the bar, to pork with black pudding, potato rôsti and apple sauce, or duck with pickled oranges in the more formal evening restaurant.
Principal beers: Morland Original, Bass, Flowers Original, Everards Tiger.
Directions Off the A415
Brewery/Company Morland
Open 12-3 (ex Mon) 6-11 (Sun 10.30)
Bar food 12-3 Av main course £7
Restaurant 12-3 6.30-11 Av 3 course à la carte £18 Av 3 course fixed price £12.95

STANTON ST JOHN Oxfordshire *Map 04 SP50*

Star Inn
STANTON ST JOHN
OX33 1EX ☎ 01865 351277
Originally a butchers shop and abbatoir, this 17th-century village inn has a peaceful, secluded garden and two, traditionally furnished bar. Home-cooked bar food is listed on a daily-changing blackboard and may include salmon with hollandaise, broccoli and mushrooms au gratin, and apple pie. **Principal beers:** Wadworth 6X & Henrys IPA.
Directions At A40/Oxford ring road rdbt take Stanton exit, follow rd to T junct, R to Stanton, 3rd L, pub on L 50yds
Brewery/Company Wadworth
Open 11-2.30 6.30-11
Bar food 12-2 6.30-10 Av main course £6.75

The Talk House
STANTON ST JOHN
Wheatley Rd OX33 1EX
☎ 01865 351648
Well converted and extended 17th-century inn within easy reach of Oxford and the M40. A Gothic-style ambience pervades throughout the attractive bars, where you can sample Thai prawn curry, half shoulder of lamb with rosemary and garlic, vegetarian pasta dishes, and good fish specials from the appealing menus on offer. **Principal beers:** Morland Original & Old Speckled Hen.
Directions Stanton St John signed from the Oxford ring road
Brewery/Company Free House
Open 12-11
Bar food 12-2 7-10 Av main course £9

Restaurant 12-2 7-10 Av 3 course à la carte £20
Accommodation (Min) s£40 d£49.50

STEEPLE ASTON Oxfordshire *Map 04 SP42*

Red Lion
STEEPLE ASTON

South Side OX6 3RY ☎ 01869 340225

The art of conversation and the enjoyment of fresh food is positively encouraged at this traditional pub. The 17th-century building comprises a bar, separate dining room, library and floral terrace. Typical dishes include Arbroath smokies en cocotte, jugged hare with forcemeat balls, and a soufflé of fresh lime. **Principal beers:** Badger Tanglefoot, Hook Norton, Wadworth 6X.

Directions Off A4260 between Oxford & Banbury
Brewery/Company Free House
Open 11-3 6-11 (Sun 7-10.30/restaurant closed Sun-Mon)
Bar food 12-2 Av main course £4.80
Restaurant 7.30-9.15 Av 3 course à la carte £22.50

STEVENTON Oxfordshire *Map 04 SU49*

The Cherry Tree
STEVENTON

33 High St OX13 6RZ ☎ 01235 831222

Inviting roadside tavern, full of old world charm. Home made specials might include liver and bacon casserole with a giant Yorkshire pudding, and chicken en croûte layered with pâté and ham. Celeriac and potato bake and mushroom Stroganoff are typical vegetarian options **Principal beers:** Wadworth Henrys IPA, 6X, Farmers Glory, & Old Timer and guest ales.

Directions Leave A34 at Milton Interchange, follow signs for Steventon, go into village, over railway bridge, pub on R
Brewery/Company Wadworth
Open 11.30-2.30 5-11 (Fri-Sun 11.30-11)
Bar food 12-2 6.30-9 Av main course £5.50

STOKE ROW Oxfordshire *Map 04 SU68*

Crooked Billet
STOKE ROW

RG9 5PU ☎ 01491 681048

Built in 1642, this off-the-beaten-track cottage was once the hideout of notorious highwayman Dick Turpin. Delightfully unspoilt inside, with beams, open fires and rustic furnishings, it offers an imaginative menu, including skate with lemon and cockle butter sauce, scallops with pancetta, wok-fried baby squid, and venison with port and juniper sauce. **Principal beers:** Brakspear.

Directions From Henley to Oxford A4130.Turn L at Nettlebed for Stoke Row
Brewery/Company Brakspear
Open 12-4.30 7-12.30
Restaurant 12-4.30 7-12.30 Av 3 course à la carte £25 Av 3 course fixed price £14.95

SUTTON COURTENAY Oxfordshire *Map 04 SU59*

The Fish
SUTTON COURTENAY

4 Appleford Rd OX14 4NQ
☎ 01235 848242

Unassuming, 100-year-old building situated in an attractive Thames-side village. Although informal, the interior atmosphere is more restaurant than pub. Drinkers are welcome, but most come for the creative food and decent wines. From filled baguettes and coq au vin, the menu extends to sea bass with ratatouille, and Angus beef fillet in red wine. **Principal beers:** Morland Original & Old Speckled Hen.

Directions From A415 in Abingdon take B4017 then L onto B4016 to village
Brewery/Company Morland
Open 12-3.30 6-11 (Sat 6.30-11, Sun 7-10.30)
Bar food 12-3.30 Av main course £5.85
Restaurant 12-3.30 7-11 Av 3 course à la carte £22.50 Av 3 course fixed price £16.95
Accommodation (Min) s£35 d£45

THAME Oxfordshire Map 04 SP70

Abingdon Arms
THAME

21 Cornmarket OX9 2BL

☎ 01844 260116

Known locally as 'The Abo', this 18th-century former coaching inn offers a friendly atmosphere and hearty traditional pub food in its long, rug-strewn bar. Choose from 'doorstop' sandwiches, home-made pasta dishes, ploughman's platters, bangers and mash, and lemon sole. Regular live music in a converted 300-year-old barn. **Principal beers:** Wadworth 6X, Brakspears, Hook Norton, Boddingtons.

Directions M40 J8 A418 to Thame

Brewery/Company Free House

Open 11-11 (Fri 11am-1am, closed Sun eve)

Bar food 12-2.30 6-9 Av main course £4.50

Restaurant 6-9.30 Av 3 course à la carte £14

TOOT BALDON Oxfordshire Map 04 SP50

The Crown Inn NEW
TOOT BALDON

OX44 9NG ☎ 01865 343240

Enjoying a pleasant rural location close to Oxford, this welcoming, 300-year-old village pub is a popular destination for some honest home cooking and summer barbeques. Bar meals range from hearty ploughman's and plaice and chips, to devilled kidney's, venison with red wine, and chicken with ginger, spring onions and coriander on the specials board.

Principal beers: Mansfield, Morland, Ruddles.

Directions Exit Oxford via Cowley, after 2m on the Stadhampton road R for the Paldons

Brewery/Company Free House

Open 11-3 6.30-11

Bar food 12-2 7-9 Av main course £6.50

Restaurant 12-2 7-9 Av 3 course à la carte £15

WANTAGE Oxfordshire Map 04 SU38

The Star Inn
WANTAGE

Watery Ln, Sparsholt OX12 9PL

☎ 01235 751539 &751001

Situated in horse racing downland country, close to the Ridegway trail, this 400-year-old village local is popular with the racing fraternity. Fairly straightforward bar food includes some home-made dishes like steak and Guinness pie, cottage pie, lambs' liver and bacon, alongside filled baguettes and mixed grill with hand-cut chips.

Principal beers: Morland Original, Butts.

Directions Sparsholt is 4m west of Wantage, take the B4507 Wantage to Ashbury road and turn off R to the village, the Star Inn is signposted

Brewery/Company Free House

Open 12-3 6-11 (Sat 12-11,Sun 12-10.30)

Bar food 12-2 7-9 Av main course £7.50

Restaurant 12-2 7-9 Av 3 course fixed price £14.50

Accommodation (Min) d£55

WESTCOTT BARTON Oxfordshire Map 04 SP42

The Fox Inn
WESTCOTT BARTON

Enstone Rd OX7 7BN ☎ 01869 340338

The Italian owner offers traditional Italian dishes alongside traditional English fare at this 14th-century country inn. Typical dishes include rigatoni al forno, with home-made Italian sausages, a spicy tomato sauce and mozzarella cheese, and a range of home-made chicken, steak and venison pies.

Principal beers: Hook Norton Best, Theakston XB.

Brewery/Company Free House

Open 11-2.30 5-11

Bar food 12-2.15 7-9.30 Av main course £4.95

Restaurant 7-9.30 Av 3 course à la carte £18

WESTON-ON-THE-GREEN Oxfordshire Map 04 SP51

The Chequers
WESTON-ON-THE-GREEN

Northampton Rd OX6 8QH

☎ 01869 350319

17th-century coaching inn built of Cotswold stone. Bar offers a traditional English pub menu while the restaurant is devoted to Thai food. Menu includes soups, Kwaitiew noodle dishes, Pad (stir fry), Kaeng (Thai curry), Khoa (rice dishes), salads, and Pla (fish and seafood).

Principal beers: Fullers London Pride, Fullers ESB.

Directions M40 J9 A34 S take 1st exit
Brewery/Company Fullers
Open 11-3 6-11
Bar food 12-2.30 Av main course £3
Restaurant 11.30-3 6-11 Av 3 course à la carte £14

WHEATLEY Oxfordshire

Map 03 ST64

Bat & Ball Inn

WHEATLEY

28 High St OX44 9HJ ☎ 01865 874379

In a picturesque village with views over the Chilterns and Berkshire Downs, this old coaching inn is renowned for its collection of cricketing memorabilia. One menu is offered throughout, and may include avocado and fresh crab meat salad, fillet steak topped with Stilton sauce, and an apple and calvados crêpe.
Principal beers: Marstons Pedigree, Morland Original.
Directions Pass thru Wheatley towards Garsington, take only L turn, signed Cuddesdon
Brewery/Company Marstons
Open 11-11
Bar food 12-2.30 6.30-9.30 Av main course £7.50
Accommodation (Min) s£44 d£56

WOODSTOCK Oxfordshire

Map 04 SP41

The Feathers Hotel

WOODSTOCK

Market St OX20 1SX ☎ 01993 812291

Situated in the heart of this small country town on the edge of Blenheim Estate, this fine 17th-century inn has a fine reputation for its food. In the relaxing Winchat Bar you might expect salmon fishcakes with mustard hollandaise, and salad niçoise, while dishes in the restaurant might include shank of lamb with olive salsa. **Principal beers:** Wadworth 6X.
Directions From M40 J9 take 1st L in Woodstock. Hotel on L
Brewery/Company Free House
Open 12-2.15 7-11
Bar food 12.30-2.15 7.30-9.15 Av main course £8.50
Restaurant 12.30-2.15 7.30-9.15 Av 3 course à la carte £40 Av 6 course fixed price £44
Accommodation (Min) s£88 d£105

Kings Head Inn NEW

WOODSTOCK

Chapel Hill, Wootton OX20 1DX
☎ 01993 811340

Pretty 16th-century stone inn tucked away in an attractive village close to Woodstock and Blenheim Palace. With pine-furnished bedrooms and enjoyable food prepared from top quality ingredients, the inn is the perfect country base. Imaginative dishes include scallops with chilli and lime, fish stew, steamed sea bass, chargrilled venison, and vanilla yoghurt and Mascarpone terrine.
Principal beers: Ruddles Best, Marston's Pedigree, Wadworth 6X.
Directions On A44 2m N of Woodstock then R to Wootton. Inn near church on Chapel Hill
Brewery/Company Free House
Restaurant 12-2 7-9.30 Av 3 course à la carte £17.50
Accommodation (Min) s£54 d£65

WOOTTON Oxfordshire

Map 04 SP41

The Killingworth Castle Inn

WOOTTON

Glympton Rd OX20 1EJ
☎ 01993 811401

Built in 1637 by Thomas Killingworth as a coaching inn, this impressive, three-storey building enjoys a peaceful village-edge location close to Woodstock and Blenheim Palace. Useful base from which to explore the Cotswolds. Expect straightforward pub food, good Morland ales and popular live folk and jazz evenings. **Principal beers:** Morland Original, Ruddles Best.
Directions Exit A34 onto B4027, cross over A4260, pub on N edge of Wootton
Brewery/Company Morland
Open 12-2.30 6.30-11
Bar food 12-2 7-9 Av main course £3.50
Restaurant 12-2 7-9 Av 3 course à la carte £12.50
Accommodation (Min) s£35 d£50

WYTHAM Oxfordshire

Map 04 SP40

White Hart

WYTHAM

OX2 8QA ☎ 01865 244372

In the pretty, thatched village of Wytham (owned by Oxford University), this attractive, creeper-covered pub has flagstone floors and open fires. It has frequently been used in the television series Inspector Morse. There is a salad,

contd.

cold meat, and quiche buffet, as well as hot dishes, and in summer excellent barbecues. **Principal beers:** Tetley, Adnams.
Directions Just off A34 NW of Oxford
Brewery/Company Allied Domecq
Open 11.30-2.30 6-11 (Summer-Sat 11.30-11, Sun 12-10.30)
Bar food 12-2 7-9 Av main course £7

Rutland

COTTESMORE Rutland *Map 08 SK91*

The Sun Inn NEW
COTTESMORE
25 Main St LE15 7DH ☎ 01572 812321
Thatched 17th-century pub set in a pretty village close to Rutland Water. Tastefully refurbished by enthusiastic licensees, expect a civilised dining atmosphere and imaginative pub food. From toasted ciabatta sandwiches (marinated spicy chicken), and home-made pasta meals, the menu may offer roast partidge with honeyed turnips and tarragon, calves' liver with Parma ham and lime jus, and lime crème brûlée with plum compote. **Principal beers:** Adnams, Everards Tiger, Courage Directors.
Brewery/Company Everards Brewery
Open 11-2.30 6-11.30
Bar food 12-2 6.30-10 Av main course £7
Restaurant 12-2 6.30-10 Av 3 course à la carte £18

EMPINGHAM Rutland *Map 04 SK90*

White Horse Inn
EMPINGHAM
Main St LE15 8PS ☎ 01780 460221
Located in the ancient county of Rutland, this 17th-century stone-built inn lies close to the largest man-made lake in Europe. Appetising specials include Rutland chicken with smoked bacon and steak and kidney pie, while Italian lasagne, lamb cutlets and Whitby scampi feature on the bar food menu.
Principal beers: Courage Directors, Ruddles, Batemans, John Smiths.
Directions From A1 take A606 signed Oakham & Rutland Water
Brewery/Company Grand Metropolitan
Open 7am-11pm (Sun 8-10.30)
Bar food 12-2.15 7.15-9.45 Av main course £8
Restaurant 12-2.15 7.15-10 Av 3 course à la carte £18 Av 3 course fixed price £17.95
Accommodation (Min) s£50 d£63

LYDDINGTON Rutland *Map 04 SP89*

Old White Hart NEW
LYDDINGTON
5 Main St LE15 9LF ☎ 01572 821703
17th-century stone pub standing by the green in an attractive village high above the Welland valley. Good range of interesting, freshly prepared bar food and more elaborate restaurant fare. Expect mussels in white wine and garlic, salmon fishcakes with lemon and dill, deep-fried Grimsby haddock, and herb-crusted rack of lamb with rosemary jus. **Principal beers:** Greene King IPA & Abbot Ale, Blacksheep, Taylor Landlord.
Brewery/Company Free House
Open 12-3 6-11
Bar food 12-2 6.30-9.30 Av main course £7
Restaurant 12-3 6.30-9.30 Av 3 course à la carte £7

MARKET OVERTON Rutland *Map 08 SK81*

Black Bull NEW
MARKET OVERTON
2 Teigh Rd LE15 7PW ☎ 01572 767677
Neatly thatched 15th-century building enjoying a pretty village setting close to Rutland Water. Relaxed and traditional beamed interior with popular lounge bar serving a good range of home-cooked dishes. Main course choices may feature Rutland chicken, whole lemon sole, and Thai-style monkfish, sirloin with peppercorn sauce, and sandwiches (lunchtimes only). **Principal beers:** Marstons Pedigree, Hook Norton, Theakstons, Greene King IPA.
Brewery/Company Free House

Open 11.30-2.30 6-11
Bar food 12-1.45 6.30-9.45 Av main course £6
Restaurant 12-1.45 6.30-9.45
Accommodation (Min) s£30 d£45

OAKHAM Rutland *Map 04 SK80*

The Blue Ball
OAKHAM

6 Cedar St, Braunston-in-Rutland LE15 8QS ☎ 01572 722135

Splendidly rufurbished village inn, formerly called The Globe, dating from the early 1600s, and reputedly Rutland's oldest pub. Thatched and quaint, it boasts a wealth of beams and timbers and a civilised atmosphere. A varied menu ranges from fishcakes and steak and ale pie, to baracuda with mango salsa, and pheasant wrapped in bacon. **Principal beers:** Ruddles, Theakstons, John Smiths.
Directions From A1 take A606 to Oakham.Village SW of Oakham
Brewery/Company Old English Pub Co
Open 12-3 6.30-11
Bar food 12-2.30 7-9.30 Av main course £6.95
Restaurant 12-2.30 7-9.30 Av 3 course à la carte £18.95

The Finch's Arms NEW
OAKHAM

Oakham Rd, Hambleton LE15 8TL ☎ 01572 756575

From the restaurant and terrace of this upmarket and tastefully refurbished 17th-century inn diners have stunning views across Rutland Water. Set in a sleepy village, it offers good range of modern dishes, perhaps including salmon tagliatelle, warm Roquefort tart with red onion jus, pork on celeriac mash with caramelised apples, and marinated tuna with shallot and tomato compôte.
Principal beers: Marstons Pedigree, Theakstons, Greene King Abbotts Ale.
Brewery/Company Free House
Open 10.30-3 6-11.30
Bar food 12-3 6.30-10 Av main course £6
Restaurant 12-3 6.30-10 Av 3 course à la carte £16 Av 3 course fixed price £14.95
Accommodation (Min) s£75 d£90

STRETTON Rutland *Map 08 SK91*

Ram Jam Inn
STRETTON

The Great North Rd LE15 7QX ☎ 01780 410776

Popular A1 roadside inn, named after a house brew advertised over the door in a manner more prominent than the original sign (the Winchilsea Arms). More than a transit stop, it offers good quality food, with dishes such as duck terrine, Rutland sausage with onion marmalade, and stir-fried squid with chilli and ginger dressing. **Principal beers:** Ruddles - Best, County.
Directions On A1 northbound carriageway past B1668 turn off, through service station into hotel car park
Brewery/Company Free House
Open 7am-11pm (bar food 7am-10pm)
Restaurant 12-2.30 6.30-9.30 Av 3 course à la carte £15
Accommodation (Min) s£45 d£55

WHITWELL Rutland *Map 04 SK90*

Noel Arms Inn
WHITWELL

Main St LE15 8BW ☎ 01780 460334

A short walk from Rutland Water, this country pub has a cosy lounge with log fire that forms part of the original thatched building. Sample steak and kidney pie or pork ribs in honey and cider in the modern bar, and grilled sea bass, or game terrine with juniper berries from the imaginative restaurant menu. **Principal beers:** Marstons Pedigree, John Smiths, Vale Notley Ale , Grainstore Cooking.
Directions From A1 take A606 to Oakham
Brewery/Company Free House
Open 11-11 (Breakfast 7.30-9.30)
Bar food 12-2.30 6.30-10 Av main course £8
Restaurant 12-2.30 7-10 Av 3 course à la carte £20
Accommodation (Min) s£50 d£65

WING Rutland *Map 04 SK80*

The Cuckoo Inn
WING

3 Top St LE15 8SE ☎ 01572 737340

A truly traditional village pub dating from the 17th century, the thatched and unpretentious Cuckoo Inn offers a warm

contd.

welcome, open fires and an unusual range of guest beers for travellers en route to nearby Rutland Water. Simple bar food supplemented by home-cooked pies, casseroles and authentic curries.
Principal beers: Bass, Marston's Pedigree.
Directions A6003 from Oakham, turn R then L
Brewery/Company Free House
Open 11.30-3 6.30-11 (closed Tue eve)
Bar food 11.30-2.30 7-9.30 Av main course £5.50

Kings Arms
WING
Top St LE15 8SE ☎ 01572 737634
Attractive 17th-century stone inn with beamed bars and log fires nestling in a peaceful village close to Rutland Water. Traditional bar snacks are supplemented by interesting specials and restaurant dishes such as chicken liver pâté with onion marmalade, red snapper with Vermouth and dill butter sauce, seafood platter, and lamb steak with redcurrant and port sauce. **Principal beers:** Bateman XB, Ruddles County.

Directions 1m off A6003 between Uppingham & Oakham
Brewery/Company Free House
Open 11-11
Bar food 12-2 6-10.30 Av main course £6
Restaurant 12-2 6-10.30 Av 3 course à la carte £15
Accommodation (Min) s£35 d£50

Staffordshire

ABBOTS BROMLEY Staffordshire — Map 07 SK02

The Crown Inn
ABBOTS BROMLEY
Market Place WS15 3BS
☎ 01283 840227
Traditional country inn situated in a conservation village - the home of the Horn Dance which dates from 1226. Food ranges from sandwiches and snacks, to a choice of steaks, swordfish, jumbo cod in crispy batter, and chicken breast in lemon and lime sauce. **Principal beers:** Bass, Wadworth 6X, Morland Old Speckled Hen, Greene King Abbot Ale.
Directions On B5013, in centre of village, opposite Butter Cross
Brewery/Company Enterprise Inns
Open 12-3 6-11
Bar food 12-2.30 7-9.30 Av main course £4.50
Restaurant 12-2.30 7-9.30 Av 3 course à la carte £10 Av 3 course fixed price £10
Accommodation (Min) s£23 d£45

The Royal Oak
ABBOTS BROMLEY
Bagot St WS15 3DB ☎ 01283 840117
There is a friendly village atmosphere at this black and white pub, with its open fires, beamed ceilings and oak-panelled restaurant. Typical dishes are breast of chicken with Dijon mustard sauce, roast duck, and medallions of beef fillet with a mushroom, tomato and red wine sauce.
Principal beers: Marstons Pedigree, Greene King Abbot Ale.
Brewery/Company Free House
Open 12-2.30 6-11
Bar food 12-2 7-9.30
Restaurant 12-2 7-9.30 Av 3 course à la carte £16

ACTON TRUSSELL Staffordshire — Map 07 SJ91

The Moat House NEW
ACTON TRUSSELL
Lower Penkridge Rd ST17 0RJ
☎ 01785 712217
Impressive 17th-century timbered building enjoying a peaceful canalside setting, just a short drive from the M6 (J13). High standard of accommodation and imaginative, carefully prepared bar meals and restaurant food. Latter may offer truffle- and garlic-studded beef fillet

with wild mushroom jus, lamb with ratatouille timbale, and a deliciously rich chocolate terrine. **Principal beers:** Bank's Bitter, Marstons Pedigree.

Brewery/Company Free House
Open 11.30-3 5.30-11 (Sun 12-10.30, Sat 11-11)
Restaurant 12-2 7-10 Av 3 course à la carte £18 Av 3 course fixed price £14.95

BIDDULPH Staffordshire *Map 07 SJ85*

The Talbot
BIDDULPH
Grange Rd ST8 7RY ☎ 01782 512608

The rugged charm and character of rural Staffordshire is reflected in Biddulphs oldest pub. Although it was built in 1868, there has been a pub on this site since the 18th century. **Principal beers:** Bass.
Directions follow Congleton rd, turn off by Biddulph Garage, pub about 1m on L
Brewery/Company Vintage Inns
Open 12-11 (Sun 12-10.30)

BUTTERTON Staffordshire *Map 07 SK05*

The Black Lion Inn
BUTTERTON
ST13 7SP ☎ 01538 304232

Situated on the edge of Manifold Valley with splendid views across the Peak National Park, this 18th-century inn offers a good range of traditional snacks and blackboard specials. The latter may include steak and stout hotpot, lamb Creole, chicken, leek and Stilton pie, and speciality steaks from the village butcher.
Principal beers: Theakston Best, Marstons Pedigree, Hartington IPA & Whim Arbor Light, Wells Bombardier.
Directions From A52 (between Leek & Ashbourne) take B5053
Brewery/Company Free House
Open 12-3 7-11 (closed Wed lunch)

Bar food 12-2 7-9 Av main course £5.50
Restaurant 12-2 7-9 Av 3 course à la carte £20
Accommodation (Min) s£35 d£55

NORBURY JUNCTION Staffordshire *Map 07 SJ72*

Junction Country Inn & Restaurant
NORBURY JUNCTION
ST20 0PN ☎ 01785 284288

Situated near the Shropshire Union Canal, this pub offers a range of bar snacks and light lunches. Typical meals on the blackboard menu include chicken balti, beef curry, sweet and sour pork and salmon hollandaise. Among the vegetarian options there might be nut and mushroom fettucine.
Principal beers: Banks Bitter, Marstons Bitter & Pedigree, guest ale.
Directions From M6 take road for Eccleshall, L at Gt Bridgeford & head for Woodseaves, L there & head for Newport, L for Norb Junct
Brewery/Company Free House
Open 11.30-3 6.30-11 (11.30-11 wknd)
Bar food 11.30-2 6.30-9 Av main course £5

ROLLESTON Staffordshire *Map 08 SK22*

Spread Eagle
ROLLESTON
Church Rd DE13 9BE ☎ 01283 813004

An inn or alehouse may have occupied this site in the quiet village of Rolleston for 1,000 years, although the present structure, incorporating old cottages and the schoolhouse, is mostly 16th century. The walled garden has charming archways. **Principal beers:** Bass.
Directions Close to the A38, drive thru Rolleston, pub is by the river
Brewery/Company Vintage Inns
Open 11-11 (Sun 12-10.30)

STAFFORD Staffordshire Map 07 SJ92

The Hollybush Inn NEW
STAFFORD

Salt ST18 0BX ☎ 01889 508234

Thatched and dating from the 14th-century, the flower-adorned Holly Bush is Staffordshire's oldest licensed premises. Beamed main bar with cosy alcoves and open fires, and a huge rear lawn for summer jazz concerts and hog roasts. Food inside ranges from traditional pub dishes to interesting specials like venison with port and redcurrant sauce and monkfish with shallots and Pernod sauce. **Principal beers:** Bass, Burtonwood James Forshaw.
Brewery/Company Free House
Open 12-3 6-11 (open all day Sat-Sun)
Bar food 12-3 6-11 Av main course £8

TATENHILL Staffordshire Map 08 SK22

Horseshoe Inn
TATENHILL

Main St DE13 9SD ☎ 01283 564913

Much of the original character has been retained at this historic pub, parts of which are thought to be over 500 years old. Good quality specials range from steak and mushroom pudding and rainbow trout to speciality sausages and pork chop with Stilton sauce. **Principal beers:** Marstons.
Directions From A38 at Branston follow signs for Tatenhill
Brewery/Company Marstons
Open 11-11 (Sun 12-10.30)
Bar food 12-2.30 6-9.30 Av main course £5.50
Restaurant 12-2.30 6-9.30

TUTBURY Staffordshire Map 08 SK22

Ye Olde Dog & Partridge Inn
TUTBURY

High St DE13 9LS ☎ 01283 813030

Splendid timber-framed coaching inn dating back to the 15th century and extended in subsequent years. Near the romantic ruins of Tutbury Castle, besieged by Parliamentary forces. Expect Turkish spiced lamb and baked monkfish in the Brasserie Restaurant which uses fresh market produce. Various home-made specials and a newly introduced alfresco buffet. **Principal beers:** Marstons Pedigree, Morland Old Speckled Hen.

Directions On A50 NW of Burton upon Trent(signposted from A50 as A511)
Brewery/Company Free House
Open 11.45-2 6-11 (Sun 11.45-11)
Restaurant 11.45-2 6-9.45 Av 3 course fixed price £7.95
Accommodation (Min) s£55 d£55

YOXALL Staffordshire Map 07 SK11

The Crown
YOXALL

Main St DE13 8NQ ☎ 01543 472551

A cosy, friendly village pub with old beams and open fires. Simple but tasty food is served, including sandwiches, snack dishes and salads. Main courses range through pizzas, grills and dishes such as fillet of duckling, breaded plaice, and Barnsley chops with mint and redcurrant gravy. **Principal beers:** Marstons Pedigree.
Directions On A515 N of Lichfield
Brewery/Company Marstons
Open 11.30-3 5.30-11 (Sat-Sun open all day)
Bar food 12-2 6-9 Av main course £4.25
Restaurant 12-2 6-9 Av 3 course à la carte £10

Suffolk

ALDEBURGH Suffolk Map 05 TM45

The Mill Inn
ALDEBURGH

Market Cross Place IP15 5BJ
☎ 01728 452563

A genuine traditional fisherman's inn frequented by the local lifeboat crew - the licensee is a longstanding member - The Mill stands opposite the 17th-century Moot Hall and enjoys a sea view. Good value food ranges from filled baguettes, and ham, egg and chips, to home-made fish bake, steak and ale pie, and fresh local fish, perhaps cod and Dover sole.

Principal beers: Adnams-Bitter, Broadside, Old, Mild.
Directions Follow Aldeburgh signs from A12 on A1094. Pub last building on L before sea
Brewery/Company Adnams
Open 11-3 6-11 (Fri-Sun 11-11; cl Sun & Thu eve winter)
Bar food 12-2 7-9 Av main course £5
Restaurant 12-2 7-9 Av 3 course à la carte £14 Av 3 course fixed price £14
Accommodation (Min) s£20 d£40

BILDESTON Suffolk — Map 05 TL94

The Crown Hotel NEW
BILDESTON
High St IP7 7EB ☎ 01449 740510
15th-century timber-framed building, formerly a wool merchants house and coaching inn, featuring oak beams, inglenook fireplaces and a two-acre garden. Reputedly the most haunted pub in Britain, it offers traditional snacks alongside daily dishes like vegetable and lentil soup, black olive pâté, cod in beer batter, honey-spiced lamb, and whole lemon sole. **Principal beers:** Adnams, Nethergate.
Directions On B1115 between Hadleigh & Stowmarket
Brewery/Company Free House
Open 11-2.30 6-11
Bar food 12-2 6.30-9.30 Av main course £7
Restaurant 12-2 6.30-9.30 Av 3 course à la carte £15
Accommodation (Min) s£35 d£55

BLYFORD Suffolk — Map 05 TM47

Queens Head Inn
BLYFORD
Southwold Rd IP19 9JY
☎ 01502 478404
Supposedly haunted by up to seven ghosts, this 15th-century inn is characterised by its antique furniture and low beams. A variety of pub fare is offered, including an enterprising menu that might include fresh Lowestoft cod, roast Welsh lamb, home-made cottage pie and venison. **Principal beers:** Adnams - Bitter, Broadside.
Directions From A12 at Blythburgh take B1123 for 1m
Brewery/Company Adnams
Open 11-3 6.30-11
Bar food 12-2 6.45-9 Av main course £5.50
Restaurant 12-2 7-9.15 Av 3 course à la carte £11.75
Accommodation (Min) d£60

BRANDESTON Suffolk — Map 05 TM26

The Queens Head
BRANDESTON
The Street IP13 7AD ☎ 01728 685307
Approximately 400 years old, this family run village pub has wooden panelling, quarry tile floors and open fires, as well as camping facilities at the rear. Home-cooked fare includes Suffolk stew and dumplings, pork and leek pie, and fish crumble. A range of bar snacks is also served. **Principal beers:** Adnams Broadside, Bitter & seasonal ale.
Directions From A14 take A1120 to Earl Soham, then S to Brandeston
Brewery/Company Adnams
Open 11.30-2.30 6-11 (Sun 12-3, 7-10.30)
Bar food 12-1.50 7-9.30 Av main course £5
Accommodation (Min) s£18 d£36

BROCKLEY GREEN Suffolk — Map 05 TL74

The Plough Inn
BROCKLEY GREEN
CO10 8DT ☎ 01440 786789
Sympathetically modernised and extended country pub commanding views across the Stour valley. Cosy bars with old oak timbers, pine furnishings and well-kept Suffolk ales. Bar meals include sandwiches and a popular 'hunky lamb', minted and pot-roasted, and the restaurant might offer duck with cherry and lime sauce. **Principal beers:** Greene King IPA, Adnams Best.
Directions Take B1061 from A143, approx 1.5m beyond Kedington
Brewery/Company Free House
Open 12-2.30 5-11
Bar food 12-2.30 6.30-11 Av main course £7.50
Restaurant 12-3 7-11 Av 3 course à la carte £18
Accommodation (Min) s£40 d£65

BROME Suffolk — Map 05 TM17

Cornwallis Arms NEW
BROME
IP23 8AJ ☎ 01379 870326
Set in 20 acres of parkland, this striking 16th-century dower house offers

contd.

delightful accommodation, an elegant restaurant, and a bustling Tudor bar where excellent ales and home-cooked food are served. Expect mushroom soup, John Dory with red onion and tomato dressing, lamb cutlets with couscous and red wine sauce, and ginger bread pudding for dessert. **Principal beers:** St Peters Best, Strong Ale & Old-Style Porter.

Cornwallis Arms

Directions Just off A140 at Brome
Brewery/Company St Peters Brewery
Open 11-11
Bar food 12-2.30 6.30-9.30 Av main course £8.95
Restaurant 12-2.30 6.30-10 Av 3 course à la carte £30
Accommodation (Min) s£75 d£87.50

BURY ST EDMUNDS Suffolk *Map 05 TL86*

The Nutshell
BURY ST EDMUNDS
17 The Traverse IP33 1VJ
☎ 01742 764867

Known as the smallest pub in Britain, this novel thatched inn covers an area of 15ft x 7ft 6 inches and features in the Guinness Book of Records. It is very popular, though they do not serve food (presumably not enough elbow room!). **Principal beers:** Greene King IPA & Abbot Ale.
Brewery/Company Greene King
Open 11am-11pm (closed Sun)

Six Bells Inn
BURY ST EDMUNDS
The Green, Bardwell IP31 1AW
☎ 01359 250820

Late 15th-century coaching inn with an inglenook fireplace and an old Suffolk range, including a copper and bread oven. Lunchtime meals include local pork sausages, and seafood and broccoli chardonnay. At dinner you might expect grilled sea bass or pot-roasted tipsy lamb steak. **Principal beers:** Adnams Best, Marston Pedigree.
Directions From A143 take turning marked Bardwell Windmill, premises 1m on L just before village green
Brewery/Company Free House
Open 12-2 6.45-10.30 (Fri-Sat 6-11)
Bar food 12-1.30 Av main course £3
Restaurant 12-1.30 6.45-9.15 Av 3 course à la carte £17 Av 3 course fixed price £12.50

CAVENDISH Suffolk *Map 05 TL84*

Bull Inn NEW
CAVENDISH
High St CO10 8AX ☎ 01787 280245

The unassuming Victorian facade of this pub, set in one of Suffolk's most beautiful villages, hides a splendid 15th-century beamed interior. Expect a good atmosphere and decent food, the daily-changing blackboard menu listing, perhaps, fresh Dover sole, squid with chilli and garlic, home-made curries, hearty ploughman's lunches, and local game in season. **Principal beers:** Adnams Bitter & Broadside.
Directions A134 Bury St Edmunds to Long Melford, then R at green, pub 5m on R
Brewery/Company Adnams
Open 11-3 6.30-11
Bar food 12-3 6.30-10 Av main course £7.95
Restaurant 12-3 6.30-10 Av 3 course à la carte £17
Accommodation (Min) s£20 d£45

CHILLESFORD Suffolk *Map 05 TM35*

The Froize Inn
CHILLESFORD
The Street IP12 3PU ☎ 01394 450282

15th-century inn built on the site of Chillesford Friary from the distinctive local red brick, and attracting discerning diners for the imaginative fish and seafood dishes on offer. From Normandy fish stew, red snapper with Creole sauce, crab gratin, and delicious oysters, the extensive menu may also list braised partidge with horseradish mash, and salads and filled rolls at lunchtime.
Principal beers: Woodforde's, Adnams, St Peter's, Mauldons.

Directions From the A12 (towards Lowestoft) take B1084, Chillesford 5m
Brewery/Company Free House
Open 12-3 6-11 (all day wknd; cl Mon & 3wks Feb/Mar)
Bar food 12-3 7-9 Av main course £7.50
Restaurant 12-3 7-9 Av 3 course à la carte £24
Accommodation (Min) s£30 d£50

COCKFIELD Suffolk *Map 05 TL95*

Three Horseshoes
COCKFIELD

Stow's Hill IP30 0JB ☎ 01284 828177
Pink-washed 14th-century thatched inn situated in open countryside with fine views. Features one of the oldest king posts in Suffolk and a wide range of traditional bar meals. Home-cooked choices may include fresh battered cod, steak and kidney pie and home-baked ham, egg and chips. **Principal beers:** Greene King IPA, Adnams Broadside, Nethergate, Tapsters Choice.
Directions A134 towards Sudbury, then L onto A1141 towards Lavenham & Cockfield
Brewery/Company Free House
Open 11-3 5.30-11 (no food Tue eve)
Bar food 12-2 6.30-9.30 Av main course £4.50
Restaurant 12-2 6.30-9.30 Av 3 course à la carte £11.50

COTTON Suffolk *Map 05 TM06*

The Trowel & Hammer Inn
COTTON

Mill Rd IP14 4QL ☎ 01449 781234
Rambling 15th-century inn with a large garden, a character oak-beamed bar and a comfortably appointed restaurant. Expect moules marinière, haddock with pesto crust, lamb with parmesan and rich red wine gravy, and more traditional dishes like Cumberland sausage, and steak, kidney and ale pie on the interesting menu. Good real ales and welcoming owners. **Principal beers:** Adnams, Greene King IPA & Abbot Ale, Nethergate.
Directions From A14 follow signs to Haughley,then Bacton,then turn left for Cotton.
Brewery/Company Free House
Open 11.30-3 (Sat 11.30-11,Sun 12-10.30) 6-11
Bar food 11.30-2 6-10 Av main course £6.75
Restaurant 11.30-2 6-10 Av 3 course à la carte £14.50

DUNWICH Suffolk *Map 05 TM47*

The Ship Inn
DUNWICH

St James St IP17 3DT ☎ 01728 648219
A once thriving medieval port, most of Dunwich has since disappeared into the sea leaving a pretty village of period properties, the nautical memorabilia-adorned Ship among them. Freshly battered plaice or cod with hand-cut chips are favourite meals, along with Ship's fish pie, pork and bean stew, sirloin steak, and home-made passion cake for pudding. **Principal beers:** Adnams.
Directions N on A12 from Ipswich thru Yoxford, R signed Dunwich
Brewery/Company Free House
Open 11-3.30 6-11
Bar food 12-2 7-9.30 Av main course £4.75
Restaurant 12-2 7-9.30
Accommodation (Min) s£38 d£52

EARL SOHAM Suffolk *Map 05 TM26*

Victoria
EARL SOHAM

The Street IP13 7RL ☎ 01728 685758
Friendly, down-to-earth village pub with its own brewery attached to the rear of the building. Traditional pub fare on offer such as corned beef hash, home-made meat and vegetarian lasagnes, various casseroles, goulash, fish pies, and cashew nut curry. Desserts include meringue and nut surprise. **Principal beers:** Earl Soham-Victoria Bitter, Albert Ale, & Gannet Mild (all brewed on site).
Directions From the A14 at Stowmarket, Earl Soham is on the A1120

contd.

Brewery/Company Free House
Open 11.30-2.30 5.30-11
Bar food 11.30-2 5.30-10 Av main course £4.95

EASTBRIDGE Suffolk *Map 05 TM46*

The Eels Foot Inn
EASTBRIDGE
IP16 4SN ☎ 01728 830154
Edge of village pub once the haunt of smugglers and named after apparatus used by local cobbler who occupied these premises. Close to Minsmere Bird Reserve. Most of the food is home-made, including steak, pork and venison casserole, fish pies, and vegetable lasagne for vegetarians. **Principal beers:** Adnams - Bitter, Broadside, Old, Regatta.
Directions From A12 at Yoxford take B1122 (signed Leiston/Sizewell).Turn L at Theberton
Brewery/Company Adnams
Open 11-11 (winter 12-3 ex Mon, 7-11)
Bar food 12-2 7-9 Av main course £5
Accommodation (Min) d£32

ERWARTON Suffolk *Map 05 TM23*

The Queens Head
ERWARTON
The Street IP9 1LN ☎ 01473 787550
Handsome mid-16th-century building in traditional Suffolk style, enjoying fine views of coast and countryside. Look out for the fascinating display of navigational maps in the loos. Dishes range from scampi platter to stuffed lemon sole with crab meat, or pheasant in apple and cider sauce. **Principal beers:** Greene King IPA, Adnams-Best, Broadside, Regatta.
Directions From Ipswich take B1456 to Shotley
Brewery/Company Free House
Open 11-3 6.30-11
Bar food 12-2 7-10 Av main course £6.95
Restaurant 12-2 7-10 Av 3 course à la carte £12.95

FRAMLINGHAM Suffolk *Map 05 TM26*

The Station Hotel
FRAMLINGHAM
Station Rd IP13 9EE ☎ 01728 723455
Victorian pub near a former railway station with a large main bar and an intimate snug at the rear. Fresh fish is a speciality at weekends, including seafood salad, lobster Thermidor and red bream. Treacle tart and menzigne supreme feature among the desserts.
Principal beers: Earl Soham Victoria, Albert & Mild, guest beers.
Directions Bypass Ipswich heading toward Lowestoft on the A12
Brewery/Company Earl Soham
Open 12-3 5-11
Bar food 12-2 7-10 Av main course £5

FRAMSDEN Suffolk *Map 05 TM15*

The Dobermann Inn
FRAMSDEN
The Street IP14 6HG ☎ 01473 890461
A 16th-century thatched free house, with beams, open fire and antique furniture. The pub, previously known as the Greyhound, was re-named by the current owner, a prominent owner, breeder and judge of dobermans. Home-made fare includes beef in red wine, St Etienne chicken, and fish gratin.
Principal beers: Adnams Best & Broadside, Greene King Abbot Ale,Courage Directors, Morlands.
Directions S off A1120 (Stowmarket/Yoxford)
Brewery/Company Free House
Open 12-3 7-11
Bar food 12-2 7-10 Av main course £7.50
Restaurant 12-2 7-10
Accommodation (Min) s£30 d£40

GREAT GLEMHAM Suffolk *Map 05 TM36*

The Crown Inn
GREAT GLEMHAM
IP17 2DA ☎ 01728 663693
Cosy, extensively renovated 17th-century village pub overlooking the Great Glemham Estate and within easy reach of the Suffolk Heritage Coast. Good choice of fish dishes includes salmon marinated in lime and coriander, fresh cod or haddock cooked in beer batter, whole lemon sole and Basque-style baked cod.
Principal beers: Greene King Abbot Ale & IPA.
Directions A12 Ipswich to Lowestoft, in Stratford-St-Andrew L at Shell garage. Crown 1.5m
Brewery/Company Free House
Open 11.30-2.30 6.30-11 (closed Mon)
Bar food 11.30-2 6.30-10 Av main course £5.50

HADLEIGH Suffolk Map 05 TM04

The Marquis of Cornwallis
HADLEIGH

Upper St, Layham IP75 5JZ
☎ 01473 822051

Situated in two acres of garden sloping down to the River Brett, this 17th-century inn uses traditional country recipes and specialises in home-made pies. Dishes are prepared from local Suffolk produce. Beef and beer pie, chicken stir-fry, pork spare ribs and pink trout are typical examples. **Principal beers:** Adnams, Greene King IPA & Abbot Ale, Fullers London Pride.
Directions From Colchester take A12 then B1070 towards Hadleigh. Layham signed on L, last village before Hadleigh
Brewery/Company Free House
Open 12-3 6-11
Bar food 12-3 7-11 Av main course £6.50
Restaurant 12-3 7-11 Av 3 course à la carte £15

HALESWORTH Suffolk Map 05 TM37

The Queen's Head NEW
HALESWORTH

The Street, Bramfield IP19 9HT
☎ 01986 784214

Just minutes from the coast, this welcoming village pub enjoys a delightful setting opposite the thatched church. Interesting, home-made food is the draw here and may feature Stilton and port terrine with Cumberland sauce, steak, kidney and 'Adnams' ale pie, and venison with mustard mash and red wine sauce. Good sandwiches, and home-made chips and ice creams. **Principal beers:** Adnams Bitter & Broadside.
Directions 2m from A12 on the A144 towards Halesworth
Brewery/Company Adnams
Open 11.45-2.30 6.30-11
Bar food 12-2 6.30-10 Av main course £6.95

HARTEST Suffolk Map 05 TL85

The Crown
HARTEST

The Green IP29 4DH ☎ 01284 830250

Once known as Hartest Hall, this heavily beamed 15th-century building is set on the village green next to the church. One menu is offered throughout, with the emphasis on an impressive range of fresh fish from Lowestoft. Special set meals during the week provide particularly good value. **Principal beers:** Greene King Abbot Ale & IPA.
Directions On B1066 S of Bury St Edmunds
Brewery/Company Greene King
Open 11-2.30 6-11
Bar food 12-2 6.30-9.30 Av main course £7.50
Restaurant 12-2 6.30-9.30 Av 3 course à la carte £13.50

HOLBROOK Suffolk Map 05 TM13

The Compasses
HOLBROOK

Ipswich Rd IP9 2QR ☎ 01473 328332

Traditional country pub situated on the Shotley peninsula, in an area of outstanding natural beauty, and has an extraordinary collection of over 1,000 key rings. Bar food ranges from standard snacks, lasagne, fish pie, and steaks, to daily fish choices, including the popular fresh battered cod and chips. **Principal beers:** Tetley, Greene King IPA.

Directions From A137 S of Ipswich, take B1456/B1080
Brewery/Company Free House
Open 11-2.30 6-11
Bar food 11.30-2.15 6-9.30 Av main course £6.50
Restaurant 11.30-2.15 6-9.30 Av 3 course à la carte £12.50

HONEY TYE Suffolk Map 05 TL93

The Lion
HONEY TYE

CO6 4NX ☎ 01206 263434

Traditional country dining pub on the Essex/Suffolk border, with low-beamed ceilings and an open log fire. Same menu throughout offers dishes like steak and ale pie, poached supreme of salmon, rack of lamb, medallions of pork and casserole of mixed seafood.

contd.

Principal beers: Greene King IPA, Adnams Best & Broadside.
Directions On A134 between Colchester & Sudbury
Brewery/Company Free House
Open 11-3 5.45-11 (Sun 12-10.30 - food all day)
Bar food 12-2 6-9.30 Av main course £7.95
Restaurant 12-2 6-9.30

HORRINGER Suffolk *Map 05 TL86*

Beehive
HORRINGER
The Street IP29 5SN ☎ 01284 735260
Pretty flintstone cottage, dated approximately 1860, set in a lovely garden with patio seating. It comprises several small rooms with stone floors and antique pine furnishings, where above average pub food may include salt beef and horseradish sandwich, seared tuna with salad niçoise, and braised pork with coriander and fragrant rice. **Principal beers:** Greene King - IPA, Abbot Ale.
Directions From A14, 1st turning for Bury St Edmunds, sign for Westley & Ickworth Park
Brewery/Company Greene King
Open 11.30-3 7-11.30
Bar food 12-2.30 7-10 Av main course £7.95
Restaurant 12-2.30 7-10 Av 3 course à la carte £16

ICKLINGHAM Suffolk *Map 05 TL77*

The Red Lion
ICKLINGHAM
The Street IP28 6PS ☎ 01638 717802
Fine 16th-century village inn situated on the edge of the King's Forest. Furnished with antiques and rugs, and featuring log fires and candlelight, the beamed interior offers a relaxing ambience in which to enjoy warm salads, home-made soups, rack of lamb, fresh Lowestoft fish, and, perhaps, partridge with elderberry sauce. **Principal beers:** Greene King Abbot Ale & IPA.
Directions On A1101 between Mildenhall & Bury St Edmunds
Brewery/Company Greene King
Open 12-3 6-11 (Sun 7-10.30)
Bar food 12-2.30 6-10 Av main course £8
Restaurant 12-2.30 6-10 Av 3 course à la carte £20

IXWORTH Suffolk *Map 05 TL97*

Pykkerell Inn
IXWORTH
38 High St IP31 2HH ☎ 01359 230398
15th-century coaching inn with original beams, inglenook fireplace, wood-panelled library room, and 14th-century barn enclosing a patio with barbeque. Menu boards highlight fresh fish, such as sea bass on basil mash with herb dressing, alongside steak and ale pie, venison with red wine and mushroom sauce, and beef Stroganoff. **Principal beers:** Greene King IPA & Abbot Ale.
Directions A14 trunk rd/jct Bury St Edmunds central to A143, towards Diss
Brewery/Company Greene King
Open 12-3 6-11
Bar food 12-2.30 Av main course £5.50
Restaurant 12-2.30 6-10 Av 3 course à la carte £18

KERSEY Suffolk *Map 05 TM04*

The Bell Inn
KERSEY
IP7 6DY ☎ 01473 823229
Splendid 14th-century timbered inn in one of Suffolk's most picturesque villages. With a wealth of old beams, flagstone floors and log fires, it makes a character destination for a meal. Lookout for the monthly fish nights and traditional dishes like game pie, lamb casserole, mixed grill and lemon and ginger sponge on the extensive menu. **Principal beers:** Shepherd Neame Spitfire, Marstons Pedigree, Websters, Wells Bombardier.
Directions Follow A1171 from Bury St Edmunds thru Lavenham, follow signs for Kersey
Brewery/Company Old English Pub Co
Open 12-3 7-11
Bar food 12-2.30 7-9.30 Av main course £6.25
Restaurant 12-2.30 7-9.30 Av 3 course à la carte £13 Av 3 course fixed price £9.95

KETTLEBURGH Suffolk *Map 05 TM26*

The Chequers Inn
KETTLEBURGH
IP13 7JT ☎ 01728 723760 & 724369
The inn was erected in 1912 to replace a much older building destroyed by fire. The grounds border the River Deben and the area is a haven for wildlife. Snacks and a bargain menu are offered in the bar, while restaurant dishes include steak, skate and game in season. **Principal beers:** Greene King IPA, Adnams Southwold, Marstons Pedigree, Tolly Cobbold.

Directions From Ipswich A12 onto B1116, L onto B1078 then R through Easton
Brewery/Company Free House
Open 11-2.30 6-11
Bar food 12-2 7-9.30 Av main course £3.50
Restaurant 12-2 7-10.30 Av 3 course à la carte £12.50

LAVENHAM Suffolk *Map 05 TL94*

Angel Hotel
LAVENHAM
Market Place CO10 9QZ
☎ 01787 247388
Situated in one of England's finest medieval towns, this quaint inn retains much of its 15th century character. Welcoming bar with beams and open fire. Expect to find decent soups, pies and casseroles, fresh fish, and game in season on the imaginative menu. Sample skate wing, rabbit with tomatoes and olives or steak and ale pie. **Principal beers:** Adnams, Mauldons Suffolk Pride, Nethergate, Greene King IPA.
Directions From A14 take Bury East/Sudbury turn off A143, after 4m take A1141 to Lavenham, Angel is off the High Street
Brewery/Company Free House

Open 11-11 (Sun 12-10.30)
Bar food 12-2.15 6.45-9.15 Av main course £8
Restaurant 12-2.15 6.45-9.15 Av 3 course à la carte £15
Accommodation (Min) s£42.50 d£69

LAXFIELD Suffolk *Map 05 TM27*

The Kings Head
LAXFIELD
Gorams Mill Ln IP13 8DW
☎ 01986 798395
Virtually unchanged since Victorian times, this charming inn is known locally as The Low House. Beer is served from the tap room. There is no bar and customers sit on original high-backed settles and enjoy traditional Suffolk music on Tuesday lunchtimes. Home-cooked fare includes game duck and steak and kidney pie.
Principal beers: Adnams Best & Broadside, Greene King IPA.
Brewery/Company Free House
Open 11-3 6-11 (Sun 12-3, 7-10.30)
Bar food 12-2 7-9 Av main course £5.50

LEVINGTON Suffolk *Map 05 TM23*

The Ship Inn
LEVINGTON
Church Ln IP10 0LQ ☎ 01473 659573
A lovely 14th-century thatched village inn overlooking the River Orwell. The nautically-themed bars are often busy with walkers, sailors and birdwatchers, who seek out the home-made bar food. Dishes may include steak and kidney pudding, sausages in cider sauce, mussels in wine and garlic, and salmon fishcakes.
Principal beers: Greene King IPA & Abbott Ale, Flowers IPA, Tetley, Ship Inn Bitter.

contd.

Directions off the A14 towards Felixstowe
Brewery/Company Pubmaster
Open 11.30-3 6-11
Bar food 12-2 7-9 Av main course £6.25
Restaurant 12-2 7-9 Av 3 course à la carte £12.50

LIDGATE Suffolk Map 05 TL75

Star Inn
LIDGATE

The Street CB8 9PP ☎ 01638 500275

Mediterranean, in particular Spanish, cuisine attracts discerning diners from far afield to this attractive, 500-year-old pub, set in a charming rural village. Expect good Greene King ales, a superb atmosphere within the heavily-beamed bars, and delicious dishes like paella, lamb in garlic and red wine, fish soup, prawns in garlic, and monkfish meunière. **Principal beers:** Greene King IPA, Greene King Abbot Ale.
Directions From Newmarket, clocktower in High st, follow signs toward Clare on B1063. Lidgate 7m from Newmarket
Brewery/Company Greene King
Open 11-3 5-11
Bar food 12.30-2 Av main course £4.50
Restaurant 12.30-2 7-10 Av 3 course à la carte £18.50

LINDSEY Suffolk Map 05 TL94

White Rose Inn
LINDSEY

Rose Green IP7 6QA ☎ 01787 210664

In idyllic rural surroundings, this 15th-century thatched and beamed inn specialises in quality cuisine at affordable prices, complemented by fine wines. Leek and Stilton tartlet, chicken breast with wild mushroom fricassée and summer pudding with a bramble coulis are temptations from a regularly varying selection.

Principal beers: Greene King Abbot Ale, Adnams Bitter.
Directions From A1071 take A1141, take 2nd turning to Kersey & follow signs to St James Chapel, pub approx 0.5m beyond chapel
Brewery/Company Free House
Open 12-3 6-11.30 (closed Mon)
Bar food 12-2.30 6.30-9 Av main course £8
Restaurant 12.30-3 7-11 Av 3 course à la carte £20

MARKET WESTON Suffolk Map 05 TL97

The Mill Inn NEW
MARKET WESTON

Bury Rd IP22 2PD ☎ 01359 221018

Old Chimney ales from the nearby micro-brewery boost the excellent choice of beers available at this refurbished, early Victorian farmhouse, set in rolling Suffolk countryside close to Diss. Traditional, home-made bar food is also proving popular, the menu features lasagne, steak and stout pie, mixed grill, and seafood tagliatelle. Regular curry nights **Principal beers:** Greene King, Adnams Best, Old Chimneys Great Raft & Military Mild.
Directions A14 Bury St Edmunds, follow A143 to Great Barton & Stanton, L on B1111 thru Barningham, next village M Weston
Brewery/Company Free House
Open 11-3 7-11 (closed Mon)
Bar food 12-2 7-9.30 Av main course £5
Restaurant 12-2 7-9.30 Av 3 course à la carte £14

MELTON Suffolk Map 05 TM25

Wilford Bridge
MELTON

Wilford Bridge Rd IP12 2PA
☎ 01394 386141

Busy pub close to Sutton Hoo, the world famous Saxon burial ship. There is a good range of snacks and light meals, and an impressive choice of fresh fish and seafood. Other options might be pan-fried calves' liver, chargrilled lamb cutlets with rosemary, and lentil and mushroom cannelloni. **Principal beers:** Adnams Best.
Directions Head to the coast from the A12, follow signs to Bawdsey & Orford, cross railway lines, next pub on L

Brewery/Company Free House
Open 11-3 6.30-11
Bar food 11-3 6.30-11 Av main course £6
Restaurant 12-3 7-11 Av 3 course à la carte £15

NAYLAND Suffolk *Map 05 TL93*

White Hart at Nayland
NAYLAND
11 High St CO6 4JF ☎ 01206 263382
Dating from the mid-15th-century, this pub is situated alongside the Nayland millstream. Look out for two naive 18th-century paintings by John Gainsborough, brother of famous artist Thomas Gainsborough. The recently overhauled menu now has a decidedly Mediterranean influence. **Principal beers:** Adnams, Greene King IPA.
Directions 6m N of Colchester on A134
Brewery/Company Free House
Open 12-3 6.30-11 (Sun 7-10.30; closed Mon)
Bar food 12-2 6.30-9.30
Restaurant 12-2 6.30-9.30 Av 3 course à la carte £23
Accommodation (Min) s£65

ORFORD Suffolk *Map 05 TM45*

Jolly Sailor Inn
ORFORD
Quay St IP12 2NU ☎ 01394 450243
A lovely quayside smugglers' inn, made up of several cosy rooms served from a central bar area. Local fish is a particular feature, including freshly battered cod or skate and chips. Alternative choices range from steak pie, and home-cooked ham, egg and chips to local game in season.
Principal beers: Adnams Bitter & Broadside.
Directions On B1084 E of Woodbridge
Brewery/Company Adnams
Open 11.30-2.30 7-11
Bar food 12-1.45 7.15-8.45 Av main course £5.50
Accommodation (Min) d£35

Pubs offering a good choice of seafood on the menu

POLSTEAD Suffolk *Map 05 TL93*

The Cock Inn
POLSTEAD
The Green CO6 5AL ☎ 01206 263150
Quintessential 17th-century English pub overlooking the village green in the heart of Constable country. Freshly prepared food, cooked with flair, highlight the interesting daily menus. Expect carrot and coriander soup, sea bass with straw potatoes and salsa verde, tiger prawn and scallop kebabs, steak and kidney pudding, and lemon tart with raspberry coulis. **Principal beers:** Badger Tanglefoot, Black Sheep, Everards Tiger, Greene King IPA.
Directions Colchester/A134 towards Sudbury then R
Brewery/Company Free House
Open 11-3 6-11 (closed Mon)
Bar food 11-3 6-11 Av main course £7
Restaurant 6-11 Av 3 course à la carte £22

RAMSHOLT Suffolk

Ramsholt Arms NEW
RAMSHOLT
Dock Rd IP12 3AB ☎ 01394 411229
Enjoying a glorious, unrivalled position on a tidal beach overlooking the River Deben, this 18th-century, pink-washed, former ferryman's cottage and smugglers' inn is the perfect summer evening destination for a pint and home-cooked meal. Expect a civilised atmosphere, picture windows, sunny patio, and a short menu offering oysters, local lobster, freshly battered fish and chips and local estate game. Rewarding riverside walks.
Principal beers: Adnams, Boddingtons, Wadworth 6X, Brakspear.
Directions End of lane on beach at Ramsholt, signed off B1083 Woodbridge to Bawdsey
Brewery/Company Free House
Open 11.30-3 6.30-11
Bar food 12-2 7-9
Accommodation (Min) s£37.50 d£75

RATTLESDEN Suffolk *Map 05 TL95*

Brewers Arms
RATTLESDEN
Lower Rd IP30 0RJ
☎ 01449 736377 737059
Beamed 17th-century pub enjoying a remote rural location west of

contd.

Stowmarket. Simply furnished interior with open fires and bread oven. A regularly-changing menu lists home-cooked dishes, perhaps Thai red prawn curry, salmon with herb butter, beef medallions with red wine, mustard and cream sauce, and toffee and banana sponge. **Principal beers:** Greene King IPA & Abbot Ale.
Directions From A14 take A1088 towards Woolpit, Rattlesden 2.8m from Woolpit
Brewery/Company Greene King
Open 12-2.30 6.30-11 (closed Mon)
Bar food 12.30-2.30 7-10.30 Av main course £6
Restaurant 12.30-2.30 7-10.30 Av 3 course à la carte £17.50

REDE Suffolk *Map 05 TL85*

The Plough
REDE
IP29 4BE ☎ 01284 789208
Picture-postcard thatched 16th-century pub set beside a pond on the village green. Worth the effort in finding for the freshly-prepared food served in the rambling, low-beamed bars. Blackboard-listed dishes may include beef and pigeon pie, Tuscan rabbit casserole, Moroccan lamb, sea bass with ginger and lime, and pork in mustard. **Principal beers:** Greene King IPA & Abbot Ale.
Directions on the A143 between Bury St Edmunds and Haverhill
Brewery/Company Greene King
Open 11-3 7-11 (closed Mon)
Bar food 11-3 7-11 Av main course £6.95
Restaurant 11-3 7-11

RISBY Suffolk *Map 05 TL86*

The White Horse Inn
RISBY
Newmarket Rd IP28 6RD
☎ 01284 810686
A 17th-century coaching inn with open fires, exposed beams and period furniture, creating the setting for a weekly changing range of six real ales. This impressive choice is complemented by a menu offering up to 25 main courses and a variety of daily specials.
Principal beers: guest ales.
Directions A14 from Bury St Edmunds
Brewery/Company Free House
Open 11-3.30 6-11
Bar food 12-2.30 6.30-9.30 Av main course £5.95
Restaurant 12-2.30 6.30-9.30 Av 3 course à la carte £17

ST PETER SOUTH ELMHAM Suffolk *Map 05 TM38*

St Peter's Hall
ST PETER SOUTH ELMHAM
NR35 1NQ ☎ 01986 782322
Former monastery dating back to the 13th century, with its own moat and many fine architectural features. Adjacent brewery, with tours available. Expect fillets of sole, Suffolk pork fillet, darne of salmon, and imaginative desserts on the good restaurant menu, and a choice of oven-baked baguettes in the character bar.

Principal beers: St Peters.
Directions From A143/A144 follow brown and white signs to St Peter's Brewery
Brewery/Company St Peters Brewery
Open 11-11 (closed Mon-Thu ex BH)
Bar food 12.30-2.30 6-9 Av main course £6.95
Restaurant 12.30-2.30 7-9.30 Av 3 course à la carte £25

SNAPE Suffolk *Map 05 TM35*

The Crown Inn
SNAPE
Bridge Rd IP17 1SL ☎ 01728 688324
Charming 15th-century inn, close to Snape Maltings, with a wealth of beams, brick floors, open fires and a particularly fine double Suffolk settle. Good food, notably fresh fish and seafood, real ale and Adnams wines attract discerning diners. Expect sea bass with roasted fennel and salsa verde, venison and chestnut casserole, and Thai red chicken curry.

Principal beers: Adnams Best & Broadside.
Directions A12 N to Lowestoft, R to Aldeburgh, then R again in Snape at crossroads by church, pub at bottom hill
Brewery/Company Adnams
Open 11-3 6-11
Bar food 12-2 7-9 Av main course £7.95
Restaurant 12-2 7-9 Av 3 course à la carte £20
Accommodation (Min) s£35 d£50

SOUTHWOLD Suffolk *Map 05 TM57*

Crown Hotel
SOUTHWOLD
The High St IP18 6DP ☎ 01502 722275
Posting inn, dating from 1750, fulfilling the purposes of pub, wine bar, restaurant and small hotel. As flagship for Adnams brewery, it offers excellent ales and wines, and good food in both the bar and restaurant. Typical imaginative dishes might be roast supreme of chicken with peppers, watercress and red wine, and panache of seafood with rissole potatoes. **Principal beers:** Adnams.
Directions off A12 take A1094 to Southwold, stay on main road into town centre, hotel on L in High St
Brewery/Company Adnams
Open 10.30-3 6-11 (closed 1wk Jan)
Bar food 12.15-2 7-9.30 Av main course £8.50
Restaurant 12.30-1.30 7.30-9.30 Av 3 course à la carte £23 Av 3 course fixed price £23
Accommodation (Min) s£47 d£72

STOKE-BY-NAYLAND Suffolk *Map 05 TL93*

The Angel Inn
STOKE-BY-NAYLAND
CO6 4SA ☎ 01206 263245
Splendid 16th-century coaching inn situated in one of Constable's favourite villages. Food is prepared from fresh ingredients, in particular fresh fish and shellfish from East Coast ports. Fishcakes with remoulade sauce, liver and bacon with Madeira sauce, fresh haddock or skate, and German-style bread pudding are typical examples from the chalkboard menu. **Principal beers:** Greene King IPA & Abbot Ale, Adnams Best.

Directions From A12 take Colchester R turn, then A134, 5m to Nayland. From A12 S take B1068
Brewery/Company Free House
Open 11-2.30 6-11 9
Bar food 12-2 6.30-9 Av main course £6.95
Restaurant 12-2 6.30-9
Accommodation (Min) s£47.50 d£61

THORNHAM MAGNA Suffolk *Map 05 TM17*

The Four Horseshoes
THORNHAM MAGNA
Wickham Rd IP23 8DH ☎ 01379 678777
Fine 12th-century inn, with a splendid thatched roof and timber-framed walls, situated in a delightfully unspoilt village close to Thornham Country Park and the interesting thatched church at Thornham Parva. Varied bar food includes Mediterranean fish stew, rib-eye steak with garlic butter, and cod with Adnams beer batter. **Principal beers:** Courage Best & Directors, Adnams Southwold, Theakstons Old Peculier, Morland Old Speckled Hen.
Directions From Diss on A140 turn R and follow signs for Finningham, 0.5m turn R for Thornham Magna
Brewery/Company Old English Pub Co.
Open 12-2.30 7-11
Bar food 12-2 7-9.30 Av main course £6.50
Restaurant 7-9.30 Av 3 course à la carte £25
Accommodation (Min) s£35 d£45

WALBERSWICK Suffolk *Map 05 TM47*

Bell Inn
WALBERSWICK
Ferry Rd IP18 6TN ☎ 01502 723109
Long, white-painted classic pub which can be reached on foot or by ferry from neighbouring Southwold. Low beams, log

contd.

fires and old settles add to the charm. In addition to tip-top Adnams ales and interesting daily specials, expect fish dishes including sea bream, hearty ploughman's, half-shoulder of lamb and, for dessert, vanilla terrine. **Principal beers:** Adnams - Best, Broadside & Old.
Directions From A12 take B1387 to Walberswick
Brewery/Company Adnams
Open 11-3 6-11 (end Jul-4 Sep 11-11)
Bar food 12-2 6-9 Av main course £6.75
Accommodation (Min) s£40 d£60

WESTLETON Suffolk — Map 05 TM46

The Crown at Westleton NEW
WESTLETON
IP17 3AD ☎ 01728 648777
Bustling old coaching inn nestling in a quiet village close to the coast and bird reserves. Well established and offering genuine hospitality in a relaxed atmosphere, it also features sound home cooking and good wines and whiskies. Menu choices range from salads and ploughman's, to interesting summer barbecue fare, seafish crumble and duck with Cassis and blackcurrant sauce. Good home-made breads and ice creams. **Principal beers:** Adnams, Greene King IPA.
Directions Turn off the A12 just past Yoxford Northbound, follow the AA signs for 2 miles
Brewery/Company Free House
Open 11-3 6-11
Bar food 12-2.15 7-9.30
Restaurant 12-3 7-9.30
Accommodation (Min) s£58.50 d£80.50

WITHERSFIELD Suffolk — Map 05 TL64

The White Horse Inn NEW
WITHERSFIELD
Hollow Hill CB9 7SH ☎ 01440 706081
Picture pretty 15th-century thatched inn set in beautiful Suffolk countryside. Original character and charm has been retained in the low-beamed bar and comfortably furnished dining room, where you can sample some reliable home-cooked food. Expect Stilton and port mousse, beef in Beamish pie, smoked haddock fishcakes, and steak au poivre. **Principal beers:** Greene King IPA & Abbot Ale, Courage, John Smiths.
Brewery/Company Free House
Open 12-2.30 6-11

Restaurant 7-12 Av 3 course à la carte £12.50
Accommodation (Min) s£38.50 d£55

Warwickshire

ALDERMINSTER Warwickshire — Map 04 SP24

The Bell
ALDERMINSTER
CV37 8NY ☎ 01789 450414
Once a coaching inn, the Bell, a tall, three-storied Georgian building, now serves imaginative and well prepared food to a discerning clientele in its immaculately maintained interior. Typical dishes may include smoked venison with sweet onion relish, salmon with hollandaise, game pie, chicken and coconut curry, and lemon tart. Special dinners, including 'symphony suppers', and decent wines. **Principal beers:** Greene King IPA & Abbot Ale.
Directions just off A3400 S of Stratford-upon-Avon
Brewery/Company Free House
Open 12-2.30 7-11.30
Restaurant 12-2 7-10 Av 3 course à la carte £16.50 Av 2 course fixed price £6.50
Accommodation (Min) s£25 d£40

BROOM Warwickshire — Map 04 SP05

Broom Tavern
BROOM
High St B50 4HL ☎ 01789 773656
Charming, brick and timbered, 16th-century inn, reputedly haunted by a cavalier killed on the cellar steps. The same menu is offered throughout the beamed rooms. Fresh fish is available daily, and other favourites include rack of lamb, beef Stroganoff and apple pie and custard made with organic apples.

Principal beers: Hook Norton, Bass.
Directions N of B439 W of Stratford-upon-Avon
Brewery/Company Free House
Open 11-3 6-11
Bar food 12-2 6.45-9.30
Restaurant 12-2 6.45-9.30 Av 3 course à la carte £13.50

DUNCHURCH Warwickshire Map 04 SP47

Dun Cow
DUNCHURCH
The Green CV22 6NJ ☎ 01788 810305
Apparently, the original dun cow was a monstrous beast four yards high and six yards long which provided milk to the local villages. A witch caused it to go on a rampage, until it was killed by Guy, Earl of Warwick. **Principal beers:** Bass, Caffreys.
Directions In Dunchurch at crossroads of B4429 & A426
Brewery/Company Vintage Inns
Open 11-11 (Sun 12-10.30)

EDGEHILL Warwickshire Map 04 SP34

The Castle Inn
EDGEHILL
OX15 6DJ ☎ 01295 670255
Also known as the Radway Tower, this 18th-century battlemented folly enjoys far-reaching views, and is said to mark the spot where Charles I's army stood before the Battle of Edgehill. Built to mark the 100th anniversary of the conflict it one of the most unusual inns in the country. Straightforward bar food. **Principal beers:** Hook Norton - Best, Old Hooky, Generation.
Directions M40 then A422. 6m until Upton House, then turn next R 1.5m
Brewery/Company Hook Norton
Open 11.30-2.30 6.30-11 9
Bar food 12-2 6.30-9 Av main course £4.50
Accommodation (Min) s£32.50 d£52.50

ETTINGTON Warwickshire Map 04 SP24

The Chequers Inn & Restaurant NEW
ETTINGTON
C37 7SR ☎ 01789 740387
Well refurbished 17th-century village inn with a neat, carpeted bar and comfortable rear restaurant. Now a serious dining venue, offering decent snacks like pesto pasta with salmon, bacon and pea soup, and sausages with garlic mash, alongside confit of rabbit, halibut with noodles, Asian vegetables and lime broth, and beef medallions with pepper jus. Good-value wines. **Principal beers:** Fullers London Pride, Adnams, Hook Norton, Bank's.
Directions 5m S of Stratford on A422, 1m S of Jct between A422 & A429, 1/4m from Jct between Fosse Way & A422
Brewery/Company Free House
Open 12-2.30 6.30-10.30 (closed Mon)
Bar food 12-3 6.30-11 Av main course £6
Restaurant 12-2.30 6.30-10.30 Av 3 course à la carte £22 Av 3 course fixed price £13.50

The Houndshill
ETTINGTON
Banbury Rd CV37 7NS ☎ 01789 740267
Conveniently situated for Shakepeare's Stratford-upon-Avon, this friendly, family-run inn overlooks a pleasant tree-lined garden. Very popular with families, it offers play areas and wide-ranging menus to cater for all tastes. Typical dishes include chicken Basque, steak and kidney pie, and fresh sea bass. **Principal beers:** Hook Norton Best, Bass.
Directions On A422 SE of Stratford-upon-Avon
Brewery/Company Free House
Open 12-3 6-11
Bar food 12-2.30 7-10.30 Av main course £6.50
Restaurant 12-2 7-9.30 Av 3 course à la carte £12.50
Accommodation (Min) s£30 d£50

GREAT WOLFORD Warwickshire
Map 04 SP23

Fox & Hounds Inn
GREAT WOLFORD
CV36 5NQ ☎ 01608 674220

Dating from the 15th century, this traditional country inn offers diners an imaginative, daily-changing specials board. Typical choices range from home-made soups and pâtés, various pies and filled jacket potatoes, to local game, stuffed pork fillet wrapped in bacon, and fresh fish such as plaice with lobster cream sauce. **Principal beers:** Shepherd Neame Spitfire,Hook Norton, Blacksheep, Boddingtons.
Directions Off A44 NE of Moreton-in-Marsh
Brewery/Company Free House
Open 12-3 7-11 (closed Mon)
Bar food 12-2.30 7-9.30 Av main course £7.50
Restaurant 12-2.30 7-9.30 Av 3 course à la carte £15
Accommodation (Min) d£35

ILMINGTON Warwickshire
Map 04 SP24

Howard Arms
ILMINGTON
Lower Green CV36 4LT
☎ 01608 682226

Inviting 17th-century Cotswold-stone building nestling beside the village green. Linked to nearby Foxcote House and one of England's most illustrious families, it features stone floors, open fires and keen new owners. Interesting daily menus may list warm salads, lamb and rosemary pie, crispy cod in beer batter, and mixed seafood in saffron sauce. **Principal beers:** Everards Tiger, Marstons Pedigree.
Directions Off A429 or A34
Brewery/Company Free House
Open 11-3 6-11
Bar food 12-2 7-9.30 Av main course £7.75
Restaurant 12-2 7-9.30 Av 3 course à la carte £15
Accommodation (Min) s£35 d£55

Pubs offering a good choice of seafood on the menu

LAPWORTH Warwickshire
Map 07 SP17

The Boot NEW
LAPWORTH
Old Warwick Rd B94 6JU
☎ 01564 782464

Expect to find modern, brasserie-style food at this busy, smartly refurbished, red-brick pub, attractively positioned by the Grand Union Canal. Sample imaginative sandwiches or choose pancetta and Cashel Blue cheese soup, roast cod with peppers and roquette mash, or confit of duck with smashed roots and balsamic jus, followed by chocolate parfait and decent coffee. **Principal beers:** Tetley, Morland Old Speckled Hen.
Brewery/Company Free House
Open 11-3 5.30-11
Bar food 12-2.30 5.30-9.30 Av main course £8
Restaurant 12-2.30 7-9.30 Av 3 course fixed price £20

LOWER BRAILES Warwickshire
Map 04 SP33

The George Hotel
LOWER BRAILES
High St OX15 5HN ☎ 01608 685223

Fine 16th-century stone coaching inn on the edge of the Cotswolds, with an inglenook fireplace and a lovely summer garden. Ideal base for good local walks. Wholesome home-cooked food ranges from hot bacon and Brie sandwich, and venison casserole, to rabbit stew, mixed grill and fillet steak. **Principal beers:** Hook Norton.
Directions B4035 toward Shipston on Stour
Brewery/Company Hook Norton
Open 12-3 6-11
Bar food 12-2 7-9.30 Av main course £6
Restaurant 12-2 7-9.30 Av 3 course à la carte £12
Accommodation (Min) s£25 d£50

LOWSONFORD Warwickshire
Map 04 SP16

Fleur De Lys
LOWSONFORD
Lapworth St B95 5HJ ☎ 01564 782431

Converted from three cottages and a mortuary, this pub is where the original Fleur de Lys pies were made. It's alongside the Stratford-upon-Avon to

Birmingham canal, and has a large garden. The style is casual dining with traditional pies, bangers and mash, vegetable korma and lemon chicken. **Principal beers:** Flowers Original, Wadworth 6X.
Directions A34 (Birmingham to Stratford)
Brewery/Company Whitbread
Open 11.30-11 (Sun 12-10.30 - food 12-8)
Bar food 12-2.30 6-9.30 Av main course £6

MONKS KIRBY Warwickshire — Map 04 SP48

The Bell Inn
MONKS KIRBY
Bell Ln CV23 0QY ☎ 01788 832352
Originally the gatehouse for a Benedictine Priory, this handsome building was converted into an inn and further restored in 1970. Flagstone floors and old beams surround you as you choose from English or Spanish dishes. Expect tapas dishes, including gambas al pil pil (prawns with chilli), and sardinas a la plancha (griddled sardines), as well as seafood specialities and grills. **Principal beers:** Flowers, Boddingtons.
Directions Off the Fosseway Intersection with B4455
Brewery/Company Free House
Open 12-2.30 7-11 (closed Mon)
Bar food 12-2.30 7-11 Av main course £4.50
Restaurant 12-2.30 7-11 Av 3 course à la carte £16

PRINCETHORPE Warwickshire — Map 04 SP47

The Three Horseshoes

PRINCETHORPE
Southam Rd CV23 9PR ☎ 01926 632345
Traditional coaching inn dating from 1856 and situated on the Fosse Way, overlooking rolling Warwickshire countryside. Beams, horsebrasses and an open fire characterise the bar, where a blackboard menu may list home-made pies, Mexican enchilladoes, seasonal game dishes, steaks from locally-reared cattle, and fresh fish specials. **Principal beers:** Adnams, Banks, Ruddles County, John Smiths.
Directions On A423 at X of B4455 & B4453
Brewery/Company Free House
Open 11-2.30 6-11
Bar food 11.30-2 6-10 Av main course £6.50
Restaurant 11.30-2 6-10
Accommodation (Min) s£20 d£30

RATLEY Warwickshire — Map 04 SP34

The Rose and Crown

RATLEY
OX15 6DS ☎ 01295 678148
Following the Battle of Edgehill nearby, a Roundhead was discovered in the chimney of this 11th-century pub and beheaded in the hearth. His ghost reputedly haunts the building. Enjoy its peaceful village location and the traditional pub food, perhaps including beef bourguignon and tagliatelle carbonara. **Principal beers:** Wells Bombadier & Eagle IPA, Badger Tanglefoot, Morland Old Speckled Hen.
Directions Follow Edgehill signs
Brewery/Company Free House
Open 12-2.30 6.30-11
Bar food 12-2 7-9.30 Av main course £5.95
Accommodation (Min) d£49

SHIPSTON ON STOUR Warwickshire — Map 04 SP24

The Red Lion
SHIPSTON ON STOUR
Main St, Long Compton CV36 5JS
☎ 01608 684221
Grade 11 listed building dating from 1748 and set in an area of outstanding natural beauty on the edge of the Cotswolds. With plenty of beams and exposed stone walls in the comfortable bars, it offer traditional dishes including sizzling steaks and barbecued spare ribs, salmon supreme, and chicken with Stilton. **Principal beers:** Webster Yorkshire, Ruddles, Adnams, Courage Directors.
Directions On B3400 between Shipston on Stour & Chipping Norton
Brewery/Company Free House
Open 11-2.30 6-11
Bar food 12-2 7-9 Av main course £6
Restaurant 12-2 7-9 Av 3 course à la carte £15
Accommodation (Min) s£29.50 d£45

White Bear Hotel NEW
SHIPSTON ON STOUR
High St CV36 4AJ ☎ 01608 661558
A fine old coaching inn, partly 16th-century, overlooking the market place. Two beamed bars, one warmed by a log-burning stove, are full of character. Decent food ranges from roast beef baguette, pork and game terrine and fish chowder, to chargrilled tuna with chilli and soy glaze, and interesting bistro fare. **Principal beers:** Marstons Pedigree, Bass.
Brewery/Company Punch Taverns
Open 11-11 (Sun 12-10.30)
Bar food 12-2.30 6.30-10.30 Av main course £7
Restaurant 12-2.30 6.30-10.30 Av 3 course à la carte £12.50
Accommodation (Min) s£22.50 d£50

STRATFORD-UPON-AVON Warwickshire *Map 04 SP25*

The Dirty Duck
STRATFORD-UPON-AVON
Waterside CV37 6BA ☎ 01789 297312
Frequented by members of the Royal Shakespeare Company from the nearby theatre, this traditional, partly Elizabethan inn has a splendid front terrace with peaceful views across the River Avon. View the gallery of autographed photographs of famous actors, or choose a meal from the 'theatre of gastronomic arts' menu. **Principal beers:** Flowers Original, Morland Old Speckled Hen, Wadworth 6X.
Brewery/Company Whitbread
Open 11-11 (Sun 12-10.30)
Bar food 12-3 5.30-11 Av main course £6
Restaurant 12-2 5.30-11 Av 3 course à la carte £15

TEMPLE GRAFTON Warwickshire *Map 04 SP15*

The Blue Boar
TEMPLE GRAFTON
B49 6NR ☎ 01789 750010
17th-century inn situated in what remains of the Forest of Arden where Shakespeare set As You Like It. Menus caters for all tastes and includes a good selection of bar meals - seafood pasta, ploughman's and salads. Guinea fowl with mushroom and port jus, and fillet steak with red wine jus are typical restaurant meals. **Principal beers:** Hook Norton, Morland Old Speckled Hen, Theakston XB.

Brewery/Company Free House
Open 11.30-3 5-11 (Sat-Sun 11.30-11)
Bar food 12-2.30 6-10 Av main course £6.95
Restaurant 12-2.30 6-10
Accommodation (Min) s£39.50 d£59.50

WARWICK Warwickshire *Map 04 SP26*

The Tilted Wig
WARWICK
11 Market Place CV34 4SA
☎ 01926 410466 411534
A restaurant bar and brasserie, all rolled into one, set in historic Warwick, overlooking the market square and just two minutes walk from the castle. The name stems from its proximity to the Crown Court. A wide variety of food includes baguettes, salads and ploughman's plus specials like pork and cider casserole, salmon fishcakes and chicken stir-fry.
Principal beers: Tetley, Marstons Pedigree, Morland Old Speckled Hen.
Directions From M40 J15 follow A429 into Warwick, after 1.5m L into Brook St on into Market Place
Brewery/Company Vanguard
Open 11-11 (Sun 12-10.30)
Bar food 12-3 6-9
Accommodation (Min) d£55

The Tudor House Inn
WARWICK
90-92 West St CV34 6AW
☎ 01926 495447
Built in 1472, this ornately framed, half-timbered building stands opposite the gates to Warwick Castle. Full of character, with swords and armour on display, it offers varied bar food to weary visitors. Menu choices may include cod with

partridge mousse, lasagne, beef and ale stew, and cod with mustard sauce.
Directions A429 into Warwick, inn opp car park entrance of Warwick Castle
Brewery/Company Old English Pub Co
Open 12-11
Bar food 12-2.30 6-9 Av main course £6.95
Accommodation (Min) s£30 d£65

WELFORD-ON-AVON Warwickshire
Map 04 SP15

The Four Alls
WELFORD-ON-AVON

Binton Rd CV37 8PW ☎ 01789 750228
17th-century inn situated on the banks of the River Avon, two miles from historic Stratford. Shakespeare loved this area and drank in many of the local taverns. Steaks and mixed grills feature prominently on the varied menu, and other dishes include lemon chicken, traditional cod, and vegetable curry. **Principal beers:** Whitbread.
Directions B439 from Stratford then L
Brewery/Company Whitbread
Open 11-11
Bar food 12-2.30 6.30-9.30 Av main course £5
Restaurant 12-2.30 6.30-9.30 Av 3 course à la carte £9.30

WHATCOTE Warwickshire
Map 04 SP24

Royal Oak
WHATCOTE

CV36 5EF ☎ 01295 680319
Historic 12th-century inn built for workers building churches in the area. Cromwell reputedly stopped here for a drink after the Battle of Edge Hill. All home-cooked food and fresh vegetables, with dishes such as chef's pâté and toast, fresh trout, chicken in garlic, steaks, and mushroom in pastry. **Principal beers:** Hook Norton, Theakston.
Brewery/Company Hook Norton
Open 12-3 6.30-11 (closed Mon lunch)
Bar food 12-2 7-9.30 Av main course £6
Restaurant 12-2 7-9.30 Av 3 course à la carte £13

Pubs offering a good choice of seafood on the menu

WITHYBROOK Warwickshire
Map 04 SP48

The Pheasant
WITHYBROOK

Main St CV7 9LT ☎ 01455 220480
Originally known as the Half Moon, this charming 17th-century coaching inn is located next to the brook from which the village takes its name. Inglenook fireplace, farm implements and horse-racing photographs inside. Extensive menu and daily blackboard specials, including, perhaps, beef Stroganoff, cottage pie, fresh sardines and spaghetti Bolognese. **Principal beers:** Courage Directors, Theakstons Best.

Directions Off B4112 NE of Coventry
Brewery/Company Free House
Open 11-3 6-11 (Sun 12-10.30 - food 12-10)
Bar food 12-2 6.30-10 Av main course £7.50

WOOTTON WAWEN Warwickshire
Map 04 SP16

The Bulls Head
WOOTTON WAWEN

Stratford Rd B95 6BD ☎ 01564 792511
There is plenty of atmosphere at this picturesque inn, originally two large cottages. Low beams, flagstones and old pews can be found inside. The accent is on fresh fish and the daily blackboard may feature smoked fish salad and monkfish tails marinated in balsamic vinegar, tomatoes and fresh herbs.
Principal beers: Marstons Pedigree, Banks Bitter, guest ales.
Directions On A3400
Brewery/Company Free House
Open 12-3 6-11
Bar food 12-2.30 7-10 Av main course £10
Restaurant 12-2.30 7-10 Av 3 course à la carte £18

West Midlands

ALDRIDGE West Midlands Map 07 SK00

Plough & Harrow
ALDRIDGE

770 Chester Rd, Mill Green WS9 0LR
☎ 01922 457847

Delightful country pub, well-loved by locals, nestling in unspoilt countryside. There is a beautiful garden with decorative borders, a low-beamed ceiling, and a large Inglenook fireplace. Sutton Park and Lichfield are within easy reach. **Principal beers:** Bass.

Directions From A5 junction at Muckley Corner, S along A461 towards Brownhills, L at traffic lights, pub 1m on R

Brewery/Company Vintage Inns

Open 11-11 (Sun 12-10.30)

BARSTON West Midlands Map 04 SP27

Bulls Head
BARSTON

Barston Ln B92 0JU ☎ 01675 442830

The unassuming outward appearance of this homely village local belies its Tudor, oak-beamed interior, Built in 1490 it posesses a priests hole that dates back to Cromwell's time. Devoid of music and electronic games, it offers traditional snacks and home-made specials like fish pie, pheasant in red wine, and fresh lemon sole. **Principal beers:** Bass, Fullers London Pride.

Directions M42 J5 take A4141 towards Warwick.Turn L 0.25m. Straight on at staggered junc. Pub 1m

Brewery/Company Free House

Open 11-2.30 5.30-11 (Sat-Sun 11-11)

Bar food 12-2 7-8.30 Av main course £5.50

Restaurant 12-2 7-8.30 Av 3 course à la carte £11

COVENTRY West Midlands Map 04 SP37

The Rose and Castle
COVENTRY

Ansty CV7 9HZ ☎ 01203 612822

Small canalside pub with moorings available. A wide range of bar snacks and light meals is offered, speciality dishes might include Ansty chicken , comprising breast of chicken wrapped inbacon and smothered with barbecuesauce or Rosie's rump, 10oz steak topped with mushrooms and onion and glazed with cheese. **Principal beers:** Tetley, Bass.

Directions From junc of M6/M69 at Walsgrave follow signs for Ansty.0.75m to pub

Brewery/Company Free House

Open 12-3 (Sun 12-11) 6-11

Bar food 12-3 6-11 Av main course £5.50

WEST BROMWICH West Midlands Map 07 SP09

The Vine
WEST BROMWICH

Roebuck St B70 6RD ☎ 0121 5532866

Real ale and curry is the winning combination at this popular pub. Home-made tandoori dishes, curries and balti meals are prepared to traditional recipes by the landlord and his wife, and there is an authentic Indian barbecue serving sizzling chicken and lamb tikka kebabs. Prices are equally attractive. **Principal beers:** 8-12 regularly changing real ales.

Brewery/Company Free House

Open 11.30-2.30 5-11 (Fri-Sun all day)

Bar food 12-2 5-10.30 Av main course £3.25

Restaurant 12-2 6-9.30 Av 3 course à la carte £7

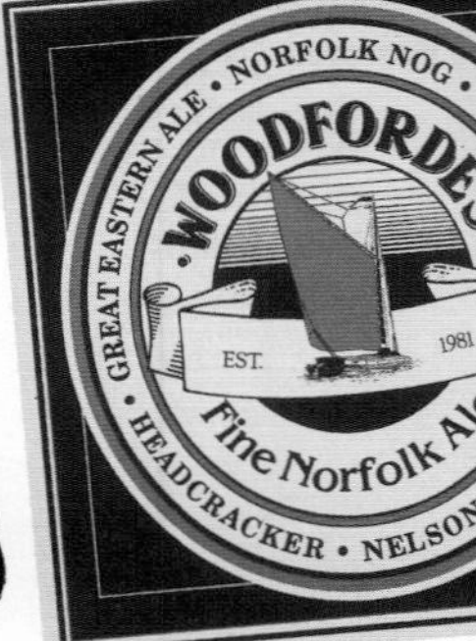

NELSON'S
Norfolk
Wherry
BEST BITTER
Trust Woodforde's to brew Wherry, a beer that combines the purest ingredients to bring out the best in Norfolk.
WOODFORDE'S
Norfolk Ales
WOODFORDE'S NORFOLK ALES · Broadland Brewery · Woodbastwick · Norwich · Norfolk · Tel: 01603 720353
Norfolk • Tel: 01603 720353
Broadland Brewery

The Sun Inn, Winforton, Hereford

Steak, Kidney & Porter Pie

Ingredients for filling:

- 2lb/900g **rump steak**, trimmed & cut into 1½ inch chunks
- 12 **button mushrooms**
- 8oz/225g **lambs' kidneys**, cleaned and sliced in half
- 12 baby **onions**, skinned
- 1 **garlic clove**, crushed
- 1 teaspoon each of **tomato ketchup**, **demerera sugar**, **Worcester sauce**, **English mustard**, **HP sauce**.
- 3oz/75g **butter**
- 2fl oz/55ml light **olive oil**
- **flour**
- **sea salt and black pepper**

Ingredients for marinade:

- 1pt/570ml **beer**
- ½pt/275ml **Guinness**
- 1 **onion**, chopped
- 1 **bayleaf** & **bouquet garni**
- 1 **carrot** (chopped) & **celery stick** (chopped)

Place all in a saucepan, bring to the boil and simmer for 15 minutes. Allow to cool.

Ingredients for topping:

- 3oz/75g **butter**
- ¼pt/150ml **water**
- ¼pt/150ml **lager**
- 4 **eggs, beaten**
- 5oz/150g **plain flour**

Method for filling:

Place **steak** and **kidney** in a bowl, pour over **marinade** (see ingredients) leave for at least 24 hours, turning occasionally. Remove **meat** from marinade and pat dry with kitchen paper. Roll **meat** in **flour** to totally cover. Heat **butter** and **oil** in large frying pan and place **meat** in, sealing all over. In another pan, sauté **onions** and **garlic** until soft, then add **mushrooms** and seal. In a large casserole layer the **onions**, **mushrooms** and **meat**. Mix marinade with **sauces**, **sugar** and **mustard**, then pour over **meat**. Season and cover with lid. Simmer over a low heat for 1-1½ hours. Allow to cool. Pour into 5-6 individual pie dishes (depending on size).

Method for topping:

Place **water**, **lager** and **butter** in a medium-sized pan and bring to the boil. Remove from the heat and add **flour**. Beat vigorously until mixture is smooth and shiny. Beat in **eggs** a little at a time until mixture is smooth and shiny. Spoon **pastry** on top of pie dishes and cover with greaseproof paper. Top with pleated foil. Tie with string and place pies in a large pan (a fish kettle is ideal) of water, making sure the water does not cover pies. Cover with lid and place in the oven.

Cooking time and oven temp:

Gas mark 6/Electric (Centigrade) 200 for 45 minutes. Serves 6 people.

Bridgend

KENFIG Bridgend *Map 03 SS88*

Prince of Wales Inn
KENFIG
CF33 4PR ☎ 01656 740356
Dating from 1440, this stone-built inn has been many things in its time - school, hotel and courtroom - and it's the only pub that still holds a weekly Sunday school. The landlord's own home-grown vegetables and salad appears wherever possible on the menu, and fresh fish is a speciality. **Principal beers:** Bass Triangle, Worthington Best, Marstons Pedigree, Thomas Watkin OSB.
Directions M4 J37 into North Cornelly & follow signs for nature reserve, Kenfig
Brewery/Company Free House
Open 11-4 6-11
Bar food 12-2.30 7-10 Av main course £5
Restaurant 12-2.30 7-10 Av 3 course à la carte £15

Caerphilly

CAERPHILLY Caerphilly *Map 03 ST18*

Travellers Rest
CAERPHILLY
Thornhill Rd CF83 1LY ☎ 01222 859021
This delightful 18th-century thatched inn really lives up to its name. Standing atop a crest in the land, it provides an ideal resting place for those exploring the Caerphilly area. The pub marks the ancient boundary between areas of Norman and Welsh rule. **Principal beers:** Bass, Hancocks HB.
Directions On the A469, travelling N from Cardiff
Brewery/Company Vintage Inns
Open 11-11 (Sun 12-10.30)

Cardiff

CREIGIAU Cardiff *Map 03 ST08*

Caesars Arms
CREIGIAU
Cardiff Rd CF4 8NN ☎ 01222 890486
Excellent fresh fish and seafood, Welsh lamb and prime steaks attract diners to this popular dining pub set in 3 acres close to the M4 and Cardiff. Choose from sea bass, monkfish, hake and turbot, or, perhaps. venison steak from the display cabinet. Other dishes include fish soup, game terrine and honey-roast duck.

Principal beers: Hancocks.
Directions 1m from M4 J34
Brewery/Company Free House
Open 12-3 6-10.30
Restaurant 12-2.30 7-10.30 Av 3 course à la carte £17

Carmarthenshire

ABERGORLECH Carmarthenshire *Map 02 SN53*

The Black Lion
ABERGORLECH
SA32 7SN ☎ 01558 685271
Small 16th-century black and white beamed inn on the banks of the River Cothi. Good selection of bar food includes sandwiches, jacket potatoes, lasagne, chicken tikka, seafood pasta, and plaice. Restaurant main courses tend to be minted lamb chops, trout, peppered pork, and duck with orange sauce.
Principal beers: Worthington, Welsh Bitter.
Directions From Carmarthen take A40 eastwards,then B4310 signposted Brechfa & Abergorlech
Brewery/Company Free House
Open 12-3 7-11.30
Bar food 12-2.30 7-10 Av main course £4.50
Restaurant 12-2.30 7-10 Av 3 course à la carte £12.50

BRECHFA Carmarthenshire *Map 02 SN53*

Forest Arms
BRECHFA
☎ 01267 202339
Stone-built, early 19th-century inn nestling in a pretty village in the beautiful Cothi Valley. Fishing mementoes adorn the unspoilt, traditional bars, where the daily menu features a varied selection of home-cooked favourites, served in generous

quantities and made from good ingredients. **Principal beers:** Dylan's, Brains Buckleys Best, Worthington.
Brewery/Company Free House
Open 12-2 6-11 (closed Sun)
Bar food 12-2 6-9 Av main course £5
Restaurant 12-2 6-9
Accommodation (Min) s£18 d£36

LLANARTHNE Carmarthenshire *Map 02 SN52*

Golden Grove Arms
LLANARTHNE
SA32 8JU ☎ 01558 668551
Family-run country inn, recently completely refurbished, set in an area of outstanding natural beauty in the Towy Valley. Steak pie, Welsh lamb chops, and chicken Odessa are favourites in the bar, while in the restaurant you can expect fresh Towy sewin, and Welsh black ribeye steak. **Principal beers:** Brains Buckleys Best, & Reverend James Original Ale, Watkin's Woosh.
Directions From end M4 take A48 toward Carmarthen, then R at Pantyeynon, 2 or 3m to Llanarthne
Brewery/Company Free House
Open 12-11
Bar food 12-9.30 Av main course £6.50
Restaurant 12-2.30 6-10 Av 3 course à la carte £14.95
Accommodation (Min) s£25 d£40

LLANDEILO Carmarthenshire *Map 03 SN62*

The Angel Inn
LLANDEILO
Salem SA19 7LY ☎ 01558 823394
Beamed ceilings and a large collection of interesting artefacts and pictures characterise this village pub, which comprises two bars and a 100-seater restaurant. There is popular bar food, a children's menu, a selection of vegetarian dishes and daily specials such as local sea trout and Cajun chicken.
Principal beers: Worthington, Dylans.
Directions A40 then B4302, turn L 1m after leaving A40 then turn R at T.Junct and travel 0.25m to Angel Inn. Located on the right hand side
Brewery/Company Free House
Open 5.30-12 (Sun 12-4/lunch available Sun only)
Bar food 6.30-10 Av main course £4.75
Restaurant 6.30-10 Av 3 course à la carte £12.50
Accommodation (Min) s£30 d£40

The Castle Brewery
LLANDEILO
113 Rhosmaen St SA19 6EN
☎ 01558 823446
Dating from 1830, this renovated Edwardian-style hotel has a micro-brewery attached at the rear of the building - Watkins OSB was recently voted "Premium Ale of Wales". Good selection of snacks and light lunches, plus hearty dishes like spicy chicken curry, mushroom Stroganoff, roasted duck breast, and poached salmon with dill cream sauce. **Principal beers:** Watkins Best, Watkins OSB.
Brewery/Company Tomos Watkin & Sons
Open 12-12
Bar food 12-2.15 6-9 Av main course £5.50
Restaurant 12-2.15 5.30-9.30 Av 3 course à la carte £10.50
Accommodation (Min) s£25 d£40

The Nags Head Inn
LLANDEILO
Pentrefelin SA19 6SD ☎ 01558 822890
Old timbered coaching inn nestling in the lush Towy Valley surrounded by ancient castles. Bar food includes home-made pies, fish and curries, while the restaurant offers a choice of Welsh black fillet steaks, crab thermidor and puddings such as apple pie and treacle tart.
Principal beers: Thomos Watkins, Boddingtons.
Directions On main A40 between Brecon & Carmarthen, 1.5 miles W of Llandeilo
Brewery/Company Free House
Open 12-3 6-11
Bar food 12-2.30 6-9.30 Av main course £6
Restaurant 12-2.30 6-9.30 Av 3 course à la carte £16 Av 4 course fixed price £10.95

PONT-AR-GOTHI Carmarthenshire *Map 02 SN52*

The Salutation Inn
PONT-AR-GOTHI
SA32 7NG ☎ 01267 290336
Black and white half-timbered building in the heart of the Towy Valley. Exposed stone walls and beams give a convincing sense of its 300-year past and the food on offer has given the pub a good reputation. Interesting specials may include beef Stroganoff, lamb in red wine, and local fish and game. **Principal beers:** Felinfoel - Double Dragon, Dragon Bitter.
Directions On A40 between Carmarthen & Llandeilo
Brewery/Company Felinfoel
Open 12-3 6-12
Bar food 12-2 6.30-10 Av main course £7.95
Restaurant 12-2 6.30-9.30 Av 3 course à la carte £16

RHOS Carmarthemshire *Map 02 SN33*

Lamb of Rhos NEW
RHOS
SA44 5EE ☎ 01559 370055
Interesting mix of country pub with beams and antiques and a continental villa festooned with flowers. Seasonally changing menu draws on fresh local produce. Dishes include laverbread, cockles and bacon, followed by Teifi salmon with honey and citrus sauce, or shank of Welsh lamb with champ. Hearty pies, ploughman's and fish and chips at lunchtime. **Principal beers:** Morland Old Speckled Hen, Worthington Best, Cains Formidable Ale.
Brewery/Company Free House
Open 11-3 6-11
Bar food 12-3 6-10
Accommodation (Min) s£24.50 d£33

Ceredigion

CARDIGAN Ceredigion *Map 02 SN14*

Webley Hotel
CARDIGAN
Poppit Sands SA43 3LN
☎ 01239 612085
Overlooking the Teifi Estuary and Cardigan Island, this hotel is located on the coastal path, and is within walking distance of Poppit Sands. Bar food ranges from local mussels and battered cod, to daily specials like chick pea and lentil curry, beef goulash, and pork in black bean sauce.

Directions A484 from Carmarthen to Cardigan
Brewery/Company Free House
Open 11.30-3 6.30-11.30
Bar food 11.30-2 6.30-9 Av main course £5.60
Accommodation (Min) s£21 d£40

LLWYNDAFYDD Ceredigion *Map 02 SN35*

Crown Inn & Restaurant
LLWYNDAFYDD
SA44 6BU ☎ 01545 560396
Traditional 18th-century Welsh longhouse with original beams and open fireplaces, close to Cardigan Bay. Bar menu features home-made steak and kidney pie and braised beef in red wine and mushroom sauce, while the restaurant offers dressed crab salad and veal cooked in vermouth, lemon and caper butter. **Principal beers:** Flowers Original & IPA, Wadworth 6X.
Directions Off A487 NE of Cardigan
Brewery/Company Free House
Open 12-3 6-11
Bar food 12-2.30 6-9.15 Av main course £6.35
Restaurant 12-2.30 6.30-9.30 Av 3 course à la carte £17.50

Conwy

ABERGELE Conwy *Map 06 SH97*

Kinmel Arms
ABERGELE
St George LL22 9BP ☎ 01745 832207
Recently refurbished 17th-century coaching inn overlooking the Rhuddlan Marshes. Interesting and varied menus may feature cod in beer batter, Kinmel

Estate sausage and mash, and lamb rogan josh in the bar, while restaurant dishes might include roast Kinmel venison with elderberry sauce, or sea bass with tapenade crust and lime butter sauce. **Principal beers:** Marstons Bitter & Pedigree, Thwaites.
Directions from Bodelwyddan towards Abergele take slip road at St George. Take 1st L and Kinmel Arms is on L at top of hill
Brewery/Company Free House
Open 12-3 7-11
Bar food 12-2.30 7-9.30 Av main course £5.50
Restaurant 12-2 7-9 Av 3 course à la carte £17 Av 3 course fixed price £12.95

BETWS-Y-COED Conwy — *Map 06 SH75*

Ty Gwyn Hotel
BETWS-Y-COED
LL24 0SG ☎ 01690 710383 710787
Former coaching inn overlooking the River Conwy in the marvellous mountain scenery of the Vale of Conwy. Good, imaginative food ranges from home-made soups, lasagne and curry, to chargrilled lamb steak with rosemary and garlic crust, spicy gumbo prawns, sauteed breast of wild mallard, and decent fresh seafood choices - squid and crayfish Provencal and salmon and sea bass en croûte. **Principal beers:** Flowers.
Directions At Juction of A5/A470, 100 yards S of Waterloo Bridge.
Brewery/Company Free House
Open 12-2 7-9.30
Bar food 12-2 7-9 Av main course £5.95
Restaurant 12-2 7-9 Av 3 course à la carte £17.95
Accommodation (Min) s£20 d£34

CAPEL CURIG Conwy — *Map 06 SH75*

Cobdens Hotel
CAPEL CURIG
LL24 0EE ☎ 01690 720243
Situated at the foot of Moel Siabod in the heart of Snowdonia, this 230-year-old inn is a popular centre for outdoor pursuits. There are two bars and one has an impressive, exposed rock face, Good-value meals include shepherd's pie, leek and potato soup, fisherman's pie and Welsh sirloin steak. **Principal beers:** Tetley, Morland Old Speckled Hen, Carlsberg-Tetley ABC.
Directions On A5, 4m N of Betws-Y-Coed
Brewery/Company Free House
Open 11-11 (Sun 12-10.30)
Bar food 12-2.30 6.30-9 Av main course £7
Restaurant 12-2.30 6.30-9
Accommodation (Min) s£25 d£50

CONWY Conwy — *Map 06 SH77*

The Groes Inn
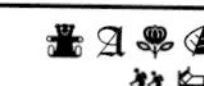
CONWY
LL32 8TN ☎ 01492 650545
Built around 500 years ago in the River Conwy Valley, the Groes Inn gained its licence in 1573, reputedly making it the first Licenced House in Wales. A speciality is the home-made ice cream. Flavours include Cream of Summer Roses, coconut and Malibu, and After Eight Mint. **Principal beers:** Tetley, Burton Ale.
Directions Off A55 to Conwy, L at mini r'about by Conwy castle onto B5106, 2 1/2m inn on R
Brewery/Company Free House
Open 12-3 6.30-11
Bar food 12-2 6.30-9 Av main course £8
Restaurant 12-2 6.30-9 Av 3 course fixed price £22.50
Accommodation (Min) s£63.25 d£80.50

GWYTHERIN Conwy — *Map 06 SH86*

Lion Inn Hotel & Restaurant
GWYTHERIN
LL22 8UU ☎ 01745 860244
The village inn is thought to be over 300 years old, but various extensions have been added over the years. Bar menu may include Anglesey eggs, cod in beer batter or beef and Guinness pie, while the restaurant offers dishes such as duck terrine, game pie and home-made soups. **Principal beers:** Ansells, Tetley, Marstons Pedigree.
Directions 3m off A548 (Llanrwst/Abergele rd) on B5384
Brewery/Company Free House
Open 12-3 6-11 (Sun 12-3, 7-10.30)
Bar food 12-2 7-9 Av main course £5.50
Restaurant 12-2 7-9 Av 3 course à la carte £14
Accommodation (Min) s£27 d£40

LLANDUDNO JUNCTION Conwy — Map 06 SH87

The Queens Head
LLANDUDNO JUNCTION

Glanwydden LL31 9JP ☎ 01492 546570

At one time this country pub was a wheelwright's cottage, and while retaining its traditional pub appeal it offers imaginative pub food. The same menu is available throughout, featuring local seafood platters, Glanwydden lamb cutlets, served with a plum and port wine sauce, and local Welsh black beef.
Principal beers: Burton, Tetley, Benskins.
Directions Take A470 from A55 towards Llandudno, at 3rd roundabout R towards Penrhyn Bay, then 2nd R into Glanwydden, pub on L
Brewery/Company Allied Domecq
Open 11-3 6-11
Bar food 12-2 6-9

LLANNEFYDD Conwy — Map 06 SH97

The Hawk & Buckle Inn
LLANNEFYDD

LL16 5ED ☎ 01745 540249

Situated 200m up in the hills, this 17th-century coaching inn affords wonderful views over rolling fields to the sea beyond. Menus offer a good choice of food based on local produce. Expect home-made pâtés, beef Wellington, rack of lamb, pork Stroganoff, and various steak and fresh fish dishes.
Brewery/Company Free House
Open 12-2 (closed Mon lunch) 7-11
Bar food 12-2 7-10 Av main course £6.50
Restaurant 7-10.30 Av 3 course à la carte £20
Accommodation (Min) s£38 d£50

Denbighshire

BODFARI Denbighshire — Map 06 SJ07

The Dinorben Arms
BODFARI

LL16 4DA ☎ 01745 710309

Heavily beamed 17th-century inn with flower-decked, tiered patios and extensive hillside gardens. Popular locally for farmhouse buffets, weekend carvery, and traditional bar food, including cod and chips, Welsh lamb with mint and rosemary, seafood mornay, steak au poivre, and chicken, ham and mushroom pie. **Principal beers:** Tetley.
Directions Come off A55 onto B5122 through Caerwys, R onto A541, R after 2.5m in Bodfari. Pub 100yrds of B541 next to church
Brewery/Company Free House
Open 12-3.30 6-11 (Sun 12-11)
Bar food 12-2.30 6-10
Restaurant 12-2.30 6-10 Av 3 course à la carte £5.50

LLANGOLLEN Denbighshire — Map 07 SJ24

The Famous Britannia Inn
LLANGOLLEN

Horseshoe Pass LL20 8DW
☎ 01978 860144

14th-century coaching inn set in its own award-winning gardens with beautiful views of the Vale of Llangollen. Situated at the foot of the famous Horseshoe Pass. Typical main course dishes range from Britannia steak pie and leek and mushroom crumble, to salmon with cucumber sauce, and stuffed plaice.
Principal beers: Theakston Old Peculiar & Best, Morland Old Speckled Hen.
Directions From Llangollen take A542 N 2m
Brewery/Company Free House
Open 11-3 6-11
Bar food 12-2.30 6-9.30 Av main course £4.95
Restaurant 12-2.30 6-9.30 Av 3 course à la carte £14.95
Accommodation (Min) s£30 d£40

LLANYNYS Denbighshire — Map 06 SJ16

Cerrigllwydion Arms
LLANYNYS

LL16 4PA ☎ 01745 890247

Rambling inn built in about 1400 by Edward Edwards, attorney of Cerrigllwydion Hall, for the benefit of his churchgoers. Pleasant garden with views of the Clwydian Hills, and atmospheric rooms in which to sample chicken, ham and mushroom pie, pork chops in cider and apple sauce, mixed grill, or a traditional bar snack. **Principal beers:** Bass, Tetley.
Directions A525 towards Denbigh, R after 1.5m, then L and 1m to pub
Brewery/Company Free House
Open 12-3 7-11 (closed Mon)
Bar food 12-3 Av main course £5
Restaurant 12-3 7-11 Av 3 course à la carte £13.50

Flintshire

BABELL Flintshire Map 03 SN83

Black Lion Inn
BABELL
CH8 8PZ ☎ 01352 720239
Grade II listed, 13th-century former drovers' inn, run by the present management for over 30 years. The restaurant and bar menus are written daily and might feature beef in red wine, poached wild salmon Florentine, and roast duckling with black cherry or peach and brandy sauce. **Principal beers:** Boddingtons.
Directions From Holywell take B5121 towards A541 (Mold to Denbigh road) & take 2nd R to Babell
Brewery/Company Free House
Open 7-11 (closed Sun, Mon & Wed)
Bar food 7.30-9.30 Av main course £7
Restaurant 7.30-9.30 Av 3 course à la carte £17.50
Accommodation (Min) s£15 d£25

CILCAIN Flintshire Map 07 SJ16

White Horse Inn
CILCAIN
CH7 5NN ☎ 01352 740142
Dating from the 14th century, this cosy inn enjoys a lovely village setting opposite the church. Rambling interior with old beams, roaring fire, an ever-changing choice of real ales, and plenty of home-cooked dishes, including Madras prawn curry, steak and kidney pie, chilli, Corsican chicken, venison and cranberry pie, and generously-filled baps. **Principal beers:** Thwaites, Fullers London Pride, Taylor Landlord, Greene King Abbot Ale.
Directions From Mold take A541 towards Denbigh. After approx 6m turn L
Brewery/Company Free House
Open 12-3 6.30-11
Bar food 12-2 7.30-9.30 Av main course £6

HALKYN Flintshire Map 07 SJ27

Britannia Inn
HALKYN
Pentre Rd CH8 8BS ☎ 01352 780272
500-year-old stone pub on an old coach route between Chester and Holyhead, with views over the Dee estuary and Wirral. It features a family farm with chickens, ducks and Fleur the spotted pig. Typical dishes are black pudding with mustard sauce, lamb casserole, beef in Moonraker Ale pie, and shark steak. **Principal beers:** Lees Bitter, GB Mild & Moonraker.
Directions Off A55 on B5123
Brewery/Company J W Lees
Open 11-11 (Sun 12-10.30)
Bar food 12-2.30 6.30-9 Av main course £5
Restaurant 12-2.30 6.30-9 Av 3 course à la carte £10
Accommodation (Min) s£25 d£30

LIXWM Flintshire Map 07 SJ17

The Crown Inn NEW
LIXWM
☎ 01352 781112
Early 17th-century inn enjoying a pretty village setting near the Clwydian Mountains and the Offa's Dyke Path. Typical dishes on the wide-ranging menu may include home-made soup, followed by steak and kidney pie, shoulder of lamb with red wine, mushroom and mint gravy, and lemon and ginger brûlée. **Principal beers:** Tetleys.
Directions Off the B5121 S of Holywell
Brewery/Company Free House
Open 5.30-11 (Sun 12-10.30, Sat 12-3, 5.30-11)
Restaurant 12-3 5.30-9.30 Av 3 course à la carte £12

MOLD Flintshire Map 07 SJ26

The Druid Inn
MOLD
Ruthin Rd, Llanferres CH7 5SN
☎ 01244 810225
At this 17th-century coaching inn, overlooking the Alyn Valley and the Craig Harris mountains, a daily blackboard menu features decent home-cooked food such as braised shoulder of lamb in red wine, salmon wrapped in bacon with hollandaise, steak, ale and mushroom pie, and imaginatively-filled granary baps. **Principal beers:** Burtonwood Top Hat, Caledonian.
Directions A494 from Mold, Druid 4 1/2m along road on R
Brewery/Company Burtonwood
Open 11.30-3 5.30-11 (Sat, Sun & BH all day & food 12-10)
Bar food 12-3 6-10 Av main course £7.25
Restaurant 12-3 6-10 Av 3 course à la carte £12
Accommodation (Min) s£25 d£36.50

Gwynedd

ABERDYFI Gwynedd Map 06 SN69

Penhelig Arms Hotel & Restaurant
ABERDYFI
LL35 0LT ☎ 01654 767215
Overlooking the Dyfi estuary, this delightful 18th-century inn's imaginative menu is characterised by fresh local fish and interesting meat dishes. Quality ingredients are used in preparing carrot and coriander roulade, chicken with tarragon cream sauce, and herb-crusted lamb. Good seafood choices may include seafood chowder, bream baked with herbs, peppers, garlic and white wine, and cod with bacon, Stilton butter and roast peppers. **Principal beers:** Tetley, Bass, Wadworth 6X, Brains.

Directions On A493 (coastal rd) W of Machynlleth
Brewery/Company Free House
Open 11.30-3.30 6-11
Bar food 12-2 6.45-9.15 Av main ourse £7.95
Restaurant 12-2 7-9.30 Av 3 course fixed price £19.50
Accommodation (Min) s£39 d£68

BONTDDU Gwynedd Map 06 SH61

The Halfway House
BONTDDU
LL40 2UE ☎ 01341 430635
Situated near the Mawddach estuary, much-loved by the poet Wordsworth, and the Clogau goldmine, this 18th-century pub is an ideal refreshment spot for walkers enjoying the beautiful surrounding countryside. Popular dishes include Welsh cheese ploughman's, steak and mushroom pie, home-baked cider ham, and fresh haddock with mustard sauce. **Principal beers:** Marstons Pedigree, Tetley.
Directions On A436 between Dolgellau & Barmouth
Brewery/Company Free House
Open 12-3 6-11
Bar food 12-2 6-9 Av main course £5.50
Restaurant 12-2 6-9 Av 3 course à la carte £10 Av 3 course fixed price £10

DOLGELLAU Gwynedd Map 06 SH71

George III Hotel
DOLGELLAU
Penmaenpool LL40 1YD
☎ 01341 422525
Superbly situated at the head of the Mawddach estuary, this fine 17th-century building enjoys magnificent views, especially from the terrace. Beyond the popular afternoon tea menu, the varied range of bar food may feature smoked fish platter, steak and kidney pie, crab and salmon fishcakes, and specials like honey-glazed ham hock. Separate restaurant carte. **Principal beers:** Ruddles Best, John Smiths.
Directions 2m West of A493 beyond RSPB Centre
Brewery/Company Free House
Open 11-11
Bar food 12-2.30 6.30-9.30 Av main course £5.75
Restaurant 12-2 7-9 Av 3 course à la carte £25
Accommodation (Min) s£40 d£70

LLANENGAN Gwynedd Map 06 SH22

The Sun Inn
LLANENGAN
LL53 7LG ☎ 01758 712660
Friendly and welcoming pub, reputedly haunted, with a wishing well in the garden, and where the locals are likely to burst into song. The changing menu includes steaks, lasagne, chicken breast and rack of lamb. **Principal beers:** Robinson Best, Old Stockport Bitter.
Directions From Pwllheli take A499 S to Abersoch.Then 1.5m towards Hells Mouth Beach
Brewery/Company Robinson
Open 12-3 5.30-9 (open all day in summer)
Bar food 12-3 5.30-9 Av main course £6.95

For Pubs with AA food rosettes see page 430

MAENTWROG Gwynedd *Map 06 SH64*

Grapes Hotel
MAENTWROG
LL41 4HN ☎ 01766 590208 & 590365
The present hotel dates from 1834, though the cellars were built in the 1300s, and the veranda overlooks the beautiful Vale of Ffestiniog. Interesting guest ales and a good bar menu, including traditional snacks and daily game and fish specialities, such as sea bass stuffed with spring onions, ginger and ham. **Principal beers:** Bass, Plassey, Wye Valley, Phoenix.

Directions A5 thru Corwen to Bala, A487 to Maentwrog, onto A496, pub 100yrds
Brewery/Company Free House
Open 11-11 (Sun 12-10.30)
Bar food 12-2.15 6-9.30 Av main course £7
Restaurant 7-12 Av 3 course à la carte £14
Accommodation (Min) s£25 d£50

NANTGWYNANT Gwynedd *Map 06 SH56*

Pen-Y-Gwryd
NANTGWYNANT
LL55 4NT ☎ 01286 870211
Located in the Snowdonia National Park, this cosy inn is the home of British mountaineering and was the base for the successful 1953 Everest team. Hearty fare from the daily-changing menu might include Welsh cheese ploughman's, home-made pâté, fish pie, and beef and mushroom pie. Short evening menu offering home-made soup, roast lamb and walnut tart. **Principal beers:** Bass.
Directions 6m S of Llanberis at head of Gwryd river, close to junction of A4086 & A498
Brewery/Company Free House
Open 11-11 (closed Nov-New Year)
Bar food 12-2 Av main course £4
Restaurant 7.30-8 Av 3 course à la carte £15
Accommodation (Min) s£22 d£44

PORTHMADOG Gwynedd *Map 06 SH53*

The Ship
PORTHMADOG
Lombard St LL49 9AP ☎ 01766 512990
Roomy 19th-century pub with non-smoking lounge bar and children's playground opposite. One menu serves everyone and features roast cod with pesto, conger eel steaks and lamb with Dijon mustard and tarragon. Beef bourguignon and salmon with lobster and brandy sauce are also popular dishes. **Principal beers:** Morland Old Speckled Hen, Tetley Bitter, Dark Mild, Burton Ale.
Directions From A55 take A470 S toward the coast
Brewery/Company Vanguard
Open 11-11 (Sun 12-10.30)
Bar food 12-2.15 6.30-9.30 Av main course £7.50

TUDWEILIOG Gwynedd *Map 06 SH23*

Lion Hotel
TUDWEILIOG
LL53 8ND ☎ 01758 770244
A village inn with a courtyard, not far from the coast. There is a selection of bar snacks plus main course options such as steak and kidney pie, fresh trout, chicken or lamb balti, and local gammon. Vegetarian dishes include cannelloni, tagliatelle niçoise and wheat casserole. **Principal beers:** Marstons Pedigree, Boddingtons, Theakston, Wadworth 6X.
Directions A499 from Caernarfon, B4417 Tudweiliog
Brewery/Company Free House
Open 12-3 6-11 (shorter hours in winter)
Bar food 12-2 6-9.30 Av main course £5
Accommodation (Min) d£40

Herefordshire

AYMESTREY Herefordshire *Map 03 SO46*

Riverside Inn
AYMESTREY
HR6 9ST ☎ 01568 708440
16th-century half timbered coaching inn with its own brewery, prettily situated on the banks of the River Lugg and directly

contd.

on the route of the 30-mile Mortimer Trail. Everything is produced freshly to order and wild duck, roast turbot, Cornish crab and haunch of venison are typical examples of the constantly changing menu.

Riverside Inn

Principal beers: Woodhampton.
Directions Situated on A4110 between Hereford & Knighton
Brewery/Company Free House
Open 12-3 6.30-11 (7 in winter)
Bar food 12-2.30 7-9.30 Av main course £6
Restaurant 12-2.30 7-9.30 Av 3 course à la carte £20 Av 3 course fixed price £16
Accommodation (Min) s£25 d£45

BRIMFIELD Herefordshire *Map 03 SO56*

The Roebuck Inn
BRIMFIELD

SY8 4NE ☎ 01584 711230

Civilised 15th-century country inn comprising two lounge bars, a locals' snug bar and an airy modern dining room. Above average bar food includes beef fillet stuffed with Stilton and wrapped in bacon and 'famous fish pie'. The restaurant offers an excellent choice of seafood, perhaps including monkfish with lobster and scallop sauce. **Principal beers:** Morland Old Speckled Hen, Tetley.
Directions Just off the A49 between Ludlow & Leominster
Brewery/Company Free House
Open 11.30-3 6.30-11
Bar food 12-2.30 7-9.30 Av main course £12
Restaurant 12-2.30 7-9.30
Accommodation (Min) s£45 d£60

CANON PYON Herefordshire *Map 03 SO44*

The Nags Head Inn
CANON PYON

HR4 8NY ☎ 01432 830252

Flagstone floors, open fires and beams characterise this friendly 16th-century inn. The restaurant area is more modern and has a glass-topped well discovered during building work. Traditional bar food includes filled jacket potatoes, stir-fries, curries, and, perhaps, game casserole.
Principal beers: Wadworth 6X, Brains, Buckleys, Hook Norton.
Brewery/Company Free House
Open 11-2.30 6-11
Bar food 12-2 6.30-9 Av main course £5
Restaurant 12-2 6.30-9 Av 3 course à la carte £14
Accommodation (Min) s£30 d£40

CAREY Herefordshire *Map 03 SO53*

Cottage of Content
CAREY

HR2 6NG ☎ 01432 840242

500-year-old building which was formerly three cottages, situated beside a stream. Specials board is likely to feature char-grilled chicken with apricot, mango and green pepper sauce, salmon with saffron and herb butter sauce, cauliflower cheese, and fillet of beef with wild mushrooms and port sauce.
Principal beers: Hook Norton.
Directions From A40 W of Ross-on-Wye take A49 towards Hereford.Follow signs for Hoarwithy,then Carey
Brewery/Company Free House
Open 12-2.30 7-11
Bar food 12-2 7-9.30 Av main course £9

DORSTONE Herefordshire *Map 03 SO34*

The Pandy Inn
DORSTONE

HR3 6AN ☎ 01981 550273

Oliver Cromwell frequented the inn during the 17th-century, though it dates back even further to 1185. The Pandy has been taken over by a South African family and their parrot, and South African dishes such as beef bobotie and tomato bredie, a lamb dish, are going down very well. **Principal beers:** Butty Buch, Wye Valley Dorothy Goodbody.

Directions Off B4348 W of Hereford
Brewery/Company Free House
Open 12-3 7-11
Bar food 12-3 7-10 Av main course £6

FOWNHOPE Herefordshire
Map 03 SO53

The Green Man Inn
FOWNHOPE

HR1 4PE ☎ 01432 860243

Black and white former coaching inn dating back to 1485, with oak beams throughout. It has an attractive garden and is located close to the river in the heart of the Wye Valley. Food includes snacks, a range of steaks, and dishes such as trout with cream cheese and prawns.
Principal beers: Marstons Pedigree, Courage Directors, Hook Norton,.
Directions From M50 take A449 then B4224 to Fownhope
Brewery/Company Free House
Open 11-11
Bar food 12-2 6-10 Av main course £5.60
Restaurant 12-2 7-10 Av 3 course à la carte £15
Accommodation (Min) s£34.50 d£56

HAMPTON BISHOP Herefordshire
Map 03 SO53

The Bunch of Carrots
HAMPTON BISHOP

HR1 4JR ☎ 01432 870237

Friendly pub with real fires, old beams and flagstones. Its name comes from a rock formation in the River Wye which runs alongside the pub. There is an extensive menu (steaks, lemon sole and Cajun chicken) plus a daily specials board, a carvery, salad buffet and simple bar snacks.
Principal beers: Bass, Boddingtons, Hook Norton.
Directions From Hereford take A4103, A438, then B4224
Brewery/Company Free House
Open 11-3 6-11
Bar food 12-2 6-10 Av main course £6.95
Restaurant 12-2 6-10 Av 3 course à la carte £11

HEREFORD Herefordshire
Map 03 SO54

The Ancient Camp Inn
HEREFORD

Ruckhall HR2 9QX ☎ 01981 250449

Spectacular views of the River Wye can be enjoyed from the front terrace of this delightful country inn/restaurant, built on the site of an Iron Age fortress. Quality cooking attracts discerning diners here, the interesting menus possibly listing home-cured gravlax, beef medallions with mushroom and foie gras, and lemon and lime cheesecake.
Principal beers: Hook Norton.
Directions Take A465 from Hereford, then B4349.Follow signs 'Belmont Abbey/Ruckhall'
Brewery/Company Free House
Open 12-2 7-11 (closed Mon)
Restaurant 12-2 7-9 Av 3 course à la carte £22.50 Av 3 course fixed price £22.50
Accommodation (Min) s£45 d£55

The Crown & Anchor
HEREFORD

Cotts Ln, Lugwardine HR1 4AB
☎ 01432 851303

Small half-timbered pub dating from the early 18th century. There are always at least eight vegetarian dishes, such as aduki bean bake, and eight fish dishes including Lugg pike filo pastries. Meat dishes might offer chargrilled Herefordshire sirloin steak with brandied blue cheese sauce. **Principal beers:** Worthington Best, Bass, Hobsons Best.
Directions 2 miles from Hereford city centre on A438, turn left into Lugwardine down Cotts Lane
Brewery/Company Free House
Open 11.30-11
Bar food 12-2 7-10 Av main course £6

HOWLE HILL Herefordshire
Map 04 SO62

The Crown
HOWLE HILL

HR9 5SP ☎ 01989 764316

Roses round the door greet visitors to this simple 19th-century country pub nestling in a sheltered spot of this scattered hamlet. The barber visits on the first Tuesday of each month. Get a haircut or simply enjoy a homemade pie or pudding in the bar. **Principal beers:** Whitbread, Marstons Pedigree.

contd.

Directions End M50 thru Ross to B4234, 1st L after entering Walford, then 1st R signed Howle Hill
Brewery/Company Free House
Open 12-2.30 (except Tues) 7-11
Bar food 12-2 7-9.30 Av main course £5.25

KIMBOLTON Herefordshire — Map 03 SO56

Stockton Cross Inn
KIMBOLTON

HR6 0HD ☎ 01568 612509
Pretty,16th-century, black and white timbered drovers' inn featured on many calendars and chocolate boxes. Hearty lamb casserole, proper fish and chips, braised sirloin, lasagne verde, and local venison sausages are among the appetising dishes on varied blackboard menu. **Principal beers:** Castle Eden Ale, Whitbread OB Mild.
Directions On the A4112 off A49 between Leominster and Ludlow
Brewery/Company Free House
Open 12-3 7-11
Bar food 12-3 7-9.30 Av main course £6.50
Restaurant 12-3 7-11 Av 3 course à la carte £19

LEDBURY Herefordshire — Map 04 SO73

The Feathers Hotel
LEDBURY

High St HR8 1PS ☎ 01531 635266
A striking black and white Elizabethan coaching inn, with exposed beams and log fires. Quills Restaurant offers modern Anglo-French cooking, while dishes in Fuggles Brasserie include home-made salmon fishcakes, spiced coconut lamb cutlets and a strudel of roasted Mediterranean vegetables and Ricotta cheese. **Principal beers:** Worthington Best, Bass.
Directions S from Worcester A449, E from Hereford A438, N from Gloucester A417.
Brewery/Company Free House
Open 11-11 (Sun 12-10.30)
Bar food 12-2 7-9.30
Restaurant 12-2.30 7-9.30
Accommodation (Min) s£69.50 d£89.50

The Talbot
LEDBURY

14 New St HR8 2DX ☎ 01531 632963
Coaching inn set among other black and white buildings in old Ledbury (New Street was completed in the 14th century). It has a carved oak dining/function room dated 1596, with a particularly fine overmantle. Favourite dishes include venison, fillet steaks, home-made pies, fish specials, and good Sunday roasts. **Principal beers:** Fullers London Pride, Hancocks,Ledbury Northdown Winter.
Directions follow Ledbury signs, turn into Bye St, 2nd L into Woodley Rd, over bridge to jct, L into New St. Talbot on R
Brewery/Company Free House
Open 11.30-3 5-11 (Sun 12-4, 7-10.30)
Bar food 12-2.30 6.30-9.30 Av main course £4.95
Restaurant 12-2.30 6.30-9.30
Accommodation (Min) s£25 d£44.50

LEOMINSTER Herefordshire — Map 03 SO45

The Royal Oak Hotel
LEOMINSTER

South St HR6 8JA ☎ 01568 612610
A Grade II listed coaching inn dating back to before 1723 and situated in the heart of this ancient market town. After strolling the old streets, relax in the cosy bar with a pint of Woods Special and peruse the mainly traditional pub food menu. Lookout for home-made soups and pies. **Principal beers:** Brains SA Best, Woods Special Bitter.
Directions Junc A44/A49
Brewery/Company Free House
Open 10-2.30 6-10.30
Bar food 12-2 6.30-9 Av main course £4
Restaurant 12-2 6.30-9 Av 3 course à la carte £15 Av 4 course fixed price £10.25
Accommodation (Min) s£35 d£48

LITTLE COWARNE Herefordshire — Map 04 SO65

The Three Horseshoes Inn
LITTLE COWARNE

HR7 4RQ ☎ 01885 400276
One customer can still remember bringing his horse to be shod here when this quaint country inn was an ale house and blacksmith's shop. Lovely walks nearby and views of the Black Mountains. Pork Normandy, lasagne, and

a range of fish dishes with herbs from the garden may feature on the varied menu. **Principal beers:** Ruddles County, Websters Yorkshire, Marstons Pedigree.

Directions Off A456 (Hereford/Bromyard). At Stokes Cross, take turning signed Little Cowarne/Pencombe
Brewery/Company Free House
Open 11-3 6.30-11
Bar food 12-2 6.30-10 Av main course £5
Restaurant 12-2 6.30-10 Av 3 course à la carte £15 Av 3 course fixed price £7.75
Accommodation (Min) s£25 d£40

MADLEY Herefordshire *Map 03 SO43*

The Comet Inn NEW
MADLEY
Stoney St HR2 9NJ ☎ 01981 250600
Located on a prominent corner position and set in two and a half acres, this black and white 19th-century inn has beamed walls and ceilings, and a large open fire. A typical menu features double noisette of lamb loin, fresh cod in beer batter, and steak and stout pie. **Principal beers:** Hook Norton, Wye Valley.
Directions approx 6m from Hereford on the B4352
Brewery/Company Free House
Open 12-2.30 7-11
Bar food 12-2 7-9.30 Av main course £5.50
Restaurant 12-2 7-9.30 Av 3 course à la carte £18

MUCH COWARNE Herefordshire

Fir Tree Inn NEW
MUCH COWARNE
HR7 4JN ☎ 01531 640619
Set in three acres of grounds with fishing lake and small caravan site, this modernised inn is situated in unspoilt countryside between Hereford and Worcester. Look to the daily specials board for such dishes as John Dory with lemon and chive butter, home-made chicken and bacon pie, and lamb knuckle with minted gravy. **Principal beers:** Ansells, Banks, Old Sam.
Directions off the A4103 Hereford to Worcester
Brewery/Company Free House
Open 12-3 6-11
Bar food 12-2.30 6.30-10 Av main course £3.50
Restaurant 12-2.30 6.30-10 Av 3 course à la carte £12.50 Av 1 course fixed price £9.95

MUCH MARCLE Herefordshire *Map 04 SO63*

The Slip Tavern
MUCH MARCLE
Waterbury Ln HR8 2NG
☎ 01531 660246
Named after a 16th-century landslip which buried a church and a herd of cattle, this pleasant country pub sits adjacent to cider apple orchards and unspoilt countryside. Straightforward home-cooked fare includes beef in ale, chilli, faggots, a range of fresh fish and a selection of jacket potatoes and rolls. **Principal beers:** Hook Norton, Wadworth 6X.
Directions Follow the signs off the A449 at the Much Marcle junction
Brewery/Company Free House
Open 11.30-2.30 6.30-11 (Sun 12-2.30, 6.30-11)
Bar food 12-2.30 7-11 Av main course £6
Restaurant 12-2.30 7-11 Av 3 course à la carte £11

PEMBRIDGE Herefordshire *Map 03 SO35*

New Inn
PEMBRIDGE
Market Square HR6 9DZ
☎ 01544 388427
Black and white timbered 13th-century village inn with cobbled front courtyard facing the market square. Full of beams, flagstone floors and old furniture, it offers a short range of home-cooked dishes. Expect seafood stew, venison sausage with marmalade mash, beef and Guinness pie, and chicken casserole with herb dumplings. **Principal beers:** Ruddles Best & Country.

contd.

Directions From M5 J7 take A44 W through Leominster towards Llandrindod Wells
Brewery/Company Free House
Open 11-3 6-11
Bar food 12-2 7-9.30 Av main course £5.90
Restaurant 12-2 6.30-9.30
Accommodation (Min) s£18.50 d£37

ST OWEN'S CROSS Herefordshire Map 03 SO52

The New Inn
ST OWEN'S CROSS
HR2 8LQ ☎ 01989 730274
16th-century timbered coaching inn with heavily beamed interior and bread oven. Colourful hanging baskets and good views of the distant Black Mountains. Expect carved ham and deep-fried scampi and chips among the bar meals, while the candlelit restaurant offers oven-baked salmon, trout and bacon, and roast rack of lamb. **Principal beers:** Smiles, Wadworth 6X, Tetley, Bass.
Directions Off A4137 W of Ross-on-Wye
Brewery/Company Free House
Open 12-2.30 6-11
Bar food 12-2 6.30-10 Av main course £6
Restaurant 12-2 6-10 Av 3 course à la carte £17.50
Accommodation (Min) s£35 d£70

SELLACK Herefordshire Map 03 SO52

The Lough Pool Inn
SELLACK
HR9 6LX ☎ 01989 730236
Half-timbered building, dating from 1631, tucked down narroe lanes close to the River Wye. Character interior with original flagstone floor and open fireplaces. Bar food ranges from pitta pockets and ploughman's to steak and kidney pie. Restaurant specialities are beef, red wine and chestnut pie, Greek-style goat casserole, and trout with almonds. **Principal beers:** Wye Valley, John Smiths, Bass.
Directions A49 from Ross-on-Wye toward Hereford, side rd signed Sellack/Hoarwithy, pub 2m from R-on-W
Brewery/Company Free House
Open 11.30-2.30 6.30-11
Bar food 12-2 7-9.30 Av main course £5.20
Restaurant 12-2 7-9.30 Av 3 course à la carte £16

SHOBDON Herefordshire Map 03 SO46

The Bateman Arms
SHOBDON
HR6 9LX ☎ 01568 708374
Black and white coaching inn dating back 400 years. Traditional interior with open fire, wooden settles and a welcoming atmosphere. To start you might try grilled goat's cheese with bramble relish, followed by 'elegant fish and chips', steamed steak and kidney pudding, lamb steak with apple mint jelly, and home-made sticky toffee pudding. **Principal beers:** Wood Ales, Bass.
Directions On B4362 off A4110 NW of Leominster
Brewery/Company Free House
Open 12-2.30 7-11
Bar food 12-2 7-10 Av main course £7.50
Restaurant 12-2 7-10 Av 3 course à la carte £18

ULLINGSWICK Herefordshire Map 03 SO54

Three Crowns Inn
ULLINGSWICK
HR1 3JG ☎ 01432 820279
One of Herefordshire's few remaining original pubs, the 300-year-old Three Crowns Inn prides itself on an ethos of simple sophistication. The menu is always changing, but may include roast pheasant with choucroute and braised pancetta, smoked cheese and onion pudding with ratatouille, and steamed cod with butterbeans, fennel and aioli. **Principal beers:** Hobsons Best, Tetley.
Directions From Burley Gate rdbt take A465 toward Bromyard, after 2m L to Ullingswick, L after 0.5m, pub 0.5m on R
Brewery/Company Free House
Open 12-2.30 7-11 (closed Tue)
Bar food 12-2 7-10 Av main course £12.50

WALTERSTONE Herefordshire
Map 03 SO32

Carpenters Arms
WALTERSTONE

HR2 0DX ☎ 01873 890353

Dating back over 300 years, this popular Black Mountains pub retains lots of character, with beams, antique furniture and a leaded fireplace, where open fires burn all winter. The food ranges from bar snacks to home-cooked dishes such as chilli, chicken curry, plaice and steak.
Principal beers: Wadworth 6X, Worthington Best.
Directions Off the A465 between Hereford & Abergavenny at Pandy
Brewery/Company Free House
Open 11-11
Bar food 12-3 7-9.30 Av main course £5
Restaurant 12-3 7-9.30

WEOBLEY Herefordshire
Map 03 SO45

Ye Olde Salutation Inn
WEOBLEY

Market Pitch HR8 8SJ ☎ 01544 318443

Traditional black and white inn at the heart of a medieval village. The focus is on fine food, ranging from imaginative bar snacks and lounge bar specials such as fillet of cod with ratatouille, to restaurant dishes of braised guinea fowl with lardons and mushrooms, or courgette fritters with chilli sauce from the separate vegetarian carte.

Principal beers: Hook Norton Best, Fullers London Pride.
Directions In the village centre facing Broad St.
Brewery/Company Free House
Open 11-11
Bar food 12-2 7-9.30 Av main course £6.95
Restaurant 12-2 7-9 Av 3 course à la carte £23
Accommodation (Min) s£40 d£65

WHITNEY-ON-WYE Herefordshire
Map 03 SO24

Rhydspence Inn
WHITNEY-ON-WYE

HR3 6EU ☎ 01497 831262

14th-century drovers' inn on the English side of the Welsh Borders, with a spacious dining room overlooking the Wye valley. Very much a dining pub, it offers an imaginative menu ranging from sizzling Cajun chicken and Hereford rabbit, to salmon fishcakes, garlic-roasted monkfish, rack of lamb, and organic Devon sausages. **Principal beers:** Robinsons Best, Bass.
Directions N side of A438 1m W
Brewery/Company Free House
Open 11-2.30 7-11 (closed 2wks Jan)
Bar food 12-2, 7-10 Av main course £7
Restaurant 12-2 7-10 Av 3 course à la carte £22
Accommodation (Min) s£32.50 d£65

WINFORTON Herefordshire
Map 03 SO24

The Sun Inn
WINFORTON

HR3 6EA ☎ 01544 327677

18th-century Herefordshire longhouse furnished with settles, wooden armchairs, and farm implements. The notorious 'hanging Judge Jefferies' supposedly held court in Winforton. Home-made Game pie, pheasant with wild mushrooms, sea bass with saffron dressing, steak and Guinness pie and treacle tart with caramelized oranges feature on the interesting daily menus.
Principal beers: Jennings, Hook Norton, Brain's,Robinsons.
Brewery/Company Free House
Open 11-3 6.15-11 (closed Tue)
Bar food 12-2 6.45-9.30 Av main course £7.50
Restaurant 12-2 6.45-9.30 Av 3 course à la carte £17
Accommodation (Min) s£30 d£48

WOOLHOPE Herefordshire
Map 03 SO63

The Butchers Arms
WOOLHOPE

HR1 4RF ☎ 01432 860281

A black and white half-timbered building dating from the 14th century, in idyllic rural surroundings. Bar food is available

contd.

all week, and the small restaurant is open Friday and Saturday night, Sunday lunchtime, and every day in summer for lunch and dinner. The menu ranges from sandwiches to rack of lamb. **Principal beers:** Hook Norton Best & Old Hooky.
Directions Off B4224 between Hereford & Ross-on-Wye
Brewery/Company Free House
Open 11.30-3 6.30-11
Bar food 12-2.15 6.30-10 Av main course £7
Restaurant 12-2.15 7-10

The Crown Inn
WOOLHOPE
HR1 4QP ☎ 01432 860468
Stone-built inn circa 1750, which has grown with Victorian and more recent extensions. There is a beamed bar and restaurant, both serving the same menu. The home-made fare includes potted Stilton with mushrooms, grilled bacon chop with plum sauce, and treacle tart and custard. **Principal beers:** Hook Norton Best, Smiles Best.
Directions from Hereford take B4224 to Mordiford, L immediately after Moon Inn. Crown Inn is in village centre
Brewery/Company Free House
Open 12-2.30 6.30-11 (Sun till 10.30, times vary in winter)
Bar food 12-2.30 6.30/7-10 Av main course £6.95
Restaurant 12-2.30 6.30/7-10 Av 3 course à la carte £13.50

Isle of Angelsey

BEAUMARIS Isle of Anglesey
Map 06 SH67

The Liverpool Arms Hotel NEW
BEAUMARIS
Castle St LL58 8BA ☎ 01248 810362
Handsome 18th-century inn located close to Beaumaris Castle and the sea. The Admiral's Tavern bar is filled with nautical memorabilia and relics, including timbers from Nelson's Victory. Daily-changing blackboard menus offer home-made soups, pies and casseroles, alongside fresh fish in beer batter, grilled tuna, shoulder of lamb, and Welsh cheeses. **Principal beers:** Tetley.
Directions A5 across the Menai Straits, R onto A545 through Menai Bridge
Brewery/Company Free House
Open 11-11
Bar food 12-2.15 6-9.15 Av main course £5.95
Restaurant 12-2.15 6-9.15 Av 3 course à la carte £5.95 Av 3 course fixed price £10
Accommodation (Min) s£35 d£50

Ye Olde Bulls Head Inn
BEAUMARIS
Castle St LL58 8AP ☎ 01248 810329
Dating from 1472, this pub is situated near Beaumaris Castle, built by Edward I in 1295. An imaginative menu ranges from rabbit, apple and sage pie, and smoked chicken with date and orange chutney, to turbot with leeks and Menai oyster sauce. **Principal beers:** Bass, Hancocks, Worthington.
Directions From Brittania Road Bridge follow A545
Brewery/Company Free House
Open 11-11 (Sun 12-10.30)
Bar food 12-2 6-9
Restaurant 7-9.30 (not Sun)
Accommodation (Min) s£57 d£81

RED WHARF BAY Isle of Anglesey
Map 06 SH58

The Ship Inn NEW
RED WHARF BAY
LL75 8RJ ☎ 01248 852568
Low, white-painted building situated right on the shore overlooking the sweep of the bay. Quarry-tiled floors, exposed beams and stonework and maritime memorabilia make for an interesting interior in which to enjoy freshly-cut sandwiches, ham shank with horseradish and parsley sauce, Moroccan chicken with saffron rice, or sea bass with lemon butter. **Principal beers:** Friary Meux, Burton Ale.
Brewery/Company Free House
Open 11-11
Bar food 12-2.30 7-9.30 Av main course £6.50
Restaurant 7-9.30 Av 3 course à la carte £18.50

Monmouthshire

ABERGAVENNY Monmouthshire
Map 03 SO21

Clytha Arms
ABERGAVENNY
Clytha NP7 9BW ☎ 01873 840206
Replacing the old local, washed away by the Usk River in the 1940s, this former dower house became a pub in 1952.

Imaginative bar snacks include wild boar sausages, leek and laverbread rissoles, and faggots and peas. The restaurant might offer grilled queen scallops, and monkfish and shellfish with saffron potatoes. **Principal beers:** Bank's, Bass, Felinfoel Double Dragon.
Directions From A449/A40 junction (E of Abergavenny) follow signs for 'Old Road Abergavenny/Clytha'
Brewery/Company Free House
Open 12-3 6-11 (Sat 12-11)
Bar food 12.30-2.30 7-9.30 Av main course £5.50
Restaurant 12.30-2.30 7-9.30 Av 3 course à la carte £19
Accommodation (Min) s£45 d£50

Llanwenarth Arms Hotel
ABERGAVENNY
Brecon Rd NP8 1EP ☎ 01873 810550
There are splendid views of the Blorenge mountain and the Usk Valley from this 16th-century hotel, situated on the River Usk. Starters include home-made pork and liver pate, and Greek salad, followed, perhaps, by fresh hake, deep fried in batter, and roast rack of local spring lamb. **Principal beers:** Bass, Marstons Pedigree.
Directions On A40 between Abergavenny & Crickhowell

Brewery/Company Free House
Open 11-3 6-11
Bar food 12-2 7-10 Av main course £10
Restaurant 12-2 7-10 Av 3 course à la carte £19
Accommodation (Min) s£53 d£63

Walnut Tree Inn
ABERGAVENNY
Llandewi Skirrid NP7 8AW
☎ 01873 852797
This whitewashed building is no ordinary pub! A perennial favourite among food lovers the world over, Franco and Ann Tarushio's pub/restaurant offers imaginative, daily-changing menus with a distinct Mediterranean flavour. Typical dishes may include crispy crab pancake, tagliolini with Parma ham and artichokes, sea bass with wild mushrooms and pancetta, and pheasant with cabbage and quince.
Principal beers: no real ale.
Directions 3m NE of Abergavenny on B4521
Brewery/Company Free House
Open 12-4 7-12 (closed 1wk Xmas & 2wks Feb)
Restaurant 12-4.30 7-12 Av 3 course à la carte £28

BETTWS-NEWYDD Monmouthshire
Map 03 SO30

Black Bear Inn
BETTWS-NEWYDD
NP5 1JN ☎ 01873 880701
Traditional pub in the Usk Valley, with tiled floors, oak beams and a large log fire. Inventive pub food features tip-top local produce, the short, daily menu listing, perhaps, Stilton and chicken terrine, avocado with monkfish and a white wine, cream and mushroom sauce, and beef stuffed with Stilton and finished with Madeira sauce. **Principal beers:** Eccleshall Slaters, Bath SPA, Bass.
Directions Off B4598 N of Usk
Brewery/Company Free House
Open 12-2 6-12.30
Bar food 12-2 6-12.30 Av main course £10
Restaurant 12-2 6-12.30 Av 3 course à la carte £23

CHEPSTOW Monmouthshire
Map 03 ST59

Castle View Hotel
CHEPSTOW

16 Bridge St NP6 5EZ ☎ 01291 620349
Originally a private residence called Woodfield House, whose first owner was the local factory manager, this 300-year-old building is close to Chepstow Castle. Its main course options range from fillet steak bordelaise, and poached darne of salmon in lemon butter sauce, to duck marinated in soy, ginger and garlic.
Principal beers: Tetley.
Directions Opposite Chepstow Castle
Brewery/Company Free House
Open 12-2.30 6-11
Bar food 12-2.30 6.30-9.30 Av main course £3.95

contd.

Restaurant 12-2 6.30-9.30 Av 3 course à la carte £14.95 Av 3 course fixed price £14.95
Accommodation (Min) s£39.95 d£49.95

LLANTRISANT Monmouthshire
Map 03 ST39

Greyhound Inn
LLANTRISANT
NP5 1LE ☎ 01291 672505 & 673447
A 17th-century longhouse with two acres of landscaped gardens, including a pond with a fountain. Lovely beer garden for summer drinking, and in winter there are three log fires in the welcoming bars. A good range of home-cooked dishes includes ploughman's, fresh fish and Welsh steaks. **Principal beers:** Flowers Original, Marstons Pedigree, Wadworth 6X, Greene King Abbot Ale.
Directions From M4 take A449 towards Monmouth, 1st jct to Usk, L into Usk Sq. Take 2nd L signed Llantrisant. 2.5m to inn
Brewery/Company Free House
Open 11-11
Bar food 11.45-2.15 6-10.30 Av main course £6
Accommodation (Min) s£48 d£62

LLANVAPLEY Monmouthshire
Map 03 SO31

Red Hart Inn
LLANVAPLEY
NP7 8SN ☎ 01600 780227
An old fashioned country pub, where families are welcome, opposite the 12th-century parish church. Home cooked food with an international flavour is served, including Italian, Indian, and Thai-style dishes. A particular favourite is the high quality chargrilled rump steak. **Principal beers:** Bass, Cottage Brewery - Golden Arrow & Southern Bitter.
Directions On B4233 E of Abergavenny
Brewery/Company Free House
Open 12-3 7-11 (not Tue)
Bar food 12-2 7-9
Restaurant 12-2 7-9 Av 3 course à la carte £13

For Pubs with AA food rosettes see page 430

PENALLT Monmouthshire
Map 03 SO51

The Boat Inn
PENALLT
Lone Ln NP5 4AJ ☎ 01600 712615
Dating back over 350 years, this pub has served as a hostelry for quarry, mill, paper and tin mine workers, and even had a landlord operating a ferry across the Wye at shift times. Extensive choice of main meals are offered with dishes such as fish pie, moussaka, and pork chilli. **Principal beers:** Theakston Old Peculiar, Freeminer Speculation, Wadworth 6X, Fuller London Pride.
Directions From Monmouth take A466.In Redbrook the pub car park is signposted. Park & walk across rail bridge over R Wye
Brewery/Company Free House
Open 11.30-3 6-11 (Sat 11-11, Sun 12-10.30 - food all day)
Bar food 12-2.30 6-9.30 Av main course £5.25

SHIRENEWTON Monmouthshire
Map 03 ST49

The Carpenters Arms
SHIRENEWTON
Usk Rd NP6 6BU ☎ 01291 641231
A 400-year-old hostelry, formerly a smithy and carpenter's shop, with flagstone floors, open fires and a pleasant wooded valley location near the Wye and Usk valleys. Straightforward bar food includes steak and mushroom pie, game pie, salmon, and chicken in leek and Stilton sauce. **Principal beers:** Fullers London Pride, Wadworth 6X, Marstons Pedigree, Taylor Landlord.

Directions M48 J2 take A48 to Chepstow then A4661, B4235.Village 3m on L
Brewery/Company Free House
Open 11-2.30 6-11
Bar food 12-2 7-9.30 Av main course £5

Tredegar Arms
SHIRENEWTON
The Square NP6 6RQ ☎ 01291 641274
Curios, farm implements and a sugar tong collection decorate the interior of this welcoming, old fashioned, village square local. Snack on a granary sandwich (hot lamb and mint) or choose home-cooked poacher's pot, 'Bullyhole' pepper pot pie, pheasant in shallot and port sauce, or king prawns in garlic and cream. **Principal beers:** Hancocks HB, Hook Norton, Bass, Tomos Watkin.
Directions From Chepstow B4235, L towards Caldicot
Brewery/Company Free House
Open 12-3 6-11.30
Bar food 12-3 6.45-9.30 Av main course £8
Restaurant 12-3 6.45-9.30 Av 3 course à la carte £12
Accommodation (Min) s£25 d£40

TAL-Y-COED Monmouthshire *Map 03 SO41*

The Halfway House Inn
TAL-Y-COED
NP7 8TL ☎ 01600 780269
Originally a drovers' inn dating from the 17th century, this handsome, wisteria-clad inn is situated in tranquil countryside within easy reach of the Wye Valley and the Brecon Beacons. Traditional home-produced food ranges from soup and sandwiches, to steaks, venison in red wine, beef Wellington, and lamb in herb sauce.
Principal beers: Felinfoel, Bass.
Directions On B4233 (between Abergavenny & Monmouth)
Brewery/Company Free House
Open 12-3 6-11
Bar food 12-2 7-10 Av main course £4
Restaurant 12-2 7-10 Av 3 course à la carte £12
Accommodation (Min) s£18.50 d£37

TRELLECK Monmouthshire *Map 03 SO50*

The Lion Inn
TRELLECK
NP5 4PA ☎ 01600 860322
Located opposite the church and reputedly haunted, this former brew and coach house offers traditional pub food. Choices range from home-made lasagne, ham, egg and chips, ploughman's and freshly-cut sandwiches on the printed menu, to specials like pork and rosemary pie, chicken tarragon, and mixed grill.
Principal beers: Bass, Bath Ales, SP Sporting Ales, Wadworth 6X.
Directions From A40 just south of Monmouth take B4293 and follow signs for Trelleck
Brewery/Company Free House
Open 12-3 6-11 (Mon 7-11; closed Sun eve)
Bar food 12-3 6-9.30 Av main course £5.50
Restaurant 12-3 6-9.30 Av 3 course à la carte £15

USK Monmouthshire *Map 03 SO30*

The Nags Head Inn
USK
Twyn Square NP5 1BH ☎ 01291 672820
Flower-adorned 15th-century inn overlooking the town square and just a short stroll from the River Usk. Local game in season, including pheasant cooked in port, and wild Usk salmon are specialities on the menu. Regular dishes include steak pie, ham platter and chicken in red wine, followed by home-made apple pie. **Principal beers:** Brains-Bitter, Dark, Buckleys Best & Reverend James.
Directions On A472
Brewery/Company Free House
Open 10-3 5.30-11
Bar food 10-3 5.30-10.30 Av main course £5.50
Restaurant 10-3 5.30-10.30 Av 3 course à la carte £12 Av 3 course fixed price £12
Accommodation (Min) s£16 d£32

Pembrokeshire

AMROTH Pembrokeshire *Map 02 SN10*

The New Inn
AMROTH
SA67 8NW ☎ 01834 812368
400-year-old coaching inn, once the haunt of smugglers, with an inglenook fireplace and a splendid Flemish chimney. Close to sandy beaches safe for bathing. Popular dishes from the bar menu include fresh local lobster and crab, home-made lasagne, steak and kidney pie, home-baked ham, and Pembrokeshire turkey. **Principal beers:** Burton, Tetley.

contd.

Directions A48 to Carmarthen, A40 to St Clears, A477 to Llanteg then L
Brewery/Company Free House
Open 11.30-3 5.30-11 (closed Nov-Mar)
Bar food 12-2 6-9 Av main course £5
Restaurant 12-2 6-9

CAREW Pembrokeshire Map 02 SN00

Carew Inn
CAREW
SA70 8SL ☎ 01646 651267

A traditional stone-built country inn situated opposite the Carew Celtic cross and Norman castle, which is a regular venue for activities by 'The Sealed Knot'. A typical menu included pork tenderloin in mustard sauce, Scottish salmon fillet with chive sauce, potato, leek and mushroom pie, and tagliatelle with Stilton sauce. **Principal beers:** Crown Buckley Reverend James, Worthington, guest ale.
Directions From A477 take A4075. Inn 400yds opp castle & celtic cross
Brewery/Company Free House
Open 12-2.30 4.30-11 (Summer 11-11)
Bar food 12-2 6.30-9 Av main course £5.95

CILGERRAN Pembrokeshire Map 02 SN14

Pendre Inn
CILGERRAN
Pendre SA43 ☎ 01239 614223

A 14th-century inn located close to the impressive Cilgerran Castle, the amazingly quiet Cilgerran Gorge with the River Teifi flowing through, and a National Trust wildlife park. Local produce is used to good effect on a menu that might include trout with onion and honey cream. **Principal beers:** Bass, Worthington, Thomas Watkins.
Directions Off A478 south of Cardigan
Brewery/Company Free House
Open 11.30-11.30 (Winter 11.30-3, 6-11.30; food all day)

LAMPHEY Pembrokeshire Map 02 SN00

The Dial Inn
LAMPHEY
The Ridgeway SA71 5NU
☎ 01646 672426

Friendly village pub, built as a dower house for the local squire. Interesting food ranges from Welsh cawl served with farmhouse cheese, and sewin with laverbread in the homely bar, to duck with jasmine, cherry brandy and kumquat sauce, or Welsh black beef with carmelised shallots and Madeira in the restaurant.
Principal beers: Hancocks HB, Bass.
Directions Just off A4139 (Tenby to Pembroke rd)
Brewery/Company Free House
Open 11-3 6-11
Bar food 12-2 7-9 Av main course £6.50
Restaurant 12-2 7-9 Av 3 course à la carte £16

LANDSHIPPING Pembrokeshire Map 02 SN01

The Stanley Arms
LANDSHIPPING
SA67 8BE ☎ 01834 891227

Admire the views of Picton Castle and the Cleddau Estuary from the garden of this 200-year-old building, with its summer flower-adorned façade, and original slate floor in the public bar. Home-cooked pub food includes Welsh lamb casserole, honey-roast ham, liver and bacon hotpot, and raspberry meringue roulade. **Principal beers:** Worthington, Bass, Greene King Abbot Ale.
Directions Off A40 at Canaston Bridge onto A4075, R at Cross Hands
Brewery/Company Free House
Open 12-3 6-11
Bar food 12-3 6.30-9.15 Av main course £5.50

LETTERSTON Pembrokeshire Map 02 SM92

The Harp Inn
LETTERSTON
31 Haverfordwest Rd SA62 5UA
☎ 01348 840061

The inn offers an extensive and attractively priced bar food menu. The restaurant, with its lovely inglenook fireplace, features an impressive range of fresh fish, including sea bass and local plaice. Other options may include venison, goose breast with port and pear sauce, or a choice of popular steak dishes.
Directions Located on main A40
Brewery/Company Free House
Open 11-3 6-11

Bar food 12-2.30 6-9.30 Av main course £5.95
Restaurant 6.30-9.30 Av 3 course à la carte £15

NEVERN Pembrokeshire *Map 02 SN04*

Trewern Arms
NEVERN
SA42 0NB ☎ 01239 820395

Handsome, ivy-clad 16th-century inn set in attractive grounds astride the River Nevern. The public bar, 'The Brew House' is a popular local, with original flagstone floors and old settles. Local salmon with a whisky and honey sauce, sirloin steak, and Preseli lamb with redcurrant and rosemary sauce are favoured dishes.
Principal beers: Flowers Original, Whitbread Castle Eden Ale, Wadworth 6X.
Directions On the A487 between Cardigan and Fishguard
Brewery/Company Free House
Open 11-3 6-11
Bar food 12-3 6-8.45 Av main course £6.50
Restaurant 12-1.45 7-8.45 Av 3 course à la carte £18
Accommodation (Min) s£35 d£50

PEMBROKE DOCK Pembrokeshire *Map 02 SM90*

Ferry Inn
PEMBROKE DOCK
Pembroke Ferry SA72 6UD
☎ 01646 682947

Creeper-clad,16th-century riverside inn situated under Cleddau Bridge with splendid views across the estuary from the nautical themed bar, and waterside terrace. Expect good fresh local fish, perhaps cod and sea bass, pork schnitzel, home-cured ham, and lamb kebabs marinated in honey and mint on the menu. **Principal beers:** Hancocks HB, Bass.
Directions A477, off A48, R at garage, signs for Cleddau Bridge, L at roundabout
Brewery/Company Free House
Open 11.30-2.45 7-11
Bar food 12-2 7-10 Av main course £6.25

Pubs offering a good choice of seafood on the menu

PORTHGAIN Pembrokeshire *Map 02 SM83*

The Sloop Inn
PORTHGAIN
SA62 5BN ☎ 01348 831449

Popular, long and low pub dating from 1743 and set in a tiny coastal hamlet with wonderful cliff scenery. Porthgain crab salad, moules marinière and fresh local fish are offered alongside home-made chilli, lasagne and various pies in the spacious bar, and there are options such as grilled swordfish, or sirloin steak in the restaurant. **Principal beers:** Felinfoel, Worthington, Brains SA.
Brewery/Company Free House
Open 11-11 (Sun 12-4, 6-10.30)
Bar food 12-2.30 6-9.30 Av main course £5.40
Restaurant 12-2.30 6-9.30 Av 3 course à la carte £13.80

ROSEBUSH Pembrokeshire *Map 02 SN02*

Tates at Tafarn Newydd
ROSEBUSH
SA66 7RA ☎ 01437 532542

The oldest part of this former farmhouse and drovers' inn dates back to the 17th-century. Charming unspoilt interior and interesting pub food, perhaps including mushroom and pistachio pâté, crostini of smoked salmon and goat's cheese, Tuscan-style beef casserole, and monkfish with mint and saffron cream sauce. For pudding try the lemon fudge tart.
Principal beers: Wye Valley.
Directions From A40 between Haverfordwest & Camarthen take B4313 N
Brewery/Company Free House
Open 12-3.30 6-11 (closed Tue & 2wks mid Jan)
Bar food 12-2 7-9 Av main course £7.25
Restaurant 12-2 7-9 Av 3 course à la carte £21

SOLVA Pembrokeshire *Map 02 SM82*

The Cambrian Inn
SOLVA
Main St SA62 6UU ☎ 01437 721210

In an attractive coastal village, this listed 17th-century pub features beams, open coal fires and a cosy atmosphere. Large patio area for summer imbibing. Home-made dishes with an Italian influence are prepared with local produce and may

contd.

include fish chowder, crab thermidor, chicken cacciatore, lamb cobbler and Welsh black steak. **Principal beers:** Worthington Best, Marstons Pedigree.
Directions 13m from Haverfordwest on the St David's Rd
Brewery/Company Free House
Open 12-3 7-11
Bar food 12-2 7-9.30 Av main course £5.50
Restaurant 12-2 7-9.30 Av 3 course à la carte £16.25 Av 2 course fixed price £6

STACKPOLE Pembrokeshire — Map 02 SR99

Armstrong Arms
STACKPOLE
SA71 5DF ☎ 01646 672324
On the edge of the Stackpole Estate (NT), close to the coast path, this delightful pub began life as the village post office. Slate floors, stone walls and an inglenook fireplace complete the picture. The menu might offer marinated monkfish with tomato sauce, and delicious home-made puddings such as banoffee pie or cheesecake. **Principal beers:** Brains Buckleys Reverend James & Buckleys Best, Wells Bombardier.
Directions From Pembroke take B4319 & follow signs for Stackpole
Brewery/Company Free House
Open 11-11 (winter 11-3, 7-11)
Bar food 12-2.30 7-9.30
Restaurant 12-2.30 7-9.30

WOLF'S CASTLE Pembrokeshire — Map 02 SM92

The Wolfe Inn
WOLF'S CASTLE
SA62 5LS ☎ 01437 741662
An old farmhouse (reputedly haunted) with low doorways and beamed ceilings. Promising food includes home-made sausages and mash, and smoked haddock with scrambled egg in the bar, with Welsh lamb and black beef fillet, and local trout, lobster and crab featuring on the interesting restaurant menu.
Principal beers: Worthington, guest beers.
Directions On A40 between Haverfordwest and Fishguard
Brewery/Company Free House
Open 11-3 6.30-11.30
Bar food 12-2 7-9 Av main course £5
Restaurant 12-2 7-9 Av 3 course à la carte £20
Accommodation (Min) s£25 d£40

Powys

BERRIEW Powys — Map 07 SJ10

Lion Hotel
BERRIEW
SY21 8PQ ☎ 01686 640452
Expect a friendly family welcome at this 17th-century timbered inn situated in a pretty black and white village. From traditional bar snacks, the bistro menu, supplemented by daily fish options and chef's specials, may offer shoulder of Welsh lamb with herbs and garlic, and pan-fried peppered salmon with lemon and herb hollandaise. **Principal beers:** Bass, Worthington, Morland Old Speckled Hen, Shepherd Neame Spitfire.
Directions 5m from Welshpool on A483, R to Berriew. Centre of village next to church.
Brewery/Company Free House
Open 11.30-3 5.30-11
Bar food 12-2 7-8.45 Av main course £8.95
Restaurant 12-2 7-8.45 Av 3 course à la carte £19 Av 3 course fixed price £9.95
Accommodation (Min) s£40 d£80

CARNO Powys — Map 06 SN99

Aleppo Merchant Inn
CARNO
SY17 5LL ☎ 01686 420210
Named after his ship by a a retired sea captain, this 17th-century stone-built inn is located in beautiful countryside between the Snowdonia and Brecon Beacons National Parks. Modernised bar with open fire and simple, home-cooked pub food such as lasagne, seafood Creole and game pie.
Principal beers: Boddingtons.
Directions From Newtown, A489 and A470
Brewery/Company Whitbread
Open 11.30-2.30 6-11
Bar food 11.30-2 6.30-9 Av main course £6.50
Restaurant 11.30-2 6.30-9 Av 3 course à la carte £11
Accommodation (Min) s£30 d£45

COEDWAY Powys Map 07 SJ31

Ye Old Hand and Diamond
COEDWAY

SY5 9AR] ☎ 01743 884379

Close to the Shropshire border and the River Severn, this 19th-century inn still retains much of its original character and has had the same chef for around twenty years. Typical menu includes Welsh lamb chops, wild rabbit with game sauce, venison, pheasant, and grilled trout and almonds.

Principal beers: Bass, Worthington.
Brewery/Company Free House
Open 11-11
Bar food 11-3 6-10 Av main course £8

CRICKHOWELL Powys Map 03 SO21

The Bear
CRICKHOWELL

Brecon Rd NP8 1BW ☎ 01873 810408

Dating from the 15th century, The Bear is still a hub of community life in this small market town in the Brecon National Park. Typical fare may include fillet of cod on a bed of spinach, braised hock of Welsh lamb, goats' cheese and fried onion pie, and bread and butter pudding with rum and bananas served with brown bread ice cream.

Principal beers: Bass, Ruddles Best, Ruddles County, John Smiths.

Directions On A40 between Abergavenny & Brecon
Brewery/Company Free House
Open 10-3 6-12
Bar food 12-3 6-12 Av main course £8
Restaurant 12-3 7-12 Av 3 course à la carte £25
Accommodation (Min) s£42 d£56

Gliffaes Country House Hotel
CRICKHOWELL

NP8 1RH ☎ 01874 730371

Family-owned country house - a Victorian Italianate mansion - set in dramatic countryside with the River Usk rolling through the extensive grounds. Expect some accomplished cooking, the interesting menu listing, perhaps, lambs' liver with mustard mash, pheasant supreme, and seared salmon with lemon butter sauce. Sandwiches and light lunch menu in the bar.

Principal beers: John Smiths.
Directions 1m off the A40, 2.5m W of Crickhowell
Brewery/Company Free House
Open 12-3 6-11
Bar food 12-2.30
Restaurant 7.30-9.15 Av 3 course fixed price £23.50
Accommodation (Min) s£50.35 d£60.70

Nantyffin Cider Mill
CRICKHOWELL

Brecon Rd NP8 1SG ☎ 01873 810775

16th-century drovers' inn and cider mill situated in the beautiful Usk Valley, close to the Brecon Beacons. Character beamed interior, and an interesting modern menu which makes good use of fish and game. Expect salmon and spinach fishcakes, shank of Welsh lamb with rosemary and garlic sauce, and Brecon venison with cassis and red wine sauce.

Principal beers: Morland Old Speckled Hen, Shepherd Neame Spitfire.
Directions At junction of A40 & A479, 1.5m west of Crickhowell
Brewery/Company Free House
Open 12-2.30 6-11 (closed Mon, 1st wks Nov & Jan)
Bar food 12-2.30 6.30-9.30 Av main course £7.50
Restaurant 12-2.30 6.30-9.30 Av 3 course à la carte £20

CWMDU Powys *Map 03 SO12*

The Farmers Arms NEW
CWMDU

NP8 1RU ☎ 01874 730464

Handy for exploring the surrounding Black Mountains, this unpretentious stone village inn is fast attracting discerning diners for the imaginative home-cooked food. From carrot and coriander soup and Llanboidy and laverbread soufflé, the blackboard menu may list sea bream with tomato and basil butter, duck with beetroot compôte and Cumberland sauce, and chocolate briôche pudding. **Principal beers:** Uley Old Spot Prize Ale, Tomos Watkin OSB, SP Sporting Ales, Wye Valley Dorothy Goodbody.

Directions From A40 take A479 signed Builth Wells, Cwmdu is 3m along this road
Brewery/Company Free House
Open 11-3 6-11 (Mon pm only in winter)
Bar food 12-2.30 Av main course £5.95
Restaurant 12-2.30 7-9.30 Av 3 course à la carte £17 Av 3 course fixed price £15
Accommodation (Min) s£20 d£30

ELAN VILLAGE Powys *Map 03 SN96*

Elan Valley Hotel
ELAN VILLAGE

LD6 5HN ☎ 01597 810448

Situated on the doorstep of the lovely Elan Valley, this Victorian fishing lodge welcomes locals and tourists alike. Snacks are served in the bar, and there is a separate children's menu. Restaurant dishes include fish soup, rack of Welsh lamb and aubergine and mushroom moussaka. **Principal beers:** Hancocks HB, Brains Buckley Reverand James, Morland Old Speckled Hen,Watkin OSB.

Directions A44 to Rhayader then B4518 for 2m
Brewery/Company Free House
Open 6-11 (weekends 11.30-3.30, 6-11) (Etr-Nov 1/2term 11.30-3.30 Tue-Sun)
Bar food 12-2.30 6-9.30 Av main course £5.50
Restaurant 7-9 Av 3 course à la carte £15
Accommodation (Min) s£30 d£50

HAY-ON-WYE Powys *Map 03 SO24*

The Famous Old Black Lion
HAY-ON-WYE

Lion St HR35 5AD ☎ 01497 820841

Part 14th-century coaching inn with bags of old- world charm and some first-rate cooking served in the beamed and panelled bar and Cromwell Restaurant. In addition to salads, ploughman's, pasta and steaks, the extensive menu may offer Loch Fyne oysters, spicy peppered venison, sea bream with sage and garlic sauce, followed by tangy lemon posset.

Principal beers: Old Black Lion Ale, Wadworth 6X.
Directions Town centre
Brewery/Company Free House
Open 11-11
Bar food 12.30-2.30 7-9.30
Restaurant 12.30-2.30 7-11 Av 3 course à la carte £20
Accommodation (Min) s£28 d£55

Kilverts Inn
HAY-ON-WYE

The Bullring HR3 5AG ☎ 01497 821042

Stone-built hotel, named after the famous diarist, Reverend Kilvert, who lived and worked in the area. It has an oak-beamed bar and a restaurant with a jazz scene mural. Pizza and pasta are features of the bar menu, while the restaurant offers Welsh lamb and plenty of fresh fish. **Principal beers:** Hancock's HB, Bass, Highgate Saddlers Best.

Directions From A50 take A49, then L onto B4348 into Hay-on-Wye. In town centre near Butter Market
Brewery/Company Free House
Open 11-11
Bar food 12-2 7-9.30 Av main course £8
Restaurant 7-9.30 Av 3 course à la carte £17.50
Accommodation (Min) s£30 d£60

LLANDINAM Powys *Map 06 SO08*

The Lion Hotel NEW
LLANDINAM
SY17 5BY ☎ 01686 688233

Llandinam is perhaps best known as the home of the first electric light in Wales. It was also a centre for Welsh girl guides, while The Lion itself is a centre for international para and hang-gliding. It also occupies an attractive riverside setting. Menu includes lasagne, mushroom pie and grilled gammon. **Principal beers:** Tetley.
Directions on the A470 midway between Newtown and Llanidloes
Brewery/Company Free House
Open 12-3 6.30-11
Bar food 12-3 Av main course £5.75
Restaurant 12-3 6.30-11 Av 3 course à la carte £13
Accommodation (Min) s£30 d£30

LLANDRINDOD WELLS Powys *Map 03 SO06*

The Bell Country Inn NEW
LLANDRINDOD WELLS
Llanyre LD1 6DY ☎ 01597 823959

Standing in the hills above Llandrindod Wells, and within easy reach of the Elan and Upper Wye valleys, this former 18th-century drover's inn offers comfortable accommodation and a varied menu. Look to the specials board for such dishes as oven-baked sea bass, beef with whisky and Drambuie sauce, salmon supreme and pan-fried venison. **Principal beers:** Worthington, Bass.
Directions 1 1/2m NW of Llandrindod Wells on the A4081
Brewery/Company Free House
Open 11-3 6-11
Bar food 12-2 6.30-9.30 Av main course £6.25
Restaurant 12-2 6.30-9.30 Av 3 course à la carte £20
Accommodation (Min) s£36 d£49.50

LLANFYLLIN Powys *Map 06 SJ11*

Cain Valley Hotel
LLANFYLLIN
High St SY22 5AQ ☎ 01691 648366

A 17th-century coaching inn with a Jacobean staircase and an attractive restaurant with all original beams and brickwork. Snacks, steaks and pies are served in the bar, while the restaurant offers trout fillet with white wine and cream sauce and Welsh lamb with honey and rosemary. **Principal beers:** Worthington, Ansells.
Directions from Shrewsbury & Oswestry follow signs for Lake Vyrnwy & onto A490 to Llanfyllin.Hotel on R
Brewery/Company Free House
Open 11.30-11 (Sun 12-10.30)
Bar food 12-2 7-9 Av main course £5.75
Restaurant 12-2 7-9 Av 3 course à la carte £18
Accommodation (Min) s£36 d£59

The Stumble Inn NEW
LLANFYLLIN
Bwlch-y-Cibau SY22 5LL
☎ 01691 648860

Standing opposite the church in a rural farming hamlet in unspoilt mid-Wales countryside close to Lake Vyrnwy, this popular stone-built inn offers a traditional pub atmosphere and food. From ploughman's, chicken curry and steak in the bar, the monthly restaurant menu may list beef goulash and Welsh lamb steak. **Principal beers:** Tetley, Calders.

Directions A458 to Welshpool, B4393 to Four Crosses and Llansantfraid, A495 Melford, A490 to Bwlch-y-Cibau
Brewery/Company Free House
Open 11-3 6-12 (closed Mon)
Bar food 12-2 6-9 Av main course £7
Restaurant 12-2 6-10 Av 3 course à la carte £20

LLANGATTOCK Powys *Map 03 SO21*

The Vine Tree Inn
LLANGATTOCK
The Legar NP8 1HG ☎ 01873 810514
Situated in the beautiful Usk Valley overlooking the medieval bridge, the Vine Tree is predominantly a dining pub. Traditional, freshly prepared food includes stockpot soup, chicken and ham pie, venison casserole, and monkfish in a white wine, Pernod and leek sauce. Baguettes and ploughman's available lunchtimes only. **Principal beers:** Flowers IPA, Boddingtons, Wadworth 6X.
Directions Take A40 W from Abergavenny then A4077 from Crickhowell
Brewery/Company Free House
Open 12-2.30 6-11
Bar food 12-2.30 6-10

LLOWES Powys *Map 03 SO14*

The Radnor Arms NEW
LLOWES
HR3 5JA ☎ 01497 847460
Fine 400-year-old stone building, formerly a drovers' inn, enjoying stunning views of the Wye Valley and Black Mountains. Freshly-cooked food is served in the small bar with its open fire, friendly atmosphere and blackboard menu. Typical dishes include cod and chips, lemon sole, marinated venison, and various filled rolls and ploughman's.
Directions A438 Brecon-Hereford Rd between Glasbury & Clyro
Brewery/Company Free House
Open 11-2.15 6.30-10 (closed Mon ex BHs & 2 wks Nov)
Bar food 12-3 6.30-11 Av main course £7.50
Restaurant 12-3 6.30-11 Av 3 course à la carte £10 Av 3 course fixed price £13.50

LLYSWEN Powys *Map 03 SO13*

The Griffin Inn
LLYSWEN
LD3 0UR ☎ 01874 754241
15th-century ivy-clad sporting inn, popular with anglers who fish the River Wye nearby. Beamed bars, large inglenook fireplace and displays of fishing memorabilia. Impressive menus might include braised knuckle of Welsh lamb, crispy duck on apple and onion compôte, pheasant with quince jelly, and bread and butter pudding. Well-chosen list of wines. **Principal beers:** Tomos Watkin, Flowers IPA, Robinsons, Brains Buckley Reverend James.
Directions On A470 (Brecon to Builth Wells rd)
Brewery/Company Free House
Open 12-3 7-11
Bar food 12-2 7-9 Av main course £9.90
Restaurant 12-2 7-9 Av 3 course à la carte £17
Accommodation (Min) s£45 d£55

MACHYNLLETH Powys *Map 06 SH70*

Dolbrodmaeth Inn
MACHYNLLETH
Dinas Mawddwy SY20 9LP
☎ 01650 531333
Much restored and modernised late 19th-century inn set in the tranquil Dovey valley amid spectacular mountain scenery. The inn is popular with anglers and has its own fishing club. Menu features locally-sourced beef and lamb steaks, a comprehensive range of fresh fish dishes, and a good vegetarian selection. **Principal beers:** Tetley, Ansells, Calders.

Directions A54 to A458, W to jct with A470, R for 0.5m, edge of Dinas Mawddwy on L between road & river
Brewery/Company Free House
Open 11-11 (out of season 7-11 only)
Bar food 12-2 7-9 Av main course £4.50
Restaurant 7-9 Av 3 course à la carte £9
Accommodation (Min) s£40 d£63

MONTGOMERY Powys *Map 07 SO29*

Dragon Hotel
MONTGOMERY
SY15 6PA ☎ 01686 668359
Parts of this old coaching inn date from the mid 1600s. The local hangman used to sit in the restaurant and watch the gallows being built - his signature is on

the window. Typical bar food is served, and the restaurant might offer escalopes of pork with prune and Armagnac sauce.

Principal beers: Flowers IPA, Wood Special.
Directions A483 toward Welshpool, R onto B4386 then B4385, Behind the town hall
Brewery/Company Free House
Open 8am-11pm
Bar food 12-2 7-9 Av main course £8
Restaurant 12-2 7-9 Av 3 course à la carte £17.95 Av 3 course fixed price £17.95
Accommodation (Min) s£44 d£74

NEW RADNOR Powys *Map 03 SO26*

Red Lion Inn
NEW RADNOR
Llanfihangel-nant-Melan LD8 2TN
☎ 01544 350220
Whitewashed, slate-roofed drovers' inn, circa 16th century, retaining much of its original character. Above-average pub food, prepared from fresh local ingredients, is offered in throughout the simply furnished interior. Expect Red Lion pâté, parsnip and apple soup, Welsh lamb cutlets with rowan jelly, peppered duck, and various fish and game dishes. **Principal beers:** Hook Norton.
Directions A483 to Crossgates then R onto A44
Brewery/Company Free House
Open 12-2.30 (Sun only) 7-11 (closed Tue in winter, 1 wk Nov)
Restaurant 12-2.30 7-11
Accommodation (Min) s£20 d£40

OLD RADNOR Powys *Map 03 SO25*

Harp Inn NEW
OLD RADNOR
LD8 2RH ☎ 01544 350655
Wonderful views across the Radnor Valley are offered from this renovated 15th-century pub set on a high hillside by a churchyard. Tuck into a hearty home-made steak and ale pie or, perhaps, moussaka, vegetable curry, fish and chips, or soup and sandwiches in the three beamed and flagstone floored interlinked rooms. **Principal beers:** Shepherd Neame, Batemans, Robinsons, Brains.
Directions A44 from Leominster to Gore, then L to Old Radnor
Brewery/Company Free House
Open 12-3 (Fri-Sat only) 6-11
Bar food 12-2 7-10 Av main course £4.50
Restaurant 12-2 7-10 Av 3 course à la carte £14
Accommodation (Min) s£30 d£45

PENYBONT Powys *Map 03 SO16*

Severn Arms Hotel
PENYBONT
LD1 5UA ☎ 01597 851224 & 851344
White-painted 19th-century coaching inn at the heart of the Ithon Valley. Much loved by J B Priestley, it features exposed timbers and beams throughout, and makes a comfortable base from which to explore mid Wales. Traditional bar food includes home-made steak and kidney pie and lasagne; separate restaurant carte. **Principal beers:** Bass, Worthingtons, Brain.

Directions On A44 at Jct with A488
Brewery/Company Free House
Open 11-2.30 6-11
Bar food 11-2.30 6-11 Av main course £4.60
Restaurant 11-1.45 6.30-8.45 Av 3 course à la carte £17.30 Av 4 course fixed price £13.90
Accommodation (Min) s£28 d£50

PWLLGLOYW Powys — Map 03 SO03

Seland Newydd
PWLLGLOYW

LD3 9PY ☎ 01874 690282

Simple, traditional, 16th-century village pub, offering seafood chowder, wild mushroom tortellini with tomato, onion and garlic sauce, and salmon fishcakes in the rustic bar. Cooking shifts up a gear in the restaurant where you may find stuffed quail with balsamic vinaigrette, monkfish with mussel, white wine and dill sauce, and a sublime coffee cheesecake on the daily menu. **Principal beers:** Worthington Best, Courage Directors.

Directions 4m N of Brecon on B4520 to Builth Wells, 1m before Lower Chapel
Brewery/Company Free House
Open 11-3 6-11
Bar food 12-2 6.30-9 Av main course £7.95
Restaurant 12.30-2 7-9 Av 3 course à la carte £21 Av 5 course fixed price £24.95

TALYBONT-ON-USK Powys — Map 03 SN12

Star Inn
TALYBONT-ON-USK

LD3 7YX ☎ 01874 676635

Traditional 200-year-old village pub located beside the River Usk and the Monmouth & Brecon Canal; popular with walkers. Other than its position, the appeal is the choice of real ales (12), and the hearty bar food. Home-made choices include carbonnade of beef, lambs' liver casserole, Hungarian pork goulash, and decent ploughman's lunches. **Principal beers:** Felinfoel Double Dragon, Theakston Old Peculiar, Freeminer Best, Bullmastiff Best.

Brewery/Company Free House
Open 11-3 6-11
Bar food 12-2.15 6.30-9.30 Av main course £5
Accommodation (Min) s£25 d£45

TRECASTLE Powys — Map 03 SN82

Castle Coaching Inn
TRECASTLE

LD3 8UH ☎ 01874 636354

Fine 17th-century inn with many original features located on the old coaching route through the Brecons. Good food ranges from lunchtime sandwiches, oven-baked lasagne and steak and kidney pie in the bar, to pork fillet with Dijon mustard sauce, and roast saddle of Welsh lamb with port and rosemary sauce served in the dining room. **Principal beers:** Greene King Abbot Ale, Adnam's Broadside, Fuller's London Pride, Shepherd Neame Spitfire.

Directions On A40 W of Brecon
Brewery/Company Free House
Open 12-3 6-11
Bar food 12-2 6.30-9.30 Av main course £6.50
Restaurant 6.30-9.30 Av 3 course à la carte £20 Av 3 course fixed price £22
Accommodation (Min) s£40 d£45

Shropshire

BISHOP'S CASTLE Shropshire — Map 07 SO38

The Three Tuns Inn NEW
BISHOP'S CASTLE

Salop St SY9 5BW ☎ 01588 638797

The Three Tuns not only serves traditional real ales brewed at its own brewery across the yard, but also has a little museum dedicated to the history of brewing. An ideal stop for the thirsty walker. The kitchen specialises in using local produce, and organic vegetables, game and fish. **Principal beers:** Three Tuns Sexton, Tuns Offa's Ale, & Tuns XXX.

Directions 22m W of Shrewsbury
Brewery/Company Free House
Open 12-3 5-11 (12-11 Fri-Sun)
Bar food 12-2.30 7-9.30 Av main course £8
Accommodation (Min) s£55 d£75

BRIDGNORTH Shropshire — Map 07 SO79

The Lion O'Morfe
BRIDGNORTH

Upper Farmcote WV15 5PS
☎ 01746 710678

The Manor of Morf was mentioned in the Domesday Book, and the name derives from the Welsh for 'marsh'. The pub dates from 1854 and now offers dishes such as Shropshire pie, breaded trout and almonds, spicy beef pancake, and steak and kidney pie.
Principal beers: Banks, Bass.

Directions Off A458(Bridgnorth/ Stourbridge) 2.5m from Bridgnorth follow signs for Claverley on L,0.5m up hill on L
Brewery/Company Free House
Open 12-2.30 7-1
Bar food 12-2 7-9.30 Av main course £4
Restaurant 12-2 7-9.30 Av 3 course à la carte £11

CLEOBURY MORTIMER Shropshire
Map 07 SO67

The Crown at Hopton
CLEOBURY MORTIMER

Hopton Wafers DY14 0NB
☎ 01299 270372

A 16th-century coaching inn of great period character with inglenook fireplaces and original oak beams. Choose a meal from the carte in the restaurant, or from the bar food selection, including daily specials like salmon with seafood sauce, duck with spicy plum sauce, and rack of lamb with redcurrant and rosemary jus. **Principal beers:** Marstons-Bitter, Pedigree.

Directions On A4117 8m west of Ludlow, 2m east of Cleobury Mortimer
Brewery/Company Free House
Open 11-3 6-11
Bar food 12-3 6-10 Av main course £8
Restaurant 12-3 7-11 Av 3 course à la carte £24 Av 4 course fixed price £19.95
Accommodation (Min) s£40 d£64

The Kings Arms Hotel NEW
CLEOBURY MORTIMER

DY14 8BS ☎ 01299 270252

Beams, oak floors and a fine inglenook fireplace characterise this 15th-century coaching inn which nestles in the heart of this picturesque village. Bar food ranges from filled baked potatoes and chilli, to lamb cassoulet and beef in orange and Guinness, while restaurant dishes may include pork with mushrooms and brandy, fillet steak with red wine gravy. **Principal beers:** Hobsons Best, Hobsons Town Cryer, Taylor Landlord, Enville.
Directions take A456 from Kidderminster the A4117 to Cleobury Mortimer
Brewery/Company Free House
Open 11.30-11 (Sun 12-10.30)
Bar food 12-2 7-9.30 Av main course £5.99
Restaurant 12-2 7-9.30 Av 3 course à la carte £13
Accommodation (Min) s£28 d£50

COALPORT Shropshire
Map 07 SJ60

The Woodbridge Inn & Restaurant
COALPORT

TF8 7JE ☎ 01952 882054

A 16th-century coaching inn overlooking the Severn Gorge by Coalport Bridge. The garden offers riverside seating and a weekend barbecue, weather permitting. Food ranges from bar snacks to coq au vin, steaks and vegetable balti in the restaurant. **Principal beers:** John Smiths, Wells Bombardier.
Directions Off A442 S of Telford
Brewery/Company Unique Pub Co
Open 12-1am (winter 12-3, 6-11)
Bar food 12-3 6-9 Av main course £4
Restaurant 6-9 Av 3 course à la carte £13

CRESSAGE Shropshire
Map 07 SJ50

The Cholmondeley Riverside Inn
CRESSAGE

SY5 6AF ☎ 01952 510 900

Situated on a spectacular bend of the River Severn, this 17th-century inn was originally built to serve the busy river ferry. All the food is freshly prepared, with local Shropshire produce and fresh fish featuring on the imaginative menu. Expect baguettes, decent soups and, perhaps, duck with port, spring onion and ginger sauce.
Directions On A458 Shrewsbury-Bridgnorth rd
Brewery/Company Free House
Open 9-3.30 6.30-10.30
Bar food 12-2.30 7-10.30 Av main course £5.50
Restaurant 12-2.30 7-10.30 Av 3 course à la carte £14
Accommodation (Min) s£50 d£65

HEATHTON Shropshire Map 07 SO89

The Old Gate Inn
HEATHTON
WV5 7EB ☎ 01746 710431

16th-century country inn with a lovely south-facing garden - perfect for dining alfresco. Expect Old Gate steak and ale pie, lamb noisettes, pork fillet with a caramel sauce, halibut steak and classic lasagne among the home-made favourites. Extensive wine list and impressive range of whiskies. **Principal beers:** Enville, Taylor Landlord, Morland Old Speckled Hen, Tetley.

Directions From Bridgnorth take A454 towards Wolverhampton. Village on minor rd on R
Brewery/Company Vanguard
Open 12-3 6.30-11
Bar food 12-2 6.30-9 Av main course £7.95
Restaurant 12-2 6.30-9.30 Av 3 course à la carte £17

HODNET Shropshire Map 07 SJ62

The Bear Hotel
HODNET
TF9 3NH ☎ 01630 685214 & 685788

An illuminated cellar garden, once a priest hole, is one of the more unusual attractions at this 16th-century coaching inn. Hodnet Hall Gardens are close by. Extensive menu includes bar snacks and restaurant meals. Fidget pie, chicken goujons and traditional fish and chips are among the blackboard dishes. **Principal beers:** Theakston, John Smiths.
Directions Junction A53 & A442 on sharp corner in middle of small village
Brewery/Company Free House
Open 11-11
Bar food 12-2 6.30-9.30 Av main course £5
Restaurant 12-2 6.30-9.30 Av 3 course à la carte £17
Accommodation (Min) s£40 d£60

IRONBRIDGE Shropshire Map 07 SJ68

The Malthouse NEW
IRONBRIDGE
The Wharfage TF8 7NH
☎ 01952 433712

Stylishly refurbished 18th-century ale house situated just 300 yards from the Ironbridge Visitor Centre. A contemporary decor fills the relaxing Malthouse Bar where imaginative, carefully prepared dishes can be sampled. Choose from onion and Stilton tart or pork and apricot terrine, followed by duck confit, calves' liver and pancetta, or Cajun red mullet with roasted chilli and onion pickle. **Principal beers:** Bass, Flowers Original, Wadworths 6X.
Brewery/Company Greenalls
Open 11-3 6-11
Bar food 12-3 6.30-9.45 Av main course £6.50
Restaurant 12-2.30 6.30-9.30
Accommodation (Min) s£45 d£55

LLANFAIR WATERDINE Shropshire Map 07 SO27

Red Lion Inn
LLANFAIR WATERDINE
LD7 1TU ☎ 01547 528214

16th-century low stone, whitewashed drovers' inn nestling in a tiny village and set beside the River Teme. Traditional snacks like scampi, fish and chips, and sirloin steak are offered in the heavily-beamed bar, while speciality home-cooked dishes include pork chop Normandy style, with Calvados, mustard and cream sauce. **Principal beers:** Wye Valley Dorothy Goodbody, Lionheart Bitter.
Directions 4m NW of Knighton, just of the Newtown road
Brewery/Company Free House
Open 12-2.30 (except Tue) 7-11
Bar food 12-2.30 7-9 Av main course £6
Restaurant 12-2.30 7-9 Av 3 course à la carte £13
Accommodation (Min) s£25 d£40

LUDLOW Shropshire *Map 07 SO57*

The Church Inn
LUDLOW

Buttercross SY8 1AW ☎ 01584 872174

Occupying one of the oldest sites in Ludlow, going back at least seven centuries, the Church Inn stands close to the old Buttercross. Apart from decent ale and en suite accommodation, it offers a short menu of traditional dishes such as chilli, mixed grill, salmon with hollandaise, and lamb with Provençale sauce. **Principal beers:** Courage Directors, Ruddles County, Websters Yorkshire, Woods Shropshire Lad.

Directions Town centre
Brewery/Company Free House
Open 11-11 (Sun 12-2.30, 7-10.30)
Bar food 12-2 6.30-9 Av main course £4.50
Restaurant 12-2 6.30-9 Av 3 course à la carte £10
Accommodation (Min) s£28 d£50

Unicorn Inn
LUDLOW

Corve St SY18 1DU ☎ 01584 873555

Tiny half-timbered pub built in 1635 on the site of an old tannery and backing on to the River Corve. Ancient timbers and panelling and log fires are notable features in the bar, where blackboard menus may list sea bass with peppercorn sauce, farmhouse grill, bacon, mushroon and cauliflower bake, and rack of lamb with Cumberland sauce. **Principal beers:** Worthington Best, Bass.

Directions A49 to Ludlow
Brewery/Company Free House
Open 12-3 6-11
Bar food 12-2.30 6-9.15 Av main course £5
Restaurant 12-2.30 6-9.30 Av 3 course à la carte £15
Accommodation (Min) s£18 d£36

MADELEY Shropshire *Map 07 SJ60*

The New Inn
MADELEY

Blists Hill Victorian Town, Legges Way TF7 5DU ☎ 01952 586309

Victorian pub set in the Blists Hill Open Air Museum, part of the complex of Ironbridge Gorge Museums which celebrate Britain's industrial heritage. Staff dress in Victorian costumes, the pub is gaslit, and there is sawdust on the floors. Filled rolls and hot dishes such as beef in ale and pork in cider available in Club Room. **Principal beers:** Banks.

Directions Between Telford & Broseley
Brewery/Company
Open 11-5
Bar food 12-2.30 Av main course £4.50
Restaurant 12-2.30 Av 3 course fixed price £10

MINSTERLEY Shropshire *Map 07 SJ30*

The Stables Inn
MINSTERLEY

Drury Ln, Hopesgate SY5 0EP
☎ 01743 891344

Built around 1680 to serve the drovers travelling between Montgomery and Shrewsbury markets, this inn is situated in a tiny hamlet of just eight houses. Traditional pub fare is on offer, including a selection of steaks and home-made casseroles, curries, lasagne, and chilli con carne. **Principal beers:** Worthington, Wells Bombardier.

Directions From Shrewsbury A488 turn L at r'about in Minsterly. At Plox Green x-roads turn R. Pub approx 3m.
Brewery/Company Free House
Open 12-3 (Sat-Sun) 6-11 (Sat-Mon 7-11)
Bar food 12-2 7-9.30 Av main course £7.50
Restaurant 12-2 7-9.30 Av 3 course à la carte £11

MORVILLE Shropshire *Map 07 SO69*

Acton Arms
MORVILLE

WV16 4RJ ☎ 01746 714209

Believed to be England's most frequently haunted inn, with three resident spooks, the Acton Arms, a former coaching inn, is situated close to Upper Cresset Hall. Traditional pub food ranges from freshly battered haddock or pork, apple and leek pie, to Oriental Thai duck, and navarin of lamb. **Principal beers:** Banks, Marston Pedigree.

Directions On A458, 3m W of Bridgnorth
Brewery/Company W'hampton & Dudley
Open 12-2.30 6.30-11
Bar food 12-2 Av main course £5.95
Restaurant 7-9.30 Av 3 course à la carte £14

MUCH WENLOCK Shropshire — Map 07 SO69

Longville Arms
MUCH WENLOCK

Longville in the Dale TF13 6DT
☎ 01694 771206

The pub is set in the most beautiful part of Shropshire, convenient for the Long Mynd and the Stretton Hills. It serves simply prepared dishes such as prime Shropshire beef steak, fresh rainbow trout, and chicken Kiev. Additional attractions are the children's menu and the choice of home-made desserts. **Principal beers:** Courage Directors, John Smiths.
Directions From Shrewsbury take A49 to Church Stretton, then B4371 to Longville
Brewery/Company Free House
Open 12-3 7-11 (Sat-Sun 12-3 6-11, closed Tue)
Bar food 12-2 7-10 Av main course £6.95
Restaurant 12-2 7-9 Av 3 course à la carte £12
Accommodation (Min) s£27 d£42

The Talbot Inn
MUCH WENLOCK

High St TF13 6AA ☎ 01952 727077

Dating from 1360, the Talbot is a black and white timbered inn which formed part of the almonry to Wenlock Priory in the 15th century. Daily specials highlight the varied menu, which may include Shropshire pie, lamb casserole, Stilton and walnut mousse, beef medallions with pepper sauce, fresh market fish, and raspberry and lemon roulade. **Principal beers:** Courage Directors, John Smiths, Boddingtons.
Brewery/Company Free House
Open 10.30-3 6.15-11
Bar food 12-2 7-9.30 Av main course £4.50
Restaurant 12-2 7-9.30 Av 3 course à la carte £20
Accommodation (Min) s£45 d£90

Wenlock Edge Inn
MUCH WENLOCK

Hilltop, Wenlock Edge TF13 6DJ
☎ 01746 785678

Originally quarrymen's cottages, built in the 17th century of Wenlock limestone, later a farmhouse, and an inn since the 1920s. Food is all home made using as much organic produce as possible. The range of pies is popular, with fillings such as venison, steak and mushroom, and oink and apple. **Principal beers:** Hobsons Best & Town Crier.
Directions 4.5m from Much Wenlock on B4371
Brewery/Company Free House
Open 11.30-2.30 6.30-11 (Sun 12-2.30, 6.30-10.30)
Bar food 12-2 7-9
Restaurant 12-2 7-9
Accommodation (Min) s£45 d£65

MUNSLOW Shropshire — Map 07 SO58

The Crown
MUNSLOW

SY7 9ET ☎ 01584 841205

Home-brewed ales and freshly-prepared food draw visitors to this impressive-looking Georgian pub which hides a welcoming Tudor interior. Chalkboards list traditional meals such as filled baguettes, ploughman's and chilli plus interesting dishes like fish soup, Thai tiger prawns in lemon sauce, salmon Normandy and pork with prosciutto and pimento sauce. **Principal beers:** Crown Inn Boys Pale Ale, Crown Inn Hundred.
Directions On B4368 between Craven Arms & Much Wenlock
Brewery/Company Free House
Open 12-2.30 7-11
Bar food 12-2 7-9.30 Av main course £6.50
Restaurant 12-2 7-9.30 Av 3 course à la carte £16
Accommodation (Min) s£35 d£45

NESSCLIFFE Shropshire — Map 07 SJ31

The Old Three Pigeons Inn
NESSCLIFFE

SY4 1DB ☎ 01743 741279

Built of sandstone, ship's timbers, wattle and daub, this 15th-century inn features highwayman's carved wooden seat. Characteristic dishes include sardines with tomato and garlic sauce, venison with Madeira sauce, rabbit casserole, herb-crusted rack of lamb, and fresh market fish - monkfish with bacon and garlic. **Principal beers:** Marston Pedigree, Wadworth 6X, John Smiths, Weetwood Old Dog.
Directions On A5 London road
Brewery/Company Free House
Open 11.30-2.30 7-11 (closed Mon in winter)
Bar food 11.30-2.30 Av main course £5.95
Restaurant 11.30-2.30 7-10.15

NORTON Shropshire Map 07 SJ70

Hundred House Hotel & Country Inn
NORTON

Bridgnorth Rd TF11 9EE
☎ 01952 730353

Primarily Georgian, family-run hotel offering well-equipped bedrooms and good, freshly-prepared food in the cosy panelled bars and restaurant. Interesting dishes include Thai beef and noodle soup, rock oysters, braised partridge with cinnamon and orange sauce, fish casserole with saffron cream sauce, and treacle tart. **Principal beers:** Smiles Heritage, Wood Shropshire Lad, Shepherd Neame Spitfire.

Directions On A442 6m N of Bridgnorth
Brewery/Company Free House
Open 7am-11pm (Sun 8.30-2.30, 7-10.30)
Bar food 12.15-2.30 6.15-9.45 Av main course £8.95
Restaurant 12.15-2.30 6.15-9.45 Av 3 course à la carte £25 Av 3 course fixed price £20
Accommodation (Min) s£69 d£95

OSWESTRY Shropshire Map 07 SJ22

The Bradford Arms
OSWESTRY

Llanymynech SY22 6EJ ☎ 01691 830582

Originally a coaching inn, Victorianised in 1900, it has been neatly furnished to retain the style, and soft lighting and an open fire help create an intimate atmosphere at this popular dining pub. Good food, prepared from fresh ingrediants, may include veal in caper sauce, Oriental stir-fried steak, and gooseberry and honey cream pudding. **Principal beers:** Greene King Abbot Ale, Shepherd Neame-Spitfire, Bishops Finger.

Directions On A483 in village centre
Brewery/Company Free House
Open 12-3 7-11 (closed Mon & 3 wks Jan)
Bar food 12-3 7-11 Av main course £9
Restaurant 12-3 7-12 Av 3 course à la carte £19

The Old Mill Inn NEW
OSWESTRY

Candy SY10 9AZ ☎ 01691 657058

A scenic riverside setting in the Candy Valley and interesting food make this country inn worth a detour. Fresh local produce is used in preparing such dishes as duck liver terrine, venison casserole, braised guinea fowl in red wine jus, chicken and cashew nut stir-fry, and seafood rendezvous. Traditional bar snacks and puddings. **Principal beers:** Ruddles Best, Morland Old Speckled Hen, Courage Directors.

Directions from B4579 follow signs for Trefonen then Llansillin, after the Ashfield on R, take 1st R towards Llansillin, 1st R down hill
Brewery/Company Free House
Open 11-3 6-11 (closed Tue)
Bar food 12-2.30 6-9.30 Av main course £4
Restaurant 12-2.30 6-9.30 Av 3 course à la carte £11
Accommodation (Min) s£17 d£34

PICKLESCOTT Shropshire Map 07 SO49

Bottle & Glass Inn
PICKLESCOTT

SY6 6NR ☎ 01694 751345

17th-century stone-built inn nestling among scenic Shropshire hills. Retains many original features, including beamed ceilings and open fireplaces. Casserole of beef in Guinness and home-made sweet and sour pork are typical examples of the blackboard specials. Menu also features home-made pies and hot baguettes. **Principal beers:** Hook Norton, Ushers, Worthington.

Directions Turn off A49 at Dorrington between Shrewsbury & Church Stretton
Brewery/Company Free House
Open 11.30-3 7-11
Bar food 12-2 7-9 Av main course £5.50
Restaurant 12-3 7-9 Av 3 course à la carte £12
Accommodation (Min) s£30 d£45

SHIFNAL Shropshire *Map 07 SJ70*

Oddfellows Wine Bar NEW
SHIFNAL

Market Place TF11 9AU
☎ 01952 461517

Originally known as the Star, this interesting single room bar has high ceilings, an elevated dining area and a conservatory. The seasonal menu may include zucchini and capsicum lasagne, seafood gumbo skillet, pork escalope with apples and Calvados, or sirloin steak with blue cheese and bacon. **Principal beers:** Bathams, Taylor Landlord & Shropshire Lad, Wood Hopping Mad.
Directions 3rd exit from Mway rdbt, at next rdbt take 3rd exit, past petrol station, round bend under railway bridge, bar on L
Brewery/Company Free House
Open 12-3 5.30-12 (Sun & Fri open all day)
Bar food 12-2 Av main course £5.50
Restaurant 12-2 7-10 Av 3 course à la carte £17.50

SHREWSBURY Shropshire *Map 07 SJ41*

The Armoury
SHREWSBURY

Welsh Bridge, Victoria Quay SY1 1HH
☎ 01743 340525

Once an armoury, this old warehouse overlooking the river was rebuilt in its present position when bricks were in short supply after the war. An interesting choice of dishes might include wild mushroom risotto cake with broad bean and spinach sauce, and medallions of beef fillet with tomato and basil mash. **Principal beers:** Wood Shropshire Lad, Wadworth 6X, two guest ales.
Open 12-11 (weekends 11-11/food all day)
Bar food 12-2.30 6-9.30 Av main course £8

The Castle Vaults
SHREWSBURY

16 Castle Gates SY1 2AB
☎ 01743 358807

An early 19th-century ale house, the Castle Vaults has a roof garden and nestles beneath the shadow of Shrewsbury Castle. Food is Mexican style, at Pancho's Mexican Eating House - try cheese nachos, tacos, burritos, chimichangas and the appetite-sating Rio Grande.
Principal beers: Hobsons Best, Marstons Pedigree.
Directions From S: M6, M54, A5. From N: M6, A49
Brewery/Company Free House
Open 11.30-3 6-11
Bar food 11.30-2.30 Av main course £8
Restaurant 11.30-2.30 6-10 Av 3 course à la carte £10 Av 2 course fixed price £10
Accommodation (Min) s£30 d£50

WEM Shropshire *Map 07 SJ52*

The Raven Inn
WEM

Tilley SY4 5HE ☎ 01939 234419

Family-run 17th-century inn with award winning terrace, overlooking fields and paddocks. Among the specials are sweet pepper chicken, spinach pie with tomato coulis, fillet steak with Stilton sauce, and salmon with lemon and dill sauce. Desserts include Mississippi mud pie, lemon brûlée and sherry trifle.
Directions A49 signed to Wem
Brewery/Company Free House
Open 11.30-2.30 6-11 (closed Mon)
Bar food 12-2 6-10 Av main course £6
Restaurant 12-2 6-10 Av 3 course à la carte £12

WENTNOR Shropshire *Map 07 SO39*

The Crown Inn
WENTNOR

SY9 5EE ☎ 01588 650613

17th-century inn buried deep in the countryside of South Shropshire. Striking view of the Long Mynd, and ideally placed for walking, fishing and riding. Fresh, home-cooked food ranges from locally-made Cumberland sausages, ploughman's bake and ocean crumble, to calpyso chicken, Mediterranean beef and fresh cod. **Principal beers:** Hobsons, Worthington, Morland Old Speckled Hen, Wood Shropshire Lad.

Directions From Shrewsbury A49 to Church Stretton, follow signs over Long Mynd to Asterton, R to Wentnor
Brewery/Company Free House
Open 12-3 7-11
Bar food 12-2 7-9 Av main course £8
Restaurant 12-2 7-9 Av 3 course à la carte £14
Accommodation (Min) s£22.50 d£53

WESTON HEATH Shropshire Map 07 SJ71

The Countess's Arms NEW
WESTON HEATH
TF11 8RJ ☎ 01952 691123
Revamped and revitalised over the past year, this now thriving rural Shropshire pub sports a spacious, wood-floored bar with a first-floor gallery, and an interesting menu featuring modern pub food. Lookout for herb-crusted cod with basil pesto and salad, honey-glazed duck with citrus sauce, Thai chicken curry, Caesar salad, and game pie.
Principal beers: Banks's, Whitbread Boddingtons, Marstons Pedigree.
Brewery/Company Free House
Open 11-12.30am (Sun 12-10.30)
Bar food 11-11 Av main course £5
Restaurant 11-11 Av 3 course à la carte £10 Av 3 course fixed price £10

WHITCHURCH Shropshire Map 07 SJ54

The Horse & Jockey
WHITCHURCH
Church St SY13 1LB ☎ 01948 664902
Built in three stages during the 17th, 18th and 19th centuries, the oldest area of this pub is an oak-beamed three-storey building. A wide-ranging menu offers potted peppered prawns and seafood gratin for starters, followed by beef Wellington, rack of lamb, or sea bass with garlic butter sauce. **Principal beers:** Vaux Bitter, Ward Bitter.
Directions In town centre next to church
Brewery/Company Vaux
Open 11.30-2.30 6-11 (closed Mon ex BH when food all day)
Bar food 11.30-2.30 6-10 Av main course £4.95
Restaurant 11.30-2.30 6-10 Av 3 course à la carte £12

Willey Moor Lock Tavern
WHITCHURCH
Tarporley Rd SY13 4HF
☎ 01948 663274
Former lock keeper's cottage idyllically situated beside the Llangollen Canal in rural South Cheshire. Neatly decorated low-beamed rooms with teapot collection, open log fires and a good choice of real ales for the afficionado. Traditional pub food includes freshly battered cod, steak pie, and a generous mixed grill. **Principal beers:** Theakston.
Directions 2m N of Whitchurch on A49 (Warrington/Tarporley)
Brewery/Company Free House
Open 12-2.30 6-11 (Sun 7-10.30)
Bar food 12-2.30 6-11 Av main course £5

Swansea

REYNOLDSTON Swansea Map 02 SS48

King Arthur Hotel
REYNOLDSTON
Higher Green SA3 1AD
☎ 01792 390775
Traditional country inn close to Arthur's stone, said to be the most famous prehistoric monument in Wales. Cosy atmosphere, log fires and good ales. Same menu throughout offers home-made curries and pies, a selection of fresh fish dishes, including hake, cockles and monkfish, while game in season features pheasant and venison.
Principal beers: Felinfoel Double Dragon, Worthington, Bass.
Directions Just N of A4118 SW of Swansea
Brewery/Company Free House
Open 11-11
Bar food 12-2.30 6-9.30 Av main course £7
Restaurant 12-2.30 6-9.30 Av 3 course à la carte £12.50 Av 3 course fixed price £8.95
Accommodation (Min) s£30 d£40

Vale of Glamorgan

EAST ABERTHAW Vale of Glamorgan Map 03 ST06

Blue Anchor Inn
EAST ABERTHAW
CF62 3DD ☎ 01446 750329
Old-world thatched inn established in 1380, a haunt of smugglers and wreckers, believed to have a secret passage down to

contd.

the sea. The interesting daily bar menu might offer Welsh faggots with herb mash, while restaurant fare may feature Cornish crab cakes, and baked red mullet topped with Welsh rarebit.

Blue Anchor Inn

Principal beers: Brains Buckleys Best, Theakston Old Peculiar, Wadworth 6X, Boddingtons.
Brewery/Company Free House
Open 11-11 (Sun 12-10.30)
Bar food 12-2 6-8 Av main course £5.50
Restaurant 12-2.30 7-9.30 Av 3 course à la carte £20

PENMARK Vale of Glamorgan *Map 03 ST06*

Six Bells Inn
PENMARK

CF62 3BP ☎ 01446 710229

Dating from 1623, this pub has a distinctive Norman archway and takes its name from the bell peel in the Norman church opposite. Typical dishes include wild rabbit casserole cooked in cider and honey, duck with plum and peppercorn sauce, and halibut with chive butter sauce. Plus blackberry crème brûlée for dessert. **Principal beers:** Hancocks HB.
Directions M4 J33 take A4045, follow signs for 'Cardiff Wales airport' then 'Penmark'
Brewery/Company Free House
Open 12-11 (Sun 12-10.30)
Bar food 12-3 Av main course £8
Restaurant 12-3 7-10 Av 3 course à la carte £17

ST HILARY Vale of Glamorgan *Map 03 ST07*

The Bush Inn
ST HILARY

CF71 7DP ☎ 01446 772745

A 14th-century thatched inn situated in a pretty village opposite the church. Favourite dishes in the bar include Welsh rarebit, chicken curry, and steak and ale pie, while the restaurant might offer sirloin steak, or trout with bacon. Lemon cheesecake and treacle tart are among the home-made puddings.
Principal beers: Hancocks HB, Bass, Morland Speckled Hen.
Directions S of A48, E of Cowbridge
Brewery/Company Punch Taverns
Open 11.30-11
Bar food 12-2.30 7-10 Av main course £5.50
Restaurant 12-2.30 7-10 Av 3 course à la carte £16 Av 3 course fixed price £10.95

Worcestershire

BEWDLEY Worcestershire *Map 07 SO77*

Little Pack Horse
BEWDLEY

31 High St DY12 2DH ☎ 01299 403762

Open fires, low beams and an elm timber bar are among the charming features at this ancient, heavily timbered pub. First recorded landlord was in 1818. Allotment pies, balti's, Moby cod and chips, and poultry, pig and fungi pie are among the more unusually-named dishes on the varied menu.
Principal beers: Ushers - Best, Four Seasons, Founders.
Brewery/Company Ushers
Open 11.30-3 6-11 (Sat-Sun 11.30-11)
Bar food 12-2 6.30-8.30 Av main course £5.25

BREDON Worcestershire *Map 03 SO93*

Fox & Hounds Inn & Restaurant
BREDON

Church St GL20 7LA
☎ 01684 772377 & 772471

Pretty, flower-adorned, 16th-century thatched pub close to the River Avon. Neatly furnished, the friendly bars offer a wide-ranging menu, including traditional pub favourites, home-made pies, beef and bacon Stroganoff, Thai-style fish and herb-crusted leg of lamb. Fresh fish and seasonal game feature on the specials board. **Principal beers:** Greene King Abbot Ale, Banks, Marstons Pedigree, Morland Old Speckled Hen.
Directions M5 J9 into Tewkesbury take B4080 towards Pershore. Bredon 3m

Brewery/Company Whitbread
Open 11-2.30 6-11
Bar food 12-2 6.30-10 Av main course £5.75
Restaurant 12-2.30 6.30-10 Av 3 course à la carte £15

BRETFORTON Worcestershire — *Map 04 SP04*

The Fleece Inn
BRETFORTON

The Cross WR11 5JE ☎ 01386 831173

Originally a medieval farmhouse, the Fleece, which is described by staff as 'a living museum', has been a pub since 1848 and is now owned by the National Trust. Typical menu includes steak and kidney pie, Gloucester sausages, and ratatouille lasagne. **Principal beers:** Uley Beer, Everards.

Directions B4035 from Evesham
Brewery/Company Free House
Open 11-2.30 6-11
Bar food 12-2 7-9 Av main course £4.50

FLADBURY Worcestershire — *Map 03 SO94*

Chequers Inn
FLADBURY

Chequers Ln WR10 2PZ
☎ 01386 860276

Much of the character has been retained in the beamed bars of this personally-run, early 14th-century village inn, which enjoys views of the Bredon Hills. A good base from which to explore the Malvern and Cotswold Hills, it offers straightforward bar food and a popular weekend carvery. **Principal beers:** Theakstons, Wells Bombadier, John Smiths.

Directions Off A4538 between Evesham and Pershore
Brewery/Company Free House
Open 11-3 6-11

Bar food 12-2 6.30-10 Av main course £9
Restaurant 12-2 6.30-10 Av 3 course à la carte £18
Accommodation (Min) s£45 d£58

FLYFORD FLAVELL Worcestershire — *Map 03 SO95*

The Boot Inn NEW
FLYFORD FLAVELL

Radford Rd WR7 4BS ☎ 01386 462658

Part 13th-century former coaching inn enjoying a quiet village location on the Wychavon Way. Well placed for the Cotswolds and Malvern Hills, it offers en suite accommodation, and traditional pub food in the timbered bars. Look to the specials board for lemon sole, beef, Guinness and mushroom pie, haddock with mustard sauce, and chicken Madras. **Principal beers:** Boddingtons, Wadworth 6X, Morland Old Speckled Hen.

Directions Take Evesham rd, L at 2nd rdbt onto A422, Flyford Flavell signed after 3m
Brewery/Company Free House
Open 11-3 6.30-11
Bar food 12-2 6.30-10 Av main course £5.95
Restaurant 12-2 6.30-11 Av 3 course à la carte £15
Accommodation (Min) s£37.50 d£55

KEMPSEY Worcestershire — *Map 03 SO84*

Walter de Cantelupe Inn
KEMPSEY

Main Rd WR5 3NA ☎ 01905 820572

Named after the mid 13th-century Bishop of Worcester, this 16th-century inn sports a boldly decorated interior, candle-topped tables and an open fire. Imaginative, home-made dishes,

contd.

displayed on a large blackboard, range from hearty ploughman's lunches and thick soups, to baked sea bass with tomato and Mozzarella, and lamb, mint and date pie. **Principal beers:** Marstons Bitter, Talyor Landlord, Woods Shropshire Lad.
Directions 4m S of Worcester city centre, on A38
Brewery/Company Free House
Open 11.30-2.30 6-11 (Sun 6-10.30; closed Mon ex BH)
Bar food 12-2.30 6.30-9.30 Av main course £5
Restaurant 12.30-2 6-9 Av 3 course à la carte £14

KNIGHTWICK Worcestershire *Map 03 SO75*

The Talbot at Knightwick
KNIGHTWICK
WR6 5PH ☎ 01886 821235
500-year-old country inn standing by the River Teme. It is run by two sisters who offer home-brewed ales and an eclectic, ever-changing range of dishes, and nearly everything is made on the premises, using vegetables from the chemical-free garden. Dishes include saffron fish soup, pheasant casserole, marinated monkfish with Puy lentils, and cod fillet Charente. **Principal beers:** Teme Valley, Hobsons.
Directions A44 through Worcester, 8m W turn onto B4197
Brewery/Company Free House
Open 11-11
Bar food 12-2 6.30-9.30 Av main course £7
Restaurant 12-2 6.30-9.30 Av 3 course fixed price £16.95
Accommodation (Min) s£30 d£50

MALVERN Worcestershire *Map 03 SO74*

Farmers Arms
MALVERN
Birts St, Birtsmorton WR13 6AP
☎ 01684 833308
Expect a friendly welcome at this 15th-century black and white timbered pub which nestles in a quiet parish close to the Malvern Hills. Cosy, low-beamed rooms in which to sample decent Hook Norton ales and homely bar food, perhaps steak and kidney pie, lasagne, mixed grill, and nursery puddings like treacle tart. **Principal beers:** Hook Norton Best & Old Hooky.
Directions On B4208 S of Great Malvern
Brewery/Company Free House
Open 11-2.30 6-11
Bar food 11-2 6-10 Av main course £4.50

OMBERSLEY Worcestershire *Map 03 SO86*

The Kings Arms NEW
OMBERSLEY
Main Rd WR9 0EW ☎ 01905 620142
Some 600 years old, the pub is an impressive, black and white timbered building dating from 1411. Inviting, with its open fires, flagstone floors and antique bric-a-brac, it offers an imaginative modern menu. Expect fish stew, monkfish with olive mash and sorrel sauce, smoked haddock and crab fishcakes, and seared duck with honey and Chinese five spices. **Principal beers:** Bass, Banks's, Marstons Pedigree, Camerons Strongarm.
Directions Just off A449
Brewery/Company Free House
Open 11-3 5.30-11
Bar food 12-2.15 6-10 Av main course £8.50

PENSAX Worcestershire *Map 03 SO76*

The Bell Inn
PENSAX
WR6 6AE ☎ 01299 896677
Built around 1840 as a hunting lodge, the Bell is a black and white inn, beautifully situated with idyllic valley views from the lounge. The traditional bar serves a constantly changing range of ales (over 400 a year), and there is a choice of popular home-cooked bar food.
Principal beers: Enville Best, Archers Golden.
Directions From Kidderminster A456 to Clows Top, B4202 towards Abberley, pub 2m on L
Brewery/Company Free House
Open 12-2.30 5-11 (Sun 12-10.30; closed Mon lunch)
Bar food 12-2 6-9.30 Av main course £5
Restaurant 12-2 6-9.30 Av 3 course à la carte £12

POWICK Worcestershire *Map 03 SO85*

The Halfway House
POWICK
Bastonford WR2 4SL ☎ 01905 831098
Situated at the foot of the Malvern Hills, halfway between Worcester and Malvern.

Lunchtime meals include filled baguettes, whitebait and nacho bowls. The evening menu may offer steaks, pan-fried chicken with white wine and chive sauce, or lamb noisettes with mint and redcurrent glaze. **Principal beers:** Taylor, John Smiths.
Directions From A15 J7 take A4440 then A449
Brewery/Company Free House
Open 12-2.30 6-11
Bar food 12-2 6.30-9 Av main course £5.95
Restaurant 12-2 6.30-9 Av 3 course à la carte £15

SHATTERFORD Worcestershire *Map 07 SO78*

The Bellmans Cross NEW
SHATTERFORD
Bridgnorth Rd DY12 5RN
☎ 01299 861322

Large, recently refurbished 19th-century village inn offering a good range of freshly prepared food, including French-inspired dishes in 'Dominiques' restaurant. From lambs' liver with bacon, and steak and kidney pie, the choice includes monkfish with black noodles and pink peppercorn sauce, duck leg confit, and beef fillet on garlic purée with red wine sauce.

Principal beers: Bass.
Directions on A442 5m outside Kidderminster
Brewery/Company Free House
Open 11-3 6-11
Bar food 11-3 6-11 Av main course £5.70
Restaurant 11-3 6-11 Av 3 course à la carte £22.50 Av 3 course fixed price £20

TENBURY WELLS Worcestershire *Map 03 SO56*

Peacock Inn
TENBURY WELLS
WR15 8LL ☎ 01584 810506

Rambling, 14th-century inn nestling in the picturesque Teme Valley. Dine on the sunny front patio or in the relaxing, oak-panelled bar. Excellent fresh fish (halibut with onion marmalade and tarragon butter), rack of lamb with roasted vegetables and thyme jus, and chicken with juniper and liquorice sauce are typical examples of the imaginative food available. **Principal beers:** Bass, Burton, Tetley.
Directions A456 from Worcester then A443 to Tenbury Wells. Inn is 1.25m E of Tenbury Wells
Brewery/Company Free House
Open 11.30-3 6-11
Bar food 12-3
Restaurant 12-3 6-11
Accommodation (Min) s£55 d£65

WYRE PIDDLE Worcestershire *Map 03 SO94*

The Anchor Inn
WYRE PIDDLE
Main St WR10 2JB ☎ 01386 552799

Originally a boatman's cottage, this 17th-century inn has terraced gardens running down to the River Avon and views of the Malverns and the Cotswolds. Seafood is the speciality and locally-grown fresh produce is prepared in traditional style. Sample grilled sea bass or try the sausage, mash and black pudding. **Principal beers:** Banks, Flowers Original, Boddingtons, Marston's Pedigree.
Directions From M5 J6 take A4538 S towards Evesham
Brewery/Company Whitbread
Open 11-2.30 6-11
Bar food 12-2.15 7-9 Av main course £7.95
Restaurant 12-2 7-9 Av 3 course à la carte £15

Wrexham

HANMER Wrexham *Map 07 SJ43*

Hanmer Arms Village Hotel
HANMER
SY13 3DE ☎ 01948 830532 & 830640

Village hotel close to a 19th-century church and within easy reach of Hanmer

contd.

Mere. From traditional pub snacks, the extensive menu selection offers duck terrine, steamed mussels with garlic, ginger and soy, prime steaks, and house specialities like Dover sole, rack of lamb, beef Stroganoff and, for vegetarians, aubergine lasagne. **Principal beers:** Tetley.
Directions Between Wrexham & Whitchurch on A539, off A525
Brewery/Company Free House
Open 7am-11pm (Bar food all day)
Bar food 12-3 6-10
Accommodation (Min) s£25 d£40

LLANARMON DYFFRYN CEIRIOG Wrexham *Map 06 SJ13*

The West Arms Hotel NEW
LLANARMON DYFFRYN CEIRIOG
LL20 7LD ☎ 01691 600665
An attractive 400-year-old inn with riverside garden standing in a picturesque hamlet at the foot of the Berwyn Mountains. Log fires warm the reception hall and traditional, oak-beamed bars provide the setting in which to enjoy terrine of duck, steamed halibut with lemon and crème fraîche, and scallop and artichoke salad. **Principal beers:** Whitbread Flowers IPA, Whitbread Boddingtons.
Directions Leave A483 at Chirk, follow signs for Ceiriog Valley B4500, hotel is 11m from Chirk
Brewery/Company Free House
Open 11-4 6-11
Bar food 12-3 7-10.30 Av main course £6
Restaurant 12-2.30 7-10.30 Av 3 course à la carte £10 Av 5 course fixed price £19.50

MARFORD Wrexham *Map 07 SJ35*

Trevor Arms Hotel
MARFORD
LL12 8TA ☎ 01244 570436 & 571550
Haunted 17th-century coaching inn - the scene of public hangings. It takes its name from Lord Trevor of Trevallin, who was killed in a duel. Venison, kangaroo and shark feature on the restaurant menu, and bar food includes steak, chicken and chips, and prawn curry.

Principal beers: Greenalls, Tetley.
Directions off A483 onto B5102 then R onto B5445 into Marford
Brewery/Company Free House
Open 9am-11pm
Bar food 11-.9.30 Av main course £5.50
Restaurant 11-9.30 Av 3 course à la carte £15 Av 3 course fixed price £7.50
Accommodation (Min) s£31 d£35

Best
on the
Millennium
Menu-
Feast on Fish
Find the perfect seafood pub by looking for the special symbol in this guide.
SEAFISH
Sea Fish Industry Authority,
18 Logie Mill, Logie Green Road, Edinburgh EH7 4HG
Tel: 0131 558 3331 Fax: 0131 558 1442
E-mail: development@seafish.co.uk

Rose & Crown, Romaldkirk, Co Durham

Steak & Kidney Pie with Theakston's Ale Gravy

Ingredients for filling:

- **3lb/1.35kg** stewing **steak**
- **1lb/450g** ox **kidney**
- **3oz/75g** plain flour
- **1** Large **onion**
- **1fl oz/25ml** sunflower oil
- **5oz/150g** Button/field **mushrooms**
- **2pt/1.2ltr** Theakston's **Ale**
- **seasoning**
- **Tomato purée**

Ingredients for topping:

- **8oz/225g** plain flour
- **4oz/110g** lard
- **3** tablespoons **water**
- **1** **egg** (for egg wash)
- **seasoning**

Method for filling:

Heat **oil** in pan. Add diced trimmed **steak** and **kidney** and seal well over high heat on stove until well browned. Add **tomato purée** and cook for 5 minutes on lower heat. Add **flour** and mix well in. Add **beer**, bring to boil and then simmer for 2 hours until meat is tender. Add **mushrooms** (cut into chunks) and cook for 5 minutes. **Season**. Chill before use.

Method for topping:

Whizz **seasoning**, **flour** and **lard** to fine crumb stage. Add **water** until mix comes together by hand (not too wet or pastry will be tough). Put in fridge for 30 minutes. Roll out to ⅛" and use. Brush with egg before cooking.

Cooking time and oven temp:

Gas Mark 8/Electric (centigrade) 230 for 20 minutes until pastry is crisp. Serves 6 people.

Cheshire

ALDFORD Cheshire Map 07 SJ45

The Grosvenor Arms NEW
ALDFORD
Chester Rd CH3 6HJ ☎ 01244 620228
Interesting bistro-style food, decent wines and good ales are attracting a discerning clientele to this comfortably refurbished and relaxing Victorian inn. Daily-changing menus may feature filled baguettes, leek and Caerphilly tart with red onion marmalade, tuna with lemon and thyme butter, marinated pork fillet with mustard sauce, and pear and almond tart. **Principal beers:** Boddingtons, Flowers IPA, Wells Bombardier, Beartown Bearskinful.
Directions on B5130 S of Chester
Brewery/Company Free House
Open 11-11 (Sun 12-10.30)
Bar food 12-10 Av main course £7.95

ALSAGER Cheshire

Wilbraham Arms NEW
ALSAGER
Sandbach Rd North ST7 2AX
☎ 01270 877970
Set in well manicured grounds on the edge of town, this large and busy dining pub, complete with conservatory restaurant and live trad jazz on Thursday, offers a friendly welcome and appetising food. Expect steak and kidney pie, beer battered cod and chips, sizzling Thai chicken with lemon grass rice, and a huge bacon, cheese and chicken filled baguette. **Principal beers:** Robinsons Best, Robinson's Frederics, Hartleys XB.
Brewery/Company
Open 12-3 6-11 (Sat 5.30-11, Sun 7-10.30)
Bar food 12-2 6.30-9.30
Restaurant 12-2 6.30-9.30

ASTON Cheshire Map 07 SJ64

The Bhurtpore Inn NEW
ASTON
Wrenbury Rd CW5 8DQ
☎ 01270 780917
Unassuming and unpretentious stone village pub, renowned for its real ales, bottled beers, and interesting home-cooked food served in the rambling, traditional bars. From hot filled baguettes and steak and kidney pie, the choice extends to excellent curries and baltis, salmon in filo with watercress sauce, and lamb with sherry and mint gravy.

Principal beers: Hanbys Drawwell.
Directions between Nantwich & Whitchurch on the A530
Brewery/Company Free House
Open 12-2.30 6.30-11
Bar food 12-2 6.30-9.30 Av main course £6.50
Restaurant 12-2 6.30-9.30 Av 3 course à la carte £13

BARTHOMLEY Cheshire Map 07 SJ75

The White Lion Inn
BARTHOMLEY
CW2 5PG ☎ 01270 882242
Historic half-timbered and thatched inn with character bars and a lovely rural setting. It offers bar food ranging from hot beef, pork or lamb sandwiches to home-made hotpot, chicken curry, or chilli con carne. Special ploughman's come with Stilton and bacon, local roast ham or chicken breast. **Principal beers:** Burtonwood Bitter, James Forshaw's, & Top Hat.
Brewery/Company Burtonwood
Open 11.30-11 (Thurs 5-11, Sun 12-10.30)
Bar food 12-2 Av main course £3.50

BOLLINGTON Cheshire Map 07 SJ97

The Church House Inn
BOLLINGTON
Church St SK10 5PY ☎ 01625 574014
Convenient for both the natural landscape of the Peak District National Park and the bright lights of Manchester, this village inn has a varied menu. Diners may enjoy diced lamb in cranberry and ginger sauce, swordfish steak in a white wine and tarragon sauce, or Bollington-made black pudding. **Principal beers:** Theakston Best, Tetley, Jennings, Kilkenny.

Directions Macclesfield turnoff on A34, thru Prestbury, follow Bollington signs.
Brewery/Company Free House
Open 12-3 5.30-11
Bar food 12-2 6.30-9.30 Av main course £6
Accommodation (Min) s£27.50 d£37.50

BROXTON Cheshire *Map 07 SJ45*

The Copper Mine
BROXTON

Nantwich Rd CH3 9JH ☎ 01829 782293

Convenient for the Candle Factory at Cheshire Workshops, Cheshire Ice Cream Farm, and 14th-century Beeston Castle, this pub has a conservatory with fine views of the surrounding countryside. A wide selection of light lunches are available, plus dishes such as chicken pastorella, and halibut with lobster, shrimp and white wine sauce. **Principal beers:** Boddingtons, Bass.
Directions A41 from Chester, L at r'about onto A534, pub 0.5m on R
Brewery/Company Paramount
Open 12-3 7-11
Bar food 12-2.30 7-9.30 Av main course £6.95
Restaurant 12-2.30 7-9.30 Av 3 course à la carte £12.95

BURWARDSLEY Cheshire *Map 07 SJ55*

The Pheasant Inn
BURWARDSLEY

CH3 9PJ ☎ 01829 770434

A 300-year-old sandstone inn, set in a beautiful village among the hills with views of five counties. Beamed and timbered bar with nautical artefacts and a huge log fire. Typical dishes are home-made salmon fishcakes with tartare sauce, beef and ale pie, and noisettes of lamb with herb crust. **Principal beers:** Bass, Weetwood, Fullers London Pride, Hanby.

Directions From Chester A41 to Whitchurch, after 4m L to Burwardsley. Follow signs 'Cheshire Workshops'
Brewery/Company Free House
Open 11-3 6-11
Bar food 12-2.30 7-9.30 Av main course £6.95
Restaurant 12-2.30 7-9.30 Av 3 course à la carte £14.50 Av 3 course fixed price £14.50
Accommodation (Min) s£49.50 d£70

CHOLMONDELEY Cheshire *Map 07 SJ55*

The Cholmondeley Arms
CHOLMONDELEY

SY14 8BT ☎ 01829 720300

Set in the heart of the lovely Cholmondeley Estate, the building was the village school until 1982, and converted to a pub in 1988. Interesting blackboard menus offer a choice of sandwiches, various curries and grills, and excellent specials such as hot crab pâté, rabbit in wine, mustard and thyme, and salmon fishcakes with hollandaise.
Principal beers: Marstons, Greene King IPA, Taylor Landlord, Weetwood.
Directions on A49, between Whitchurch & Tarporley
Brewery/Company Free House
Open 11-3 7-11 (Sat 6.30-11)
Bar food 12-2.15 7-10 Av main course £8.95
Accommodation (Min) s£50 d£65

CONGLETON Cheshire *Map 07 SJ86*

Plough Inn Hotel
CONGLETON

Macclesfield Rd, Eaton CW12 2NH
☎ 01260 280207

17th-century half-timbered coaching inn alongside the original London to Manchester turnpike. The bar menu might offer beef bourguignon and vegetarian lasagne. A typical restaurant dish is roasted monkfishfillet with red cabbage and baby fennel,fresh garden peas and foie gras velonte and essence of red pepper.
Principal beers: Boddingtons, Morland Old Speckled Hen, Marstos Pedigree.
Directions on A536(Congleton to Macclesfield road)
Open 12-3 6-11

contd.

Bar food 12-2 7-10 Av main course £8
Restaurant 12-2 7-9.30 Av 3 course à la carte £27.50 Av 6 course fixed price £37.50
Accommodation (Min) s£60 d£75

COTEBROOK Cheshire Map 07 SJ56

Alvanley Arms NEW
COTEBROOK
Forest Rd CW6 9DS ☎ 01829 760200
Former farmhouse set in affluent Cheshire countryside close to Beeston Castle (NT). Two comfortable beamed bars with open fires, and a large garden with fishing lake. Enjoy a pint of Robinsons and, perhaps, fresh cod and mushy peas, Greek lamb, tuna with olives and garlic, or halibut with mussels from the varied menu. **Principal beers:** Robinsons Best.

Directions On the A49, 10m from Chester, 12m from M6 J16
Brewery/Company Robinsons
Open 11.30-3 6-11
Bar food 12-2.15 6-9.30 Av main course £6.95
Restaurant 12-2.15 6-9.30 Av 3 course à la carte £15 Av 3 course fixed price £9.50
Accommodation (Min) s£25 d£45

HANDLEY Cheshire Map 07 SJ45

The Calveley Arms
HANDLEY
Whitchurch Rd CH3 9DT
☎ 01829 770619
Old coaching inn in a quiet village location, once part of the Calveley estate. Beamed ceilings and open fires add to the atmosphere. Good choice of appetising starters, sandwich and baguette fillings. For something more substantial choose from a range of steak and pasta dishes. **Principal beers:** Boddingtons, Boddingtons Mild, Castle Eden, Wadworth 6X.

Directions 5m S of Chester, signposted from A41
Brewery/Company Enterprise Inns
Open 12-3 6-11
Bar food 12-2.30 6-9.30 Av main course £7

KNUTSFORD Cheshire Map 07 SJ77

The Dog Inn
KNUTSFORD
Well Bank Ln, Over Peover WA16 8UP
☎ 01625 861421
Delightful18th-century inn, enhanced in summer by dazzling flowerbeds, tubs and baskets. Noted for using the freshest of local produce, with beef, poultry, game, vegetables and herbs competently used in preparing dishes like rabbit casserole, lamb with apricot gravy, steak and ale pie, and roast Cheshire beef. Puddings include sticky toffee pudding. **Principal beers:** Tetley, Moorhouse Black Cat, Flowers IPA, Weetwood Old Dog.
Directions From Knutsford take A50 S. Turn L at 'The Whipping Stocks'. Pub in 2m
Brewery/Company Free House
Open 11.30-3 5.30-11.30 (Sun 12-4, 7-11)
Bar food 12-2.30 7-9.30 Av main course £8.95
Accommodation (Min) s£50 d£70

LYMM Cheshire Map 07 SJ68

Green Dragon
LYMM
2 Mill Ln, Heatley WA13 9SB
☎ 01925 750921
Allegedly haunted by the benign spirit of the first landlord, who opened the doors in 1850, this welcoming pub is the annual setting for the Dickensian Day on December 13th, and the crowning of the May Queen. **Principal beers:** Bass.
Directions On A6144, 1.5m from village centre
Brewery/Company Vintage Inns
Open 11-11 (Sun 12-10.30)

OVER PEOVER Cheshire Map 07 SJ77

Ye Olde Parkgate Inn
OVER PEOVER
Stocks Ln WA16 8TU ☎ 01625 861455
Ivy-covered village pub surrounded by fields and woodland. Attractively furnished beamed bars and comfortable

lounge where home-cooked food is served. Blackboard daily specials supplement the traditional pub menu, the latter listing steak and kidney pie, hot beef roll, ham salad, and roast of the day. **Principal beers:** Samuel Smith Old Brewery.
Directions A50 from Knutsford. Inn 3m on L after Radbroke Hall
Brewery/Company Samuel Smith
Open 11.30-11 (Sun 12-3.30, 7-10.30)
Bar food 12-2 6.30-9 Av main course £5.50

PENKETH Cheshire Map 07 SJ58

The Ferry Tavern
PENKETH
Station Rd WA5 2UJ ☎ 01925 791117
Old ale house by the river on its own island (the ferry is the original Ferry Cross the Mersey). Snacks and light bites are available, while the full menu offers steaks, fish and chips, a range of sausages, and King Henry's feast (roast shoulder of lamb with rosemary and mint). **Principal beers:** Courage Directors, Boddingtons, Ruddles County, Theakston Old Peculier.
Directions A57 - A562, Fiddler's Ferry signposted
Brewery/Company Free House
Open 12-3 5.30-11 (open all day wknd)
Bar food 12-2 6-7.30 Av main course £5
Restaurant 12-2 6-9 Av 3 course à la carte £10

PLUMLEY Cheshire Map 07 SJ77

The Smoker
PLUMLEY
WA16 0TY ☎ 01565 722338
A 400-year-old thatched coaching inn with beamed ceilings, panelled walls and period fireplaces, named after the Prince Regent's favourite racehorse. Expect good Robinsons ales and decent bar food, including specials like Thai lamb curry, seafood bake, hake with prawn and mushroom sauce, and various steaks. Extensive garden with play area.
Principal beers: Robinsons Best & Mild.
Directions from M6 J19 take A556 W. Pub is 1.75m on L
Brewery/Company Robinsons
Open 11-3 5.30-11
Bar food 11-2.30 6-10 Av main course £7
Restaurant 11-2.30 6-10 Av 3 course à la carte £15

PRESTBURY Cheshire Map 07 SJ87

The Legh Arms & Black Boy Restaurant
PRESTBURY
Prestbury Village Centre SK10 4DG
☎ 01625 829130
Centrally located in historic Prestbury village, this 15th-century pub and restaurant takes pride in catering for special occasions. The menu may include medallions of Chelford pork, honey roasted breast of Barbary duckling, or aubergine with Mediterranean vegetable compôte. A wide choice of speciality coffees is also available. **Principal beers:** Robinsons.
Directions From M6 thru Knutsford to Macclesfield, turn to Prestbury at Broken Cross. Pub in village centre
Brewery/Company Robinsons
Open 8-1am
Bar food 12-2 7-10 Av main course £5
Restaurant 12-2 7-10 Av 3 course à la carte £22 Av 3 course fixed price £11.95

STRETTON Cheshire Map 07 SJ68

Stretton Fox
STRETTON
Northwich Rd WA4 4PG
☎ 01925 732991
Large old 19th-century farmhouse spread over a considerable area, with lots of interesting nooks and crannies. There are three open fireplaces, an orchard and gardens. Typical menu includes minted lamb cutlets, hot chicken salad, Hunter's chicken, roasted vegetable upside down pie, and beef and Bass Ale pie. **Principal beers:** Bass.
Brewery/Company Vintage Inns
Open 11-11 (Sun 12-10.30)

SWETTENHAM Cheshire Map 07 SJ86

The Swettenham Arms
SWETTENHAM
Swettenham Ln CW12 2LF
☎ 01477 571284
Picturesque, white-painted village pub hidden away behind the church in the lovely Dane valley. Open fires and lots of beams add to the relaxing ambience. Good traditional menu with an extensive choice of dishes which might include baked cod, sugar-baked ham, mild beef curry and duck and apricot pie.

contd.

Principal beers: Tetley, Greenalls Original, Jennings, Beartown.
Directions M6 J18 to Holmes Chapel, then A535 towards Jodrell Bank. 3m take rd on R (Forty Acre Lane) to Swettenham
Brewery/Company Free House
Open 11.30-3 6.30-11 (Sun 12-4, 7-11)
Bar food 12-2.30 7-9.30 Av main course £8.95

TARPORLEY Cheshire Map 07 SJ56

The Boot Inn NEW
TARPORLEY
Boothsdale, Willington CW6 0NH
☎ 01829 751375
Close to 'Little Switzerland', the Boot Inn was originally a beerhouse set in a row of cottages. It now occupies the whole row and has quarry-tiled floors, open fires, and a penny-farthing bicycle made from pennies and farthings. Typical dishes include turkey and ham pie, smoked trout kedgeree and mushroom Stroganoff.
Principal beers: Weetwood Oasthouse Gold, Old Dog & Eastgate; Cains, Bass.
Directions off the A54 Kelsall by-pass
Brewery/Company Free House
Open 10-3 6-11
Bar food 10-2.30 6-9.30 Av main course £7.50
Restaurant 10-2.30 6-9.30 Av 3 course à la carte £17.50

TUSHINGHAM CUM GRINDLEY Cheshire Map 07 SJ54

Blue Bell Inn
TUSHINGHAM CUM GRINDLEY
SY13 4QS ☎ 01948 662172
Exceptionally friendly pub with a warm welcome extending to children and dogs. The building dates from the 17th century and has an abundance of beams, open fires, horse brasses, and a 400-year-old mummified rat. Favourite dishes include garlic and lime chicken, trout, lasagne and steaks.
Principal beers: Hanby Ales.
Directions On the A41 N of Whitchurch
Brewery/Company Free House
Open 12-3 6-11
Bar food 12-3 6-9 Av main course £4.95
Restaurant 12-3 6-9 Av 3 course à la carte £8

WARMINGHAM Cheshire Map 07 SJ76

The Bears Paw Hotel
WARMINGHAM
School Ln CW11 9QN ☎ 01270 526317
Country hotel close to the River Wheelock. Luncheon menu ranges from lamb cutlets with redcurrant and rosemary sauce, and chicken breast wrapped in smoked bacon with Stilton and port sauce, to broccoli and cauliflower bake for vegetarians. Seafood dishes include grilled halibut fillets with lemon, prawns and almonds. **Principal beers:** Bass, Boddingtons, Flowers IPA.
Directions From M6 J18 take A54 then A533 towards Sandbach. Follow signs for village
Brewery/Company Free House
Open 11-11 (Sun 12-10.30)
Bar food 12-2 6-9.30 Av main course £5.45
Restaurant 12-2 7-12 Av 3 course à la carte £20
Accommodation (Min) s£50 d£66

WINCLE Cheshire Map 07 SJ96

The Ship Inn
WINCLE
SK11 0QE ☎ 01260 227217
Situated near the River Dane in the folds of the lower Pennines, this quaint, 16th-century, red sandstone pub remains delightfully unspoilt. Expect a friendly welcome, decent ale and hearty, home-cooked food. Typical dishes include good soups, lasagne, Tuscan chicken, pork and bean casserole, oven-baked cod with tapenade, and gammon and eggs.
Principal beers: Taylor, Wye Valley, Boddingtons, Courage Directors.
Directions Leave A54 at Fourways Motel x-rds, towards Danebridge, Inn 0.5m before bridge on L
Brewery/Company Free House
Open 12-3.30 7-11.30 (closed Mon Nov-Mar)
Bar food 12-2.30 7-9.30 Av main course £5.95
Restaurant 12-3.30 7-11 Av 3 course à la carte £12.95

WRENBURY Cheshire Map 07 SJ54

The Dusty Miller NEW
WRENBURY
CW5 8HG ☎ 01270 780537
Beautifully converted 19th-century mill set beside a canal and the River Weaver;

splendid rose-covered terrace for summer alfresco drinking. Sample the full range of Robinsons ales and interesting bar food. Dishes may include sea bass, smoked haddock rarebit, chargrilled chicken with cider and mustard sauce, pizzas, and ham and eggs. **Principal beers:** Robinson's: Best, Frederics, Old Tom, Hatters Mild; Hartleys XB.
Brewery/Company Robinsons
Open 11.30-11 (closed winter Mon lunch)
Bar food 12-2.30 6.30-9.30 Av main course £7.95
Restaurant 12-2.30 6.30-9.30 Av 3 course à la carte £15

WYBUNBURY Cheshire *Map 07 SJ64*

The Swan
WYBUNBURY

Main Rd CW5 7NE ☎ 01270 841280
Registered as an alehouse in 1580, situated next to the church in the village centre. Main course includes a range of steak, poultry and seafood dishes, such as home-made Cumberland sausages and mash, fishcakes, ramblers' lunch plus daily specials using fresh local produce. **Principal beers:** Jennings, Marston Pedigree.
Directions M6 J16 towards Chester/Nantwich.Turn L at trafic lights in Wybunbury
Brewery/Company Jennings
Open 12-11
Bar food 12-2.30 6-9.30 Av main course £5.50

Cumbria

AMBLESIDE Cumbria *Map 07 NY30*

Drunken Duck Inn
AMBLESIDE

Barngates LA22 0NG ☎ 015394 36347
Stunningly situated in 60 acres in the heart of Cumbria's scenic Lakeland, this 16th-century inn has its own tarn and micro-brewery. Imaginative food ranges from Cumberland cheese and pickles at lunchtime, to confit of duck, coriander-crusted salmon with crab sauce, chicken, mushroom and tarragon suet pudding, and pan-fried scallops with lemon grass butter sauce. **Principal beers:** Yates, Jennings, Theakston Old Peculier, Cracker Ale.

Directions A592 from Kendal, follow signs for Hawkshead, 2.5m sign for inn on R, 1m up the hill
Brewery/Company Free House
Open 11.30-3 6-11
Bar food 12-2.30 6-9 Av main course £8.50
Restaurant 6-9 Av 3 course à la carte £17.95
Accommodation (Min) s£55 d£70

APPLEBY-IN-WESTMORLAND Cumbria *Map 12 NY62*

The Royal Oak Inn
APPLEBY-IN-WESTMORLAND

Bongate CA16 6UN ☎ 017683 51463
Medieval coaching inn where the blackboard menu features starters such as leek and watercress soup, fillet of smoked mackerel with rhubarb chutney, and smoked duck with lime dressing. Main course dishes include chicken with white wine and tomato sauce, roast salmon with lobster sauce, and lemon sole with nut brown butter. **Principal beers:** Yates Biter,Black Sheep Bitter,Fraoch,Theakston Best Bitter.

Directions M6 J38 take A66 east. Village on B6542 on R.

Brewery/Company Free House
Open 11-3 6-11 (Sun 12-10.30)
Bar food 12-2 6.30-9.30
Restaurant 12-2 6.30-9
Accommodation (Min) s£30 d£60

Tufton Arms Hotel NEW
APPLEBY-IN-WESTMORLAND
Market Square CA16 6XA
☎ 017683 51593
Victorian coaching inn situated in the heart of this popular market town. From home-made lasagne and fresh fish and chips, served in the traditional bar, the menu choice extends to such cosmopolitan dishes as carpaccio of beef, sea bass with champagne butter sauce, pigeon with rösti potatoes, and iced nougat parfait in the conservatory restaurant. **Principal beers:** Tetley, Theakstons.

Brewery/Company Free House
Open 10.30-11
Bar food 12-2 6.30-9 Av main course £5.50
Restaurant 12-2 6.30-9 Av 3 course à la carte £21
Accommodation (Min) s£47.50 d£85

ARMATHWAITE Cumbria — Map 12 NY54

The Dukes Head Hotel
ARMATHWAITE
Front St CA4 9PB ☎ 016974 72226
Named after the Duke of Clarence (Queen Victoria's son), and opened as a pub when the Settle to Carlisle Railway was being built. Popular with walkers exploring the beautiful Eden Valley. One menu offers dishes such as hot potted shrimps, trout with almonds and pistachio butter, and tuna with lime and ginger. **Principal beers:** Boddingtons, Morland Old Speckled Hen, Burton Ale, Whitbread Castle Eden Ale.
Directions A6, turn at Armathwaite turning
Brewery/Company Pubmaster
Open 11.45-3 5.30-11
Bar food 12-3 6.15-11 Av main course £7.25
Restaurant 12-3 6.15-11 Av 3 course à la carte £14.50
Accommodation (Min) s£26.50 d£46.50

ASKHAM Cumbria — Map 12 NY52

The Punchbowl Inn
ASKHAM
CA10 2PF ☎ 01931 712443
An-easy-to-find haven in a beautiful Cumbrian village, this 16th-century coaching inn offers the best in old world charm and hospitality. There is a good choice of starters or light lunch alternatives, while main courses include fisherman's crust, salmon supreme, tagliatelle pescatori, and braised beef in ale. **Principal beers:** Whitbread Castle Eden Ale, Wadworth 6X, Flowers IPA, Morland Old Speckled Hen.
Directions From M6 N on A6 for 7m
Brewery/Company Whitbread
Open 12-3 6.30-11
Bar food 12-2 6.30-9 Av main course £6.50
Accommodation (Min) s£28.50 d£53

BARBON Cumbria — Map 07 SD68

The Barbon Inn
BARBON
LA6 2LJ ☎ 015242 76233
A 17th-century coaching inn, off the main road, nestling at the foot of the Yorkshire Dales. Bar food ranges from sandwiches to steak and kidney pie, and the à la carte dinner menu might offer hot smoked salmon roulade, and roast rack of lamb with redcurrant and elderflower sauce. **Principal beers:** Theakston.
Directions 3.5m N of Kirkby Lonsdale on A683
Brewery/Company Free House
Open 12-3 6.30-11
Bar food 12-2 7-9 Av main course £5.50
Restaurant 12.30-1.30 7.30-9 Av 3 course à la carte £15
Accommodation (Min) s£32 d£60

BASSENTHWAITE Cumbria Map 11 NY23

The Pheasant
BASSENTHWAITE
CA13 9YE ☎ 017687 76234

Old coaching inn close to Bassenthwaite Lake, with an inglenook fireplace in the bar. There is a light lunch menu available throughout the inn, and a fixed-price menu for lunch and dinner in the restaurant. Typical offerings are Cumberland smoked ham and local rainbow trout. **Principal beers:** Theakston, Bass, Jennings Cumberland.

Directions A66 to Cockermouth, 8m N of Keswick on L
Brewery/Company Free House
Open 11.30-2.30 5.30-10.30
Bar food 12-2.30 Av main course £5.50
Restaurant 12-1.30 7-8.30 Av 3 course fixed price £19.50
Accommodation (Min) s£46 d£72

BEETHAM Cumbria Map 07 SD47

The Wheatsheaf Hotel
BEETHAM
LA7 7AL ☎ 015395 62123

Fine, timbered, 16th-century coaching inn enjoying a peaceful village setting close to Morecambe Bay and the Lake District. Neatly refurbished bar offering good choice of food, including air-dried Cumbrian ham with home-made chutney, Bury black pudding with mashed roots and stewed sweet onion, and honey-scented rack of Lakeland lamb with blackberry gravy. **Principal beers:** Jennings Cumberland, Jennings Bitter, Theakston.

Directions On A6 5m N of J35
Brewery/Company Free House
Open 11-3 6-11
Bar food 12-2 6-9 Av main course £7.95
Restaurant 12-2 6-9 Av 3 course à la carte £15 Av 3 course fixed price £10.95
Accommodation (Min) s£45 d£55

BLENCOGO Cumbria Map 11 NY14

The New Inn
BLENCOGO
CA7 0BZ ☎ 016973 61091

A late Victorian sandstone pub, with an open fire and a friendly atmosphere, in a farming hamlet with splendid views of the north Cumbrian fells. Hearty bar food ranges from 'light bites' like tagliatelle carbonara and cheese and herb pate with Cumberland sauce, to main dishes such as sirloin steak, and pork fillet with peppercorn sauce. **Principal beers:** Black Sheep.

Directions Toward Wigton on B5305, then B5302 toward Silloth, after 4m Blencogo signed on L
Brewery/Company Free House
Open 12-3 (Thu-Sun) 7-11 (closed Wed)
Bar food 12-1.30 7-9 Av main course £9

BOOT Cumbria Map 07 NY10

The Burnmoor Inn NEW
BOOT
CA19 1TG ☎ 019467 23224

Located in the stunning Eskdale Valley, at the foot of Scafell Pike, England's highest mountain, this 16th-century inn offers an ideal rest stop for walkers. A typical menu includes Pad's local game pie, sirloin steak, homemade vegetable crumble, and Bewley's Cumberland sausage. **Principal beers:** Jennings Cumberland, Black Sheep Bitter.

Brewery/Company Free House
Open 10am-11pm
Bar food 12-9 Av main course £4.50
Restaurant 12-2 7-9 Av 3 course à la carte £16 Av 4 course fixed price £17.50
Accommodation (Min) s£27 d£54

BOUTH Cumbria Map 07 SD38

The White Hart Inn NEW
BOUTH
LA12 8JB ☎ 01229 861229

Surrounded by fells, this 17th-century inn is family owned and run by locals. Locally reared beef is a speciality, but as one of the proprietors is a vegetarian, there's plenty available in that direction too. Typical menu includes game pie, pasta Siciliana, halibut steak and vegetable balti. **Principal beers:** Blackpool Bitter, Black Sheep, Jennings Cumberland Ale, Barnsley.

Brewery/Company Free House

contd.

Open 12-2 6-11 (Mon & Tue 6-11 only)
Bar food 12-2 6-8.45 Av main course £6.50
Restaurant 12-2 6-8.45 Av 3 course à la carte £12.50
Accommodation (Min) s£28 d£36

BUTTERMERE Cumbria *Map 11 NY11*

Bridge Hotel
BUTTERMERE
CA13 9UZ ☎ 017687 70252
A perfect Lakeland retreat, standing next to an old packhorse bridge which in its day carried Wordsworth, Ruskin and Southey to marvel at the Buttermere fells and their twin lakes, this traditional 18th-century inn offers good food and a warm welcome, as well as comfortable accommodation. **Principal beers:** Tetley, Calders.
Directions Take B5289 from Keswick
Brewery/Company Free House
Open 10-11 (food 12-2.30, 3-5.30, 6-9.30 in summer)
Bar food 12-2.30 6-9.30 Av main course £5.50
Restaurant 7-8.30 Av 3 course à la carte £25 Av 4 course fixed price £18.95
Accommodation (Min) s£42 d£84

CARTMEL Cumbria *Map 07 SD37*

The Cavendish
CARTMEL
LA11 6QA ☎ 015395 36240
Cartmel's oldest hostelry, dating from the 15th century, with oak beams and log fires creating a cosy atmosphere. Bar food ranges from soup and sandwiches to lamb Henry or bangers and mash. Typical restaurant dishes might be stuffed fillet steak, sea bass and local ostrich.
Principal beers: Jennings Cumberland, Mitchell's Lancaster Bomber, Tetleys.
Directions M6 J36 take A590 follow signs for Cartmel. In village take 1st R
Brewery/Company Free House
Open 11.30-11
Bar food 12-2.15 6-9.30 Av main course £5.95
Restaurant 12-2.15 6-9.30 Av 3 course à la carte £18.50 Av 3 course fixed price £18.50
Accommodation (Min) s£27 d£54

CONISTON Cumbria *Map 07 SD39*

Black Bull Inn NEW
CONISTON
1 Yewdale Rd LA21 8DU
☎ 015394 41335 41668
Wordsworth and Turner stayed at this 400-year-old coaching inn which nestles beneath Coniston 'Old Man'. After an invigorating fell walk, enjoy a home-brewed pint and tuck into a good meal from the extensive menu. From favourite snacks and Cumberland grills, the choice includes game pie, duck with damson sauce, Esthwaite trout and fresh market fish. **Principal beers:** Coniston Blue Bird, Old Man Ale, & Opium, Coniston Blacksmith.
Brewery/Company Free House
Open 11-11 (Sun 12-10.30)
Bar food 12-9 6-9 Av main course £6
Restaurant 6-9 Av 3 course à la carte £18
Accommodation (Min) s£40 d£65

CROSTHWAITE Cumbria *Map 07 SD49*

The Punch Bowl Inn
CROSTHWAITE
LA8 8HR ☎ 015395 68237
A 16th-century inn nestling in the picturesque Lyth Valley, featuring three welcoming fires in winter, a popular summer patio, and superior, modern pub food. Well-cooked dishes include seafood hors d'oeuvre, warm game salad, braised shank of lamb with red wine and rosemary sauce, duck with soy, ginger and honey, and sticky Tunisian-style orange cake. **Principal beers:** Theakston, Black Sheep, Jennings Cumberland Ale, Morland Old Speckled Hen.

Directions From M6 J36 take A590 towards Barrow, then A5074 & follow signs for Crosthwaite. Pub next to church on L
Brewery/Company Free House

Open 11-11 (Sun 12-10.30, closed 2wks in Nov)
Restaurant 12-2 6-9 Av 3 course à la carte £15 Av 3 course fixed price £11.95
Accommodation (Min) s£37.50 d£55

DENT Cumbria   Map 07 SD78

Sun Inn
DENT

Main St LA10 5QL ☎ 01536 25208

Situated in a quaint, narrow cobbled street, the oldest parts of this Dales inn dates from the 15th and 16th centuries. Traditional pub fare and home-brewed ales are served in the cosy beamed bars. Typical dishes include home-made steak and kidney pie, beefburger, toasted sandwiches, Brie and courgette bake, and a selection of daily specials. **Principal beers:** Dent.
Directions From M6 through Sedburgh, Dent signed, 4.5m
Brewery/Company Free House
Open 11-2.30 6.30-11 (Jul/Aug 11-11, no food Mon-Thu Jan-Mar)
Bar food 12-2 6.30-8.30 Av main course £4.95
Accommodation (Min) s£20 d£37

DOCKRAY Cumbria   Map 11 NY32

The Royal Hotel
DOCKRAY

CA11 0JY ☎ 017684 82356

Wordsworth and Mary Queen of Scots both visited this 16th-century family-run inn, a mile from the shores of Ullswater. A blazing log fire and flagstone floor help to create a cosy, inviting atmosphere. Typical examples from the specials board include medallions of monkfish, half a braised guinea fowl, and Caribbean pork. **Principal beers:** Whitbread Castle Eden, Jennings Cumberland, Black Sheep, Wadworths 6X.
Directions A66 towards Keswick for 8m, turn L onto A5091 signposted Dockray
Brewery/Company Free House
Open 11-11
Bar food 12-2.30 Av main course £6
Restaurant 12-2.30 6-9 Av 3 course à la carte £13
Accommodation (Min) s£30 d£60

ELTERWATER Cumbria   Map 07 NY30

The Britannia Inn
ELTERWATER

LA22 9HP ☎ 015394 37210

Traditional 16th-century Lakeland inn on the village green, surrounded by magnificent fell scenery, and convenient for walkers exploring the Langdale Valley. Home-made dishes include steak and mushroom pie, Cumberland pie, chicken with wild mushroom ragout, and rack of lamb with parsnip crumble. Sweets include lemon brûlée and sticky toffee pudding. **Principal beers:** Jennings, Coniston Bluebird, Dent Aviator.
Directions A593 from Ambleside, then B5343 to Elterwater
Brewery/Company Free House
Open 11-11
Bar food 12-2 6.30-9.30 Av main course £6.95
Accommodation (Min) s£24 d£48

ESKDALE GREEN Cumbria   Map 06 NY10

Bower House Inn
ESKDALE GREEN

CA19 1TD ☎ 019467 23244

Typical Lakeland inn, around 300 years old, and a farmhouse before World War 1. There is a lovely oak beamed bar with log fires, a restaurant and a relaxing lounge. From decent sandwiches and traditional Cumberland sausage, daily specials may include pheasant in red wine, trout Jeanette, and rum Nickie. **Principal beers:** Theakston Bitter, Jennings Bitter, Morland Old speckled Hen.
Directions 4m off A595 1/2m W of Eskdale Green
Brewery/Company Free House
Open 11-11
Bar food 12-2 6.30-9.30 Av main course £7.25
Restaurant 7-8.30 Av 3 course à la carte £21 Av 4 course fixed price £21
Accommodation (Min) s£53.50 d£74

King George IV Inn
ESKDALE GREEN

CA19 1TS ☎ 019467 23262

Centuries-old Lakeland inn situated at the heart of the delightful Eskdale Valley. Cosy bars feature open fires and low, oak-beamed ceilings. Fresh home-cooked fare, include a traditional Cumbrian breakfast,

contd.

hearty bar snacks and daily specials, such as liver and onions, seafood platter and turkey escalope. **Principal beers:** Theakston - Best, Old Peculier & XB, Jennings Cumberland.
Directions A590 to Greenodd, A5092 to Broughton-in-Furness then over Ulpha Fell towards Eskdale
Brewery/Company Free House
Open 11-3 6-11
Bar food 12-2 6-9 Av main course £5.50
Restaurant 7-9 Av 3 course à la carte £17
Accommodation (Min) s£25 d£45

GRANGE-OVER-SANDS Cumbria Map 07 SD47

Hare & Hounds Country Inn NEW

GRANGE-OVER-SANDS
Bowland Bridge LA11 6NN
☎ 015395 68333
Set in a tiny hamlet which boasts a post office and four houses, this 17th-century pub plays host to the local hounds every January. Among the dishes produced in the kitchen are deep-fried Whitby scampi, poached swordfish steak, Hare and Hounds beef Stroganoff and a variety of pizzas, salads and jacket potatoes. **Principal beers:** Tetleys.

Directions M6 onto A591, L after 3m onto A590, R after 3m onto A5074, after 4m sharp L & next L after 1m
Brewery/Company Free House
Open 11-11 (Sun 12-10.30)
Bar food 12-2 6-9 Av main course £6.25
Restaurant 12-2 6-9 Av 3 course à la carte £12 Av 4 course fixed price £12
Accommodation (Min) s£35 d£50

For Pubs with AA food rosettes see page 430

GRASMERE Cumbria Map 11 NY30

The Travellers Rest Inn

GRASMERE
Keswick Rd LA22 9RR ☎ 0500 600725
Some of the finest scenery in the country surrounds this 16th-century former coaching inn, which offers a good range of beers and and an extensive menu of home-cooked traditional fare. Typical dishes are moules marinière, pot-roasted lamb shank, and sticky toffee pudding. **Principal beers:** Jennings Bitter, Cumberland Ale, & Sneck Lifter, Marstons Pedigree.

Directions From M6 take A591 to Grasmere, pub 1/2m N of Grasmere
Brewery/Company Free House
Open 11-11 (Sun 12-10.30)
Bar food 12-3 6-9.30 Av main course £5.95
Restaurant 12-3 6-9.30 Av 3 course à la carte £12
Accommodation (Min) s£16 d£32

GREAT LANGDALE Cumbria Map 07 NY20

The New Dungeon Ghyll Hotel

GREAT LANGDALE
LA22 9JY ☎ 015394 37213
The hotel enjoys a spectacular location at the foot of the Langdale Pikes and Pavey Ark. Bar food encompasses pasta dishes, salmon and dill fishcakes, and game pie. Restaurant dishes include chicken supreme stuffed with prawns, and venison steak with red wine and mushroom sauce. **Principal beers:** Courage Directors, Ruddles Best.
Directions From M6 into Kendal then A591 into Ambleside onto A593 to B5343, hotel 6m on R
Brewery/Company Free House
Open 11-11 (Sun 11-10.30, food served 11.30-9)

Restaurant 7-8.30 Av 3 course fixed price £17.50
Accommodation (Min) s£37.50 d£55

GRIZEBECK Cumbria Map 07 SD28

The Greyhound Inn NEW
GRIZEBECK
LA17 7XJ ☎ 01229 889224
Situated on the edge of the Lake District National Park, this late 17th-century slate-roofed inn is set at the bottom of a long deep incline, and is an ideal location for walkers to gather their strength. A typical menu includes grilled lamb cutlets, haddock in batter and spinach and ricotta cannelloni. **Principal beers:** John Smiths, Black Sheep.

Brewery/Company Free House
Open 12-3 6-11
Bar food 12-2 6-9 Av main course £5
Accommodation (Min) s£21 d£35

HAVERTHWAITE Cumbria Map 07 SD38

Rusland Pool
HAVERTHWAITE
LA12 8AA ☎ 01229 861384
Situated in open countryside at the foot of the Rusland Valley, this friendly, 18th-century coaching inn is named after the nearby river. Varied menus offer a good range of snacks - freshly battered cod, seafood pasta - and main meals like duck in plum sauce, steak with bacon and Stilton, and monkfish Provencal.
Principal beers: Wadworth 6X.
Directions M6 J36 take A590 towards Barrow-in-Furness
Brewery/Company Free House
Open 11-11 (bar food served all day, 12-9.15)
Restaurant 12-2.30 6-9.15 Av 3 course à la carte £15
Accommodation (Min) s£40 d£56

HAWKSHEAD Cumbria Map 07 SD39

Queens Head Hotel
HAWKSHEAD
Main St LA22 0NS ☎ 015394 36271
Traditional black and white building dating from the 16th century in the centre of a traffic-free village. Typical dishes include liver and onions and Mexican tortillas at lunchtime, while in the evening you might expect Hawkshead organic trout, and haggis and black pudding Wellington. **Principal beers:** Robinsons Hartleys XB & Frederics.

Directions M6 J36 A590 to Newby Bridge. Take 2nd R, 8m to Hawkshead
Brewery/Company Robinsons
Open 11-11
Bar food 12-2.30 6.15-9.30 Av main course £7
Restaurant 12-2.30 6.15-9.30 Av 3 course à la carte £16.25
Accommodation (Min) s£40 d£60

HEVERSHAM Cumbria Map 07 SD48

Blue Bell Hotel
HEVERSHAM
Princes Way LA7 7EE ☎ 015395 62018
Once a local vicarage dating back to 1460, this civilised country inn is situated close to the Kent estuary and fine local walks. Food ranges from 'light bites' like Cumbria ham and fruit chutney, and various open sandwiches, to venison casserole, Morecambe Bay shrimps, fresh sea bass, and puddings like sticky toffee pudding.
Principal beers: Samuel Smith Old Brewery.
Directions On A6 between Kendal & Milnthorpe
Brewery/Company Samuel Smith
Open 7-12

contd.

Bar food 11-6 7-9.30 Av main course £6.50
Restaurant 12-6 7-9.30 Av 3 course à la carte £11.50 Av 4 course fixed price £12.50
Accommodation (Min) s£47.50 d£64

KENDAL Cumbria Map 07 SD59

Gateway Inn
KENDAL
Crook Rd LA8 8LX
☎ 01539 720605 & 724187

Delightful, appropriately named country house inn with superb views and located at the gateway to the Lake District National Park. Welcoming atmosphere and plenty of choice for those wanting to eat. Try one of the fresh fish dishes, grilled lamb cutlets, shin of beef or, perhaps, the steak and mushroom pie.

Directions From M6 J36 take A590/A591, follow signs for Windermere, pub on L after 9m
Brewery/Company Thwaites
Open 11-11
Bar food 12-2 6-9 Av main course £8
Restaurant 12-2 6-9
Accommodation (Min) s£35 d£50

KESWICK Cumbria Map 11 NY22

The Horse & Farrier Inn NEW
KESWICK
Threlkeld Village CA12 4SQ
☎ 017687 79688

Sample excellent Jennings ales and imaginative home-cooking at this 300-year-old stone pub situated below Blencathra, a popular fell among local walkers. From salmon and dill sandwiches and cold platters, the menu extends to shoulder of lamb with spinach mash and rosemary and redcurrant sauce, and red snapper with balsamic and soy dressing.

Principal beers: Jennings: Bitter, Cocker Hoop, Sneck Lifter & Cumberland Ale.
Brewery/Company Jennings
Open 11-11 (Sun 12-10.30)
Bar food 12-2 6.30-9.30
Restaurant 12-2 6.30-9.30 Av 3 course à la carte £15

KIRKBY LONSDALE Cumbria Map 07 SD67

Pheasant Inn
KIRKBY LONSDALE
LA6 2RX ☎ 015242 71230

Ideally situated between the Yorkshire Dales and the Lake District, one mile from the centre of Kirkby Lonsdale, this 18th-century, white-painted coaching inn prides itself on its extensive, interesting choice of specials which may include beef and leek pot, fresh Loch Fyne mussels, fillet of red sea bream, and rabbit and root vegetable casserole.
Principal beers: Theakston Best, McEwans.

Directions From M6 J36 onto A65 for 7m, L onto A683 at Devils Bridge, 1m to Casterton. Village centre
Brewery/Company Free House
Open 11-3 6-11 (Restaurant closed Sun lunch Nov-Mar)
Bar food 12-2 6.30-9
Restaurant 7-9

Snooty Fox Tavern
KIRKBY LONSDALE
Main St LA6 2AH ☎ 015242 71308

Listed Jacobean inn with a white stone facade and rambling bars with roaring fires and a wealth of unuusal artefacts. Cumberland sausages with champ, and fish in beer batter are typical bar fare, while the interesting specials board might offer duck with bramble and juniper compôte, and three cheese soufflé with garlic cream.

Principal beers: Taylor Landlord, Robinsons Hartleys XB, Theakston Best.
Directions M6 J36 take A65 tavern 6m
Brewery/Company Free House
Open 11-11
Bar food 12-2.30 6.30-10 Av main course £5.95
Restaurant 12-2.30 6.30-10 Av 3 course à la carte £16
Accommodation (Min) s£32 d£50

The Sun Inn
KIRKBY LONSDALE
Market St LA6 2AU ☎ 015242 71965
The same menu is offered throughout this 16th-century inn, in the bar or 30's avante garde-style restaurant, which is called Mad Carew's from the poem by J Milton Hayes. Dishes might include seafood hors d'oeuvre, baked salmon fillet, and chargrilled Barnsley lamb chop. **Principal beers:** Black Sheep, Dent, Boddingtons.
Directions From M6 J36 take A65
Brewery/Company Free House
Open 11-11 (Sun 12-10.30)
Bar food 11-2 6-10 Av main course £8.95
Restaurant 12-2 6-10
Accommodation (Min) s£29.50 d£49.50

Whoop Hall Inn

KIRKBY LONSDALE
Skipton Rd LA6 2HP ☎ 015242 71284
Over 350 years old, Whoop Hall was once the kennels for local fox hounds, and gets its name from the huntsman's call. In an imaginately converted barn you can sample a good menu offering spare ribs, medallions of monkfish with sweet pepper sauce, and sticky toffee pudding. **Principal beers:** Theakstons, Dent, Black Sheep.
Directions A65 from M6, pub 1m SE of Kirkby Lonsdale
Brewery/Company Free House
Open 7am-11.30pm
Bar food 12-2.30 7-10 Av main course £5.75
Restaurant 12-2.30 7-10 Av 3 course à la carte £15
Accommodation (Min) s£40 d£60

Pubs offering a good choice of seafood on the menu

LAZONBY Cumbria *Map 07 SD53*

Joiners Arms
LAZONBY
Townfoot CA10 1BL ☎ 01768 898728
18th-century village inn, formerly a farmhouse and barn, close to the River Eden with fine Pennine views. The menu ranges from snacks and home-made steak and kidney pie, Cumberland sausages, and to a good choice of vegetarian dishes such as spinach and mushroom lasagne.
Principal beers: Whitbread.
Directions Take A6 N to Plumpton, R to Lazonby
Brewery/Company Free House
Open 12-3.30 6.30-11.30
Bar food 12-2 6.30-8.30 Av main course £5.25
Accommodation (Min) s£21.50 d£38

LITTLE LANGDALE Cumbria *Map 07 NY30*

Three Shires Inn
LITTLE LANGDALE
LA22 9NZ ☎ 015394 37215
100-year-old country inn, constructed of slate, and named after the meeting point of the old counties, just up the road. Beef and ale pie, and local Cumberland sausage are typical bar fare, while the restaurant might offer marinated venison with juniper and garlic served with port and Stilton sauce.
Principal beers: Jennings-Best, Cumberland, Theakston XB.
Directions Turn off A593, 2.3m from Ambleside at 2nd junct signposted for The Langdales. 1st L 0.5m, Hotel 1m up lane
Brewery/Company Free House
Open 11-11 (winter 11.30-3,8-10.30, closed Jan)
Bar food 12-2 6-9 Av main course £8.50
Restaurant 7-8 Av 4 course fixed price £17
Accommodation (Min) s£25 d£50

LOWESWATER Cumbria *Map 11 NY12*

Kirkstile Inn NEW
LOWESWATER
CA13 0RU ☎ 01900 85219
Quaint 16th-century inn in a quiet Lakeland valley which has everything - lakes, mountains, pastures and forest. The beamed bars attract locals and walkers alike for the excellent Cumbrian ales, the warm hospitality, and

contd.

traditional pub food, including braised venison in red wine, spicy lamb curry, vegetable cobbler, and fruit crumble. **Principal beers:** Jennings Bitter & Cumberland Ale.
Brewery/Company Free House
Open 11-11
Bar food 12-2.30 6-9 Av main course £6.75
Restaurant 6-8 Av 3 course à la carte £14.95 Av 4 course fixed price £14.95
Accommodation (Min) s£37 d£47

MELMERBY Cumbria *Map 12 NY63*

The Shepherds Inn
MELMERBY
CA10 1HF ☎ 01768 881217
An 18th-century sandstone inn facing the village green. It is well known for its good food and beer and draws eager diners from across the Pennines for favourite dishes like Cumberland sausage hotpot, chicken and ham cobbler, and venison and Roquefort crumble. Desserts, such as tutti frutti sponge pudding, and fine local cheeses are particularly popular. **Principal beers:** Jennings Cumberland, Holts, Black Sheep Riggwelter, Hesket Newmarket Ales.
Directions On A686 NE of Penrith
Brewery/Company Free House
Open 10.30-3 6-11 (Sun 12-3, 7-10.30)
Bar food 11-2.30 6-9.45 Av main course £6
Restaurant 11-2.30 6-9.45 Av 3 course à la carte £12

MUNGRISDALE Cumbria *Map 11 NY33*

The Mill Inn
MUNGRISDALE
CA11 0XR ☎ 017687 79632
Set in a peaceful village, this 16th-century coaching inn is handy for spectacular fell walks. Charles Dickens and John Peel once stayed here. Sample traditional Lakeland food and tuck into game casserole, Whitby scampi or chicken breast wrapped in smoked bacon with a Stilton sauce. **Principal beers:** Jennings Bitter & Cumberland, Tetley.

Directions From Penrith A66 to Keswick, after 10m R to Mungrisdale, pub 2m on L
Brewery/Company Free House
Open 8am-midnight (Sun 8-11)
Bar food 12-9 Av main course £6.95
Accommodation (Min) s£27 d£47

NEAR SAWREY Cumbria *Map 07 SD39*

Tower Banks Hotel
NEAR SAWREY
LA22 0LF ☎ 015394 36334
Situated in a tiny hamlet midway between Hawkshead and Lake Windermere, this 17th-century Lakeland pub stands next door to Hill Top (NT), Beatrix Potter's former home. The slate-flagged floored bar is popular with tourists, as is the traditional bar menu which offers ploughman's, potted shrimps, home-made pies, and local trout.
Principal beers: Theakston - Best, XB, & Old Peculier,Coniston Bluebird.
Directions On B5285 SW of Windermere
Brewery/Company Free House
Open 11-3 6-11 (Summer 5.30-11)
Bar food 12-2 6.30-9 Av main course £5.50
Restaurant 6.30-9 Av 3 course à la carte £10.50
Accommodation (Min) s£35 d£50

NETHER WASDALE Cumbria *Map 06 NY10*

The Screes Hotel
NETHER WASDALE
CA20 1ET ☎ 019467 26262
300-year-old inn situated in a quiet valley amid majestic mountain scenery. Once a Temperance House after the local vicar in the 1800s revoked its license due to drunken goings-on. Bar food includes Cumberland sausage, fresh herb-battered haddock, Thai spicy seafood salad, and swordfish with lime and ginger salsa.
Principal beers: Yates, Jennings, Black Sheep, Dent.
Directions E of A595 between Whitehaven & Ravenglass

Brewery/Company Free House
Open 12-11
Bar food 12-2.30 6-9.30 Av main course £6.50
Accommodation (Min) s£25 d£40

OUTGATE Cumbria Map 07 SD39

Outgate Inn
OUTGATE
LA22 0NQ ☎ 015394 36413

Formerly a toll house, this 18th-century Lakeland pub offers salad and fish dishes, jacket potatoes and sandwiches. Outgate grill, home-made steak and kidney pie, and grilled gammon are among the main courses, while the daily specials may include chicken in red wine and whole honey glazed ham shank.

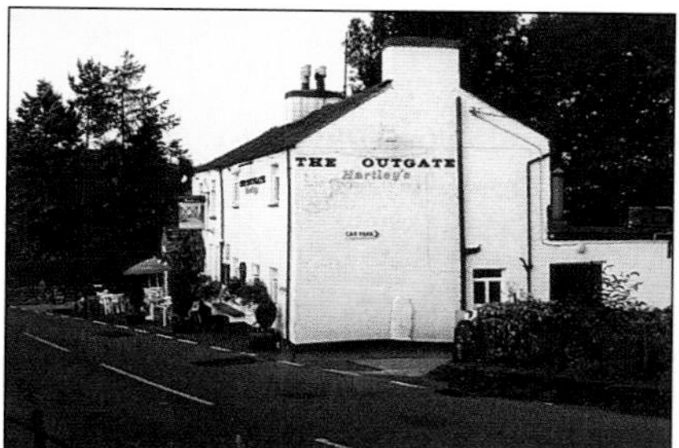

Principal beers: Hartleys XB, Robinsons Best, Fredericks.
Directions From M6, A684 to Kendal, A591 towards Ambleside. At Plumgarths take B5284 to Hawkshead then Outgate
Brewery/Company Hartleys
Open 11-3 6-11
Bar food 12-2 6.30-9 Av main course £6
Accommodation (Min) d£50

RAVENSTONEDALE Cumbria Map 07 NY70

Black Swan Hotel
RAVENSTONEDALE
CA17 4NG
☎ 015396 23204 & 0800 0741394

Built of Lakeland stone at the turn of the century, this comfortable hotel is set in a peaceful village on the edge of the Howgill Fells. A tempting menu may feature pot-roasted pork with apple dumplings, local game pie, or sea bass with warm citrus vegetables. Lovely beckside garden and character bars.
Principal beers: Black Sheep.
Directions M6 J38 take A685 E towards Brough
Brewery/Company Free House
Open 8.30-3 6-11
Bar food 12-2 6-9 Av main course £5.75
Restaurant 12-2 7-9 Av 3 course à la carte £15 Av 5 course fixed price £23
Accommodation (Min) s£45 d£70

The Fat Lamb Country Inn
RAVENSTONEDALE
Crossbank CA17 4LL ☎ 015396 23242

Dating back to the 1600s, this historic inn is beautifully situated in remote open countryside midway between the Lake District and the Yorkshire Dales. Food is produced on the premises, using fresh local ingredients, the imaginative bar menu offering baked egg Wensleydale, trout with walnuts and oats, and Cumberland sausage.

Principal beers: Tetley.
Directions On A683 between Sedbergh and Kirkby Stephen
Brewery/Company Free House
Open 12-11
Bar food 12-3 6-11 Av main course £8
Restaurant 12-3 6-11 Av 3 course à la carte £16 Av 4 course fixed price £18
Accommodation (Min) s£32 d£56

SCALES Cumbria Map 11 NY32

White Horse Inn
SCALES
CA12 4SY ☎ 017687 79241

Situated on the lower slopes of Blencathra, this former farmhouse dates from around 1650. The inn cultivates traditional values, with good food and ale and no noisy distractions. Local delicacies include air-dried Cumberland Ham, Cumberland sausage and Borrowdale trout. Options range from bar snacks to full meals.
Principal beers: Bass, Jennings, Blacksheep, Worthington.
Directions Off A66 between Keswick & Penrith

contd.

Northern England

Brewery/Company Free House
Open 12-2.30 6.30-10.30
Bar food 12-2 6.45-9 Av main course £8

SEATHWAITE Cumbria *Map 07 SD29*

Newfield Inn
SEATHWAITE
LA20 6ED ☎ 01229 716208

16th-century inn set in Wordsworth's favourite valley, popular with walkers and climbers, not least for the good range of cask ales, 25 malt whiskies and 10 authentic Polish vodkas. Free-range eggs from the inn's own hens feature in a menu of homely dishes served in generous portions.
Principal beers: Theakston Best, XB, Old Peculier.

Directions A590 toward Barrow, then R onto A5092, becomes A595, follow for 1m, R at Duddon Bri, 6m to Seathwaite
Brewery/Company Free House
Open 11-3 6-11.30 (Wknds 11-11.30)
Bar food 12-3 6-10 Av main course £4.95
Restaurant 12-3 6-10 Av 3 course à la carte £8.95

THIRLSPOT Cumbria *Map 11 NY31*

The Kings Head
THIRLSPOT
CA12 4TN ☎ 0500 600 725

Oak beams and inglenook fireplaces are features of this 17th-century coaching inn set in the heart of the Lake District National Park. Good-value bar food is served, and a four-course evening meal, with dishes such as baked Borrowdale trout and slow-cooked pork roast.
Principal beers: Theakston XB, Best & Old Peculier, Jennings, Morland Old Speckled Hen.

Directions From M6 take A66 to Keswick then A591, pub 4m S of Keswick
Brewery/Company Free House
Open 12-11
Bar food 12-3 6-9.30 Av main course £5.95
Restaurant 12-3 7-9 Av 3 course à la carte £17.95 Av 4 course fixed price £17.95
Accommodation (Min) s£15.95 d£32

THORNTHWAITE Cumbria *Map 11 NY22*

Swan Hotel & Country Inn NEW
THORNTHWAITE
CA12 5SQ ☎ 017687 78080

Family-run 17th-century inn set in stunning Lakeland scenery, complete with fell views and nearby lakeside walks. Varied menus may list braised beef in Guinness, Cumberland sausage on puréed apple, and steak with peppercorn sauce in the bar. Evening table d'hôte menus include home-made soups and local trout and pheasant.

Directions 3m out of Keswick on the A66
Brewery/Company Free House
Open 12-11

Bar food 12-2.30 6-9.30 Av main course £6.50
Restaurant 12-2 6-9 Av 3 course à la carte £12 Av 5 course fixed price £16
Accommodation (Min) s£22 d£44

TIRRIL Cumbria *Map 12 NY52*

Queens Head Inn
TIRRIL
CA10 2JF ☎ 01768 863219
Long, rambling, whitewashed building dating from 1719 and once owned by the Wordsworth family. Plenty of original beams, worn flagstones, open fires, and interesting dishes on varied menus. From ploughman's and stuffed pittas, the choice may include with redcurrant jus, venison with peppercorn sauce, and red snapper Sicillian. Fine range of malt whiskies. **Principal beers:** Black Sheep Best, Jennings Cumberland, Boddingtons, Dent Kamikaze.
Directions A66 towards Penrith then A6 S toward Shap. In Eamont Bridge take R just after Crown Hotel. Tirril 1m on B5320.
Brewery/Company Free House
Open 12-3 6-11 (Sat 12-11, Sun 12-10.30)
Bar food 12-2 6-9.30 Av main course £6.50
Restaurant 12-2 6-9.30 Av 3 course à la carte £14
Accommodation (Min) s£30 d£40

TROUTBECK Cumbria *Map 07 NY40*

Queens Head Hotel
TROUTBECK
Townhead LA23 1PW ☎ 015394 32174
Historic coaching inn situated at the base of the Kirkstone Pass amid stunning Lakeland scenery. The interior oozes character and has an excellent reputation for food and ale. Expect an imaginative menu, including sampled dishes like a full flavoured home-made soup with lovely herb bread, shank of lamb in red wine, and langoustines with lemon grass and coriander. **Principal beers:** Mitchells Lancaster Bomber, Boddingtons, Tetley, Coniston Bluebird.
Directions M6 J36, A590/591 westbound towards Windermere, R at mini-rdbt onto A592 signed Penrith/Ullswater, pub 2m on R
Brewery/Company Free House
Open 11-11
Bar food 12-2.30 6.30-9 Av main course £6.95
Restaurant 6.30-9 Av 3 course à la carte £15
Accommodation (Min) s£40 d£55

ULVERSTON Cumbria *Map 07 SD27*

The Bay Horse Hotel and Restaurant
ULVERSTON
Canal Foot LA12 9EL ☎ 01229 583972
17th-century former coaching inn overlooking the Leven estuary, with comfortable bedrooms and a long-established reputation for excellent food. Interesting bar meals (herb and cheese pâté and braised lamb pie - lunchtime only), and contemporary dishes like tomato and apricot soup, chicken with honey, Calvados and raspberry vinegar glaze, and chocolate Drambuie cream in the Conservatory Restaurant. **Principal beers:** Jennings, Marstons, Theakstons, Wells.
Directions From A590 on entering Ulverston follow signs for Canal Foot L
Brewery/Company Free House
Open 11-11 (Sun 12-10.30)
Bar food 12-2 Av main course £8.50
Restaurant 12-1.30 7.30-8 Av 3 course à la carte £25 Av 3 course fixed price £16.75
Accommodation (Min) s£85 d£140

Royal Oak
ULVERSTON
Spark Bridge LA12 8BS
☎ 01229 861006
Set in a small village, this large, 18th-century pub offers a varied menu. Dishes include grilled halibut steak, chargrilled chicken tikka, ragout of mushrooms, goat's cheese tart, and Higginson's award-winning Cumberland sausage. **Principal beers:** Tetley, Boddingtons, Wadworth 6X, Marston Pedigree.
Directions From Ulverston take A590 N.Village off A5092
Brewery/Company Enterprise Inns
Open 11-3 5.30-11 (Sun all day)
Bar food 12-2.30 6-9.30 Av main course £7.50
Restaurant 12-2.30 6-9.30

For Pubs with AA food rosettes see page 430

WASDALE HEAD Cumbria
Map 11 NY10

Wasdale Head Inn
WASDALE HEAD
CA20 1EX ☎ 019467 26229

According to the licensee, the inn has 'the mostly starkly beautiful situation anywhere in the world - probably', at the head of a remote and unspoilt valley, surrounded by magnificent fells. Birthplace of British climbing, it boasts a rustic, slate-floored bar, and hearty food, including home-made soups, local freshwater lobster, and roast leg of lamb. **Principal beers:** Wasd Ale, Jennings Cumberland,Heskett Newmarket Kern Knott's Cracking Stout.

Directions Follow signs 'Wasdale' from A595, the inn is at the head of the valley
Brewery/Company Free House
Open 11-11
Bar food 11-2 6-9 Av main course £6
Restaurant 7-9 Av 4 course fixed price £18
Accommodation (Min) s£34 d£68

WATERMILLOCK Cumbria
Map 11 NY42

Brackenrigg Inn NEW
WATERMILLOCK
CA11 0LP ☎ 017684 86206

Traditional 18th-century coaching inn with fine terrace and gardens overlooking Ullswater towards Helvellyn. Enjoy a warm welcome, excellent northern ales and interesting bar food. Typical dishes include salmon and cod fishcakes with red pepper dressing, goat's cheese and olive soufflé, roast spiced duck with honey, ginger and soy sauce, and filled baguettes. **Principal beers:** Theakstons Best, Jennings Cumberland, Black Sheep Special.

Directions A66 to Keswick, A592 for 6m to Watermillock
Brewery/Company Free House
Open 12-11
Bar food 12-2 6-9 Av main course £7
Restaurant 7-9 Av 3 course à la carte £17 Av 4 course fixed price £15
Accommodation (Min) s£32 d£54

YANWATH Cumbria
Map 11 NY52

The Yanwath Gate Inn NEW
YANWATH
CA10 2LF ☎ 01768 862386

Unassuming 17th-century village pub located two miles from the M6 (J40). Weary travellers can relax by the log fire in the beamed bar and enjoy some decent bar food. Choose, perhaps, from feta and saffron risotto or Stilton soup, followed by fish pie, Oriental duck, sea bass with garlic and ginger, and sticky gingerbread pudding. **Principal beers:** Theakston, Hesket Newmarket.

Brewery/Company Free House
Open 12-2.30 7-11
Bar food 12-2.30 6-11 Av main course £5.90
Restaurant 12-2.30 7-11 Av 3 course à la carte £15

Co Durham

BARNARD CASTLE Co Durham
Map 12 NZ24

The Morritt Arms Hotel
BARNARD CASTLE
Greta Bridge DL12 9SE
☎ 01833 627232

A good choice of food is offered at this creeper-clad, 17th-century coaching inn, situated by the River Greta. Dickens stayed here to research Nicholas Nickleby, and Dickensian murals are a feature of the bar. Expect hot ciabatta sandwiches, steak and kidney pie and spicy sausages with parmesan mash on the short bar menu.

Principal beers: Taylor Landlord, Tetley, Butterknowle Conciliation Ale, Black Sheep.
Directions At Scotch Corner take A66 towards Penrith, after 9m turn at Greta Bridge. Hotel over bridge on L
Brewery/Company Free House
Open 11-11
Bar food 11.30-2.30 6-9.30 Av main course £7
Restaurant 12-2.30 7-9.30 Av 3 course à la carte £15.95 Av 4 course fixed price £15.95
Accommodation (Min) d£75

COTHERSTONE Co Durham — Map 08 NZ01

The Fox and Hounds
COTHERSTONE
DL12 9PF ☎ 01833 650241
An 18th-century coaching inn, with heavy beams and open fires, situated in beautiful Upper Teesdale. Pub food, including the house brunch (bacon, egg, sausage, pudding, tomato and mushroom) is offered in the bar, while the restaurant might have Teesdale lamb with mint gravy, or grilled 16oz Dover sole. **Principal beers:** Black Sheep Best & Special.
Directions 4m W of Barnard Castle, from A66 turn onto B6277, Cotherstone signposted
Brewery/Company Free House
Open 11-3 6-11
Bar food 11-3 6-10 Av main course £6
Restaurant 11-3 6-10 Av 3 course à la carte £20
Accommodation (Min) s£37.50 d£55

ELWICK Co Durham — Map 08 NZ43

The McOrville Inn
ELWICK
34 The Green TS27 3EF
☎ 01429 273344
Noted for its friendly atmosphere, 'The Mac' is situated overlooking the green in a pretty village setting. Traditional home-cooked food is served in generous portions, ranging from burgers, platters and pies in the bar to chops, steaks and giant cod in the restaurant, with specials such as Cajun chicken. **Principal beers:** Castle Eden, Black Sheep.
Directions 1/4m from A19
Brewery/Company Whitbread
Open 11-3 5.30-11
Bar food 12-2 Av main course £4.50

MIDDLETON-IN-TEESDALE Co Durham — Map 08 NY92

The Teesdale Hotel
MIDDLETON-IN-TEESDALE
Market Square DL12 0QG
☎ 01833 640264 & 640537
In the heart of the High Pennines this 17th-century coaching inn has been tastefully modernised, yet retains much traditional charm. A full menu may offer Hungarian beef goulash and spinach noodles, or fillet of trout with breadcrumbs and almonds. Extensive vegetarian menu.
Principal beers: Tetley.
Brewery/Company Free House
Open 7.45am-11.30pm
Bar food 12-2 7-9 Av main course £6
Restaurant 12-2 7.30-8.30 Av 3 course à la carte £19.95 Av 4 course fixed price £19.95
Accommodation (Min) s£42.50 d£65

ROMALDKIRK Co Durham — Map 08 NY92

Rose and Crown
ROMALDKIRK
DL12 9EB ☎ 01833 650213
Classic coaching inn, built in 1733, on the middle green next to the church in a conservation village. Excellent food, immaculately prepared, is offered on informal and affordable terms. Expect chargrilled sausages and black pudding, local Cotherstone cheese ploughman's, plaice with sesame crust and tomato and thyme sauce, and hot walnut and syrup tart. **Principal beers:** Theakston Best, Marstons Pedigree.
Directions 6m NW from Barnard Castle on B6277
Brewery/Company Free House
Open 11.30-3 (Restaurant lunch on Sun only) 5.30-11
Bar food 12-1.30 6.30-9.30 Av main course £8.50
Restaurant 12-1.30 7.30-9 Av 4 course fixed price £24
Accommodation (Min) s£62 d£84

SEDGEFIELD Co Durham Map 08 NZ32

The Dun Cow Inn & Restaurant
SEDGEFIELD
43 Front St TS21 3AT
☎ 01740 620894 & 620894
Splendid old village inn with plenty of flower baskets in summer and an interesting array of bric-a-brac inside. Typical offerings include a salad of poached sea trout, crevettes, marinated squid and steamed lobster, or local wood pigeon on celeriac purée with red wine and rosemary jus. **Principal beers:** Theakston - Best, XB.
Directions At junct of A177 & A689. Inn in centre of village
Brewery/Company Free House
Open 11-3 6.30-11
Bar food 12-2 7-10 Av main course £8.50
Restaurant 12-2 7-10 Av 3 course à la carte £17
Accommodation (Min) s£49.50 d£65

Greater Manchester

ASHTON-UNDER-LYNE Greater Manchester Map 07 SJ99

The Station
ASHTON-UNDER-LYNE
2 Warrington St OL6 6XB
☎ 0161 330 6776 & 343 7778
Built in 1845 to serve railway, the Station has a collection of 'railwayana'. Lunchtime food ranges from hot baguettes and salads, through home-made pies and hot pots, to dishes such as chicken tikka with rice and poppadoms.
Principal beers: Marstons Pedigree, Tetley.
Directions A627
Brewery/Company Free House
Open 12-11
Bar food 12-2.30 Av main course £3

BAMFORD Greater Manchester Map 07 SD81

Egerton Arms
BAMFORD
Ashworth Rd, Ashworth Valley OL11 5UP
☎ 01706 646183
Old-world pub, known locally as the Chapel House, and thought to be over 500 years old. Popular bar food includes warm salads, black pudding with mustard, and liver and onions, while the restaurant may offer game pie, gigot of lamb, chicken and mushroom roulade, and halibut with spiced orange.
Principal beers: Theakston Old Peculier, Morland Old Speckled Hen, Ruddles.
Directions Bamford on B6222
Brewery/Company Free House
Open 12-3 (Restaurant lunch on Sun only) 6-11
Bar food 12-2.30 6-9 Av main course £5
Restaurant 12-6 6-10 Av 3 course à la carte £14 Av 4 course fixed price £14

DELPH Greater Manchester Map 07 SO90

Green Ash Hotel
DELPH
New Tame, Denshaw Rd OL3 5TS
☎ 01457 871035
Overlooking picturesque valley scenery, this stone-built country pub was originally a weaver's cottage before trading as a co-op until1954. Carefully restored and converted into a hotel, it offers a popular lunchtime carvery with several roasts and a salad bar. Restaurant fare includes rack of lamb, fillet steak, poached halibut and vension.
Principal beers: Black Sheep.
Directions Just off A670 NE of Oldham
Brewery/Company Free House
Open 7am-midnight (Sun 8-11)
Restaurant 12-2 7-10 Av 3 course à la carte £20 Av 4 course fixed price £15.95
Accommodation (Min) s£30 d£55

DIDSBURY Greater Manchester Map 07 SJ89

The Woodstock Tavern
DIDSBURY
139 Barlow Moor Rd M20 2DY
☎ 0161 448 7950
Woodstock is a large Victorian house converted into a tavern six years ago. Recently completely refurbished on two floors, it now includes a large patio and a petanque pitch. Dishes range from pies and bangers and mash, to more exotic fare such as kangaroo and alligator.
Principal beers: Worthington, Bass.
Directions From end of dual carrageway turn R at traffic lights) 0.5m on R
Brewery/Company Bass
Open 12-11 (Sun 12-10.30)
Bar food 12-8 12-8.30 Av main course £4.95

MANCHESTER Greater Manchester
Map 07 SJ89

Dukes 92
MANCHESTER
14 Castle St, Castlefield M3 4LZ
☎ 0161 839 8646
Located beside lock 92 of the Rochdale Canal, this chic, trendy pub has been stylishly created from a stable block for canal horses. A gallery, lockside patio, and theatre performanaces are among the attractions. Popular for its selection of 42 European cheeses, delicious pates, gourmet sandwiches, and daily pasta dishes. **Principal beers:** Taylor Landlord, Boddingtons.
Directions Town centre
Brewery/Company Free House
Open 11.30-11 (Sun 12-10.30, Sat-Sun food 12-6)
Bar food 12-3 5-8.30 Av main course £4.50
Restaurant 12-3 5-8.30

Mash & Air
MANCHESTER
40 Chorlton St M1 3HW
☎ 0161 661 6161 & 661 1111
Mash & Air is located in Manchester city centre and offers a bar on the first floor, a restaurant on the second, and fine dining on the third. The bar menu offers pizza from a wood-fired oven, calves, liver with blue cheese polenta cake, and fish prepared in a variety of styles. **Principal beers:** Mash & Air own brews.
Directions City centre
Brewery/Company Free House
Open 12-12 (Mon-Wed) 12-1am (Thu-Sat/closed Sun)
Bar food 12-12 Av main course £7
Restaurant 6-11 Av 3 course à la carte £25

The White Lion
MANCHESTER
43 Liverpool Rd, Castlefield M3 4NQ ☎ 0161 832 7373
One of the oldest licensed premises in Manchester, the White Lion is adjacent to Castlefields historic Roman fort and the Granada Studios. There is also a Manchester United FC 'shrine'. The menu features steak, curries, and homemade pies.
Principal beers: Boddingtons, Taylor Landlord, Fullers London Pride, Morland Old Speckled Hen.
Brewery/Company Whitbread
Open 11.30-11
Bar food 12-10 Av main course £5

OLDHAM Greater Manchester
Map 07 SD90

The Rams Head Inn NEW
OLDHAM
Denshaw OL3 5UN ☎ 01457 874802
Stone-built country inn, dating back 400 years, with views over Saddleworth Moor. Seafood specialities and gourmet dinners are featured, with dishes such as chargrilled fresh tuna steak with tomato salsa, and haddock on spring onion mash with a rich cheese sauce.

Principal beers: Tetley, Taylor Landlord, Golden & Best.
Directions From M62 towards Oldham, Denshaw 2m on R
Brewery/Company Free House
Open 12-2.30 (Closed Mon ex BHs) 6-11 (Sun & BH 12-10.30, no bar food Sat eve)
Bar food 12-2.30 6-10 Av main course £10
Restaurant 12-2.30 6-10 Av 3 course à la carte £20 Av 2 course fixed price £7.50

The Roebuck Inn
OLDHAM
Strinesdale OL4 3RB ☎ 0161 624 7819
An 18th-century inn located on the edge of Saddleworth Moor, offering an extensive menu of home-cooked dishes. Typical dishes include platters and ploughman's, lambs' liver and onions, steak and kidney pie, and daily specials like beef Stroganoff and rack of lamb with honey, garlic and mint sauce.
Principal beers: Oldham.
Directions From Oldham take A62 then A672 towards Ripponden. 1m turn R at petrol station into Turf Pit Lane. Pub 1m.
Brewery/Company Free House

contd.

Open 12-2.30 5-11 (Sun 12-10.30 - food all day)
Bar food 12-3 5-11 Av main course £5.25
Restaurant 12-2.30 5-10.30 Av 3 course à la carte £14 Av 2 course fixed price £5.50

The White Hart Inn
OLDHAM

Stockport Rd, Lydgate OL4 4JJ
☎ 01457 872566

A solid 18th-century stone building standing in the rugged Pennines high above Oldham. Comfortable lounge and brasserie, with stone walls and a roaring log fire, serving modern dishes cooked with flair. Expect Loch Fyne oysters, beef carpaccio, braised lamb shank with garlic and thyme mash, tempura of cod, and baked chocolate muffin. **Principal beers:** Boddingtons, Flowers IPA.
Directions From Manchester A62 to Oldham. R onto bypass, A669 through Lees. Inn 500yds past Grotton brow of hill turn R
Brewery/Company Free House
Open 12-3 6-11
Restaurant 12-2.30 7-9.30 Av 3 course à la carte £22 Av 2 course fixed price £9
Accommodation (Min) s£55 d£70

Lancashire

BELMONT Lancashire *Map 07 SD61*

Black Dog
BELMONT

2/4 Church St BL7 8AB
☎ 01204 811218

Built as a farmhouse in 1750, this traditional moorland village pub is adorned with antiques and bric-a-brac and offers well-kept Holts ales and good-value bar food. From simple snacks like soup, sandwiches and breaded cod, the menu may list home-made pizzas, smoked cod provençale, and venison in red wine. **Principal beers:** Holt-Bitter, DBA, Mild.
Directions M65 J3 onto A675
Brewery/Company Holts
Open 12-4 7-11
Bar food 12-2 7-9 Av main course £4.40
Accommodation (Min) s£32 d£42

BILSBORROW Lancashire *Map 07 SD52*

Owd Nell's Tavern
BILSBORROW

Guy's Thatched Hamlet, Canal Side
PR3 0RS ☎ 01995 640010

Busy thatched pub tucked away in an expanding thatched tourist hamlet beside the Lancaster Canal. Great for families, it features wide-ranging menus including their 'famous' steak and kidney pudding, Irish mussel hotpot, honey-roasted ham shank, hot roast beef sandwich, and fish, chips and mushy peas.

Principal beers: Boddingtons, Taylor, Chesters, Jennings.
Brewery/Company Free House
Open 7.30am-10.30pm
Bar food 11-3.30 3.30-9.30 Av main course £5.50
Restaurant 12-2.30 5.30-10.30 Av 3 course à la carte £15
Accommodation (Min) s£38 d£51.50

BLACKBURN Lancashire *Map 07 SD62*

Millstone Hotel
BLACKBURN

Church Ln, Mellor BB2 7JR
☎ 01254 813333

Dating from the 17th century, this former farm and ale house provides a comfortable rural retreat. Freshly prepared food ranges from black pudding on sage and onion mash, and beef in stout in the bar, to fish soup, beef fillet in red wine, and lamb on couscous with mint pesto on the restaurant carte. **Principal beers:** Thwaites.
Directions From M6 J31 take A59 towards Clitheroe, past British Aerospace. R at rndbt signed Blackburn/Mellor. Next rndbt 2nd L. Hotel- top of hill on R
Brewery/Company Shire Inns
Open 11-11

Bar food 12-2 6.30-9.15
Restaurant 12-2 7-9.30 Av 3 course à la carte £22 Av 3 course fixed price £22
Accommodation (Min) s£52 d£72

BLACKO Lancashire Map 07 SD84

Moorcock Inn
BLACKO

Gisburn Rd BB9 6NF ☎ 01282 614186

Situated in the heart of Pendle witch country and close to the famous Pendle Way, this former farmhouse enjoys panoramic views of the moorland valleys. A wide-ranging menu offers steak and kidney pie, whole ham shank with mustard sauce, seafood lasagne, red snapper with lemon and dill butter, and a vegetarian specials board. **Principal beers:** Thwaites.
Directions M65 J13, A682 for Kendal
Brewery/Company Thwaites
Open 12-2.30 6.30-11 (open all day wknd)
Bar food 12-2 6.30-9.30 Av main course £5.50
Restaurant 12-2 6.30-9.30
Accommodation (Min) s£20 d£35

CARNFORTH Lancashire Map 07 SD47

Dutton Arms
CARNFORTH

Station Ln, Burton LA6 1HR
☎ 01524 781225

Children are well catered for at this peaceful Lancashire pub, with a climbing frame, climbing ropes, and kid's corner menu. Adults can sample from a menu that may include mutton hotpot, char-grilled chicken Caesar salad, sirloin steak, salmon fishcakes, or spinach and mushroom roulade. **Principal beers:** Boddingtons, Morland Old Speckled Hen, Dent.
Directions from M6 take A6 signed Milnthorpe (Kendal), 3m before Milnthorpe turn R signed Burton/Holme
Brewery/Company Free House
Open 11.30-3 5.30-11 (11.30-11 winter wknd & summer evday)
Bar food 12-2.30 6-11 Av main course £5.95
Restaurant 12-2.30 6-11 Av 3 course à la carte £16

CHIPPING Lancashire Map 07 SD64

Dog & Partridge NEW
CHIPPING

Hesketh Ln PR3 2TH ☎ 01995 61201

Tucked away in a hamlet with views of the surrounding hills, this comfortably modernised rural inn dates back to 1515. Popular food includes steak and kidney pie and freshly battered haddock with hand-cut chips; evening fare features roast beef, with fresh fish and local game dishes listed on the blackboard.
Principal beers: Tetleys.
Brewery/Company Free House
Open 12-3 7-11
Bar food 12-1.30 Av main course £8
Restaurant 12-1.30 7-9 Av 3 course à la carte £15 Av 4 course fixed price £11.75

CLITHEROE Lancashire Map 07 SO74

Assheton Arms
CLITHEROE

Downham BB7 4BJ ☎ 01200 441227

Everything a village pub should be, an attractive stone-built inn tucked away opposite the church in a timeless estate village, with old beams, and a warm, welcoming atmosphere. The food ranges from home-made soup and sandwiches to dishes such as venison casserole, sea bream with caper sauce, and a range of steaks. **Principal beers:** Boddingtons, Castle Eden Ale.
Directions From A59 take Chatburn turn. In Chatburn follow signs for Downham
Brewery/Company Whitbread
Open 12-3 7-11 (closed 2nd week Jan)
Bar food 12-2 7-10 Av main course £8.50

DARWEN Lancashire Map 07 SD62

Old Rosins Inn
DARWEN

Treacle Row, Pickup Bank, Hoddlesden BB3 3QD ☎ 01254 771264

The original inn, set in the heart of the Lancashire Moors, has been extended to provide a variety of facilities. Bar food includes plate pies, beef in Old Peculier, mixed grill, and a seafood platter, while the restaurant might offer local duck and a daily choice of fresh fish. **Principal beers:** Jennings Bitter, Cumberland, Sneck Lifter, Cocker Hoop.

contd.

Directions M65 J5, follow signs for Haslingdon then R after 2m signed Egworth. 0.5m R & continue for 0.5m
Brewery/Company Jennings
Open 11-11 (Sun 12-10.30)
Bar food 11.30-10 Av main course £4.50
Restaurant 7-10 Av 3 course à la carte £17.50 Av 4 course fixed price £15
Accommodation (Min) s£42.50 d£55

FENCE Lancashire Map 07 SD83

Fence Gate Inn & Banqueting Centre
FENCE

Wheatley Lane Rd BB12 9EE
☎ 01282 618101

Built in the 17th century on the site of a building constructed in 1402, this substantial inn offers wide-ranging menus in its Topiary Brasserie. From speciality open sandwiches and starters like smoked haddock chowder, the choice extends to herb-crusted cod, tagliatelle with tomato pesto, and fillet steak with rôsti potato and claret sauce.
Principal beers: Theakston, Courage, John Smiths, Boddingtons.
Directions From M65 L 1.5m, set back on R opposite T-junction for Burnley
Brewery/Company Free House
Open 12-11
Bar food 12-3 6.30-12 Av main course £7
Restaurant 12-3 6.30-12 Av 3 course à la carte £15 Av 3 course fixed price £12.50

GALGATE Lancashire Map 07 SD45

The Stork Hotel
GALGATE

Conder Green LA2 0AN
☎ 01524 751234

Situated on the River Conder, the Stork has been a public house, under various names, since the mid-17th century. The menu ranges from traditional pub fare such as toasties and baked potatoes, to quail with apricot and Stilton stuffing, baked monkfish steak, and crocodile in lime, coriander, and vermouth sauce.
Principal beers: Boddingtons, Tetley.
Directions M6 J33 take A6 north. At Galgate turn L & next L to Conder Green
Brewery/Company Free House
Open 11-11 (Sun 12-10.30)
Bar food 12-2.30 6.30-9 Av main course £5
Accommodation (Min) s£22.50 d£36

GOOSNARGH Lancashire Map 07 SD53

The Bushell's Arms
GOOSNARGH

Church Ln PR3 2BH ☎ 01772 865235

Just 4 miles from the M6 (J32), this Georgian former farmhouse offers a warm welcome, good ale and genuine home-cooked food. One menu is offered throughout the spacious and modernised interior. Expect fresh fish from Fleetwood and a global range of dishes, including Greek beef stew (stifado), Moroccan chicken, smoked fish platter, and Lancashire hotpot.
Principal beers: Taylor Best.
Brewery/Company Whitbread
Open 12-3 6-11
Bar food 12-2.30 7-10 Av main course £5.50

Ye Horns Inn
GOOSNARGH

Horns Ln PR3 2FJ ☎ 01772 865230

An 18th-century, black and white coaching inn enjoying views across field to hills beyond. Friendly and intimate bar and dining room. Traditional cooking is the speciality of the house, with dishes ranging from steak and kidney pie and fresh battered cod, to roast duckling with apple, and salmon with hollandaise.
Principal beers: No real ale.
Directions From M6 J32 take A6 N. At traffic lights turn R onto B5269. In Goosnargh follow Inn signs
Brewery/Company Free House
Open 12-3 (ex Mon) 7-11 (no bar food Sun lunch, Sat eve)
Bar food 12-3 7-11
Restaurant 12-3 7-11 Av 5 course fixed price £16.50
Accommodation (Min) s£49 d£75

HESKIN GREEN Lancashire Map 07 SD51

Farmers Arms
HESKIN GREEN

85 Wood Ln PR7 5NP ☎ 01257 451276

Long, creeper-covered country inn with two cosy bars decorated in old pictures and farming memorabilia, and a good outdoor area, including farmyard animals, for families. The wide-ranging

traditional menu incorporates salads, sandwiches, steaks, fresh grilled plaice, home-made chicken and mushroom pie, and several vegetarian options.
Principal beers: Taylor Landlord, Castle Eden, Flowers IPA, Boddingtons.
Directions On B5250 between M6 & Eccleston
Brewery/Company Whitbread
Open 12-12
Bar food 12-9.30 Av main course £4
Accommodation (Min) s£35 d£50

HEST BANK Lancashire *Map 07 SD46*

Hest Bank Hotel NEW
HEST BANK
2 Hest Bank Ln LA2 6DN
☎ 01524 824339

A 16th-century inn, formerly a staging post for coaches crossing Morecambe Bay, situated beside the Lancaster Canal. Using fresh local produce, the menu features potted shrimps, mussel casserole, lamb hotpot, steak, mushroom and ale pie, and filled baguettes. Interesting specials may include salmon fishcakes, herrings in oatmeal, and fresh whiting.

Principal beers: Boddingtons, Marstons Pedigree.
Directions From Lancaster take A6 N, after 2m L to Hest Bank
Brewery/Company Inn Partnership
Open 11.30-11 (Sun 12-10.30)
Bar food 12-9 Av main course £5

MERECLOUGH Lancashire *Map 07 SD83*

Kettledrum Inn & Restaurant
MERECLOUGH
302 Red Lees Rd BB10 4RG
☎ 01282 424591

Inviting, well kept country inn, named after the 1861 Derby winner, offering fine views of the Pendle Hills, comfortable bars and a traditional choice of pub food. Expect breaded scampi, home-made game pie, seafood casserole, a daily roast, good vegetarian dishes, and a choice of freshly prepared curries.
Principal beers: Theakston, Tetley, Hancocks HB.
Directions from Burnley town centre, past Burnley FC, 2 1/2m, 1st pub on L
Brewery/Company Devonshire Pub Co
Open 11.30-3 5.30-11 (Sun 12-10.30)
Bar food 12-2.30 6-9.30
Restaurant 12-2.30 6-9.30 Av 3 course à la carte £13.50

PARBOLD Lancashire *Map 07 SD41*

The Eagle & Child
PARBOLD
Maltkiln Ln L40 3SG ☎ 01257 462297

Beautifully refurbished, 18th-century, brick-built inn with bowling green and wild garden. Rug-strewn flagstone floors and handsome antiques characterise the civilised interior. Imaginative, well-presented food ranges from steak and ale pie and crispy duck salad, to venison with juniper, gin and blackberries, herb-crusted pork fillet with Madeira, and baked hake with horseradish sauce.
Principal beers: Thwaites Best, Theakston Bitter, Moorhouse Black Cat, Liverpool Red.
Directions From M6 J27 to Parbold. At bottom of Parbold Hill turn R on B5246 to Hilldale. Then 1st L to Bispham Green
Brewery/Company Free House
Open 12-3 5.30-11 (Sun food 12-8.30)
Bar food 12-2 5.30-8.30
Restaurant 12-2 5.30-8.30

RIBCHESTER Lancashire *Map 07 SD63*

The White Bull
RIBCHESTER
Church St PR3 3XP ☎ 01254 878303

Four complete Tuscan pillars from a temple that formed part of the Roman town are among the more unusual features found at this listed 17th-century pub. Traditional pub food is served in the attractively furnished bars, including steak and kidney pie, lasagne, steaks and changing specials.
Principal beers: Flowers IPA, Marstons Pedigree, Boddingtons.
Brewery/Company Whitbread
Open 11.30-3 6.30-11 (Sun 12-10.30; food 12-8)

contd.

Bar food 11.30-2 6.30-9.30 Av main course £5
Restaurant 11.30-2 6.30-9.30 Av 3 course à la carte £9
Accommodation (Min) d£45

SAWLEY Lancashire Map 07 SD74

The Spread Eagle NEW
SAWLEY
BB7 4NH ☎ 01200 441202

Revitalised 18th-century inn on the banks of the River Ribble with spectacular valley views from picture windows. With talented chef/owner Steven Doherty at the helm expect superior pub food. Innovative dishes, prepared from tip-top ingredients, may include red onion tart, duck leg confit with bean, lentil and black pudding stew, lamb provençale with rosemary jus, and tarte tatin. **Principal beers:** Black Sheep, Morland Old Speckled Hen, Smiles, Theakston.
Directions N on A59 to Skipton, 3m N of Clitheroe
Brewery/Company Free House
Open 11-11 (closed 2 wks Nov)
Restaurant 12-2 6-9 Av 3 course à la carte £18
Accommodation (Min) s£37.50 d£55

SLAIDBURN Lancashire Map 07 SD75

Hark to Bounty Inn
SLAIDBURN
Townend BB7 3EP ☎ 01200 446246

Situated in the renowned Trough of Bowland, this 13th-century stone-built inn takes its name from a hunting dog whose loud barking led to his master, the village squire, calling his favourite hound the 'Hark to Bounty'. Expect rib of beef, game pie and mustard-glazed pork chops among the imaginative daily specials.
Principal beers: Theakston - Old Peculier, Mild & Bitter, Courage Directors.
Directions From M6 J31 take A59 to Clitheroe then B6478, through Waddington and Newton and on to Slaidburn
Brewery/Company Scottish Courage
Open 7.30am-midnight
Bar food 12-2 6-9 Av main course £6.50
Restaurant 12-2 6-9 Av 3 course à la carte £12.50 Av 4 course fixed price £10
Accommodation (Min) s£25 d£50

WHALLEY Lancashire Map 07 SD73

Freemasons Arms
WHALLEY
8 Vicarage Fold, Wiswell BB7 9DF
☎ 01254 822218

Originally three cottages, the building and interior of the pub remain largely unchanged, characterised by antique furniture, wooden beams and brass and copperware. The food is freshly cooked and offers a good choice of dishes, including beef fillet au poivre, rack of lamb, fresh fish platter, grilled plaice, and steak and kidney pie. **Principal beers:** Jennings Bitter & Cumberland Ale.
Brewery/Company Free House
Open 12-3 6.30-12 (closed Mon-Tue)
Restaurant 12-2 6.30-9.30 Av 3 course à la carte £15.95

WHITEWELL Lancashire Map 07 SD64

The Inn At Whitewell
WHITEWELL
Forest of Bowland BB7 3AT
☎ 01200 448222

Formerly the Keeper of the Forest's house, parts of this lovely building beside the River Hodder date from the 1300s. The inn is renowned for the quality of its food, with the likes of bangers and champ or fish pie, alongside local game dishes, Bowland lamb, and daube of beef. Individual interior and smartly refurbished bedrooms. **Principal beers:** Marstons Pedigree, Boddingtons.
Directions Take B6243 and follow signs for Whitewell
Brewery/Company Free House
Open 11-3 6-11
Bar food 12-2 7.30-9.30 Av main course £8
Restaurant 7.30-9.30 Av 3 course à la carte £26
Accommodation (Min) s£53 d£75

WREA GREEN Lancashire Map 07 SD33

The Grapes Hotel
WREA GREEN
Station Rd PR4 2PH ☎ 01772 682927

Situated in the centre of the village opposite the green and duck pond. One menu caters for everybody, offering a selection of snacks and traditional pub meals, such as chicken and ham pie, steak and mushroom pie, vintage mushrooms, and lasagne. Sweets include bread-and-butter pudding and banoffee pie.

Principal beers: Theakston, Boddingtons.
Directions From M55 J3 follow signs for Kirkham then Wrea Green
Brewery/Company Greenalls
Open 11-11 (food 12-9.30 Sun)
Bar food 12-2.30 5.30-9.30 Av main course £3.95

Merseyside

BARNSTON Merseyside *Map 07 SJ28*

Fox and Hounds
BARNSTON
Barnston Rd L61 1BW ☎ 0151 648 7685
Situated in the conservation area of Barnston Dale, this pub contains an assortment of 1920s/30s memorabilia, including a collection of policemen's helmets. Wholesome, traditional pub fare is on offer, such as Somerset pork chops baked in apple and cider sauce, cottage pie, corned beef hash, and lamb and pork casserole. **Principal beers:** Websters Yorkshire Bitter, Ruddles County, Theakston XB & Best, Courage Directors.
Directions From M53 J4 take A5137 to Heswell. R to Barnston on B5138
Brewery/Company Free House
Open 11-11 (Sun 12-10.30)
Bar food 12-2 Av main course £4.95

Northumberland

ALLENDALE Northumberland *Map 12 NY85*

Kings Head Hotel
ALLENDALE
Market Place NE47 9BD
☎ 01434 683681
Dating from 1754, the Kings Head is the oldest inn in Allendale, situated in the centre of the North Dales village. Expect a warm welcome and traditional bar food, including chicken and bacon baguette, beef in ale pie, Jester's chicken,

mixed grill, venison sausages, and freshly-battered cod with giant hand-cut chips. **Principal beers:** Jennings Cumberland, Durham, Theakston Best, Tetley.
Directions From Hexham take B6305/B6304/B6295
Brewery/Company Free House
Open 11-11 (Sun 12-10.30)
Bar food 12-2.30 6.30-9
Accommodation (Min) s£23 d£45

ALLENHEADS Northumberland *Map 12 NY84*

The Allenheads Inn
ALLENHEADS
NE47 9HJ ☎ 01434 685000
Unique 18th-century pub situated in a remote village high in the Pennines. Run by eccentric licensees, the extraordinary bar is festooned with curios and assorted bric-a-brac, including full life-size china tigers, mangles, birdcages and tailor's dummies. The straightforward bar menu steak pie, sweet and sour chicken, and lamb and vegetable pie.

Principal beers: Tetley.
Directions From Hexham take B6305, then B6295 to Allenheads
Brewery/Company Free House
Open 11-2.30 7-11 (Sat-Sun 12-4, 7-11, closed lunch winter; No bar food Mon-Thu)
Bar food 11-2 7-10 Av main course £5
Accommodation (Min) s£25 d£43

ALNWICK Northumberland *Map 12 NU11*

Masons Arms
ALNWICK
Stamford, Nr Rennington NE66 3RX
☎ 01665 577275
Stone-built coaching inn dating back some 200 years, situated in open countryside. The same menu of home-

contd.

cooked fare operates throughout, supplemented by a daily specials board. Popular dishes include steak and ale pie, salmon and broccoli bake, and lamb and rosemary casserole. **Principal beers:** Ruddles Best, Courage Directors.
Directions 3.5m from A1 on B1340
Brewery/Company Free House
Open 12-2 6.30-11 (Sun 7-10.30)
Bar food 12-2 7-9 Av main course £6
Restaurant 12-2 7-9 Av 3 course à la carte £12
Accommodation (Min) d£39

BAMBURGH Northumberland

Map 12 NU13

Victoria Hotel
BAMBURGH

Front St NE69 7BP ☎ 01668 214431
Situated in the centre of Bamburgh, the Holy Island of Lindisfarne and the Farne Islands are within easy distance of this hotel. An interesting selection of starters includes ricotta cheese and spinach tortellini, and honey roast duck with poached plums. Main courses typically feature locally caught fish, chargrilled steaks, and venison.

Principal beers: Theakston Best, Ruddles, John Smiths, McEwans.
Directions In centre of Bamburgh village green
Brewery/Company Free House
Open 10-11
Bar food 12-3 7-10 Av main course £6
Restaurant 6-10 Av 3 course à la carte £17
Accommodation (Min) s£35 d£50

Pubs offering a good choice of seafood on the menu

BELSAY Northumberland

Map 12 NZ09

The Highlander
BELSAY

NE20 0DN ☎ 01661 881220
Traditional pub meals, interesting home-cooked specials and afternoon cream teas are available at this popular, flower-adorned roadside hostelry. Choose from salads, casseroles (lamb and rosemary hotpot), pasta meals, and substantial dishes like rack of lamb with minted jus, and pork with apple and cider sauce.

Principal beers: John Smiths, Theakston Best.
Directions On A68, 2m S of Belsay
Brewery/Company Scottish & Newcastle
Open 9.30-11 (Sun 12-10.30)
Bar food 12-9.30 Av main course £7

BERWICK-UPON-TWEED Northumberland

Map 12 NT95

The Rob Roy
BERWICK-UPON-TWEED

Dock Rd, Tweedmouth TD15 2BQ
☎ 01289 306428
There is a cosy, rustic atmosphere at this stone-built pub, which has a salmon fishing theme in the bar. Quality seafood is the speciality here, the interesting menus often listing Lindisfarne oysters, creamed shellfish soup, monkfish in garlic butter, and halibut with hollandaise. Meat-eaters can order prime Border steaks and duck in cassis.
Principal beers: John Smiths, Theakston Best.
Directions Exit A1 2m S of Berwick at A1167 signed Scremerston, to rdbt signed Spittal, then R. 1m to Albion PH, L, 1m to pub
Brewery/Company Free House
Open 12-2.30 7-11 (closed Tue)

Bar food 12-2 7-9 Av main course £7.50
Restaurant 12-1.45 7-9.15 Av 3 course à la carte £25
Accommodation (Min) s£23 d£38

BLANCHLAND
Northumberland *Map 12 NY95*

Lord Crewe Arms
BLANCHLAND
DH8 9SP ☎ 01434 675251

Once the abbot's house of Blanchland Abbey, this is one of England's oldest inns. Antique furniture, blazing log fires and flagstone floors make for an atmospheric setting. Bar food ranges from sandwiches to steaks, and the restaurant offers wild boar with mustard sauce, rack of lamb with rosemary and garlic jus and daily fish dishes. **Principal beers:** Vaux Samson.
Directions 10m S of Hexham via B6306
Brewery/Company Free House
Open 11-3 6-11.30 (Restaurant lunch on Sun only)
Bar food 12-2 7-9 Av main course £5
Restaurant 12-2 7-9.15 Av 3 course à la carte £28 Av 4 course fixed price £28
Accommodation (Min) s£80 d£110

CARTERWAY HEADS
Northumberland *Map 12 NZ05*

The Manor House Inn
CARTERWAY HEADS
DH8 9LX ☎ 01207 255268

Stone-built former manor with superb views of Derwent Valley Reservoir and the moors beyond. Comfortably rustic bar and dining room, and modern menus featuring interesting pub food. Dishes may include pigeon and lamb fillet casserole with black pudding, monkfish and scallops in saffron and fennel, and sea bass stuffed with Italian vegetables. **Principal beers:** Theakstons Best, Mordue Workie Ticket, Morland Ruddles County, Taylor Landlord.
Directions A69 W from Newcastle, L onto A68 then S for 8m. Inn on L
Brewery/Company Free House
Open 11-3 6-11
Bar food 12-2.30 7-9.30 Av main course £8
Restaurant 12-2.30 7-9.30 Av 3 course à la carte £17
Accommodation (Min) s£24.50 d£43

CHATTON
Northumberland *Map 12 NU02*

The Percy Arms Hotel
CHATTON
Main Rd NE66 5PS ☎ 01665 215244

Built in the early 19th-century as a hunting lodge by the Duke of Northumberland, this ivy-covered pub enjoys a peaceful village setting in the unspoilt Till Valley. Bar food includes steak and kidney pie, local crab salad, fresh haddock and chip, lamb with mint and redcurrant sauce, and mixed seafood platter.
Directions From Alnwick take A1 N, then B6348 to Chatton
Brewery/Company Free House
Open 11-3 6-11 (Restaurant lunch on Sun only)
Bar food 12-1.30 6.30-9.30 Av main course £5.95
Restaurant 12-1.30 6.30-9 Av 3 course à la carte £12.50
Accommodation (Min) s£20 d£40

CORBRIDGE
Northumberland *Map 12 NY96*

The Angel Inn
CORBRIDGE
Main St NE45 5LA ☎ 01434 632119

Stylish 17th-century coaching inn overlooking the River Tyne. Relax with the daily papers in the panelled lounge or attractive bars, or enjoy a home-made dish or two from the extensive menu choice. Options range from freshly battered cod and chips, and deluxe sandwiches, to lamb hotpot, rabbit in mustard cream, and cheese and vegetable bake. **Principal beers:** Theakston Best, John Smiths.
Directions 0.5m off A69, signed Corbridge
Brewery/Company Scottish & Newcastle

Open 7am-11pm

contd.

Bar food 11.45-2.30 5-9 Av main course £9.95
Restaurant 11.45-2.30 5-9 Av 4 course à la carte £16.95 Av 3 course fixed price £16.95
Accommodation (Min) s£49.50 d£74

CRASTER Northumberland Map 12 NU22

Cottage Inn
CRASTER
Dunstan Village NE66 3SZ
☎ 01665 576658
An 18th-century building with a walled garden, once part of the Craster estate, situated just a few minutes from the sea. English and local dishes feature on the menus, with plenty of fresh fish and vegetarian options. Dishes include game, port and oyster pie and a fisherman's platter. **Principal beers:** Ruddles, Theakston.
Directions NW of Howick to Embleton road
Brewery/Company Free House
Open 11-3 6-11
Bar food 12-3 6-10.15 Av main course £5.25
Restaurant 12-3 7-10.15 Av 3 course à la carte £14

EGLINGHAM Northumberland Map 12 NU21

Tankerville Arms NEW
EGLINGHAM
NE66 2TZ ☎ 01665 578444
Modernised, stone-built village pub with coal fires, comfortable furnishings and a bustling atmosphere. Expect a friendly welcome and home-cooked food, including sandwiches and ploughman's, and, perhaps, sausages with caramelised onion and apple mash, Craster smoked salmon and dill fishcakes, baked cod, and venison with smoked bacon and Madeira sauce. **Principal beers:** Ruddles, Courage Theakston XB & Directors, Taylor Landlord, Bass.
Directions B6346 from Alnwick
Brewery/Company Free House
Open 11-3 6-11
Bar food 12-2 6-9 Av main course £5.95
Restaurant 12-2 6-9 Av 3 course à la carte £20 Av 4 course fixed price £16

ETAL Northumberland Map 12 NT93

Black Bull
ETAL
TD12 4TL ☎ 01890 820200
Located by the ruins of Etal Castle, this 300-year-old hostelry is the only thatched pub in Northumberland. Close to the River Till and a short distance to the grand walking country of the Cheviots. Typical dishes include liver and onions, deep-fried haddock and giant Yorkshire puddings. **Principal beers:** Stones, Tetley.
Directions 10m N of Wooler R off A697, L at Jct for 1m then L into Etal.
Brewery/Company Free House
Open 12-3 6.30-11 (11-11 summer)
Bar food 12-3 7-9 Av main course £5.95
Restaurant 6.30-9.30

FALSTONE Northumberland Map 12 NY78

The Blackcock Inn NEW
FALSTONE
NE48 1AA ☎ 01434 240200
Traditional 18th-century stone-built inn set in heart of the Northumberland National Park, close to Kielder Reservoir and Forest. Expect roaring log fires in winter and hearty pub food, the chalkboard menu offering ploughman's, chicken, ham and leek pie, poacher's pie, filled Yorkshire puddings, and pork with ginger and plum sauce. Excellent walking. **Principal beers:** Blackcock Ale, Ruddles County, John Smiths Magnet, Marston Pedigree.
Directions off unclassified rd from Bellingham (accessed from A68 or B6320)
Brewery/Company Free House
Open 11-11 (Sun 12-10.30)
Bar food 11-3 7-9 Av main course £3.95
Restaurant 7-12 Av 3 course à la carte £14.75
Accommodation (Min) s£22 d£50

The Pheasant
FALSTONE
Stannersburn NE48 1DD
☎ 01434 240382
Standing alone in a hamlet close to the attractions of Kielder Water and Forest, this attractive 350-year-old former farmhouse is the perfect base from which to explore Northumbria's National Park. Expect comfortable bedrooms, character bars, and good home cooking. Dishes include cider-baked gammon, game pie,

seafood tagliatelle, and lamb with redcurrant jus. **Principal beers:** Theakston Best, Marstons Pedigree.
Directions From A68 onto B6320, or from A69, B6079, B6320, follow signs 'Kielder Water'
Brewery/Company Free House
Open 11.30-3 (Restaurant lunch Sun only) 6-11 (Sun 12-3 7-10.30, no bar food Sun eve)
Bar food 12-2.30 7-9 Av main course £5.95
Restaurant 12-2.30 7-9 Av 3 course à la carte £15
Accommodation (Min) s£40 d£58

GREAT WHITTINGTON Northumberland *Map 12 NZ07*

Queens Head Inn & Restaurant
GREAT WHITTINGTON
NE19 2HP ☎ 01434 672267
A 15th-century coaching inn, as seen on TV in the BBC drama When The Boat Comes In. The imaginative menu offers offers local game in season and a daily supply of fresh fish such as fillet of halibut topped with king prawn and salmon mousse and set on a watercress cream. **Principal beers:** Black Sheep, Queens Head, Hambleton, guest ale.
Directions Off A68 & B6318 W of Newcastle upon Tyne
Brewery/Company Free House
Open 12-3 6-11 (closed Mon)
Bar food 12-2 6.30-9.30 Av main course £7.95
Restaurant 12-2.30 6.30-9.30 Av 3 course à la carte £17

HALTWHISTLE Northumberland *Map 12 NY76*

Milecastle Inn
HALTWHISTLE
Military Rd NE49 9NN
☎ 01434 321372 & 320682
Very small traditional stone-built inn, just 700 metres from Hadrian's Wall. Low beams, open fires and lots of copper and brass characterise the interior. Hearty pub food might include ploughman's, gammon and egg, and wild boar and duckling pie, and in the restaurant perhaps trout with hollandaise.
Principal beers: Northumberland Castles, Tetley, Butterknowle.
Directions Leave A69 at Haltwhistle, pub at junction with B6318
Brewery/Company Free House
Open 12-3 6.30-11 (restaurant open Sun am & Wed-Sat pm)
Bar food 12-2 6.30-8.45 Av main course £5.95
Restaurant 12-1.30 7-8.45

HAYDON BRIDGE Northumberland *Map 12 NY86*

The General Havelock Inn
HAYDON BRIDGE
Ratcliffe Rd NE47 6ER ☎ 01434 684376
Built as a private house in 1840, but licensed since 1890, this pub occupies a pleasant riverside setting. The food is all home-made and the wide-ranging menu offers everything from smoked salmon flan and roast duck with Cumberland sauce, to fresh dressed crab and fillet of pork rosemary. **Principal beers:** Tetley.
Directions On A69, 7m west of Hexham
Brewery/Company Free House
Open 12-2.30 7-11 (closed Mon & Tue)
Bar food 12-2 7-8.45 Av main course £6
Restaurant 12-2 7-8.45 Av 3 course à la carte £16.50 Av 4 course fixed price £19.50

HEDLEY ON THE HILL Northumberland *Map 12 NZ05*

The Feathers Inn
HEDLEY ON THE HILL
NE43 7SW ☎ 01661 843607
Situated in the heart of Northumberland, this friendly, stone-built inn has traditional oak beams and open fires, as well as individual character and lots of atmosphere. The bar menu changes regularly and among the imaginative dishes are lamb casserole, Cumberland sausage, home-cooked ham, and smoked cod and cheese pancake. **Principal beers:** Boddingtons, Mordue Workie Ticket.
Brewery/Company Free House
Open 12-3 (BHs, Sat & Sun only) 6-11 (Sun 7-10.30 only)
Bar food 12-2.30 7-9 Av main course £5

HEXHAM Northumberland *Map 12 NY96*

Dipton Mill Inn
HEXHAM
Dipton Mill Rd NE46 1YA
☎ 01434 606577
Set beside a small river in a deep hollow, this former mill house, built around

contd.

1750, features open fires, excellent local ales and wholesome, home-cooked food in its panelled and low-beamed bars. Sample dishes may include steak and kidney pie, lamb steak with red wine and mustard sauce, and mince and dumplings.
Principal beers: Tetley, Hexhamshire Shire Bitter, Devil's Water & Whapweasel.
Directions 2m S of Hexham on HGV route to Blanchland (B6306)
Brewery/Company Free House
Open 12-2.30 6-11 (Sun 12-4.30, 7-10.30)
Bar food 12-2.30 6.30-8.30 Av main course £5.50

LONGFRAMLINGTON Northumberland *Map 12 NU10*

Granby Inn
LONGFRAMLINGTON
Front St NE65 8DP ☎ 01665 570228
Situated at the heart of Northumberland, between the Cheviots and the coast, this 200-year-old coaching inn is a family-run business which retains much of its original character. Expect seafood platter, grilled ham, sirloin steak and chicken chasseur among a varied selection of dishes. Good range of desserts.

Directions On A697, 11m N of Morpeth
Brewery/Company Free House
Open 11-3 6-11
Bar food 11-2 6-9.30 Av main course £7
Restaurant 11-2 6-9.30 Av 3 course à la carte £10 Av 3 course fixed price £9.95
Accommodation (Min) s£31.50 d£56

For Pubs with AA food rosettes see page 430

LONGHORSLEY Northumberland *Map 12 NZ19*

Linden Tree Bar & Grill
LONGHORSLEY
Linden Hall Hotel NE65 8XF
☎ 01670 516611
Originally two large cattle byres, this popular bar takes its name from the linden trees in the grounds of Linden Hall Hotel. Straightforward meals range from all-day sandwiches, to main dishes such as leek, cheese and onion bake, steak and kidney pie, pan-fried sirloin steak, and poached salmon.
Principal beers: Theakston XB & Black Bull, Marston Pedigree, John Smith.
Directions Off the A1 on the A697 1m N of Longhorsley
Brewery/Company Free House
Open 10am-11pm (Sun 10-10.30)
Bar food 12-2 6-9.30 Av main course £8.25
Accommodation (Min) s£97.50 d£125

LOW NEWTON BY THE SEA Northumberland *Map 12 NU22*

The Ship
LOW NEWTON BY THE SEA
The Square NE66 3EL ☎ 01665 576262
The village of Low Newton was purpose-built as a fishing village in the 18th century and is in the shape of an open-sided square. In summer the bay is busy with yachts and boats. A simple bar menu includes plenty of fresh fish, vegetable broth, and a variety of sandwiches and toasties.
Principal beers: Ruddles Best, Northumberland Castles.
Directions NW from A1 at Alnwick
Brewery/Company Free House
Open 11-11 (Nov-Easter 11-3, 7-11/bar food as opening times)

MATFEN Northumberland *Map 12 NZ07*

The Black Bull
MATFEN
NE20 0RP ☎ 01661 886330
The pretty estate village of Matfen is the setting for this striking, 200-year-old creeper-covered inn. Comfortable restaurant and plush carpeted bar offering an interesting range of meals, including, perhaps, paella, steak and mushroom pie, Northumbrian game pie, and various fish dishes and grills.

Principal beers: Theakston Black Bull.
Directions Leave A69 at Corbridge, join B6318. 2m N sign to Matfen
Brewery/Company Free House
Open 11-3 6-11
Bar food 12-2.30 6.30-9 Av main course £5
Restaurant 12-2 6.30-9.30
Accommodation (Min) s£35 d£60

NEWTON ON THE MOOR Northumberland *Map 12 NU10*

Cook and Barker Inn
NEWTON ON THE MOOR
NE65 9JY ☎ 01665 575234

Enjoying superb views across rolling fields to the Northumbrian coast, this 17th-century roadside inn offers A1 travellers a welcome break for some good bar food. Daily blackboard dishes may feature smoked salmon fishcakes, Cajun marinated chicken, lamb and aubergine moussaka, and seafood casserole. Comfortable overnight accommodation.
Principal beers: Theakston Best & XB, Ruddles, Courage Directors, Fuller's London Pride.
Directions 0.5m from A1 S of Alnwick
Brewery/Company Free House
Open 11-3 6-11 (Sun 6-10.30)
Bar food 12-2 6-8 Av main course £4.95
Restaurant 12-2 7-9 Av 3 course à la carte £18.50 Av 3 course fixed price £18.50
Accommodation (Min) s£37.50 d£70

PONTELAND Northumberland *Map 12 NZ17*

The Badger
PONTELAND
St House Farm NE20 9BT
☎ 01661 867931

Built in the late 18th century by Newcastle merchant Shafto Coulter, The Badger once contained offices, outhouses and stabling, as well as a coach house and dovecote. The pub is full of charming nooks and crannies, has four huge fireplaces for winter, and a patio for eating out in summer. **Principal beers:** Bass, Worthingtons, Stones.
Directions A696 Newcastle to Jedburgh, 0.5m past Newcastle Airport, pub on edge of village
Brewery/Company Vintage Inns
Open 11.30-11 (Sun 12-10.30)

ROWFOOT Northumberland *Map 12 NY66*

The Wallace Arms
ROWFOOT
NE49 0JF ☎ 01434 321872

One mile from Featherstone Castle, this country pub, built in 1856, stands in a rural setting. It is a good area for walkers, and is the start point of the South Tyne Trail. Chicken in cream and lemon sauce, steak and ale pie, and salmon with a mustard crust may be part of the menu.
Principal beers: Four Rivers Moondance, Four Rivers Hadrian Legion.
Brewery/Company Free House
Open 12-2.30 4-11 (opening times vary, ring for details)
Bar food 12-2 7-9 Av main course £5.95
Restaurant 12-2 7-9 Av 3 course à la carte £12.50

SEAHOUSES Northumberland *Map 12 NU23*

The Olde Ship Hotel
SEAHOUSES
9 Main St NE68 7RD ☎ 01665 720200

Set above a tiny, picturesque harbour, this historic, family-run hotel has tremendous character within its bustling, nautically-themed bars. Expect tip-top ales and home-cooked food, perhaps including smoked fish chowder, seafood lasagne, liver and onion casserole, spicy lamb stew, followed by ginger trifle or clootie dumpling and custard. **Principal beers:** John Smiths, Theakston, Bass, McEwans.
Directions lower end of main street above harbour
Brewery/Company Free House
Open 11-3 6-11 (closed Dec & Jan)
Bar food 12-2 7-8.30 Av main course £5
Restaurant 12-2 7-8.30 Av 3 course fixed price £13.50
Accommodation (Min) s£32 d£64

WARDEN Northumberland *Map 12 NY96*

The Boatside Inn
WARDEN
NE46 4SQ ☎ 01434 602233

The pub, situated below Warden Hill and the Iron Age fort, gets its name from the rowing boat facility that ferried people across the Tyne before the bridge was built. Typical pub grub is served in the bar, and the restaurant offers steaks,

contd.

chicken and Stilton, and fish of the day. **Principal beers:** Theakston, Courage Directors, Boatside Inn Bitter.
Directions Just off A69 west of Hexham, follow signs to Warden Newborough & Fourstones
Brewery/Company Free House
Open 11-3 5.30-11
Bar food 12-2 6.30-9.30 Av main course £6
Restaurant 12-2 6.30-9.30 Av 3 course à la carte £12

WARENFORD Northumberland
Map 12 NU12

Warenford Lodge
WARENFORD
NE70 7HY ☎ 01668 213453
Look out for the village sign off the A1 or you could miss a meal to remember. Tucked away close to the Northumbrian coast, this 200-year-old former coaching inn offers an excellent menu of global, home-cooked dishes. Expect Roman lamb stew, Seahouses kipper pâté, Lindisfarne oysters, and Italian pork roasted with herbs and wine.
Directions 100yds E of A1, N of Alnwick
Brewery/Company Free House
Open 12-2 7-11 (closed Mon (ex BH) & wkday lunch)
Bar food 12-1.30 7-9.30 Av main course £7.80
Restaurant 12-1.30 7-9.30 Av 3 course à la carte £14.30

Tyne & Wear

WHITLEY BAY Tyne & Wear
Map 12 NZ37

The Waterford Arms
WHITLEY BAY
Collywell Bay Rd, Seaton Sluice
NE26 4QZ ☎ 0191 237 0450 & 296 5287
The building dates back to 1899 and is situated close to the small local fishing harbour, overlooking the North Sea. Splendid beaches and sand dunes are within easy reach. Seafood dishes are the speciality, including a large fish and chips, fresh seafood feast, Whitby scampi, and fresh lobster in season. **Principal beers:** Vaux Waggle Dance, Wards,Vaux Samson, Vaux Lorimers Best Scotch Lambtons.

Directions From A1 N of Newcastle take A19 at Seaton Burn then floow signs for A190 to Seaton Sluice
Brewery/Company Vaux
Open 11-2 5-10 (Sat-Sun open all day)
Restaurant 11-2 5-10 Av 3 course à la carte £12.45
Accommodation (Min) s£25 d£50

Yorkshire, East Riding of

BEVERLEY Yorkshire, East Riding of
Map 08 TA03

White Horse Inn
BEVERLEY
22 Hengate HU17 8BN
☎ 01482 861973
Carefully preserved 16th-century brick inn, more commonly known as 'Nellies', with spartan but very atmospheric little rooms, complete with coal fires, wooden floors, gas lighting and period funishings that evoke a distinct Victorian charm. Simple lunchtime bar food includes sandwiches, home-made pies and lasagne. **Principal beers:** Samuel Smith Old Brewery Bitter & Soveriegn Bitter.
Directions A1079 from Hull to A1174 into Beverley
Brewery/Company Samuel Smith
Open 11-11 (Sun 12-10.30/no food Mon lunch)
Bar food 12-2 Av main course £3.95

BRANDESBURTON Yorkshire, East Riding of
Map 08 TA14

The Dacre Arms
BRANDESBURTON
Main St YO25 8RL ☎ 01964 542392
Popular village pub, dating from 1806, providing an extensive range of food and seven real ales. In the bar you can choose chicken curry, lamb cobbler, chilli beef platter, haddock and chips or steak and kidney pie. Restaurant fare includes duck

with plum and Armagnac sauce, and rack of lamb. **Principal beers:** Black Sheep Best & Special, Theakston Old Peculier.
Brewery/Company Free House
Open 11.30-2.30 6-11 (open all day wknds; food all day Sun)
Bar food 12-2 6-10 Av main course £4.95
Restaurant 7-11

BREIGHTON Map 08 SE73
Yorkshire, East Riding of

Ye Olde Poachers Inne
BREIGHTON
Main St YO8 7DH ☎ 01757 288849
Medieval theme nights are among the attractions at this family-run pub and restaurant, complete with medieval rest and armour decorating the walls. Prides itself on its home-cooked food and range of specialities, including grills and steaks. Fish dishes might feature seafood medley, jumbo haddock and Tuscany pie.
Principal beers: Marstons Pedigree, Black Sheep, Morland Old Speckled Hen.
Brewery/Company Free House
Open 11.30-3 6-11.30
Bar food 12-2 6-9.15 Av main course £8.95
Restaurant 12-2 (Fri & Sat only) 6-9.15 Av 3 course à la carte £15
Accommodation (Min) s£19 d£39.50

DRIFFIELD Map 08 TA05
Yorkshire, East Riding of

The Bell
DRIFFIELD
46 Market Place YO25 6AN
☎ 01377 256661
Delightful 250-year-old coaching inn, popular locally for the informal lunches served in the rambling, old-panelled bar and lounge areas. From a good cold buffet and filled jacket potatoes, the menus extend to sweet and sour chicken, pork with apple and cider, and rack of lamb with Cumberland sauce. **Principal beers:** Hambleton, Malton, Bass, Worthington Best.
Directions Enter town from A164, turn R at traffic lights. Car park 50yrds on L behind black railings
Brewery/Company Free House
Open 10-2.30 6-11 (Sun 11-2.30,7-10)
Bar food 12-1.30 7-9.30
Restaurant 12-1.30 7-9.30 Av 3 course à la carte £20
Accommodation (Min) s£73 d£102

FLAMBOROUGH Map 08 TA27
Yorkshire, East Riding of

The Seabirds Inn
FLAMBOROUGH
Tower St YO15 1PD ☎ 01262 850242
The fishing village setting provided the inspiration for the name of this popular inn, once a traditional fisherman's local. Note the interesting nautical theme. Among the blackboard specials you might find local crab salad, grilled bacon chop, poachers pie, and smoked haddock and broccoli pie. Over 200 guest beers in two years. **Principal beers:** John Smiths.
Directions On B1255 E of Bridlington
Brewery/Company Free House
Open 11-3 7-11 (Sat 6.30-11,Sun 7-10.30)
Bar food 12-2 7-9 Av main course £5
Restaurant 12-2 7-9 Av 3 course à la carte £12

HOLME UPON SPALDING MOOR
Yorkshire, East Riding of Map 08 SE83

Ye Olde Red Lion Hotel
HOLME UPON SPALDING MOOR
Old Rd YO4 4AD ☎ 01430 860220
17th-century coaching inn with a friendly atmosphere, a wealth of brasses, oak beams, and an open fire. Traditional home-cooked pub food features good quality steaks in the bar, while the restaurant menu consists mainly of fish and seafood. Specialities include duckling and peppered steak. **Principal beers:** Tetley, Bass.
Directions off A1079 (York/Hull road). At Market Weighton take A614
Brewery/Company Free House
Open 11-2.30 6-11
Bar food 12-1.45 6.45-9.45 Av main course £6
Restaurant 12-1.30 7.15-9.30 Av 3 course à la carte £15 Av 3 course fixed price £9.25
Accommodation (Min) s£34.50 d£56

HUGGATE Map 08 SE85
Yorkshire, East Riding of

The Wolds Inn
HUGGATE
YO42 1YH ☎ 01377 288217
Dating back to 1580, this traditional coaching inn occupies a very quiet location on top of the Yorkshire Wolds. Ideal base for walking. The village has

contd.

one of the deepest wells in the country. Wholesome pub fare features a variety of dishes, including beef curry, deep-fried whitebait and chicken korma. **Principal beers:** John Smiths, Tetley, Theakston.
Directions S 0f A166 between York & Driffield
Brewery/Company Free House
Open 12-2.30 6.45-11 (closed Mon, ex BH)
Bar food 12-2.30 6.45-11 Av main course £5
Restaurant 12-3.45 6.45-9.30 Av 3 course à la carte £14.50 Av 3 course fixed price £7.95
Accommodation (Min) s£22.50 d£35

HULL *Map 08 TA02*
Yorkshire, East Riding of

The Minerva Hotel
HULL
Nelson St, Victoria Pier HU1 1XE
☎ 01482 326909
Nautical memorabilia and the history of the Hull fishing fleet characterise the interior of this handsome 19th-century riverside hotel, complete with micro-brewery and rambling, old-fashioned rooms with coal fires. Simple bar food features filled baguettes, haddock and chips and steak and ale pie. **Principal beers:** Tetley, Taylor Landlord, Black Sheep, Caledonian.
Directions M62 onto A63, then Castle St, turn R at signpost for Fruit Market
Brewery/Company Allied Domecq
Open 11-11 (Sun 12-10.30)
Bar food 12-2 6-9 Av main course £4.50
Restaurant 12-2 6-9 Av 3 course à la carte £7.25

LUND *Map 08 SE94*
Yorkshire, East Riding of

Wellington Inn
LUND
19 The Green YO25 9TE
☎ 01377 217294
Mid-19th-century village green pub. The bar snacks menu is displayed on the blackboard. In the restaurant, starters include home-made game terrine, and double baked goats cheese soufflé. Main courses on offer include Barbary duck breast with apricot and blackcurrant stuffing. There is an impressive wine list, too. **Principal beers:** Bateman, Taylor Landlord, Black Sheep Best, John Smiths.
Directions On B1284 NE of Beverley
Brewery/Company Free House
Open 12-3 7-11 (Sun 12-3, 7-10.30)
Bar food 12-2 Av main course £6.50
Restaurant 7-10 Av 3 course à la carte £17.50

STAMFORD BRIDGE *Map 08 SE75*
Yorkshire, East Riding of

The Three Cups
STAMFORD BRIDGE
York Rd YO4 1AX ☎ 01759 375901
After the Battle of Stamford Bridge in 1066, where King Harald defeated his brother and King Hardrada of Norway, troops are thought to have camped on land where this pub, which still has an 18th-century water-well in its bar, now stands. Menu includes traditional pub food and a selection of specials.
Principal beers: Bass.
Directions From York on A166, pub 5m on L
Brewery/Company Vintage Inns
Open 11-11 (Sun 12-10.30)

Yorkshire, North

ACASTER MALBIS *Map 08 SE54*
Yorkshire, North

The Ship Inn
ACASTER MALBIS
Moor End YO23 2UH
☎ 01904 705609 & 703888
17th-century coaching house with a relaxing riverside garden where one can watch the boats and barges go by. Yet, only a few miles from York city centre. Traditional pub food is on offer, including a selection of steaks and grills, chicken Kiev, Whitby haddock, and vegetarian spinach and mushroom lasagne. **Principal beers:** Tetley, Taylor Landlord.

Directions from York take A1036 south after Dringhouses take follow signs for Bishopthorpe and then Acaster Malbis
Brewery/Company Free House
Open 12-3 (1 May-30 Sep 11.30-11) 7-11 (winter Sat-Sun 12-11)
Bar food 12-2.30 6.30-9.30 Av main course £4.95
Restaurant 12-2 7-9.30 Av 3 course à la carte £15
Accommodation (Min) s£29.50 d£39.50

AKEBAR Yorkshire, North *Map 07 NZ19*

The Friar's Head
AKEBAR
Akebar Park DL8 5LY ☎ 01677 450201
Originally a farm and stud, where the Cistercian monks of Jervaulx Abbey bred their horses in the 16th century. It is now part of a golf complex with three courses. Seasonal local produce is used in dishes such as venison with port and redcurrant sauce, and monkfish with Calvados and cream. **Principal beers:** John Smith, Theakston, Black Sheep.
Directions Take A684 from Leeming Bar Motel (on A1). W towards Leyburn for 7m. Friar's Head is in Akebar Park
Brewery/Company Free House
Open 10-2.30 6-11.30
Bar food 12-2.30 6-11 Av main course £6
Restaurant 12-2.30 6-11 Av 3 course à la carte £18

APPLETREEWICK Yorkshire, North *Map 07 SE06*

The Craven Arms
APPLETREEWICK
BD23 6DA ☎ 01756 720270
Traditional, 17th-century creeper-clad village inn, named after Lord Craven, a former Mayor of London, situated close to the River Wharfe and the Dales Way. Comfortable interior with log fires and old beams. Straightforward bar food includes Cumberland sausage, steak and kidney pie and deep-fried plaice.
Principal beers: Black Sheep, Tetley, Theakston Old Peculiar.
Directions From Skipton take A59 towards Harrogate, B6160 N. Village signd on R.(Pub just outside village)
Brewery/Company Free House
Open 11.30-3 6.30-11
Bar food 12-2 7-9.30 Av main course £6

ASENBY Yorkshire, North *Map 08 SE37*

Crab & Lobster
ASENBY
YO7 3QL ☎ 01845 577286
Jazz and Blues suppers are held regulalry at this 17th-century thatched pub, which is set in six acres of lovely gardens. The restaurant menu might offer herb crusted seabass, or roast lamb fillet, while brasserie dishes include Thai red seafood curry, and lobster, king prawn and scallop thermidor. **Principal beers:** Black Sheep, Theakston, Taylor, Bass.
Directions From A1(M) junc take A168 towards Thirsk
Brewery/Company Free House
Open 11.30-3 6-11(Sun 12-10.30)
Bar food 11.30-2.30 6-9.30 Av main course £9.50
Restaurant 11.30-2.30 6-9.30 Av 3 course à la carte £25 Av 3 course fixed price £14.50
Accommodation (Min) d£60

ASKRIGG Yorkshire, North *Map 07 SD99*

Kings Arms Hotel
ASKRIGG
Market Place DL8 3HQ
☎ 01969 650258
Historic coaching inn originally built as a Georgian manor house to accommodate one of the most celebrated racing stables of the day. Sophisticated Silks Room menu might include chicken and leek pie, local venison, and seafood medley. Expect roasted cod, beef fillet with cassis and orange liquor, and hot cappuccino soufflé in the elegantly panelled Clubroom Restaurant. **Principal beers:** Theakston Black Bull, XB, John Smiths, Morland Old Speckled Hen.
Directions N off A684 between Hawes & Leyburn
Brewery/Company Free House
Open 11-3 6.30-11 (Sat 11-5, 6.30-11, Sun 7-10.30)
Bar food 12-3 6.30-11 Av main course £7
Restaurant 12-3 7-11 Av 3 course à la carte £25
Accommodation (Min) s£50 d£79

BAINBRIDGE Yorkshire, North
Map 07 SD99

Rose & Crown Hotel
BAINBRIDGE

DL8 3EE ☎ 01969 650225

Traditional 500-year-old coaching inn overlooking the village green in the heart of Wensleydale. The forest horn is blown each evening from Holyrood to Shrovetide to guide travellers safely to the village. Good choice of starters, while main courses include grilled sole, trio of lamb cutlets, and mushroom and broccoli pancake **Principal beers:** Websters Yorkshire.
Directions On A684 in centre of village
Brewery/Company Free House
Open 11-11 (Sun 12-10.30)
Bar food 12-2 6-9 Av main course £6.45
Restaurant 12-2 7-9.30 Av 3 course à la carte £18
Accommodation (Min) s£32 d£52

BEDALE Yorkshire, North
Map 08 SE28

Freemasons Arms NEW
BEDALE

Nosterfield DL8 2QP ☎ 01677 470548

Cluttered with curios and memorabilia, this inviting, long and low whitewashed building, formerly a row of 18th-century cottages, features English cooking that uses local produce. Booking is essential for the likes of Whitby cod, Masham gammon, Yorkshire steaks, baked halibut with spinach and lemon butter sauce, preceded by home-made soups. Civilised beamed bar; good Northern ales.
Principal beers: Taylor Landlord, Theakston Best, Black Sheep, Tetley.
Brewery/Company Free House
Open 12-3 6-11 (closed Mon ex BH)
Bar food 12-1.30 7-8.45

BILBROUGH Yorkshire, North
Map 08 SE54

The Three Hares Inn & Restaurant
BILBROUGH

Main St YO2 3PH ☎ 01937 832128

Inviting brick-built pub, formerly the village blacksmiths, offering imaginative food and good wine. Begin with chargrilled scallops with pepper salsa, or chicken liver parfait, then, perhaps, try beef and wild mushroom casserole, or venison with butter bean confit and roasted shallots. Good fish specials and puddings like steamed banana sponge.
Principal beers: Taylor Landlord, Black Sheep.
Directions Off A64 (York/Leeds rd)
Brewery/Company Free House
Open 12-3 7-11 (closed Mon/restaurant closed Sun eve)
Bar food 12-2 7-9.30 Av main course £7.95
Restaurant 12-2 7-9.30 Av 3 course à la carte £16.50 Av 2 course fixed price £9.95

BOROUGHBRIDGE Yorkshire, North
Map 08 SE36

The Black Bull Inn
BOROUGHBRIDGE

6 St James St YO5 9AR ☎ 01423 322413

Grade 11 listed building, 800 years old in parts and reputedly haunted, which has always been an inn. Typical dishes on the interesting menus range from crab and salmon fishcakes, and mushroom and bacon ragout, to sea bass with pesto butter sauce, venison with shallot and port sauce, and beef in creamy whisky sauce. **Principal beers:** Black Sheep, John Smiths.

Directions on A1(M) 7m N of A59 junction. Signposted to Borougbridge. 2nd L at 1st rndbt, 3rd L at 2nd rndbt, 2nd R just over hill
Brewery/Company Free House
Open 11-11 (Sun 12-10.30)
Bar food 12-2 7-9 Av main course £5.50
Restaurant 12-2 7-9.30 Av 3 course à la carte £15
Accommodation (Min) s£37 d£42

BREARTON Yorkshire, North
Map 08 SE36

Malt Shovel Inn
BREARTON

HG3 3BX ☎ 01423 862929

Occupying a remote village setting, this cosy 16th-century pub is full of character,

featuring low-beamed ceilings and a striking, ancient oak partition wall. Expect good food, including steak and ale pie, honey-spiced chicken salad, lamb braised in white wine with garlic and mint, and ham and asparagus tart on the imaginative blackboard menu. **Principal beers:** Daleside Nightjar, Durham Magus, Black Sheep, Theakston.
Directions From A61 (Ripon/Harrogate) take B6165 towards Knaresborough. Turn at Brearton - 1.5m.
Brewery/Company Free House
Open 12-3 6.45-11 (closed Mon)
Bar food 12-2 7-9 Av main course £6

BROUGHTON Yorkshire, North *Map 07 SD95*

Bull Inn
BROUGHTON
BD23 3AE ☎ 01756 792065
Resting on the edge of the Yorkshire Dales at the front of Broughton Hall, yet accessibly on the main A59, a friendly welcome awaits at this real country pub. Romany mushrooms could be an appetiser with Cumberland sausage to follow. There's a Junior Menu for children. **Principal beers:** Jennings, Theakston.
Directions On A59 4m from Skipton coming from M6
Brewery/Company Jennings
Open 11-11
Bar food 12-10 Av main course £6

BUCKDEN Yorkshire, North *Map 07 SD97*

The Buck Inn
BUCKDEN
BD23 5JA ☎ 01756 760228
Between the extensive bar menu and carte, a wide choice of imaginative dishes is on offer at this traditional Georgian coaching inn nestling in Upper Wharfedale in the Yorkshire Dales. Expect the likes of moules marinière, braised local lamb in filo pastry with thyme jus, and seared tuna loin with salsa. **Principal beers:** Theakston - Bitter, Black bull, XB, & Old Peculiar.
Directions From Skipton take B6265, then B6160
Brewery/Company Free House
Open 7.30-11
Bar food 12-2 6.30-9 Av main course £6.95
Restaurant 6.30-9 Av 3 course à la carte £23.95
Accommodation (Min) s£38 d£66

BURNSALL Yorkshire, North *Map 07 SE06*

The Red Lion
BURNSALL
By the Bridge BD23 6BU
☎ 01756 720204
Prettily situated by the Wharfe, this 16th-century ferryman's inn is deep in Yorkshire Dales walking country. Diners may find cottage pie, Irish oysters, Red Lion fish pie, breast of chicken with bacon and spinach, and Gloucester Old Spot pork on the menu. The majority of the meat cooked here comes from local farmers. **Principal beers:** Black Bull, Theakston, Morland Old Speckled Hen.

Directions From Skipton take A59 east take B6160 towards Bolton Abbey, Burnsall 7m
Brewery/Company Free House
Open 11.30-11.30 (Sun closes 10.30)
Bar food 12-3 6-9.30 Av main course £8.95
Restaurant 12-2.45 7-9.30 Av 3 course fixed price £22.95
Accommodation (Min) s£58 d£90

BYLAND ABBEY Yorkshire, North *Map 08 SE57*

Abbey Inn NEW
BYLAND ABBEY
YO6 4BP ☎ 01347 868204
Rambling rooms with a wood-burning stove, stone-flagged floors, oak and stripped pine furnishings characterise this splendid inn, which overlooks the ruins of Byland Abbey. Imaginative menus might feature beef and black sheep cobbler, apricot-filled pork with redcurrant glaze, chicken with tomato and tarragon sauce, and sea bream with pesto.

contd.

Northern England

Abbey Inn

Principal beers: Black Sheep, Tetley.
Directions From A19 Thirk/York follow signs to Byland Abbey/Coxwold
Brewery/Company Free House
Open 11-3.30 6.30-11 (Mon open pm only)
Bar food 12-2 6.30-9
Restaurant 12-2 6.30-9 Av 3 course à la carte £16

CARLTON Yorkshire, North
Map 07 SE08

Forester Arms
CARLTON

DL8 4BB ☎ 01969 640272

Country inn nestling in beautiful Coverdale, dating from 1640 and featuring beamed ceilings, flagstone floors and log fires. It is a gem in North Yorkshire's cuilnary crown, offering imaginative menus, including plenty of fresh fish. Dishes sampled were local game terrine, ragout of guinea fowl with wild mushrooms, and a rich chocolate marquise.

Principal beers: John Smiths, Theakston, Black Sheep, Ruddles.
Directions S of Leyburn off A684 or A6108
Brewery/Company Free House
Open 12-3 6.30-11 (closed Sun pm, Mon & Tue am)
Bar food 12-2 7-9.30 Av main course £8
Restaurant 12-2 7-9.30 Av 3 course à la carte £25
Accommodation (Min) s£40 d£70

CARTHORPE Yorkshire, North
Map 08 SE38

The Fox & Hounds
CARTHORPE

DL8 2LG ☎ 01845 567433

Neatly kept 200-year-old pub, formerly a smithy, in a peaceful village just off the A1. Comfortably furnished lounge bar and dining room, the latter featuring the original forge. Expect some good pub, perhaps fresh Whitby crab, chicken stuffed with Coverdale cheese, and halibut with cream and grain mustard sauce on the list of blackboard specials.
Principal beers: John Smiths.
Directions Off A1, signposted on both northbound & southbound carriageways
Brewery/Company Free House
Open 12-2.30 7-11 (closed Mon)
Bar food 12-2.30 7-10 Av main course £8.95
Restaurant 12-2.30 7-10 Av 3 course à la carte £16 Av 3 course fixed price £11.95

CLAPHAM Yorkshire, North
Map 07 SD76

New Inn
CLAPHAM

LA2 8HH ☎ 015242 51203

Family-run, former 18th-century coaching inn set in a peaceful Dales village beneath Ingleborough Mountain. Popular with walkers and pot-holers it offers a friendly welcome and honest pub food, including game pie, steak and ale pie, ploughman's lunches, mixed grill and duck with pepper sauce.
Principal beers: Fulbeck, Dent, Black Sheep, Theakston.

Directions On A65 in Yorkshire Dale National Park
Brewery/Company Free House
Open 11-3 7-11 (Sat-Sun 11-11)
Bar food 12-2 7-9 Av main course £6
Restaurant 7-9 Av 3 course à la carte £18 Av 3 course fixed price £15
Accommodation (Min) s£25 d£40

COXWOLD Yorkshire, North *Map 08 SE57*

The Fauconberg Arms
COXWOLD
Main St YO6 4AD ☎ 01347 868214

17th-century inn once patronized by leading 18th-century novelist, Laurence Sterne who lived nearby. The village and estate were given to the Fauconberg family by Henry VIII. Good range of starters and an impressive selection of main dishes might include pan-fried Barnsley chop, steak and Guinness pie and deep-fried Whitby prawns. **Principal beers:** Theakston, Tetley, Black Bull.
Directions Take A19 S from Thirsk, 2m turn L, signposted alternative route for caravans/heavy vehicles. 5m to village
Brewery/Company Free House
Open 11-2.30 6.30-11
Bar food 12-2 7-9
Restaurant 12-2 7-9
Accommodation (Min) s£30 d£55

DANBY Yorkshire, North *Map 08 NZ70*

Duke of Wellington Inn
DANBY
YO21 2LY ☎ 01287 660351

18th-century coaching inn situated in the heart of the North York Moors National Park. Perfect base for walking and riding. Straightforward menu features traditional pub food, including battered whole tail scampi, chicken curry, local lamb cutlets and giant prawn salad. **Principal beers:** John Smiths Magnet, Camerons Strongarm, Morland Old Speckled Hen.
Directions From A171 between Guisborough & Whitby take rd signed 'Danby & Moors Centre'
Brewery/Company Free House
Open 11-3 7-11
Bar food 12-2 7-9 Av main course £7.50
Restaurant 12-2 7-9 Av 3 course à la carte £13
Accommodation (Min) s£23 d£50

EAST WITTON Yorkshire, North *Map 07 SE18*

The Blue Lion
EAST WITTON
DL8 4SN ☎ 01969 624273

Civilised 18th-century Wensleydale inn overlooking the village green and classic estate village. Tastefully furnished interior with open fires, old settles, a relaxing atmosphere, and excellent, daily-changing blackboard menus All the food is freshly prepared and typical dishes are king scallops with lemon risotto and Gruyère cheese, and local partridge with braised cabbage and thyme sauce. **Principal beers:** Theakstons, Black Sheep Riggwelter, Theakston Old Peculier.
Brewery/Company Free House
Open 11-11
Bar food 12-2.15 7-9.30 Av main course £10.50
Restaurant 7-9.30 Av 3 course à la carte £19
Accommodation (Min) s£47.50 d£65

EGTON BRIDGE Yorkshire, North *Map 08 NZ80*

Horseshoe Hotel
EGTON BRIDGE
YO21 1XE ☎ 01947 895245

An 18th-century country house inn set in lovely grounds by the River Esk, with fishing rights and scenic local walks. Hearty food may range from game terrine, green-lipped mussels, and lunchtime sandwiches, to lamb shank with red wine and rosemary sauce, and baked ling with bubble and squeak. **Principal beers:** Theakston, Tetley, Durham, Black Sheep.
Directions From Whitby take A171 towards Middlesborough Village signed in 5m
Brewery/Company Free House
Open 11.30-3.30 6.30-11
Bar food 12-2 6.45-9 Av main course £6.50
Restaurant 12-2 6.45-9 Av 3 course à la carte £13
Accommodation (Min) s£26 d£38

ELSLACK Yorkshire, North
Map 07 SD94

The Tempest Arms
ELSLACK

BD23 3AY ☎ 01282 842450

Attractive stone-built pub enjoying an isolated postion amid beautiful Yorkshire Dales scenery. It comprises several small rooms and alcoves, with oak beams, wooden floors, stone walls, a log fire and a cosy atmosphere. One varied menu is offered, perhaps incluidng Cajun tuna, medallions of beef, lamb Jennings, and smoked fish platter. **Principal beers:** Jennings - Bitter, Cumberland & Sneck Lifter, Theakstons.

Directions From Skipton take A59 towards Gisburn. Elslack signed on L on A56

Brewery/Company Jennings

Open 11-11 (Sun 12-11; food served all day wknds)

Bar food 12-2.15 6-10 Av main course £6.99

Restaurant 12-2.15 6-9.30 Av 3 course à la carte £13.50

Accommodation (Min) s£50 d£59.50

ESCRICK Yorkshire, North
Map 08 SE64

Black Bull Inn
ESCRICK

Main St Y19 6JP ☎ 01904 728245

Situated at the heart of a quiet village, this 19th-century pub is within easy reach of York racecourse and the historic city centre. Dishes include 16oz prime rumpsteak, a choice of fresh fish and excellent home-made pies. **Principal beers:** Tetley, John Smiths, guest beer.

Directions From York follow the A19 for 5m, enter Escrick, take second L up main street, premises located on the L

Brewery/Company Free House

Open 11.30-3 5-11 (all day wknds)

Bar food 12-2.30 6-10 Av main course £5.50

Restaurant 12-2.30 6-10 Av 3 course à la carte £12

Accommodation (Min) d£52

FADMORE Yorkshire, North
Map 08 SE68

The Plough Inn NEW
FADMORE

Main St YO62 7HY ☎ 01751 431 515

Situated in a tranquil hamlet on the edge of the North York Moors with fine views across the Vale of Pickering, this stylishly refurbished old cottage is popular locally for imaginative food. Daily menus may list filled baguettes, herb-crusted baked halibut, venison with redcurrant and port sauce, medallions of beef with grain mustard sauce, and seafood thermidor. **Principal beers:** Tetleys, John Smiths, Black Sheep, Hambleton.

Directions 1m N of Kirkbymoorside on the A170 Thirsk to Scarborough Rd

Brewery/Company Free House

Open 12-2.30 6.30-11 (closed Mon/no food Sun eve)

Bar food 12-2 7-9 Av main course £8

Restaurant 12-2 7-9 Av 3 course fixed price £11.50

GOATHLAND Yorkshire, North
Map 08 NZ80

Mallyan Spout
GOATHLAND

The Common YO22 5AN ☎ 01947 896486

Ivy-clad, stone-built Victorian property with mullioned windows, named after the famous waterfall at the rear of the hotel. Fresh fish from Whitby is a feature of both menus, including cod and chips, and kebab of monkfish and halibut wrapped in bacon and served with basmati rice. **Principal beers:** Malton Double Chance, Whitby Brewery.

Directions Off A169 (Whitby/Pickering rd)

Brewery/Company Free House

Open 11-11 (Sun 12-10.30)

Bar food 12-2 6-9 Av main course £5.25

Restaurant 12-2 6.45-10 Av 3 course à la carte £19.50 Av 3 course fixed price £19.50

Accommodation (Min) s£50 d£65

GREAT OUSEBURN Yorkshire, North
Map 08 SE46

The Crown Inn NEW
GREAT OUSEBURN

Main St YO26 9RF ☎ 01423 330430

This cheery village pub saw the start of the Tiller Girls dancing troupe and has a landlord who played for Leeds United.

Barbeques are held in summer. Menu may include carpet-bagger fillet steak, Crown's own seafood pie, fresh battered haddock, Quorn tikka masala, and seared venison steak forestière. **Principal beers:** Black Sheep, John Smiths, Taylors Landlord.
Brewery/Company Free House
Open 5-11 (Sat-Sun 11-11)
Bar food 5-10 (12-10 Sat-Sun) Av main course £5.50

HARROGATE Yorkshire, North *Map 08 SE35*

The Boars Head Hotel
HARROGATE
Ripley Castle Estate HG3 3AY
☎ 01423 771888
Old coaching inn, luxuriously refurbished and re-opened by Sir Thomas & Lady Ingleby from nearby Ripley Castle after a drought in the village of 75 years. Creative dishes are served in both the bistro and restaurant. Typically, you may find venison sausages with mustard mash, duck with chorizo and lentil cassoulet, or medallions of Yorkshire lamb with haggis hollandaise. **Principal beers:** Theakston Best & Old Peculier, Black Bull, Marstons Pedigree, Dale Crackshot.

Directions On the A61 Harrogate/Ripon road, the Hotel is in the centre of Ripley village
Brewery/Company Free House
Open 11.30-3 5-11
Bar food 11.30-3 6-10 Av main course £7.95
Restaurant 12-2.30 6.30-11 Av 3 course à la carte £30 Av 3 course fixed price £30
Accommodation (Min) s£95 d£115

Pine Marten
HARROGATE
Otley Rd, Beckwith Knowle HG3 1PR
☎ 01423 533091
Built in 1890 in the style of a Cotswolds manor house, and decorated by William Morris, this delightful building was the home of Robert Wigglesworth, whose firm constructed the worlds largest telescope in 1863. **Principal beers:** Bass.
Directions On B6162 at Beckwith Knowle on outskirts of Harrogate
Brewery/Company Vintage Inns
Open 11-11 (Sun 12-10.30)

HAWES Yorkshire, North *Map 07 SD88*

Board Hotel
HAWES
Market Place DL8 3RD ☎ 01969 667223
Traditional Dales pub in the heart of Hawes in beautiful Wensleydale. Expect a friendly welcome and hearty traditional food, in particular home-made pies. Choose from local game, chicken and mushroom pie, and Portuguese fish pie or, perhaps, lasagne, chilli, or a roast beef lunch. **Principal beers:** Tetley, Black Sheep, Theakstons.
Directions M6 J37 - A684 east
Brewery/Company Free House
Open 11-4 6.30-11
Bar food 12-2 6.30-9 Av main course £4
Restaurant 12-2 6.30-9 Av 3 course à la carte £8
Accommodation (Min) d£42

HELMSLEY Yorkshire, North *Map 08 SE68*

The Feversham Arms Hotel NEW
HELMSLEY
1 High St YO62 5AG ☎ 01439 770766
Built in 1855 on the site of an older hostelry, this small hotel has been much extended since the 1960s and has a large garden with heated swimming pool. There are three bars and a restaurant which offers Spanish shellfish casserole, monkfish, venison and lobster thermidor. **Principal beers:** Theakstons Best.
Directions from the A1(M) jct A168 to Thirsk, then A170 for 14m to Helmsley
Brewery/Company Free House
Open 10-2.30 6-11
Bar food 12-2 6.30-9

contd.

Restaurant 12-2 7-10 Av 3 course à la carte £17.50 Av 3 course fixed price £17.50
Accommodation (Min) s£55 d£70

The Star Inn
HELMSLEY
Harome YO62 5JE ☎ 01439 770397
Charming 14th-century thatched pub featuring hand-crafted oak furniture, low beams, log fires and superior pub food. Robust, up-to-date cooking using fresh ingredients, including home-grown herbs, is evident in such dishes as steamed steak and kidney pudding, red mullet with black bean salsa, and rich pheasant casserole. Puddings may include a tangy lemon tart. **Principal beers:** Black Sheep Special, John Smiths, Theakston Best.

Directions From Helmsley take A170 towards Kirkbymoorside. 0.5m turn R for Harome
Brewery/Company Free House
Open 11.30-3 6.30-11 (Sun 12-10.30 – food 12-6; closed Mon eve)
Bar food 11.30-2 6.30-9.30 Av main course £11
Restaurant 11.30-2 6.30-9.30 Av 3 course à la carte £22

HETTON
Yorkshire, North — *Map 07 SD95*

The Angel
HETTON
BD23 6LT ☎ 01756 730263
Renowned for its innovative modern menus, this attractive dining pub and restaurant dates back some 400 years ago. From fish soup, ham shank and foie gras terrine, and confit of duck with orange sauce, blackboard specials in the brasserie may include oysters, red mullet with gazpacho dressing, and sea bass with olive mash and red wine fish sauce.

Directions From A59 take B6265 towards Grassington/Skipton
Brewery/Company Free House
Open 12-3 6-11 (closed 1 wk Jan)
Bar food 12-2 6-10 Av main course £9
Restaurant 12-2 6-9 Av 3 course à la carte £30 Av 4 course fixed price £30

HOVINGHAM
Yorkshire, North — *Map 08 SE67*

The Worsley Arms Hotel
HOVINGHAM
Main St YO62 4LA ☎ 01653 628234
Situated in one of the county's prettiest villages, birthplace of the Duchess of Kent, this mid-19th-century inn was built by eccentric equestrian Sir William Worsley. Food is available in the quality restaurant and Cricketers Bistro, with dishes ranging from pan-fried sea-bass and fillet of Yorkshire beef to seared salmon and confit of Goosnargh duck. **Principal beers:** John Smiths, Theakston.
Directions From A1 take A64 towards Malton, L onto B1257 signed Slingsby & Hovingham. 2m to Hovingham
Brewery/Company Free House
Open 12-2.30 6-11
Bar food 12-2 6-9.30 Av main course £10
Restaurant 12-2 7-9.30 Av 3 course à la carte £25 Av 3 course fixed price £25
Accommodation (Min) s£60 d£80

HUBBERHOLME
Yorkshire, North — *Map 07 SD97*

The George Inn
HUBBERHOLME
BD23 5JE ☎ 01756 760223
J B Priestley, whose ashes were scattered in Hubberholme churchyard, looked upon this 18th-century listed Dales pub as his favourite watering hole. Nearby the

waters of the Wharfe tumble over limestone pavements. Steak and kidney pie, salmon with creamy dill sauce, Dales lamb chops and Sicilian lasagne are typical examples of the varied menu.
Principal beers: Theakston Black Bull, Black Sheep, Youngers Scotch.
Directions At Buckden on B6160 take turn for Hubberholme
Brewery/Company Free House
Open 11.30-3 6.30-11 (Summer 11.30-11)
Bar food 12-2 6.30-8.45 Av main course £7
Accommodation (Min) s£27 d£41

KETTLEWELL Yorkshire, North — Map 07 SD97

Racehorses Hotel
KETTLEWELL
BD23 5QZ ☎ 01756 760233
Small 18th-century inn situated between the River Wharfe and Park Gill Beck. Bar meals range from Kilnsey trout with toasted almonds, to poached Scottish salmon. Restaurant dishes include sirloin steak with Madeira sauce, and pork medallions with honey sauce. **Principal beers:** Theakston Best, Black Bull, John Smiths, Theakston Old Peculier.
Directions From Skipton take B6265, after 6m continue on B6160 toward Kettlewell, hotel over 2nd bridge on L
Brewery/Company Free House
Open 11-11
Bar food 12-2 6.30-9 Av main course £8.50
Restaurant 6.30-9 Av 3 course à la carte £18
Accommodation (Min) s£18 d£60

KIRBY HILL Yorkshire, North — Map 12 NZ10

The Shoulder of Mutton Inn NEW
KIRBY HILL
DL11 7JH ☎ 01748 822772
200-year-old traditional inn in an elevated village position. Ideal base for exploring the Yorkshire countryside. Relax in the dining room with its stone walls and original beams, and choose from a straightforward menu characterised by good home-cooking. Favourites might include braised steak, seafood platter, half-shoulder of lamb, and Kirby haddock.
Principal beers: John Smiths, Black Sheep Bitter & Riggwelter, Darwin Richmond Ale.
Directions 4m N of Richmond, 6m from A1 A66 J at Scotch Corner
Brewery/Company Free House
Open 12-2 7-11
Bar food 12-2 7-9.30 Av main course £5.75
Restaurant 12-2 7-9.30 Av 3 course à la carte £12
Accommodation (Min) s£28 d£43

KIRKBYMOORSIDE Yorkshire, North — Map 08 SE68

George & Dragon Hotel
KIRKBYMOORSIDE
17 Market Place YO62 6AA
☎ 01751 433334
17th-century coaching inn on the southern edge of the North York Moors. Cosy bar, low beams, renowned collection of cricket and rugby sporting memorabilia. Lovely walled garden at rear. The same menu is offered throughout, with steak and ale pie, fillet of halibut toscana, and Salt Marsh lamb among the dishes. Good range of puddings. **Principal beers:** Taylor Landlord, Black Sheep, John Smiths, Boddingtons.

Directions Just off A170 between Scarborough & Thirsk in centre of the Market Town
Brewery/Company Free House
Open 10-3 6-11
Bar food 12-3 6.30-11 Av main course £8
Restaurant 12-3 6.30-11 Av 3 course à la carte £15
Accommodation (Min) d£79

Northern England

The Lion Inn NEW
KIRKBYMOORSIDE
Blakey Ridge YO62 6LQ
☎ 01751 417320
Fourth highest inn in England with an isolated moorland location. It is cosy inside with low ceilings, beams and stone walls. Typical dishes are Old Peculier casserole in the bar, along with the snacks and sandwiches, and rack of lamb, steak or duck breast in the restaurant. **Principal beers:** Tetley, Theakston Blackbull, Bitter & Old Peculier, Morland Old Speckled Hen.
Directions From A170 follow signs 'Hutton le Hole/Castleton'. Turning 6m N of Hutton le Hole.
Brewery/Company Free House
Open 10.30am-11pm
Bar food 11.30am-10pm Av main course £5.95
Restaurant 11.30am-10pm Av 3 course à la carte £16
Accommodation (Min) s£17 d£48

KIRKHAM Yorkshire, North
Map 08 SE76

Stone Trough Inn
KIRKHAM
Kirkham Abbey YO6 7JS
☎ 01653 618713
Situated opposite Kirkham Abbey and handy for visiting Castle Howard and enjoying scenic local walks, this characterful inn offers fine views across the Derwent Valley. Inside, you will find several beamed and cosy rooms warmed by log fires and, as we went to press, new owners. **Principal beers:** Tetley, Taylor Landlord, Jennings Cumberland, Theakston Old Peculier.
Directions 1 1/2m off A64, between York & Malton
Brewery/Company Free House
Open 12-2.30 6-11 (Sun 7-10.30)
Bar food 12-2 6-9
Restaurant 12-2 6.30-9.30

KNARESBOROUGH Yorkshire, North
Map 08 SE35

The General Tarleton Inn
KNARESBOROUGH
Boroughbridge Rd, Ferrensby HG5 0QB
☎ 01423 340284
Traditional 18th-century coaching inn surrounded by glorious unspoilt countryside. Well-planned brasserie menu is enhanced by an imaginative wine list. Follow carpaccio of tuna with noodle salad and Thai lemon dressing, with venison with roasted butternut squash and rocket salad. Decent lunchtime sandwiches include roasted natural chicken and roast beef. **Principal beers:** Black Sheep, Tetley, Taylors.
Directions On A6055, on crossroads in Ferrensby
Brewery/Company Free House
Open 12-3 6-11
Bar food 12-2 6.30-9.30 Av main course £9.50
Restaurant 12-2 7-9.30 Av 3 course fixed price £25
Accommodation (Min) s£65 d£65

LEYBURN Yorkshire, North
Map 07 SE19

Sandpiper Inn
LEYBURN
Market Place DL8 5AT ☎ 01969 622206
Dating from around 1640, this is the oldest building in Leyburn and has been a pub for 30 years. It is traditional in style, with a beautiful garden in summer. New owner, talented chef Jonathan Harrison, has introduced an innovative, modern pub menu, the blackboard choice perhaps featuring pave of salmon with chive and bacon sauce, pork fillet wrapped in Parma ham with roast peppers and black olives, followed by lemon tart with lime sorbet.

Principal beers: Dent Best, Black Sheep Riggwelter, Theakston.
Directions From A1 take A684 to Leyburn
Brewery/Company Free House
Open 11-3 6-11
Bar food 12-2.30 7-10 Av main course £6
Restaurant 12-2.30 7-10 Av 3 course à la carte £16
Accommodation (Min) s£27.50 d£45

LINTON Map 07 SD96 Yorkshire, North

The Fountaine Inn
LINTON
BD23 5HJ ☎ 01756 752210
A 16th-century inn located in the Yorkshire Dales National Park on the banks of the River Beck. Total refurbishment will transform the inn for the year 2000. This will include a new kitchen producing freshly prepared dishes, such as knuckle of lamb, or monkfish with king prawns and garlic.
Principal beers: Black Sheep, Theakston, Tetley.
Directions From Skipton take B6162 8m turn R for Linton
Brewery/Company Free House
Open 11-11 (11-3, 5.30-11 in winter)
Bar food 12-2.30 6.30-9 Av main course £6.95

LONG PRESTON Map 07 SD85 Yorkshire, North

Maypole Inn NEW
LONG PRESTON
BD23 4PH ☎ 01729 840219
Set in a picturesque Yorkshire Dales village, within easy reach of the Forest of Bowland and the Pennines, this friendly 300-year-old inn offers en suite accommodation and traditional home cooking. After a good moorland walk enjoy beef in ale, chicken and spinach curry, salmon fishcakes, braised shoulder of lamb with rosemary, or various sandwiches and salads. **Principal beers:** Worth Alesman, Taylor Landlord, Castle Eden, Boddingtons.
Directions On A65 between Settle and Skipton
Brewery/Company Whitbread
Open 12-3 6-11 (Sat-Sun 12-11)
Bar food 12-2 6.30-9 Av main course £6
Restaurant 12-2 6.30-9 Av 3 course à la carte £10
Accommodation (Min) s£26 d£39

MIDDLEHAM Map 07 SE18 Yorkshire, North

The White Swan Hotel
MIDDLEHAM
Market Place DL8 4PE ☎ 01969 622093
Traditional inn on the market square of the race horse training town. Special emphasis is given to providing a warm and friendly welcome. The range of dishes from the bar and restaurant menus includes ploughman's, pies, seafood risotto, and fillet steak with black pudding and red wine sauce.

Principal beers: Black Sheep, Hambleton, John Smiths.
Directions From A1, take A684 toward Leyburn then A6108 to Ripon, 1.5m to Middleton
Brewery/Company Free House
Open 10-11
Bar food 12-2.30 6.30-9.30 Av main course £6.15
Restaurant 12-2.30 6.30-9.30 Av 3 course à la carte £17.50 Av 3 course fixed price £14.50
Accommodation (Min) s£28 d£38

MOULTON Map 08 NZ20 Yorkshire, North

Black Bull Inn
MOULTON
DL10 6QJ ☎ 01325 377289
A pub divided into a number of small rooms, including an evening fish bar; a vine-adorned conservatory; and a converted Pullman carriage. Extensive menus range from oysters, game terrine, seafood linguine and French onion tart in the bar, to poached turbot hollandaise, Italian fish stew, and rack of lamb with Madeira sauce.
Directions 1m S of Scotch Corner off A1
Brewery/Company Free House
Open 12-2.30 6-10.30 (Fri-Sat 6-11, closed Sun)
Bar food 12-2.30 Av main course £5
Restaurant 12-2.30 6-10.30 Av 3 course à la carte £25 Av 3 course fixed price £14.95

MUKER Yorkshire, North *Map 07 SD99*

The Farmers Arms
MUKER

DL11 6QG ☎ 01748 886297

Favoured by walkers on the Pennine Way, this unpretentious little pub is set in the heart of beautiful Swaledale. Sit by the open fire in the simply furnished main bar and accompany a pint of Theakstons with a simple bar meal, perhaps, steak pie, lasagne, or a filled bap. **Principal beers:** Theakston-Best, Old Peculier, Butterknowle, John Smiths.

Directions From Richmond take A6108 towards Leyburn, turn R onto B6270

Brewery/Company Free House

Open 11-2.30 (Open longer hours in summer) 7-11

Bar food 12-2.30 7-9 Av main course £5.25

OSMOTHERLEY Yorkshire, North *Map 08 SE49*

Three Tuns Inn
OSMOTHERLEY

South End DL6 3BN ☎ 01609 883301

450-year-old building situated on the Yorkshire Moors near Lyke Lake. Main course dishes range from local pork with sage and apricot sauce, fresh sea bass with lemon butter, and halibut steak topped with prawns and cheese, to roast lamb with fresh strawberry and mint sauce. **Principal beers:** Theakston XB, Theakston Old Peculier, Beamish, Younger Scotch.

Directions Off A19

Brewery/Company Free House

Open 11.45-3.30 6.45-11 (no food Sun eve)

Bar food 11.45-3.30 6.45-11 Av main course £6.50

Restaurant 11.45-3.30 6.45-11 Av 3 course à la carte £12.50

Accommodation (Min) s£47.50 d£60

PATELEY BRIDGE Yorkshire, North *Map 07 SE16*

The Sportmans Arms Hotel
PATELEY BRIDGE

Wath-in-Nidderdale HG3 5PP

☎ 01423 711306

Built from mellow sandstone, this 17th-century building is situated by the River Nidd in a conservation Village. An impressive menu offers dishes such as crumbed loin of pork on chive mash with curry and sultana sauce, roast salmon with ginger and spring onions, and Toulouse sausages in red onion and butterbean gravy. **Principal beers:** Younger, Theakston, John Smiths.

Directions A39/B6451, restaurant 2m N of Pateley Bridge

Brewery/Company Free House

Open 12-2 7-11

Bar food 12-2 7-9 Av main course £9

Restaurant 12-2 7-9 Av 3 course à la carte £20

Accommodation (Min) s£45 d£70

PICKERING Yorkshire, North *Map 08 SE88*

Fox & Hounds Country Inn
PICKERING

Sinnington YO62 6SQ ☎ 01751 431577

Competently cooked modern British dishes attact diners to this attractive, stone-built village inn on the edge of the North Yorkshire Moors. Expect game terrine, garlic and herb-crusted cod, oven-baked sea bass with Mediterranean vegetables, pan-roasted pork fillet, and caramelised citrus tart, as well as steak pie and fresh haddock with mushy peas. **Principal beers:** Camerons, Theakston XB.

Directions 3m W of town, off A170

Brewery/Company Free House

Open 12-2.30 6-11

Bar food 12-2 6.30-9 Av main course £8

Restaurant 12-2 6.30-9 Av 3 course à la carte £16

Accommodation (Min) s£34 d£40

The White Swan
PICKERING

Market Place YO18 7AA

☎ 01751 472288

Delightful 16th-century coaching inn with natural historic charm, especially within the cosy panelled bars, well-appointed bedrooms, and a wide choice of appetising food. Imaginative dishes include crab risotto, roast partridge with game chips and redcurrant and onion jelly, and seared scallops with garlic and Gruyère cheese. **Principal beers:** Black Sheep Best & Special.

Directions In the market place between the church and the steam railway station

Brewery/Company Free House

Open 11-3 5.30-11

Bar food 12-3 7-11 Av main course £6.50
Restaurant 12-3 7.30-11 Av 3 course à la carte £19
Accommodation (Min) s£45 d£60

PICKHILL Yorkshire, North
Map 08 SE38

Nags Head Country Inn
PICKHILL
YO7 4JG ☎ 01845 567391
17th-century coaching inn synonymous with Yorkshire hospitality at its best, notably among weary A1 travellers who can retreat to the beamed lounge bar for welcome refreshment. Home-cooked food ranges from decent sandwiches (available all day) and Thai chicken curry, to sea bass with Oriental vegetables, and pheasant with game gravy. **Principal beers:** Hambleton Ale, Theakston Black Bull & Old Peculier.
Directions 1 E of A1(4m N of A1/A61 junction).W of Thirsk

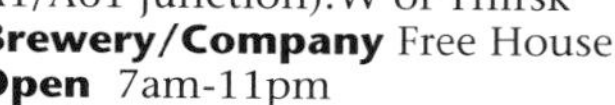

Brewery/Company Free House
Open 7am-11pm
Bar food 12-2 5.30-10 Av main course £6.95
Restaurant 12-2 5.30-10 Av 3 course à la carte £16
Accommodation (Min) s£36 d£50

RAMSGILL Yorkshire, North
Map 07 SE17

The Yorke Arms
RAMSGILL
HG3 5RL ☎ 01423 755243
Creeper-clad 18th-century stone inn in unspoilt Nidderdale, originally built as a shooting. Creative modern English cooking attracts a discerning dining clientele. Expect the likes of carrot and ginger soup, fricassée of monkfish and scallops, sweet and sour braised duck with Oriental vegetables, and quality calves' liver with thyme polenta on the imaginative menu. **Principal beers:** Black Sheep Special.
Directions Turn off at Pateley Bridge at the Nidderdale filling station on Low Wath rd. Signed to Ramsgill, continue for 3.5m
Brewery/Company Free House
Open 11-11 (Sun 12-10.30)
Bar food 12-2 7-9
Restaurant 12-2 7-9
Accommodation (Min) s£70 d£65

RICHMOND Yorkshire, North
Map 07 NZ10

Charles Bathurst Inn NEW
DABE
RICHMOND
Arkengarthdale DL11 6EN
☎ 01748 884567 884265
The 'CB Inn' lies tucked away in the remote and stunningly beautiful Arkengarthdale in the Yorkshire Dales. Open fires, wooden floors and a relaxing atmosphere characterise the interior. A good menu highlights freshly cooked food, including, perhaps spiced tomato and lentil soup, lime and ham filled guinea fowl with Madeira jus, sea bass with herbs and garlic, and venison on roast vegetables with port and honey. **Principal beers:** Theakstons, John Smiths, Black Sheep.
Brewery/Company Free House
Open 11-11
Bar food 12-2 6.30-11 Av main course £7.75
Restaurant 12-2 6.30-11 Av 3 course à la carte £17 Av 3 course fixed price £13.50

ROSEDALE ABBEY Yorkshire, North
Map 08 SE79

The Milburn Arms Hotel
ROSEDALE ABBEY
YO18 8RA ☎ 01751 417312
Comfortable 16th-century hotel, enjoying a peaceful village location on the North York Moors. Quality cooking is served in the Priory Restaurant, including a summer fish menu - red mullet with scallop risotto and tomato broth - and duck with red onion tarte tatin and redcurrant jus. Good blackboard menu in the spacious bar. **Principal beers:** Bass, Stones, Blacksheep.
Directions A170 W from Pickering 3m, R at sign to Rosedale then 7m N
Brewery/Company Free House
Open 11.30-3 6.30-11
Bar food 12-2.30 7-9.30 Av main course £7.25
Restaurant 12-2.30 7-9.30 Av 3 course à la carte £25
Accommodation (Min) s£41.50 d£64

White Horse Farm Hotel
ROSEDALE ABBEY
YO18 8SE ☎ 01751 417239
Its origins as a farm are still evident in the memorabilia displayed in the bar, and its position is enviable - high above the village with spectacular moorland views. Typical Yorkshire fare highlight the menus, such as Whitby haddock pot, roast local venison, Barnsley chop with honey glaze, and York chocolate tart. Sandwiches, salads and ploughman's are always available. **Principal beers:** Blacksheep - Bitter, Special & Riggwelter, Tetley, John Smiths.
Directions Turn off A170, follow signs to Rosedale for approx 7m, hotel sign points up steep hill out of village, hotel 300yds on left
Brewery/Company Free House
Open 12-3 6.30-11
Bar food 12-2 6.30-9.30 Av main course £8
Restaurant 12-2 7-12 Av 4 course fixed price £19
Accommodation (Min) s£33 d£66

SAWLEY Yorkshire, North
Map 08 SE26

The Sawley Arms
SAWLEY
HG4 3EQ ☎ 01765 620642
Popular dining pub at the centre of a long, straggling village. Noted for its award-winning, flower-filled garden, and for its range of unusual home-made soups (leek and coconut). Among the main courses you will find salmon and herb pancake, freshly smoked Nidderdale trout, curried chicken breast and home-made steak pie. **Principal beers:** Theakston, John Smiths, Black Sheep.

Directions A1-Knaresborough-Ripley, or A1-Ripon B6265-Pateley Bridge
Brewery/Company Free House
Open 11.30-3 6.30-10.30
Bar food 11.30-3 6.30-9 Av main course £6.50
Restaurant 11.30-2 6.30-9 Av 3 course à la carte £17.50

SAXTON Yorkshire, North
Map 08 SE43

The Plough Inn
SAXTON
Headwell Ln LS24 9PB ☎ 01937 557242
White-stone, 250-year-old building, formerly a farmhouse, offering restaurant quality food throughout the cosy dining room and adjoining bar. From lunchtime snacks like hot beef baguette or a first-rate ploughman's, the blackboard may list venison with juniper jus, monkfish on couscous with creamy pesto, and good puddings like strawberry and almond strudel. **Principal beers:** Theakston, Taylor, Rooster's, Rudgate.
Directions Off A64 join A162 thru Towton, R onto B1217, Saxton signposted
Brewery/Company Free House
Open 12-3.30 6-11 (closed Sun eve, all Mon)
Bar food 12-2 Av main course £8
Restaurant 12-2 6.30-10 Av 3 course à la carte £17.95 Av 3 course fixed price £16

SCAWTON Yorkshire, North
Map 08 SE58

The Hare Inn
SCAWTON
YO7 2HG ☎ 01845 597289
Reputedly built 800 years ago by the monks from nearby Rievaulx Abbey, this attractive stone pub enjoys a peaceful village setting on the North York Moors. Satisfying blackboard listed dishes may include rabbit casserole, monkfish with tomato and garlic sauce, steak and kidney pudding, beef Wellington, fresh Whitby haddock, and puddings like trio of chocolate. **Principal beers:** Black Sheep, Vaux Samson.
Brewery/Company Free House
Open 12-2 6.30-11 (closed Mon am, ex BHs, 1st wk Feb)
Bar food 12-2 6.30-9 Av main course £6
Restaurant 12-2 6.30-9 Av 3 course à la carte £15

SETTLE Yorkshire, North *Map 07 SD89*

Golden Lion Hotel
SETTLE
Duke St BD24 9DU ☎ 01729 822203
Built around 1640, and once a traditional coaching inn, the hotel is situated in the heart of the 17th-century market place. Food ranges from the triple-decker Bookmaker sandwich, with roast beef, mushroom and onion, to baked sea bass with creamed spinach and wine sauce.
Principal beers: Thwaites.
Directions in the town centre opposite Barclays bank
Brewery/Company Thwaites
Open 8am-11.30pm
Bar food 12-2.30 6.30-10 Av main course £6.75
Restaurant 12-2.30 6-10 Av 3 course à la carte £15
Accommodation (Min) s£23.50 d£47

STARBOTTON Yorkshire, North *Map 07 SD97*

Fox & Hounds Inn
STARBOTTON
BD23 5HY ☎ 01756 760269
A lovely limestone village in the heart of beautiful Upper Wharfedale is the setting for this welcoming 17th-century pub. Close to the Dales Way, it offers excellent Yorkshire ales and decent home-cooking. Typical dishes may include hearty ploughman's, chicken and leek crumble, Moroccan-style lamb, steak and mushroom pie, and sticky toffee pudding. **Principal beers:** Black Sheep, Taylor Landlord,Theakston Old Peculier & Black Bull.
Directions on B6160 N of Kettlewell
Brewery/Company Free House
Open 11.30-3 6.30-11 (closed Mon eve, Jan-mid Feb)
Bar food 12-2 7-9 Av main course £6.50
Accommodation (Min) d£46

SUTTON-ON-THE-FOREST Yorkshire, North *Map 08 SE56*

Rose & Crown

SUTTON-ON-THE-FOREST
Main St YO6 1DP ☎ 01347 810351
Stylish and relaxing ivy-clad village pub with a distinct bistro atmosphere and imaginative food to match. Blackboards list the daily specials such as bangers and chive mash, game pie and trio of grilled fish, alongside regular dishes like smoked salmon fishcakes, monkfish in white wine, pheasant provençale, freshly-cut sandwiches, and hot lemon pudding.
Principal beers: John Smiths, Theakston.
Directions On B1363 N of York
Brewery/Company Free House
Open 11-3 6-11 (closed Mon/no food Sun pm)
Bar food 11-2.30 6-9.30 Av main course £9.95
Restaurant 11-2.30 6-9.30 Av 3 course à la carte £17.50

TERRINGTON Yorkshire, North *Map 08 SE67*

Bay Horse Inn
TERRINGTON
YO6 4PP ☎ 01653 648416
Homely village pub with a good food trade. Game pie, fresh fish and locally produced steaks and roasts are features of the menu, supported by blackboard specials such as pork chop with Madeira and mushrooms, pheasant in red wine, and salmon with capers and prawns.

Principal beers: Theakston Black Bull, John Smiths.
Brewery/Company Free House
Open 12-3 6.30-11 (no food Sun & Tue eve)
Bar food 12-2 7-9 Av main course £6
Restaurant 12-2 7-9

THORNTON WATLASS Yorkshire, North *Map 08 SE28*

The Buck Inn
THORNTON WATLASS
HG4 4AN ☎ 01677 422461
Traditional country inn enjoying a quintessential English village setting overlooking cricket green. The wall of the pub doubles as the boundary!. Examples of the extensive menu include Masham rarebit, scrambled egg and smoked

contd.

salmon in French bread, deep-fried Whitby cod, oven-baked lasagne, seafood tagliatelle and venison casserole.

The Buck Inn

Principal beers: Theakston, Tetley, Black Sheep, John Smiths.
Directions From A1 at Leeming Bar take A684 to Bedale, then B6268. Village 2m on R, hotel by cricket green
Brewery/Company Free House
Open 11-3 6-11
Bar food 12-2 6.30-9.30 Av main course £6
Restaurant 12-2 6.30-9.30 Av 3 course à la carte £15
Accommodation (Min) s£32 d£48

THRESHFIELD Yorkshire, North — Map 07 SD96

The Old Hall Inn
THRESHFIELD
BD23 5HB ☎ 01756 752441

Popular Dales inn which takes its name from the 15th-century hall at the rear, built by monks and reputedly the oldest inhabited building in Wharfedale. Good base for excellent walking. Interesting blackboard menu listing venison steak on garlic mash, wild boar sausages, and braised lamb with lemon and garlic. Good snacks. **Principal beers:** Taylor Best, Landlord, & Golden Best.
Directions From Skipton north on B6265
Brewery/Company Free House
Open 11-3 6-11 (Sun 12-3 7-10.30)
Bar food 12-2 6-9.30 Av main course £6.50
Restaurant 12-2 6-9.30 Av 3 course à la carte £16
Accommodation (Min) d£40

WASS Yorkshire, North — Map 08 SE57

Wombwell Arms
WASS
YO6 4BE ☎ 01347 868280

Situated at the base of the lovely Hambleton Hills, the hamlet of Wass is the setting for this welcoming 17th-century stone inn. A blackboard menu offers such popular dishes as grilled Whitby cod, pot roasted lamb shank, local venison sausages, and tagliatelle with chargrilled Mediterranean vegetables and pesto. **Principal beers:** Black Sheep, Taylor Landlord and guest beers.
Directions From A1 take A168 to A19 jnct. York exit, then L after 2.5m, L at Coxwold to Ampleforth, Wass 2m
Brewery/Company Free House
Open 12-2.30 7-11 (closed Sun eve in winter & all Mon)
Bar food 12-2 7-9 Av main course £8
Accommodation (Min) s£29.50 d£49

WEST BURTON Yorkshire, North — Map 07 SE08

Fox & Hounds
WEST BURTON
DL8 4JY ☎ 01969 663279

Close to the heart of beautiful Wensleydale, this 17th-century coaching inn is attractively located by the pretty green in a totally unspoilt village. Traditional pub food is a feature here, the menu listing home-made lasagne, vegetable curry, beef in ale pie, chicken supreme, and fish pie. **Principal beers:** Black Sheep, Websters Yorkshire, Theakston - Bitter, Old Peculier.
Brewery/Company Free House
Open 11-11
Bar food 11.30-2 6.30-9 Av main course £4.75
Restaurant 6.30-9 Av 3 course à la carte £13 Av 3 course fixed price £12
Accommodation (Min) s£37 d£44

WEST TANFIELD Yorkshire, North — Map 08 SE27

The Bruce Arms NEW
WEST TANFIELD
Main St HG4 5JJ ☎ 01677 470325

Solid, stone-built, 18th-century village pub with a relaxed rustic atmosphere, log fires and candle-topped tables. An

interesting blackboard menu offers a good choice, including twice-baked cheese soufflé, braised lamb shank with parsley mash and red wine gravy, confit of duck, salmon with chargrilled red cabbage, and crème brûlée. **Principal beers:** Black Sheep.
Directions On A6108 Ripon/Masham rd, close to A1
Brewery/Company Free House
Open 12-2 6-11 (closed Sun pm & all Mon)
Bar food 12-2 6.30-9.30 Av main course £10

WEST WITTON Yorkshire, North — *Map 07 SE08*

The Wensleydale Heifer Inn
WEST WITTON
DL8 4LS ☎ 01969 622322

A 17th-century Yorkshire Dales Inn located in the heart of the National Park. Favourite dishes are home-made fish cakes, Pen Hill pie and Wensleydale chicken in the bar, while the restaurant offers rack of lamb, grilled sea trout and Aberdeen Angus steaks, followed by syrup sponge. Good themed food evenings. **Principal beers:** Theakston, John Smiths.

Directions A684, at West end of village.
Brewery/Company Free House
Open 8am-11pm
Bar food 12-2 6.30-9.30 Av main course £6.50
Restaurant 12-2 6-9.30 Av 3 course à la carte £24.50 Av 3 course fixed price £14.50
Accommodation (Min) s£55 d£76

WHITBY Yorkshire, North — *Map 08 NZ81*

The Magpie Cafe
WHITBY
14 Pier Rd YO21 3PU ☎ 01947 602058

Former merchant's house built in 1750 overlooking Whitby harbour. Not really a pub but a licensed premises serving excellent fish and seafood, notably the

ever-popular Whitby cod or haddock and chips. Further choices include Scottish mussels, king scallops, seafood chowder, skate in black butter, oven-baked sea bass, and steak with pepper sauce.
Brewery/Company Free House
Open 11.30-9 (closed Jan)

WIGGLESWORTH Yorkshire, North — *Map 07 SD85*

The Plough Inn
WIGGLESWORTH
BD23 4RJ ☎ 01729 840243

Located at the heart of Ribblesdale, in Yorkshire's Three Peaks country, this historic inn was originally a working farm forming part of a country estate. Relax in the oak panelled dining room where a bistro-style menu is available, or dine in the conservatory restaurant with its fine Pennine views, sampling haddock mornay or marinated pork shoulder. **Principal beers:** Tetley, Boddingtons.
Directions from A65 between Skipton & Long Preston take B6478 to Wigglesworth
Brewery/Company Free House
Open 8.30-2.30 5-11
Bar food 12-2 7-9 Av main course £5.75
Restaurant 12-2 7-9 Av 3 course à la carte £16.50 Av 3 course fixed price £16.50
Accommodation (Min) s£35 d£54.50

YORK Yorkshire, North Map 08 SE65

Dormouse
YORK

Clifton Park, Shipton Rd YO3 6RD
☎ 01904 640682

This new pub has been constructed from reclaimed materials, including oak beams from rail bridges, and bricks and roof slates from buildings in the Midlands and the South. The gardens are extensively planted with native species. **Principal beers:** Bass.
Directions A64 Scarborough Rd, then A1237 York Ring Road, pub is on A19 just off A1237
Brewery/Company Vintage Inns
Open 11-11 (Sun 12-10.30)

Yorkshire, South

BESSACARR Yorkshire, South Map 08 SE60

Hare & Tortoise
BESSACARR

329 Bawtry Rd DN4 7NB
☎ 01302 861901

Dating from 1789, this coaching inn on the Great North Road has recently been returned to its original function after being a private residence since 1850.
Principal beers: Bass, Stones, Worthington.
Directions On crossroads of A638 & A635 Doncaster to Bawtry Road
Brewery/Company Vintage Inns
Open 11-11 (Sun 12-10.30)

BRADFIELD Yorkshire, South Map 08 SK29

The Strines Inn
BRADFIELD

Bradfield Dale S6 6JE ☎ 0114 285 1247

Originally a manor house built in 1275, most of the building dates from the 1550s onwards, and it has been an inn since 1771. Food, served in the bar, includes home-made chicken and leek pie, giant Yorkshire pudding with roast beef and vegetables, and grilled rainbow trout. **Principal beers:** Morland Old Speckled Hen, Marston Pedigree, Mansfield Ridings Bitter.
Directions off A57 between Sheffield toward Manchester
Brewery/Company Free House
Open 10.30-3 (all day Etr-Sep & wknds) 6.30-11 (food all day Etr-Sep & wknds)
Bar food 12-2.30 7-9 Av main course £5.95
Accommodation (Min) s£35 d£59.50

PENISTONE Yorkshire, South Map 08 SE20

Cubley Hall
PENISTONE

Mortimer Rd, Cubley S36 9DF ☎ 01226 766086

Imposing stone-built 18th-century inn set in four acres with fine views over the lower Pennines. Neatly refurbished yet maintaining many original features, it offers extensive modern menus. Typical dishes include Caesar chicken and pasta, gourmet pizzas, baked salmon with pesto couscous and chive and tomato sauce, and dark chocolate and rum tart.

Principal beers: Tetley, Burton Ale, Morland Old Speckled Hen, Greene King Abbot Ale.
Brewery/Company Free House
Open 11-11 (Sun 12-10.30)
Bar food 12-10 Av main course £6
Accommodation (Min) s£48.50 d£58.50

WENTWORTH Yorkshire, South Map 08 SK39

Rockingham Arms
WENTWORTH

8 Main St S62 7TL ☎ 01226 742075

Imposing creeper-clad pub, built as a farmhouse in the 17th century. There is an orchard garden to the side, a bowling green and the village cricket pitch. The menu offers traditional pub food - filled baguettes, steak and mushroom pie, bangers and mash, and large Yorkshire puddings. **Principal beers:** Theakston XB, Old Peculier, & Best, Courage Directors.

Directions M1 J36 to Hoyland Common then B6090
Brewery/Company Scottish & Newcastle
Open 11-11 (Sun 12-10.30)
Bar food 12-2.30 5-9 Av main course £5.25
Restaurant 12-2

Yorkshire, West

CLIFTON Yorkshire, West *Map 08 SE12*

Black Horse Inn
CLIFTON
HD6 4HJ ☎ 01484 713862
A 16th-century coaching inn, once used as a meeting place for the Luddites, with oak-beamed rooms and open coal fires. Good range of traditional bar meals including steak sandwich and haddock and chips, while the restaurant features tournedos Rossini and smoked salmon cornets filled with prawns. **Principal beers:** Boddingtons, Castle Eden Ale, Taylor Landlord.

Directions N of Brighouse
Brewery/Company Whitbread
Open 11-3 5.30-11 (Sun 12-3, 5.30-10.30)
Bar food 12-2.15 5.30-9.30 Av main course £6.25
Restaurant 12-2.15 5.30-9.30 Av 3 course à la carte £18.50 Av 3 course fixed price £17.95
Accommodation (Min) s£26 d£39

DEWSBURY Yorkshire, West *Map 08 SE22*

West Riding Licensed Refreshment Rooms
DEWSBURY
Dewsbury Railway Station, Wellington Rd WF13 1HF ☎ 01924 459193
Converted 19th-century railway station building on the Trans-Pennine route. Daily blackboard specials include a range of meat, fish, vegetarian and vegan meals, such as Alaskan fishcakes, walnut escalopes, lamb pasticcio and carrot roulade with water cress filling. An always changing selection of real ales is also available. **Principal beers:** Bateman Dark, Mild, XB & XXXB.

Open 11-11 (Mon-Sat) 12-10.30 (Sun)
Bar food 12-3 Av main course £3.50

HALIFAX Yorkshire, West *Map 07 SE02*

The Rock Inn Hotel
HALIFAX
Holywell Green HX4 9BS
☎ 01422 379721
Small hotel situated in the valley of Holywell Green, close to Last of the Summer Wine and Brontë country. Expect a cosmopolitan choice of main course dishes such as Thai red chicken curry, braised lamb in red wine with apricots, pork Romana, and meatloaf Wellington, as well as a good selection of vegetarian meals. **Principal beers:** Black Sheep, Taylor Landlord.
Directions From M62 J24 follow signs for Blackley, L at crossroads, approx 0.5m on L
Brewery/Company Free House
Open 11-11
Accommodation (Min) s£45 d£50

HAREWOOD Yorkshire, West *Map 08 SE34*

Harewood Arms Hotel
HAREWOOD
Harrogate Rd LS17 9LH
☎ 0113 2886566
Former coaching inn, situated opposite Harewood House. Ideal base for touring the Yorkshire Dales. Extensive range of home-made food, prepared with fresh local produce. Good bar menu includes lasagne, Yorkshire rarebit, deep-fried

contd.

haddock, spicy lamb kebabs and sandwiches. Expect roast duck and baked salmon on the imaginative restaurant menu. **Principal beers:** Samuel Smith Old Brewery Bitter.
Directions On A61 S of Harrogate
Brewery/Company Samuel Smith
Open 11-11
Bar food 12-9.45
Restaurant 12-2 7-10 Av 3 course à la carte £21.50 Av 4 course fixed price £21.50
Accommodation (Min) d£68

HAWORTH Yorkshire, West *Map 07 SE03*

The Old White Lion Hotel
HAWORTH
Main St BD22 8DU ☎ 01535 642313
300-year-old former coaching inn located at the top of a cobbled street, close to the Brontë Museum and Parsonage. Traditionally furnished bars offer a welcome respite from the tourist trail, Theakston ales, and a wide range of generously served snacks and meals. **Principal beers:** Wilsons, Websters, Theakston, John Smiths.
Directions Turn off A629 onto B6142, hotel 0.5m past Haworth Station
Brewery/Company Free House
Open 11-3 6-11
Bar food 11.30-2.30 6.30-9.30 Av main course £5
Restaurant 7-9.30 Av 3 course à la carte £14 Av 3 course fixed price £12
Accommodation (Min) s£44.50 d£61

HORBURY Yorkshire, West *Map 08 SE21*

Quarry Inn & Cottages
HORBURY
70 Quarry Hill WE4 5NE
☎ 01924 272523
Creeper-clad stone pub built in the 19th-century in the hollow of a disused quarry. Comfortable, split-level interior adorned with brass artefacts, and a traditional range of pub food enhanced by daily specials. Typical dishes include Scottish haddock and chips, home-made lasagne, fisherman's pie, and chicken stir-fry. **Principal beers:** Marstons Pedigree & Bitter, John Smiths.
Directions On the A642 approx 2.5m from Wakefield
Brewery/Company Marstons
Open 11.30-11 (Sun 12-4, 7-10.30/no food Sun eve)
Bar food 12-2 5.30-8.30 Av main course £4
Restaurant 12-2 5.30-8.30 Av 3 course à la carte £7.25 Av 3 course fixed price £7.25
Accommodation (Min) s£27.50 d£30

LEDSHAM Yorkshire, West *Map 08 SE42*

The Chequers Inn
LEDSHAM
Claypit Ln LS25 5LP ☎ 01977 683135
Quaint creeper-clad inn situated in an old estate village. Low beams and wooden settles enhance the character. The pub is closed on Sunday because the one-time lady of the manor was offended by drunken farm labourers on her way to church over 160 years ago. Appetising specials might include Barnsley chop, Cumberland sausage and pan-griddled swordfish. **Principal beers:** Younger, Theakston Best, John Smiths.
Directions Between A1 & A656 above Castleford
Brewery/Company Free House
Open 11-3 5.30-11 (Sat 11-11/closed Sun)
Bar food 12-2.15 6.30-9.30 Av main course £5.50
Restaurant 6.30-9.30

LEEDS Yorkshire, West *Map 08 SE23*

Roundhay Fox
LEEDS
Princes Av, Roundhay LS8 2EP
☎ 0113 246 3090
Next to the beautiful Roundhay Park, and close to Tropical World, - a collection of international exotic flora - this pub is the ideal place to relax after a busy day in Leeds. **Principal beers:** Bass, Worthington, Stones.
Directions from M1 or M62 follow signs for Tropical World (pub is opp) or from Leeds city centre toward Harrogate then A6120
Brewery/Company Vintage Inns
Open 11-11 (Sun 12-10.30)

Whitelocks
LEEDS
Turks Head Yard, Briggate LS1 6HB
☎ 0113 245 3950
City centre pub tucked away in a quiet yard. The first licence was granted in

1715. Starters include Florida cocktail and Whitelocks mushrooms. Elsewhere the menu offers salmon, haddock, roast beef and Yorkshire pudding, beef and mushrooms in Younger's Scotch bitter, and home-style fruit pie to finish. **Principal beers:** Theakston - Old Peculiar, Best & XB, Younger - Scotch, IPA.
Directions next to Marks & Spencer in Briggate
Brewery/Company Scottish & Newcastle
Open 11-11 (Sun 12-10.30)
Bar food 11-7.30 Av main course £4
Restaurant 12-2.30 5.30-7.30 Av 3 course à la carte £11.50

LINTON Yorkshire, West *Map 08 SE34*

The Windmill Inn
LINTON
Main St LS22 4HT ☎ 01937 582209
A coaching inn since 1674, the building actually dates from 1314 and originally housed the owner of the long disappeared windmill. Popular bar food includes beer-battered haddock and lamb and barley casserole. Dishes such as sea bream Breton and fillet steak can be found in the restaurant. **Principal beers:** John Smiths, Theakston Best, Ruddles County.
Directions from A1 exit at Tadcaster/Otley junction and follow Otley signs. In Collingham follow signs for Linton
Brewery/Company Scottish Courage
Open 11.30-3 5-11 (Sat-Sun 11.30-11)
Bar food 12-2 5.30-9 Av main course £6
Restaurant 12-2 5.30-9 Av 3 course à la carte £16 Av 3 course fixed price £8.50

MELTHAM Yorkshire, West *Map 07 SE11*

Will's O' Nat's
MELTHAM
Blackmoorfoot Rd HD7 3PS
☎ 01484 850078
Situated on both the Kirklees and Colne Valley circular walks, this friendly, 18th-century rural pub is popular with walkers. Good food is also an attraction, the menu choice including sandwiches, baked ham with Cumberland sauce, lambs' liver and onions, fish of the day (cod with parsley sauce), and home-made puddings. **Principal beers:** Old Mill, Tetley Bitter & Mild.
Directions A62 from Huddersfield then off B6107 towards Holmfirth
Brewery/Company Vanguard
Open 11.30-3 6.30-11
Bar food 11.30-2 6-9.30 Av main course £5.30
Restaurant 11.30-2 6-9.30 Av 3 course à la carte £11

NEWALL Yorkshire, West *Map 07 SE14*

The Spite
NEWALL
LS21 2EY ☎ 01943 463063
Traditional village pub which boasts a legend of feuding landlords, and a vast collection of framed banknotes in the relaxing bars. From the Spite's 'famous' hot beef sandwich, soup, and a selection of daily roasts, the menu extends to steak pie, lambs' liver, bacon and onions, and hot chocolate fudge pudding. **Principal beers:** Websters, Black Sheep, John Smiths.
Brewery/Company Unique Pub Co
Open 11.30-3 6-11 (Sat 11.30-11, Sun 12-3,7-10.30)
Bar food 11.30-2 7-9 Av main course £5.50
Restaurant 11.30-2 7-9

POOL Yorkshire, West *Map 08 SE24*

The White Hart
POOL
Main St LS21 1LH ☎ 0113 202 7901
Situated at the centre of the village, this building was originally a farmhouse, dating from the 18th century and licensed around 1825. Classic British food is served. **Principal beers:** Bass.
Directions From M1 J47 follow signs for airport.Then A658.Village 3m
Brewery/Company Vintage Inns
Open 11-11 (Sun 12-10.30)

RIPPONDEN Yorkshire, West *Map 07 SE01*

Old Bridge Inn
RIPPONDEN
Priest Ln HX6 4DL ☎ 01422 822595
Picturesquely situated by a cobbled packhorse bridge spanning the River Ryburn, this restored 14th-century Pennine inn was visited by Daniel Defoe. Typical examples from the blackboard menu include chargrilled vegetable lasagne, fisherman's pie, chicken, broccoli pie, and deep-fried Camembert. Separate bridge across the bridge.

contd.

Old Bridge Inn

Principal beers: Taylor Landlord & Golden Best, Black Sheep Best.
Directions 5m from Halifax in village centre by church
Brewery/Company Free House
Open 12-3 5.30-11 (Sat 12-11, Sun 12-10.30/no food wknds)
Bar food 12-2 6.30-9.30 Av main course £4.75

ROYDHOUSE Yorkshire, West Map 08 SE21

The Three Acres Inn
ROYDHOUSE

HD8 8LR ☎ 01484 602606

Turn of the century stone coaching inn set high up in the Pennines above Huddersfield and renowned for its civilised atmosphere, warm hospitality and commendable bar food. Excellent menu choices range from imaginative sandwiches (crab with lemon and ginger dressing), to fresh Irish oysters, hake, prawn and Wensleydale pie, and duck confit with red wine and mushroom jus.
Principal beers: Taylor Landlord, Morland Old Speckled Hen, Adnams, Mansfield Riding Bitter.
Directions From Huddersfield take A629 then B6116,take L turn for village
Brewery/Company Free House
Open 12-3 7-11
Bar food 12-2 7-9.45 Av main course £7.95
Restaurant 12-3 7-9.45 Av 3 course à la carte £22.50 Av 4 course fixed price £25
Accommodation (Min) s£40 d£60

SHELF Yorkshire, West Map 07 SE12

Duke of York
SHELF

West St, Stone Chair HX3 7LN
☎ 01422 202056

There's a vast array of brassware and jugs at this 17th-century former coaching inn, and the atmosphere is lively. Traditional pub food is served, including a range of snacks, grills, chicken specialities, Indian dishes and vegetarian options. Daily specials include fresh fish. **Principal beers:** Taylor Best & Landlord, guest beer.
Directions M62 J25 to Brighouse.Take A644 N. Inn 500yds on R after Stone Chair r'about
Brewery/Company Whitbread
Open 11-12 (Sun 12-11)
Bar food 12-2.30 5-9 Av main course £5
Accommodation (Min) s£28 d£38

THORNTON Yorkshire, West Map 07 SE03

Ring O'Bells
THORNTON

212 Hilltop Rd BD13 3QL
☎ 01274 832296

Popular moorland pub, just three miles from Bradford, renowned for its quality home-cooked food served throughout the pubby, open-plan interior. Expect dishes such as seared salmon on chicory mash with champagne and mushroom sauce, and kleftico, an individual joint of lamb shoulder slowly roasted with fresh mint, oregano and a hint of garlic.

Principal beers: Websters Yorkshire, John Smiths, Theakston, Black Sheep.
Directions From M62 take A58 for 5m, R at crossroads onto A644, after 4.5m follow signs for Denholme, on to Well Head Rd into Hilltop Rd
Brewery/Company Free House
Open 11.30-3.30 5.30-11 (Sun 6.30-10)
Bar food 12-2 5.30-9 Av main course £7.50
Restaurant 12-2 7-9.30 Av 3 course à la carte £15 Av 2 course fixed price £6.95

UPPER HOPTON Yorkshire, West
Map 08 SE11

Hare & Hounds
UPPER HOPTON
Liley Ln WF14 8EE ☎ 01924 481021
Situated on the outskirts of the city, this bustling hostelry was once a lock-up for condemned prisoners. Unspoilt timeless atmosphere, with an intimate snug bar and walled patio. **Principal beers:** Bass, Stones, Worthington.
Directions Take the B6118 from the A62 Leeds Road, or take Huddersfield Road from Wakefield, then the B6118
Brewery/Company Vintage Inns
Open 12-11 (Sun 12-10.30)

WAKEFIELD Yorkshire, West
Map 08 SE32

Kaye Arms Inn & Brasserie NEW
WAKEFIELD
29 Wakefield Rd, Grange Moor WF4 4BQ
☎ 01924 848385
Isolated, family-run roadside pub close to the Yorkshire Mining Museum, offering a warm welcome and imaginative food. Extensive printed menus list dishes like mixed fish risotto, cheese soufflé, roast salmon with horseradish crust, and ribeye steak with chips. Evening specials may include veal with spinach and thyme risotto cake and stuffed pepper. Good wines by the glass.
Directions from M1 follow signs for mining museum, 3m further on (A642)
Brewery/Company Free House
Open 11.30-3 7-11
Bar food 12-2 7-9.30

WIDDOP Yorkshire, West
Map 07 SD93

Pack Horse Inn
WIDDOP
HX7 7AT ☎ 01422 842803
A converted laithe farmhouse dating from the 1600s, 300 yards from the Pennine Way and popular with walkers. Food includes sandwiches, burgers and steaks, plus dishes from the blackboard such as haddock mornay, rack of lamb, mega-mix grill, and game in season. Round off with home-made Pavlova or sticky toffee pudding. **Principal beers:** Thwaites, Theakston XB, Morland Old Speckled Hen.
Directions Off A646 & A6033
Brewery/Company Free House
Open 12-3 7-11
Bar food 12-2 7-10 Av main course £6.95
Accommodation (Min) s£28 d£44

SCOTLAND – Aberdeen City • Aberdeenshire • Angus • Argyll & Bute • City of Edinburgh • City of Glasgow • Dumfries & Galloway • Dundee City • East Lothian • Falkirk • Fife • Highlands • Moray • Perth & Kinross • Renfrewshire • Scottish Borders • South Ayrshire • Stirling • West Lothian • Western Isles

Town House Hotel,
Markinch,
Fife

Upside Down Fish Pie

Ingredients for filling:

- 1 fennel
- 8oz/225g monkfish
- 8oz/225g haddock
- 8oz/225g smoked haddock
- 8oz/225g salmon
- 12 cooked mussels
- 2oz/50g cooked prawns
- 5fl oz/2.75ml white wine
- 2oz/50g margarine
- 2oz/50g flour
- 10fl oz/5.5ml milk
- 5fl oz/2.75ml cream
- ½ lemon
- 1 teaspoon Pernod
- fresh dill

Ingredients for topping:

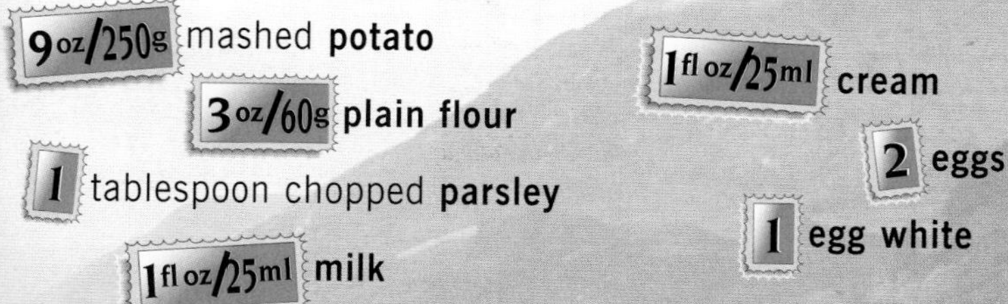

- 9oz/250g mashed **potato**
- 3oz/60g **plain flour**
- 1 tablespoon chopped **parsley**
- 1fl oz/25ml **milk**
- 1fl oz/25ml **cream**
- 2 **eggs**
- 1 **egg white**

Method for filling:

Slice **fennel**, brush with **oi**l and roast in the oven until tender (Gas mark 7/Electric (centigrade) 220. Cut **monkfish**, **haddock**, **smoked haddock** and **salmon** into bite-sized pieces. Poach slightly in **white win**e, adding **mussels** and **prawns**. Make a white sauce by making a roux with the **margarine** and **flour**, adding **milk**, **cream** and **wine** from the poached **fish**. Add the roasted **fennel**, **Pernod** and the rind and juice from the **lemon**. **Season**.

Method for topping:

To make the potato pancake, beat all the ingredients together to a thick batter. Place large spoonfuls in oil in a frying pan and cook until golden brown. Can be heated in a microwave or deep-fat fryer.

To assemble:

Arrange fish mixture on the potato pancake, spoon over the sauce and garnish with **dill.** Serves 6 people.

Aberdeen City

ABERDEEN Aberdeen City Map 15 NJ90

Prince of Wales
ABERDEEN
7 St Nicholas Ln AB10 1HF
☎ 01224 640597
The pub dates from 1850 and has the longest bar in the city at 60 feet. It has a reputation for being good value, offering a wide range of real ales, excellent coffee, and the home-cooked food might include filled baguettes, freshly-made soups, steak and ale pie, tuna and pasta bake, and a selection of salads. **Principal beers:** Theakstons Old Peculier, Bass, Caledonian 80/-.
Directions city centre
Brewery/Company Free House
Open 11am-midnight (Sunday 12.30-11)
Bar food 11.30-2.30 Av main course £4

Aberdeenshire

KINCARDINE O'NEIL Aberdeenshire Map 15 NO59

Gordon Arms Hotel
KINCARDINE O'NEIL
North Deeside Rd AB34 5AA
☎ 01339 884236
Built around 1810 and recently upgraded following a fire in late 1998, this hotel is located in the marvellous scenery of Royal Deeside. Balmoral is within easy reach. The seafood selection may feature halibut with white wine and butter sauce, local Dee salmon, and goujons of sole. Other main courses include guinea fowl Goa style and mushroom Stroganoff.
Principal beers: McEwans Export & 80/-, Calders 70/-, Tetley.
Directions on A93 (Aberdeen-Braemar road)
Brewery/Company Free House
Open 11.30-11
Bar food 12-2 5-9 Av main course £6
Restaurant 12-2 5-9 Av 3 course à la carte £8
Accommodation (Min) s£20 d£32

Pubs offering a good choice of seafood on the menu

MARYCULTER Aberdeenshire Map 15 NO89

Old Mill Inn
MARYCULTER
South Deeside Rd AB12 5FX
☎ 01224 733212
A 200-year-old country inn on the edge of the River Dee, just 10 minutes' from Aberdeen city centre. Fresh local produce is a feature of the menu, with interesting dishes such as venison cooked in beer, wine and cranberries, and chicken Highlander, stuffed with haggis, and served on a Glayva and cream sauce.
Principal beers: Bass, Deuchers IPA.
Directions 5m W of Aberdeen on B9077
Brewery/Company Free House
Open 7.30am-11pm (Fri-Sat 8-12)
Restaurant 12-2 5.30-9.30 Av 3 course à la carte £15
Accommodation (Min) s£45 d£55

NETHERLEY Aberdeenshire Map 15 NO89

Lairhillock Inn and Restaurant
NETHERLEY
AB39 3QS ☎ 01569 730001
An 18th-century coaching inn enjoying a peaceful rural setting with views over Deeside, yet a mere 15 minutes drive south of Aberdeen. Imaginative dishes on the varied menu may include cullen skink, quail and pheasant terrine, cod crumble, baked sea bass and, for dessert, chocolate parfait or mulled raspberries.

Principal beers: Flowers, Boddingtons, Deuchers IPA, Courage Directors.
Directions From Aberdeen take A90 turn R at Durris turning
Brewery/Company Free House
Open 11-2.30 5-11
Bar food 12-2 6-9.30 Av main course £7.95
Restaurant 7-11 Av 3 course à la carte £25 Av 4 course fixed price £27.95

Scotland

OLDMELDRUM Aberdeenshire *Map 15 NJ82*

The Redgarth
OLDMELDRUM

Kirk Brae AB51 0DJ ☎ 01651 872353

There are magnificent views of Bannachie and the surrounding countryside from this friendly establishment. Cask conditioned ales from all over the UK are served in the lounge bar, along with a range of snacks, and there is a varied menu of home-cooked dishes using fresh local produce. **Principal beers:** Courage Directors, Caledonian Deuchers IPA, Taylor Landlord, Burton Ale.

Directions On A947
Brewery/Company Free House
Open 11-2.30 5-11
Bar food 12-2 5-9 Av main course £8
Restaurant 12-2 5-9 Av 3 course à la carte £12
Accommodation (Min) s£40 d£50

STONEHAVEN Aberdeenshire *Map 15 NO88*

Marine Hotel
STONEHAVEN

9/10 Shorehead AB39 2JY
☎ 01569 762155

A four-storey building overlooking the harbour where, not surprisingly, fish figures prominently on an extensive menu. Look out for Cajun blackened rock turbot, local shellfish in season and Scotch fillet steaks. **Principal beers:** Taylor Landlord, Deuchars IPA, 4 guest beers.

Directions 15m south of Aberdeen on A90
Brewery/Company Free House
Open 11am-12 midnight
Bar food 12-2 5-9.15 Av main course £6
Restaurant 12-2 5-10 Av 3 course à la carte £10 Av 3 course fixed price £6
Accommodation (Min) s£27.50 d£40

Angus

GLENISLA Angus *Map 15 NO26*

The Glenisla Hotel
GLENISLA

PH11 8PH ☎ 01575 582223

The hotel has been a focal point for travellers for almost 300 years, from drovers and customs men to modern day walkers and tourists. Typical dishes include smoked salmon with Scottish cheeses, langoustines in garlic, Aberdeen Angus sirloin steak, and home-made whisky and honey ice cream. **Principal beers:** Iveralmond Independence, Theppledonser & Lia Fail.

Directions On B951
Brewery/Company Free House
Open 11-11 (Fri-Sat midnight/food served 12-8 Sun)
Bar food 12-2.30 6.30-8.30 Av main course £5.50
Restaurant 12-2.30 6.30-8.30 Av 3 course à la carte £15.70
Accommodation (Min) s£27.50 d£50

Argyll & Bute

ARDENTINNY Argyll & Bute *Map 10 NS18*

Ardentinny Hotel
ARDENTINNY

Loch Long PA23 8TR ☎ 01369 810209

One of the West Coast of Scotland's most enchanting old droving inns, dating back to the early 1700s. Local produce is sourced from the surrounding hills and lochs to produce the interesting informal lunch and supper dishes that are served in the buttery and bars or in the patio garden. **Principal beers:** McEwans.

Brewery/Company Free House
Open 11-11 (closed Nov & Feb)
Bar food 12-2.30 6-9 Av main course £6.25
Restaurant 7-9 Av 3 course à la carte £22.50 Av 3 course fixed price £22.50
Accommodation (Min) s£36 d£68

ARDFERN Argyll & Bute Map 10 NM80

The Gallery of Lorne Inn
ARDFERN

PA31 8QN ☎ 01852 500284

Modernised droving inn, popular with fishermen and 'yachties'. Seafood dishes are an important part of the menu, ranging from local langoustines, halibut with lemon butter, Islay scallops with garlic and parsley butter, and seafood chowder. Non meat-eaters may find pheasant with claret gravy, and braised beef in beer. **Principal beers:** no real ale.

Directions 25 S of Oban. A816 then B8002
Brewery/Company Free House
Open 11-midnight
Bar food 12-2 6.30-9 Av main course £6.95
Restaurant 6.30-9 Av 3 course à la carte £16
Accommodation (Min) s£33.50 d£67

ARDUAINE Argyll & Bute Map 10 NM71

Loch Melfort Hotel NEW
ARDUAINE

PA34 4XG ☎ 01852 200233

In a superb setting beside Arduaine Gardens, this charming hotel enjoys glorious views over Loch Asknish Bay. The restaurant specialises in seafood, but also caters for other tastes. Dishes include paupiettes of grey sole with squat lobsters, escalope of Ardmaddy salmon, langoustines from Luing, and Jamaican lime crunch.

Directions on the A816 20m from South Oban
Brewery/Company Free House
Open 10.30-11.30 (closed mid-Jan to mid Feb)
Bar food 12-2.30 6-9 Av main course £8.50
Restaurant 7-9
Accommodation (Min) s£72.50 d£105

BOWMORE Argyll & Bute Map 10 NR35

The Harbour Inn NEW
BOWMORE

The Square PA43 7JR ☎ 01496 810330

Some of the finest Islay seafood, beef, lamb, game and whisky are on offer at this refurbished quayside inn with views towards Jura. Lunchtime bistro fare includes crab fishcakes, Loch Gruinart oysters, and filled jumbo rolls, while evening restaurant dishes may highlight steak stuffed with leek and oysters, hare with braised red cabbage, and Thai-style fish stew. **Principal beers:** McEwan 60/- & 80/-.

Brewery/Company Free House
Open 11am-1am
Bar food 12-2.30 7-9 Av main course £10
Accommodation (Min) s£37.50 d£60

CAIRNBAAN Argyll & Bute Map 10 NR89

Cairnbaan Hotel & Restaurant
CAIRNBAAN

PA31 8SQ ☎ 01546 603668

Late 18th-century former coaching inn situated at Lock 5 on the Crinan Canal. Traditional dishes in the restaurant include chargrilled fillet of Black Angus beef, while the Bar Loch 5 might offer casserole of West Highland lamb, or Loch Etive mussels with white wine, fennel and garlic. **Principal beers:** Bass, Caledonian Deuchars IPA.

Directions From Glasgow Airport take A82/A83 to Lochilphead,then A816 to Cairnbaan
Brewery/Company Free House
Open 11-11
Bar food 12-2.30 7-9 Av main course £8
Restaurant 7-8.45 Av 3 course à la carte £20
Accommodation (Min) s£45 d£70

Pubs offering a good choice of seafood on the menu

CLACHAN-SEIL Argyll & Bute *Map 10 NM71*

Tigh an Truish Inn
CLACHAN-SEIL

PA34 4QZ ☎ 01852 300242

Traditional whitewashed pub next to historic Clachan Bridge. The name means 'House of the Trousers' as Highlanders used to swap their kilts for trousers here before travelling to the mainland. Imaginative, home-cooked food might include steak and ale pie, spicy bean casserole, Argyll lamb and fillets of wild salmon. **Principal beers:** Tennant 80/-.

Directions 14m S of Oban, take A816, 12m turn off B844 toward Atlantic Bridge

Brewery/Company Free House

Open 11-2.30 5-11.30 (Summer 11-11.30/no food winter eve)

Bar food 12-2.15 6-8.30 Av main course £5.75

Accommodation (Min) d£40

DUNOON Argyll & Bute *Map 10 NS17*

Coylet Inn
DUNOON

Loch Eck PA23 8SG ☎ 01369 840426

Comfortable 17th-century fishing inn located on the shores of Loch Eck amid beautiful mountain scenery, where the film Blue Boy was made. Blackboard menus serve both bar and restaurant and may list smoked fish pie, fresh battered cod, local scallops, salmon and venison, and home-made soups. Characters bars have open fires and a relaxing atmosphere. **Principal beers:** McEwans 80/-, Caledonian IPA.

Brewery/Company Free House

Open 11-2.30 5-12

Bar food 12.30-2 7-9.30 Av main course £5

Accommodation (Min) s£20 d£40

KILBERRY Argyll & Bute *Map 10 NR76*

Kilberry Inn
KILBERRY

PA29 6YD ☎ 01880 770223

Distinctive country inn, formerly a post office croft, reached via 16 miles of single-track road through lovely scenery, with exposed beams, stone walls and a constantly-changing menu. Home-made favourites range from country sausage pie, chicken with glayva and apricot sauce, salmon fish pie, and steak cooked in red wine and topped with Stilton. Excellent bread, cakes and shortbread are also available.

Directions From Lochgilphead take A83 south. Take B8024 signposted Kilberry

Brewery/Company Free House

Open 11-2 5-10 (closed Sun & mid Oct-Easter)

Bar food 12.15-2 6.30-9 Av main course £8.95

Restaurant 12.15-2 6.30-9 Av 3 course à la carte £25 Av 3 course fixed price £22

Accommodation (Min) s£38.50 d£67

KILFINAN Argyll & Bute *Map 10 NR97*

Kilfinan Hotel Bistro Bar NEW
KILFINAN

PA21 2EP ☎ 01700 821201

Set on the shores of Loch Fyne, this comfortable, 18th-century coaching inn is a haven for country pursuits, and offers excellent food. With plentiful local game and fresh fish from the loch, expect to find scallops, langoustines, oven-roasted salmon, and venison burger with mash and Arran mustard bistro menu. Innovative set-price restaurant menu.

Brewery/Company Free House

Open 11-11

Bar food 12-2 6-7.30

Restaurant 7.30-8.45

Accommodation (Min) s£49 d£78

PORT APPIN Argyll & Bute *Map 14 NM94*

Pierhouse Hotel & Restaurant NEW
PORT APPIN

PA38 4DE ☎ 01631 730302

Delightfully situated in a tranquil spot on the shores of Loch Linnhe, with views over Lismore to Mull, the Pierhouse is renowned for its fresh seafood, especially oysters, mussels, huge crabs and Mull lobsters which are kept in creels off the pier. You will also find seafood pasta, beef Stroganoff, and prime Angus steaks on the menu.

Principal beers: Calders Cream, Calders 70/-, Tetley.

Brewery/Company Free House

Open 11.30-11.30 (Sun 12-11)

Bar food 12.30-2.30 6.30-9.30

Restaurant 12.30-2.30 6.30-9.30 Av 3 course à la carte £15.50

Accommodation (Min) s£35 d£60

STRACHUR Argyll & Bute Map 10 NN00

Creggans Inn NEW

STRACHUR

PA27 8BX ☎ 01369 860279

Long-established and charming converted farmhouse with pleasing Loch Fyne and hillside views. Good food, in particular fresh seafood and game from owning family's estate, may include mussels, oysters and salmon from the loch, calves' liver with bacon and shallot sauce, and baked apple and vanilla crumble, alongside local scallops, sea bass, monkfish and venison. **Principal beers:** Morland Old Speckled Hen, Theakstons, Courage Directors, McEwans 80/-.

Directions A82 from Glasgow, at Tarbet take A83 to Cairndow, then A815 down coast to Strachur

Brewery/Company Free House

Open 11-11 (11-1am summer) (12-11 winter Sun, 12-1am summer Sun)

Bar food 12-2.30 6-8 Av main course £6.95

Restaurant 7-9 Av 3 course fixed price £22.50

Accommodation (Min) s£47.50 d£47.50

TAYNUILT Argyll & Bute Map 10 NN03

Polfearn Hotel

TAYNUILT

PA35 1JQ ☎ 01866 822251

Situated at the foot of Ben Cruachen, this friendly, family-run hotel is close to the shores of Loch Etive and enjoys stunning all round views. Noted for its fresh fish, perhaps including marinated herrings, local mussels in white wine and cream, and seafood chowder, the menu also features venison in red wine and herbs. **Principal beers:** no real ale.

Directions turn off A85, continue 1.5m through village down to loch shore

Brewery/Company Free House

Open 12-2.30 5.30-11

Bar food 12-2 5.30-8.45 Av main course £7.50

Restaurant 5.30-8.45 Av 3 course à la carte £18.50 Av 5 course fixed price £18.50

Accommodation (Min) s£25 d£50

TAYVALLICH Argyll & Bute Map 10 NR78

Tayvallich Inn

TAYVALLICH

PA31 8PL ☎ 01546 870282

Fresh fish and seafood straight from local boats is the speciality at this small inn on the shores of Loch Sween, overlooking a sheltered yacht anchorage. Expect to find smoked mussels and queen scallops with garlic and ginger mayonnaise, pan-fried Sound of Jura scallops, Cajun salmon with black butter, alongside prime Scottish steaks. **Principal beers:** Calders 70/-, Calders 80/-.

Directions From Lochgilphead take A816 then B841/B8025

Brewery/Company Free House

Open 11-3 6-11 (Jun-Oct 11am-midnight)

Bar food 11-2 6-8.30 Av main course £6

Restaurant 7-9 Av 3 course à la carte £25

City of Edinburgh

EDINBURGH City of Edinburgh Map 11 NT27

Royal Ettrick Hotel

EDINBURGH

13 Ettrick Rd EH10 5BJ

☎ 0131 228 6413

Period mansion, now a hotel, situated in a residential suburb west of the city. Classic lounge bar with a two-tiered conservatory extension serving good-value and well presented meals. Dishes range from smoked haddock mousse and steak pie, to creamy mushroom Stroganoff and mussel and onion stew. **Principal beers:** Caledonian, Caledonian Deuchars IPA, Broughton, Border.

Directions From W end of street follow Lothian road, turn R onto Gilmor place for 0.75m, Hotel on R behind Bowling Green
Brewery/Company Free House
Open 12-12
Bar food 12-2 5.30-8.30 Av main course £5
Accommodation (Min) s£45 d£70

The Starbank Inn
EDINBURGH
64 Laverockbank Rd EH5 3BZ
☎ 0131 552 4141
Tastefully renovated stone pub situated on the waterfront of North Edinburgh, affording splendid views over the Firth of Forth to the Fife coast. The bar menu typically offers roast lamb with mint sauce, poached salmon, haddock mornay, a vegetarian dish of the day, and chicken with tarragon cream sauce.

Principal beers: Belhaven 80/-, Belhaven Sandy Hunters Traditional, Taylor Landlord, 7 guest beers.
Brewery/Company Free House
Open 11-11 (Thu-Sat 11-12, Sun 12-11) (food wknds 12-9.30)
Bar food 12-2.30 6-9.30 Av main course £5
Restaurant 12-2.30 6-9.30

RATHO
City of Edinburgh — *Map 11 NT17*

The Bridge Inn
RATHO
27 Baird Rd EH28 8RA
☎ 0131 333 1320
Formerly a farmhouse and later a staging post for boats on the Union Canal, this historic inn dates back to about 1750. Blackboard specials might well feature poached salmon with lemon hollandaise, roast leg of lamb, and sirloin of beef. Try the Ratho haggis fillet steak from the restaurant menu. **Principal beers:** Bellhaven 80/- & IPA, Caledonian Deuchars Ale & 80/-.

Directions From Newbridge interchange B7030, follow signs for Ratho
Brewery/Company Free House
Open 12-11 (Fri & Sat 11-12, Sun 12.30-11)
Bar food 12-9 Av main course £6.50
Restaurant 12.30-2 6.30-9 Av 3 course à la carte £20

SOUTH QUEENSFERRY
City of Edinburgh — *Map 11 NT17*

Hawes Inn
SOUTH QUEENSFERRY
Newmalls Rd EH30 9TA
☎ 0131 3311990
Modernised inn that inspired Robert Louis Stevenson to write the adventure classic Kidnapped. Indeed it plays a leading role in the story, and also appears in Sir Walter Scott's The Antiquary. With fine views of the Forth bridges, it offers good ale and wide range of food, including haggis, salmon Musselburgh, and rack of lamb. **Principal beers:** Caledonian Deuchars IPA, Burtons Ale.
Directions A90 from Edinburgh
Brewery/Company Allied Domecq
Open 8am-midnight (bar food 12-10)

contd.

Restaurant 12-2 6.30-10 Av 3 course à la carte £21.95 Av 3 course fixed price £16.95
Accommodation (Min) s£34 d£55

City of Glasgow

GLASGOW City of Glasgow
Map 11 NS56

Buttery
GLASGOW
652 Argyle St G3 8UF ☎ 0141 221 8188
Former Glasgow tenement building, now a thriving restaurant and bistro with rich, wood-panelled Victorian interior. High-quality produce is simply prepared in modern global style, resulting in dishes like beef fillet teriyaki and trio of seafood with herb beurre blanc. Bar food might feature bookmaker's sandwich and deep-fried salmon goujons.
Principal beers: Calders 80/-.
Directions Town centre
Brewery/Company Allied Domecq
Open 12-2.30 7-10.30 (Closed Sun)
Bar food 12-2.30 Av main course £6.95
Restaurant 12-2.30 7-10.30 Av 3 course à la carte £35 Av 3 course fixed price £16.85

Rab Ha's
GLASGOW
53 Hutchieson St G1 1SH
☎ 0141 572 0400
Victorian building, recently refurbished, housing a pub, restaurant and bedrooms. Expect a traditional pub atmosphere and some innovative cooking. Choices include fajitas, tempura, Thai cirrues amd cullen skink in the bar. The restaurant offers fusion cooking with dishes from the ocean, the earth and from home.
Principal beers: McEwans 70/- & 80/-.
Directions City centre
Brewery/Company Free House
Open 11-12
Bar food 12-10.30 Av main course £6
Restaurant 12-12 Av 3 course à la carte £25
Accommodation (Min) s£50 d£70

Ubiquitous Chip
GLASGOW
12 Ashton Ln G12 8SJ ☎ 0141 334 5007
Situated in a cobbled mews in the West End, the Ubiquitous Chip has a spectacular green courtyard area with a trickling pool as well as a more traditional dining room. Fine Scottish ingredients are given an imaginative treatment in dishes such as vegetarian haggis and neeps, Ayrshire ham salad, and spinach and cream cheese bridie.
Principal beers: Caledonian 80/-, & Deuchars IPA.
Brewery/Company Free House
Open 11-11 (11-12 midnight Fri/Sat)
Restaurant 12-11 Av 3 course à la carte £15

Dumfries & Galloway

CANONBIE Dumfries & Galloway
Map 11 NY37

Riverside Inn NEW
CANONBIE
DG14 0UX ☎ 013873 71512 71295
White-painted Georgian inn enjoying a pretty setting overlooking the River Esk. A pleasant rural air fills the simply furnished interior where home-cooked food prepared from fresh ingredients is a major draw. Daily-changing menus may list smoked fish pâté, pheasant in red wine, organic pork chops, fresh fish (sea bass, Thai haddock), and lemon tart.

Principal beers: Yates, Caledonian Deuchars IPA.
Directions Just across Scottish border on A7, 1st R is Canonbie

Brewery/Company Free House
Open 11-11 (closed 2 wks Feb)
Bar food 12-2 7-9
Restaurant 12-2 7-9 Av 3 course à la carte £11.50
Accommodation (Min) s£55 d£78

EAGLESFIELD
Dumfries & Galloway *Map 11 NY27*

The Courtyard Restaurant NEW
EAGLESFIELD
DS11 3PQ ☎ 01461 500215
Former drapers shop built in 1914 and converted into a bar/restaurant in the mid-1980s. Popular with travellers heading for the Highlands, it offers good home cooking. Enjoy lasagne, fruity chicken curry, or steak and chips in the bar, or baked cod with cheese and mustard or venison with cranberry in the rear restaurant.

Directions 8m N of Gretna
Brewery/Company Free House
Open 12-2.30 6.30-12 (closed Mon in summer)
Bar food 12-2 6.30-9 Av main course £5.75
Restaurant 12-2 7-9 Av 3 course à la carte £16 Av 3 course fixed price £16.50
Accommodation (Min) s£19.50 d£34

ISLE OF WHITHORN
Dumfries & Galloway *Map 11 NX43*

The Steam Packet Inn
ISLE OF WHITHORN
Harbour Row DG8 8LL ☎ 01988 500334
Picture windows in the attractively modernised bar of this 18th-century quayside building afford lovely harbour views. Seafood is high on the menu here, perhaps including turbot with beetroot compôte and scallops with bacon and hollandaise. Choice extends to carrot and coriander soup, sausage casserole, chicken and leek pie, and prime Galloway steaks. **Principal beers:** Theakston XB.

Directions From Newton Stewart take A714,then A746 to Whithorn, then Isle of Whithorn
Brewery/Company Free House
Open 11-11
Bar food 12-2 7-9.30 Av main course £5
Restaurant 12-2 7-9.30
Accommodation (Min) s£22.50 d£45

MOFFAT
Dumfries & Galloway *Map 11 NT00*

Black Bull Inn
MOFFAT
Churchgate DG10 9EG
☎ 01683 220206
The main building dates from the 16th century and was used by Graham of Claverhouse as his headquarters. Scottish bard Robert Burns was a frequent visitor circa 1790. Traditional fare includes shepherd's pie, haggis and trout, and home-made puddings such as Pavlova and apple pie. **Principal beers:** McEwans, Theakston.
Brewery/Company Free House
Open 11-11
Bar food 11.30-2.15 6-9.15 Av main course £5.50
Restaurant 11.30-2.15 6-9.30 Av 3 course à la carte £11
Accommodation (Min) s£21 d£32

NEW ABBEY
Dumfries & Galloway *Map 11 NX96*

Criffel Inn
NEW ABBEY
2 The Square DG2 8BX
☎ 01387 850244
An unassuming small hotel on the village square, close to 13th-century Sweetheart Abbey, with an attractive garden for summer sipping. Unchanged for many years, it offers appetising Scottish food, including wild Solway salmon, rack of Borders lamb, prime beef fillet, and a traditional high tea menu. **Principal beers:** Belhaven IPA, Deuchars IPA, Orkney Dark Island.
Directions M/A74 leave at Gretna, A75 to Dumfries, A710 S to New Abbey
Brewery/Company Free House
Open 12-2.30 4.30-11
Bar food 12-2 4.30-8 Av main course £7.50
Restaurant 12-2 4.30-8 Av 3 course à la carte £7.50

NEWTON STEWART Dumfries & Galloway
Map 10 NX46

Creebridge House Hotel
NEWTON STEWART

Minnigaff DG8 6NP ☎ 01671 402121

Formerly the home to the Earls of Galloway, this delightful 18th-century, stone-built hotel is set in three acres of pretty gardens. Relax in the beamed and comfortable Bridge Bar & Brasserie and enjoy some decent food, perhaps, 'posh' fish & chips, cullen skink, Solway salmon on horseradish mash with basil beurre blanc, beef Stroganoff and Ecclefechan butter tart. **Principal beers:** Orkney Dark Island, Taylor Landlord, Black Sheep.

Directions From A75 into Newton Stewart, turn right over river bridge, hotel 200yds on left.
Brewery/Company Free House
Open 12-2.30 6-11.30
Bar food 12-2 6-9 Av main course £8.95
Restaurant 7-9 Av 3 course à la carte £25 Av 4 course fixed price £21
Accommodation (Min) s£55 d£79

PORTPATRICK Dumfries & Galloway
Map 10 NW95

Crown Hotel NEW
PORTPATRICK

9 North Crescent DG9 8SX
☎ 01776 810551

Bustling harbourside hotel, formerly fisherman's cottages dating from 1800, enjoying fine views across the Irish Sea. Atmospheric, rambling old bar with open fire and seafaring displays. Bar food draws on the fruits of the ocean, with dishes like scallops wrapped in bacon, fresh lobster, local prawns and seafood platter.
Brewery/Company Free House
Open 11-11.30
Bar food 12-2.30 6-10 Av main course £8
Accommodation (Min) s£48 d£72

Dundee City

BROUGHTY FERRY Dundee City
Map 12 NO43

Fisherman's Tavern
BROUGHTY FERRY

10-16 Fort St DD5 2AD
☎ 01382 775941

Unspoilt and bustling old fisherman's cottage, converted to a pub in 1857, situated on the shore of the Tay estuary. Noted for its first-rate real ales and hearty bar food. 'Fisherman's Favourites' include steak and St Andrews ale pie, soups (broccoli and Stilton), hot and sour king prawns, and fisherman's pie. **Principal beers:** Belhaven - St Andrews, IPA & 80/-, Maclays 80/-, Inveralmond Stone of Destiny.
Brewery/Company Free House
Open 11-1am (no food Sun in winter)
Bar food 11.30-2.30 Av main course £4.75
Accommodation (Min) s£17 d£34

DUNDEE Dundee City
Map 11 NO43

Mercantile Bar
DUNDEE

100/108 Commercial St DD1 2NJ
☎ 01382 225500

Busy town centre pub with upstairs restaurant. Bar snacks include filled baked potatoes and salads. Main course dishes feature traditional steak pie, chicken Mercantile, stuffed haddock with spicy prawns, and cheese and broccoli bake. This pub supports Dundee's musical talent with a songwriting club. **Principal beers:** McEwans 80/- & 70/-.
Directions Town centre
Brewery/Company Big Beat Group
Open 10-11 (Sun 12-10.30, Thu-Sat 10-12)

East Ayrshire

DALRYMPLE East Ayrshire
Map 10 NS31

The Kirkton Inn
DALRYMPLE

1 Main St KA6 6DF ☎ 01292 560241

Village centre inn situated a short stroll from the River Doon. Robert Burns was reputed to have drunk here. Popular pub food features mince and tatties with doughballs, lamb hotpot, haggis with Drambuie cream, freshly battered haddock, and wild Doon salmon.

Principal beers: Belhaven Export.
Directions Between A77 & A713 approx 5m from Ayr signed from both roads
Brewery/Company Free House
Open 11am-midnight
Bar food 11-9 Av main course £7
Accommodation (Min) s£15 d£20

GATEHEAD East Ayrshire *Map 10 NS33*

The Cochrane Inn
GATEHEAD

45 Main Rd KA2 0AP ☎ 01563 570122
Good emphasis on contemporary British food at this village centre pub, just a short drive from the Ayrshire coast. Friendly, bustling atmosphere inside. Good choice of starters may include soused herring and grilled goat's cheese, while main courses might feature stuffed pancake, pan-fried red mullet and chicken with Swiss cheese.
Directions from Glasgow A77 to Kilmarnock, then A759 to Gatehead
Brewery/Company Free House
Open 11-3 5-12
Bar food 12-2 6-9 Av main course £7.50
Restaurant 12-2 6-9 Av 3 course à la carte £15

East Lothian

EAST LINTON East Lothian *Map 12 NT57*

Drovers Inn
EAST LINTON

5 Bridge St E40 4BE ☎ 01620 860374
Originally a watering hole for sheep and cattle herders, this comfortable old inn is situated close to the River Tyne and the Linn Falls. Noted for real ales and freshly prepared food. Menu choices range from sandwiches and steaks in the bar, to monkfish thermidor, and roast suckling pig in honey and ginger in the restaurant.
Principal beers: Adnams Broadside, Caledonian 80/-, Fullers ESB, Wadworths 6X.
Directions Off A1 5m past Haddington, follow rd under railway bridge, then L
Brewery/Company Free House
Open 11.30-2.30 5-11 (Sun 11.30-11)
Bar food 11.30-2 6-9.30 Av main course £6.50
Restaurant 11.30-2.30 6-9.30 Av 3 course à la carte £20

GIFFORD East Lothian *Map 12 NT56*

Goblin Ha' Hotel
GIFFORD

EH41 4QH ☎ 01620 810244
Located by the village square and green, the Goblin Ha' is a traditional hotel offering a good atmosphere and a varied range of home-cooked dishes in its bar and adjoining conservatory. Dishes may include cullen skink, pork with apple and Stilton, lasagne, beef and mushroom casserole, and popular grills. **Principal beers:** Hopback Summer Lightning, Marstons Pedigree, Bellhaven.

Directions On A846, 100yrds from main village square on shore side of the road
Brewery/Company Free House
Open 11-2.30 5-11
Bar food 12.30-2 6.30-9 Av main course £6.50

East Renfrewshire

NEWTON MEARNS East Renfrewshire *Map 11 NS55*

The Osprey
NEWTON MEARNS

Dodside Rd G77 6NP ☎ 0141 616 5071
This cosy pub in a farmyard setting is the ideal place for lovers of golf. There are four quality courses in close proximity. There are also three roaring log fires, and plenty of old stout wooden beams.

contd.

Principal beers: Bass.
Directions 1st L after M77 J4
Brewery/Company Vintage Inns
Open 11-11 (Sun 12-10.30)

Falkirk

CASTLECARY Falkirk Map 11 NS77

Castlecary House Hotel
CASTLECARY
Main St G68 0HD ☎ 01324 840233
The main building of this friendly hotel complex is a 19th-century coaching inn. From standard pub snacks and home-made burgers, the varied menus include dressed crab, Thai fishcakes, lamb casserole, fresh haddock and chips, prime steaks with sauces, home-made sticky toffee pudding, and a good-value table d'hote restaurant menu. **Principal beers:** Tennent Velvet.

Directions Off A80 N of Cumbernauld
Brewery/Company Free House
Open 11-11 (11-11.30 Fri-Sat, 12.30-11 Sun)
Bar food 12-2 6-9 Av main course £4.20
Restaurant 12-2 7-10 Av 3 course à la carte £15
Accommodation (Min) s£33 d£48

Fife

ANSTRUTHER Fife Map 12 NO50

The Dreel Tavern
ANSTRUTHER
16 High St West KY10 3DL
☎ 01333 310727
There's plenty of atmosphere at this 16th-century coaching inn with its oak beams and coal fire. A new addition is the non-smoking conservatory dining room. The menu offers lemon and tarragon chicken, haddock Mornay, lamb steak with mint sauce, and East Neuk scampi. Desserts include Dime bar toffee crunch pie, and treacle and nut tart.
Principal beers: Calders 70/-.
Brewery/Company Free House
Open 11-12 (Sun 12.30-12)
Bar food 12-2 6-9 Av main course £5
Restaurant 12-2 6-9

ELIE Fife Map 12 NO40

The Ship Inn
ELIE
The Toft KY9 1DT ☎ 01333 330246
A 19th-century hostelry overlooking Elie Bay near one of Scotland's finest watersports centres. After windsurfing, dinghy sailing, water-skiing or perhaps sea-fishing, you might like to inspect the interesting menu which may offer green-lipped mussels in garlic butter, home-made steak pie, chicken curry, fillet steak with Arran mustard sauce, and sticky toffee pudding. **Principal beers:** Belhaven 80/- & Best, Theakston Best.
Directions Follow A915 & A917 to Elie.Follow signs from High St to Watersport Centre to the Toft.
Brewery/Company Free House
Open 11-11 (Summer 11-midnight/Sun from 12.30)
Bar food 12-2 6-9
Accommodation (Min) s£30 d£50

KIRKCALDY Fife Map 11 NT29

The Old Rectory Inn NEW
KIRKCALDY
West Quality St, Dysart KY1 2TE
☎ 01592 651211
The splendid walled garden and cosy beamed bar of this Georgian inn perched above the harbour in this pretty village make agreeable areas for enjoying some imaginative food. An extensive menu is supplemented by daily specials, perhaps including lentil broth, mussels, cockles and onion stew, venison casserole, and beef Stroganoff. Separate restaurant carte. **Principal beers:** Calders Cream Ale.

Brewery/Company Free House
Open 12-3 6.45-12 (Sun 12-4 only closed Mon, 1 wk Jan/2 wks mid-Oct)
Bar food 12-2 7-9.30 Av main course £6.75
Restaurant 12-2 6.45-9.30 Av 3 course à la carte £20.75 Av 4 course fixed price £14

LOWER LARGO Fife Map 11 NO40

Crusoe Hotel
LOWER LARGO
2 Main St KY8 6BT ☎ 01333 320759
Originally a granary, this historic inn is located in Lower Largo, birthplace of Alexander Selkirk, immortalised by Daniel Defoe in Robinson Crusoe. Constantly-changing menu might offer Cumberland sausage, blackened Cajun tuna, pan-fried fillet of lamb and crisp Barbary duck breast. Various pasta dishes and a range of filled baguettes.
Principal beers: Boddingtons.
Directions A92 to Kirkcaldy East, A915 to Lundin Links, then R to Lower Largo
Brewery/Company Free House
Open 11-12 (Fri 11-1am, Sun 12.30-12)
Bar food 12-2.30 6-9 Av main course £5
Restaurant 12-2.30 7-9.45 Av 3 course fixed price £18
Accommodation (Min) s£47.90 d£51.50

MARKINCH Fife Map 11 NO20

Town House Hotel
MARKINCH
1 High St KY7 6DQ ☎ 01592 758459
Family-run 17th-century coaching inn situated in the heart of town. Recently refurbished, it offers imaginative home-cooked dishes such as kiln roasted salmon with balsamic dressing, seafood crumble bake, ribeye steak with pepper sauce, and tagliatelle carbonara. To finish, look out for ginger sponge pudding with lemon and ginger sauce.
Principal beers: no real ale.
Directions Off A92(Dundee/ Kirkcaldy rd) Hotel opp. rail station
Brewery/Company Free House
Open 12-2.30 6-11
Bar food 12-2 6-9 Av main course £6.95
Restaurant 12-2 6-9 Av 3 course à la carte £12.95 Av 3 course fixed price £6.50
Accommodation (Min) s£25 d£50

Highland

ACHILTIBUIE Highland Map 14 NC00

Summer Isles Hotel & Bar NEW
ACHILTIBUIE
IV26 2YG ☎ 01854 622282
An oasis at the end of a single track road, this family-run hotel and bar looks out over a bay to the Summer Isles. Freshly-cooked food using local produce is worth making the journey for. Expect baguettes, seafood platter, Aberdeen Angus steak and venison casserole in the bar; imaginative 5-course dinners in the restaurant.
Directions take A835 N from Ullapool for 10m, Achiltibuie signed on L, 15m to village, hotel 1m on L
Brewery/Company Free House
Open 12-11 (2-11 in winter)
Bar food 12-2.30, from 8pm Av main course £12
Restaurant 12-2.30 8 Av 5 course fixed price £36.50
Accommodation (Min) s£55 d£77

ALTNAHARRA Highland Map 14 NC53

Altnaharra Hotel
ALTNAHARRA
IV27 4UE ☎ 01549 411222
Traditional Highland hotel with a major focus on fishing. Sandwiches, steak, and fish and chips are particular favourites in the bar, while in the restaurant the set dinner menu may offer seared scallops with caramelised lemon, and saddle of rabbit stuffed with blueberries and fresh herbs. **Principal beers:** no real ale.
Directions A9 to Bonar Bridge, A336 to Lairg & Tongue
Brewery/Company Free House
Open 12-2.30 5-10 (closed 1 Nov-1 Mar)
Bar food 12-2 5-9 Av main course £8
Restaurant 6-9 Av 3 course à la carte £25 Av 4 course fixed price £25
Accommodation (Min) s£53 d£106

APPLECROSS Highland Map 13 NG74

Applecross Inn
APPLECROSS
Shore St IV54 8LR ☎ 01520 744262
The inn is set in a sandy bay overlooking Raasay and the Isle of Skye, reached by a spectacular drive over Bealach Na Ba, rising to 2,053 feet. Fresh local fish and seafood

Scotland

feature strongly on the interesting menu, including oysters, squat lobsters, crab and queen scallops. Alternatives include venison burger or sirloin steak.

Applecross Inn

Directions From Lochcarron to Kishorn then L onto unclassifed rd to Applecross over 'Bealach Na Ba'
Brewery/Company Free House
Open 11-12 (Sun 12.30-11
Bar food 12-9 Av main course £4.95
Restaurant 6.30-9 Av 3 course à la carte £19.50 Av 3 course fixed price £17.50

ARDVASAR Highland *Map 13 NG60*

Ardvasar Hotel
ARDVASAR
IV45 8RS ☎ 01471 844223

Superbly situated at the southern end of the Sleat Peninsula, known as The Wild Garden of Skye, this traditional hotel is a perfect base for spotting wildlife and enjoying the magnificent scenery. The menu changes daily and offers dishes such as herb crunch chicken supreme and fresh local seafood.
Principal beers: Isle of Skye.
Directions From ferry terminal, 50yds & turn L
Brewery/Company Free House
Open 11-11 (closed Apr-Oct)
Bar food 12-10 Av main course £10
Restaurant 7.30-9 Av 3 course à la carte £25
Accommodation (Min) s£40 d£70

AVIEMORE Highland *Map 14 NH81*

The Old Bridge Inn
AVIEMORE
Dalfaber Rd PH22 1PU ☎ 01479 811137

Cosy and friendly Highland pub overlooking the River Spey. Dine in the relaxing bars or in the attractive riverside garden. A typical meal may begin with salmon mousse, moving on to game pie, Fraser's haggis, neeps and tattites, or speciality pasta dishes, followed by Ecclefechan tart.
Directions Exit A9 to Aviemore, 1st L to 'Ski road' then 1st L again - 200m
Brewery/Company Free House
Open 11-11 (Fri 11-1, Sun 12.30-12)
Bar food 12-2 6-9 Av main course £6
Restaurant 6-9 Av 3 course à la carte £9
Accommodation (Min) s£9 d£18

CARRBRIDGE Highland *Map 14 NH92*

Dalrachney Lodge Hotel
CARRBRIDGE
PH23 3AT ☎ 01479 841252

A sympathetically restored Victorian shooting lodge, with log fires and period furniture, set in 14 acres of mature grounds. Local ingredients, notably Aberdeen Angus beef and Scottish lamb, are used in preparing the varied range of dishes available. Choices include pesto mussels, venison casserole, haggis, and pork with brandy and cream sauce.
Directions A9 onto A938 for 1.5m, through village, pub on R
Brewery/Company Free House
Open 12-2 5.30-11
Bar food 12-2 5.30-11 Av main course £6.50
Restaurant 7-8.30 Av 3 course à la carte £25 Av 4 course fixed price £25
Accommodation (Min) s£40 d£50

CAWDOR Highland *Map 14 NH85*

Cawdor Tavern
CAWDOR
The Lane IV22 5XP ☎ 01667 404777

Originally the joiner's workshop for Cawdor Estate, this country pub, with two bars and a restaurant, is popular with locals and visitors alike. Typical dishes are breast of chicken filled with haggis and served with a mushroom cream

sauce, and sticky ginger pudding with home-made ice cream. **Principal beers:** Tennents 80/-, Deuchars IPA.
Directions from A96(Inverness-Aberdeen)take B9006 & follow signs for Cawdor Castle. Tavern in village centre.
Brewery/Company Free House
Open 11-3 5-11 (May-Oct 11-11)
Bar food 12-2 5.30-9 Av main course £6.25
Restaurant 6.30-9 Av 3 course à la carte £16.50

CONTIN Highland *Map 14 NH45*

Achilty Hotel
CONTIN
IV14 9EG ☎ 01997 421355
Well-converted 300-year-old farm steadings, situated near a fast-flowing mountain river, created this former coaching inn on the village edge. Traditional Scottish dishes highlight the menu, in particular haggis with whisky and cream, venison with port and cranberries, Aberdeen Angus steaks, and fresh local seafood - langoustines with lime mayonnaise. **Principal beers:** John Smiths, McEwans Wxport & 70/-.
Directions On A835, at the northern edge of Contin
Brewery/Company Free House
Open 11am-midnight (Sat 11-11.30, Sun 12.30-11)
Bar food 12-2.30 5.30-9.30 Av main course £6.50
Restaurant 12-2.30 5.30-9.30 Av 3 course à la carte £16
Accommodation (Min) s£24.50 d£49

DORNOCH Highland *Map 14 NH78*

Mallin House Hotel
DORNOCH
Church St IV25 3LP ☎ 01862 810335
Mallin House is a modern hotel just 200 yards from the Royal Dornoch Golf Course. Scottish cooking with an emphasis on fresh seafood - lobster, mussels, langoustines in garlic butter - local venison, and dishes like rack of lamb, pan-fried haggis and black pudding in malt whisky sauce. **Principal beers:** John Smiths, Theakston.
Directions (from Tain (on A9) take A836 to Bonar Bridge, then turn left onto A949 in direction of Dornoch (approx 10m))
Brewery/Company Free House
Open 11-2.30 5-11
Bar food 12.30-2 6.30-9 Av main course £6.50
Restaurant 12.30-2 6.30-9 Av 3 course à la carte £20
Accommodation (Min) s£27 d£64

DUNDONNELL Highland *Map 14 NH08*

Dundonnell House
DUNDONNELL
IV23 2QR ☎ 01854 633204
Sheltering beneath the massive mountain range of An Teallach, this old drovers' inn offers quality food. Casual bistro atmosphere with extensive bar menu including local salmon, steak and ale casserole and Aberdeen Angus steaks. Sample mussel and saffron soup and lemon sole with trout caviar and chive butter in the restaurant. **Principal beers:** McEwans 70/-.
Directions From Inverness W on the A835, at Braemore junct take A382 for Gairloch
Brewery/Company Free House
Open 11-11 (Sun 12.30-11/closed Jan-mid Feb)
Bar food 12-2.15 6-8.45 Av main course £7.50
Restaurant 7-8.30 Av 3 course à la carte £23 Av 4 course fixed price £26
Accommodation (Min) s£45 d£75

FORT AUGUSTUS Highland *Map 14 NH30*

The Lock Inn
FORT AUGUSTUS
Canalside PH32 4AU ☎ 01320 366302
A former bank and post office, this 19th-century building, with stone walls and oak beams, is on the banks of the Caledonian Canal, and boasts fine views across Loch Ness. Good-value food ranges from mussels in white wine and garlic, and ciabatta sandwiches, to fresh Mallaig haddock, game casserole, and prime Angus steaks. **Principal beers:** Caledonian 80/-.
Directions On the banks of Caledonian Canal in Fort Augustus
Brewery/Company Free House
Open 11-11 (Summer 11-midnight)
Bar food 12-3 6-10 Av main course £6
Restaurant 6-10 Av 3 course à la carte £18

FORT WILLIAM Highland Map 14 NN17

Moorings Hotel NEW
FORT WILLIAM
Banavie PH33 7LY ☎ 01397 772797
Peacefully set alongside the Caledonian Canal with spectacular views of Ben Nevis, this modern hotel offers good food in the bustling and informal Mariners Bar. From burgers, salad platters and steak pie, the choice includes braised Rannoch venison, haggis, neeps and tatties, Mallaig scallops, and prime Angus steaks. More elaborate evening carte. **Principal beers:** Alloa 70/-, 80/-, Calders.
Directions from A82 in Fort William follow signs for Mallaig, then L onto A830 for 1m. Cross canal bridge then 1st R signposted Banavie
Brewery/Company Free House
Open 12-11.45
Bar food 12-9 Av main course £7
Restaurant 7-9.30 Av 4 course fixed price £26
Accommodation (Min) s£48 d£68

GAIRLOCH Highland Map 14 NG87

The Old Inn NEW
GAIRLOCH
IV21 2BD ☎ 01445 712006
Former coaching inn in a lovely setting by the harbour with magnificent views. Expect a warm welcome, well-equipped bedrooms, and hearty food in the popular bars and bistro. Dishes include fish pie, steak and ale pie, locally-caught seafood platter, Angus steak on haggis with whisky sauce, and salmon with dill and lemon butter.
Directions just off main A832, near harbour at S end of village
Brewery/Company Free House
Open 11-12
Bar food 12-2.30 6-9 Av main course £6
Restaurant 6.30-9 Av 4 course fixed price £19.50
Accommodation (Min) s£27.50 d£55.50

GARVE Highland Map 14 NH36

Inchbae Lodge Hotel
GARVE
IV23 2PH ☎ 01997 455269
19th-century hunting lodge situated on the banks of the River Blackwater. Haggis is served traditionally with *neeps and tatties*. A vegetarian haggis is also provided. Seafood dishes include West Coast mussels and local smoked salmon. Wood pigeon is braised in red wine and Marsala with bacon, mushroom, celery and shallots. **Principal beers:** Belhaven, guest Scottish ale.
Directions On A835, hotel 6m W of Garve
Brewery/Company Free House
Open 11-2.30 5-11
Bar food 12-2 5-8.30 Av main course £6.50
Restaurant 12-2 6.30-8 Av 3 course fixed price £17
Accommodation (Min) s£33 d£56

GLENELG Highland Map 14 NG81

Glenelg Inn
GLENELG
IV40 8JR ☎ 01599 522273
150-year-old traditional village inn with a large garden and superb views over the sea to Skye. Fresh produce is the cornerstone here, with the accent very much on seafood. Typical main courses dishes might include beef Wellington, fresh Loch Hourn monkfish tails, and chicken supreme with haggis and whisky sauce.
Directions From Shiel Bridge (A87) take unclassified road to Glenelg
Brewery/Company Free House
Open 12-11 (closed Nov-Easter)
Bar food 12.30-2 7.30-9 Av main course £6.50

GLENFINNAN Highland Map 14 NM98

The Prince's House NEW
GLENFINNAN
PH37 4LT ☎ 01397 722246
Close to the site where Bonnie Prince Charlie raised the Jacobite standard in 1745, this 17th-century inn offers a hospitable Highland welcome, attractive bedrooms and good food. Dishes range from steak and mushroom pie and haggis with mash in the bar, to venison with plum and ginger confit, and red mullet with champagne and chive sauce in Flora's Restaurant. **Principal beers:** McEwan 70/-.
Directions 15m along A830 NW of Fort William, hotel situated 1/2m past Glenfinnan monument
Brewery/Company Free House
Open 12-11 (closed Xmas-end Jan)
Bar food 12.30-2.30 5-9 Av main course £6.95

Restaurant 7-8.30 Av 4 course fixed price £27
Accommodation (Min) s£45 d£86

ISLE ORNSAY Highland Map 13 NG71

Hotel Eilean Iarmain
ISLE ORNSAY

IV43 8QR ☎ 01471 833332
Traditional Highland inn retaining its Victorian charm and old-world character. Straightforward but appetising bar food comprises grilled salmon steak, broccoli and cream cheese bake, and mixed grill. Dinner in the formal candlelit restaurant might consist of ballotine of salmon with scallops, herb-crusted fresh cod, and baked lemon tart. **Principal beers:** McEwans-70/-, 80/-.
Directions A851, A852 right to Isle Ornsay harbour front
Brewery/Company Free House
Bar food 12.30-2.30 6.30-9.30 Av main course £7
Restaurant 12.30-2 7.30-9 Av 3 course à la carte £19.50 Av 5 course fixed price £33
Accommodation (Min) s£80 d£115

KYLESKU Highland Map 14 NC23

Kylesku Hotel
KYLESKU

IV27 4HW ☎ 01971 502231
Coaching inn on the old ferry slipway between Loch Glencool and Loch Glendhu in the Highlands of Sutherland. Both the bar and restaurant menus specialise in locally caught seafood and venison in season. Daily specials include lobster, scallops, seafood pie, and pickled salmon with mustard and mayonnaise.
Directions 35m N of Ullapool on the A838, turn into Kylesku, hotel is at the end of the road at Old Ferry Pier
Brewery/Company Free House
Open 8.30-11 (closed Nov-Feb)

Bar food 12-2.30 6-9.30 Av main course £6.50
Restaurant 12-2.30 7-9.30 Av 3 course à la carte £19.95 Av 2 course fixed price £16.95
Accommodation (Min) s£30 d£55

LYBSTER Highland Map 15 ND23

The Portland Arms Hotel
LYBSTER

KW3 6BS ☎ 01593 721721
Long a favoured stop-off point between Wick and Thurso, the Portland Arms dates from the 16-century. Dishes include roast fillet of beef with a herb and cheese crust on a shallot and red wineglaze, and pan-fried venison with a junper scented cream. **Principal beers:** Tennent 70/-.
Directions Beside the main A9 road, when travelling from Inverness, hotel situated on the left hand side of the road, 200 yrds from the Lybster sign
Brewery/Company Free House
Open 7.30am-11pm
Bar food 11.30-3 5.30-9 Av main course £6.75
Restaurant 11.30-3 5.30-9 Av 3 course à la carte £16.70 Av 3 course fixed price £16.70
Accommodation (Min) s£45 d£68

Call the AA Hotel Booking Service on 0870 5050505 to book at AA recognised hotels and B & Bs in the UK and Ireland, or through our Internet site: http://www.theaa.co.uk/hotels

For Pubs with AA food rosettes see page 430

Pubs offering a good choice of seafood on the menu

NORTH BALLACHULISH Highland Map 14 NN06

Loch Leven Hotel

NORTH BALLACHULISH

Old Ferry Rd, Onich PH33 6SA

☎ 01855 821236

Situated on the northern shore of Loch Leven, this 17th-century coaching inn is ideally placed for touring the Great Glen and Western Highlands. Steak and mushroom pie, vegetarian haggis, fresh battered haddock, venison sausages in red wine, and farmhouse chicken feature on the bar menu. Good range of Oriental and seafood dishes. **Principal beers:** John Smiths, McEwan 80/-.

Directions off the main A82 at N of Ballachulish Bridge

Brewery/Company Free House

Open 11am-midnight

Bar food 12-3 6-9 Av main course £6.50

Accommodation (Min) s£25 d£50

ONICH Highland Map 14 NN06

Onich Hotel

ONICH

PH33 6RY ☎ 01855 821214

Magnificently situated hotel on the shores of Loch Linnhe. The Deerstalker Bar, adorned with impressive stags' heads, offers snacks, fish and chip favourites and home-cooked dishes such as meatloaf, gammon and pineapple, and macaroni cheese. The dinner menu in the restaurant presents a choice of Scottish dishes.

Principal beers: Tetleys, Calders, Alloa.

Directions Beside A82, 2m N of Ballachulish Bridge

Brewery/Company Free House

Open 11-12

Bar food 12-9 Av main course £7.50

Restaurant 7-9 Av 3 course à la carte £25 Av 4 course fixed price £25

Accommodation (Min) s£36 d£92

PLOCKTON Highland Map 14 NG83

The Plockton Hotel

PLOCKTON

Harbour St IV52 8TN ☎ 01599 544274

Village centre inn overlooking Loch Carron and also enjoying views of the mountains. Inside is a collection of hand-made model boats made by a local craftsman. All fish is landed nearby, and prawns are landed in the harbour. On the menu diners may find grilled blue trout, Skye king scallops, and glazed Barbary duck.

Principal beers: Tennents.

Directions On A87 to Kyle of Lochalsh take turn at Balmacara. Plockton 7m N.

Brewery/Company Free House

Open 11am-midnight (11am-12.30am Wknds)

Bar food 12-2.30 6-9

Accommodation (Min) s£25 d£55

Plockton Inn & Seafood Restaurant

PLOCKTON

Innes St IV52 8TW ☎ 01599 544222

The inn, run by a local family, was built as a church manse in the. Great pride is taken in the use of fresh local seafood, and the hotel has its own smokehouse. Dishes may include hearty fish soup, scallops with bacon, garlic and cream, skate with black butter, and home-smoked gravlax.

Principal beers: Caledonian, Fraoch.

Directions On A87 to Kyle of Lochalsh take turn at Balmacara. Plockton 7m N

Brewery/Company Free House

Open 11-1am (Sat 11-11.30, Sun 12.30-11)

Bar food 12-2.30 5.30-10 Av main course £11.50

Restaurant 12-2.30 5.30-10 Av 3 course à la carte £14

Accommodation (Min) s£28 d£58

ULLAPOOL Highland Map 14 NH19

The Argyll Hotel

ULLAPOOL

Argyll St IV26 2UB ☎ 01854 612422

Traditional family-run hotel just a short stroll from the shores of Loch Broom. Timeless public bar and comfortable main bar, both with open fires and 80 malt whiskies to choose from. West coast scallops and halibut, chicken supreme,

venison medallions, and haggis, neeps and tatties feature on the varied menus.
Principal beers: Calders 70/-, 2 Scottish guest ales.
Brewery/Company Free House
Open 11-11.30 (Sun 12-11)
Bar food 12-2 5-9 Av main course £7.50
Accommodation (Min) s£20 d£35

The Ceilidh Place
ULLAPOOL
14 West Argyle St N26 2TD
☎ 01854 612103
Concerts, music festivals, exhibitions, plays and poetry readings are just some of the cultural events staged at this former boat shed overlooking Loch Broom. The self-service restaurant offers home-made soups, pepper terrine with Cumberland sauce, venison casserole, good fish dishes, and Lochbroom prawns grilled with garlic.
Directions On entering Ullapool, along Shore St, pass pier and take 1st R. Hotel is straight ahead at top of hill
Brewery/Company Free House
Open 11-11
Bar food 11-7.30 Av main course £5
Restaurant 7-9.30 Av 3 course à la carte £11
Accommodation (Min) s£50 d£100

Morefield Hotel & Mariners Restaurant
ULLAPOOL
North Rd IV26 2TQ ☎ 01854 612161
Popular bar and seafood restaurant, also known for its large selection of malt whiskies and ports. Possible dishes include lobster royale, seafood Thermidor, or Achiltibuie salmon and roast scallop terrine. If youre not feeling

fishy try Aberdeen Angus prime sirloin, pork fillet Stilton, or something from the vegetarian menu.

Principal beers: Belhaven, Tennent, 2 guest ales.
Brewery/Company Free House
Open 11-2.30 5-11 (11-11 summer)
Bar food 2 5.30-9.30 Av main course £9
Restaurant 6.30-9.30 Av 3 course à la carte £20
Accommodation (Min) s£35 d£50

Midlothian

PENICUIK Midlothian *Map 11 NT25*

Howgate Restaurant NEW
PENICUIK
Howgate EH26 8PY ☎ 01968 670000
Once a stable block, then a cheese-making facility, the Howgate is now a bar, bistro and restaurant sitting in a pleasant courtyard setting with a stream just a few feet away. Today's menu may include Angus beef and mushroom pie, vegetable strudel with noodles, and red snapper fillet with chilli couscous.
Principal beers: Belhaven Best.
Directions On A6094, 0.5m SE of Penicuik
Brewery/Company Free House
Open 12-2.30 6-11
Bar food 12-2.30 6-11
Restaurant 12-2.30 6-10

Moray

FOCHABERS Moray *Map 15 NJ35*

Gordon Arms Hotel
FOCHABERS
80 High St IV32 7DH ☎ 01343 820508
Comfortable public rooms retain much of their original character at this 250-year-old coaching inn. Fine Scottish ingredients are a feature of the menus, including game, lamb and beef, seafood from the Moray coast, and Spey salmon. Flambé dishes such as scampi Newburg or steak Diane are a speciality. **Principal beers:** Caledonian Deuchars IPA.
Brewery/Company Free House
Open 7am-11.30pm
Bar food 12-2.30 5-9.30 Av main course £6.95
Restaurant 12-2.30 7-9.30 Av 3 course à la carte £20 Av 3 course fixed price £16.95
Accommodation (Min) s£40 d£60

Scotland

Perth & Kinross

ABERFELDY Perth & Kinross Map 14 NN84

Ailean Chraggan Hotel
ABERFELDY
Weem PH15 2LD ☎ 01887 820346
Small hotel set in two acres looking over the River Tay to the hills beyond. Tay salmon and local game are features of the daily menu, which might include creamy seafood soup with rouille, pan-fried venison steaks with pinenuts and red cabbage, and sticky toffee pudding. **Principal beers:** no real ale.
Directions A9 N to jct at Ballinluig then A827 onto Aberfeldy, R onto B846
Brewery/Company Free House
Open 12-2 6.30-9.30 (8.30 in winter)
Bar food 1-2 6.30-9.30
Restaurant 1-2 6.30-9.30 Av 3 course à la carte £15
Accommodation (Min) s£38.50 d£67

ALMONDBANK Perth & Kinross Map 11 NO02

Almondbank Inn
ALMONDBANK
31 Main St PH1 3NJ ☎ 01738 583242
Enjoying fine views over the River Almond from its neat rear garden, this Victorian village inn specialises in prime Aberdeen Angus steaks (from the landlord's own family butcher) with a variety of sauces. The extensive menu may also list fresh haddock and scampi, roast beef and Yorkshire pudding, and chicken George. **Principal beers:** Broughton Greenmantle.
Directions From Perth take A85 towards Crieff. 3m to Almondbank
Brewery/Company Free House
Open 11-2.30 5-11 (Fri-Sat 11-2.30, 5-11.45)
Restaurant 12-2 5-8

BURRELTON Perth & Kinross Map 11 NO23

The Burrelton Park Inn NEW
BURRELTON
High St PH13 9NX ☎ 01828 670206
Long, low roadside inn in typical Scottish vernacular style. Spacious lounge bar offering an all-day menu - steak and ale pie, seafood tagliatelle, Chinese stir-fried chicken - and a well-appointed restaurant featuring a daily menu, perhaps including venison au poivre, pheasant, and Scottish salmon with Drambuie sauce. **Principal beers:** Inveralmond.
Brewery/Company Free House
Open 11-11
Bar food 12-9 Av main course £6.50
Restaurant 12-9 Av 3 course à la carte £17.50 Av 2 course fixed price £5.50 (lunch only)
Accommodation (Min) s£30 d£45

CLEISH Perth & Kinross Map 11 NT09

Nivingston House
CLEISH
KY13 7LS ☎ 01577 850216
Country house hotel set in extensive grounds with wonderful views of the Cleish Hills. Local produce is evident in the bar food and in the Orchard Restaurant, with dishes such as mussels with white wine sauce, grilled Tay salmon, pot-roasted local venison, and prime Scotch fillet steak.
Principal beers: Calders.
Directions 2m W of M90 J5
Brewery/Company Free House
Open 12-11
Bar food 12-2 7-9 Av main course £5
Restaurant 12-2 7-9 Av 3 course à la carte £25 Av 3 course fixed price £15
Accommodation (Min) s£30 d£140

GLENDEVON Perth & Kinross Map 11 NN90

Tormaukin Hotel
GLENDEVON
FK14 7JY ☎ 01259 781252
18th-century former drovers' inn occupying an idyllic rural setting encircled by the Ochil Hills. The name means 'hill of the mountain hare' in old Scots. Log fires, beamed ceilings and cosy bars. Extensive menus offer an

interesting choice of international cuisine, as well as fresh Scottish produce. **Principal beers:** Harviestown 80/-, Schiehallion & Montrose.
Directions On A823 between M90 & A9
Brewery/Company Free House
Open 11-11 (Sun 12-11/closed 10 days early Jan)
Bar food 12-2 5.30-9.30 Av main course £8.95
Restaurant 6.30-9.30 Av 3 course à la carte £24.50
Accommodation (Min) s£50 d£78

GLENFARG Map 11 NO11
Perth & Kinross

The Bein Inn NEW
GLENFARG
PH2 9PY ☎ 01577 830216
Drovers' inn dating from 1863, with open fires and a cosy lounge, situated in a wooded glen. A daily pasta dish, ribeye steak, and julienne of fresh chicken are offered in the bar. Restaurant dishes include fresh Islay scallops, seafood casserole, and supreme of Perthshire guinea fowl.

Brewery/Company Free House
Open 11-11
Bar food 12-9
Restaurant 12-2 6-9 Av 3 course à la carte £15
Accommodation (Min) s£35 d£56

KILLIECRANKIE Map 14 NN96
Perth & Kinross

The Killiecrankie Hotel
KILLIECRANKIE
PH16 5LG ☎ 01796 473220
Built as a manse in 1840, the hotel is set in extensive grounds close to the Pass of Killiecrankie. The panelled bar has a lovely sun lounge adjacent to accommodate the good bar food operation. The serious eating is done in the restaurant, which offers an innovative menu of Scottish fare.
Principal beers: no real ale.
Directions Turn off A9 at Killicrankie.Hotel 3m on B8079 on R
Brewery/Company Free House
Open 11-2.30 5.30-11 (closed Jan & Feb)
Bar food 12.30-2 6.30-9.30 Av main course £7.95
Restaurant 7-8.30 Av 4 course fixed price £31
Accommodation (Min) s£58 d£116

KINNESSWOOD Map 11 NN10
Perth & Kinross

Lomond Country Inn
KINNESSWOOD
KY13 7HN ☎ 01592 840253
Dramatically set on the slopes of the Lomond Hills overlooking Loch Leven and its famous castle, this informal, small village hotel offers an interesting bar menu. Quality ingredients are used in such dishes as cullen skink, salmon fishcakes with basil and tomato sauce, beefsteak pie, and pear and toffee crumble. **Principal beers:** Marstons Pedigree, Jennings Bitter, Greene King Abbot Ale.
Directions M90 J5, follow signs for Glenrothes then Scotlandwell, Kinnesswood next village
Brewery/Company Free House
Open 11-11
Bar food 12-2.30 6-10 Av main course £5.50
Restaurant 12-2.30 6-10 Av 3 course à la carte £18.50 Av 3 course fixed price £10
Accommodation (Min) s£40 d£60

KINROSS Map 11 NO10
Perth & Kinross

The Muirs Inn Kinross
KINROSS
49 Muirs KY13 8AS ☎ 01577 862270
Dating back almost 200 years, this whitewashed inn began life as a farmhouse. It offers a choice of bars, the Wee Still Lounge Bar featuring an original whisky still. Home-made soups are a speciality of both the bar and restaurant menus, along with steak pie and whisky ginger cream. **Principal beers:** 8 Scottish guest ales.

contd.

The Muirse Inn Kinross

Directions from M90 J6 take A922 to T-junction. Inn diagonally opposite on R
Brewery/Company Free House
Open 12-2 5-11 (Fri 12-2 5-12, Sat 11-12, Sun 12.30-11)
Bar food 12-1.30 5-9 Av main course £7.50
Restaurant 12-2 5-9 Av 3 course fixed price £8.95
Accommodation (Min) s£27.50 d£39.50

PITLOCHRY Perth & Kinross — Map 14 NN95

Moulin Hotel
PITLOCHRY
11-13 Kirkmichael Rd, Moulin PH16 5EW ☎ 01796 472196
300-year-old coaching inn at the foot of 2,757ft Ben Vrackie near Pitlochry, gateway to the Scottish Highlands. Expect grilled salmon, Angus steak, fish, chips and mushy peas, and steak and ale pie on the main menu. Dinner main courses might include braised pheasant, and home-made mushroom and aubergine bake. **Principal beers:** Moulin - Braveheart, Old Remedial, Light & Ale of Atholl, McEwans 80/-.

Directions From A9 at Pitlochry take A923. Moulin 0.75m
Brewery/Company Free House
Open 12-11 (Fri-Sat 12-11.45)
Bar food 12-6 6-9.30 Av main course £7
Restaurant 6-9 Av 3 course à la carte £17 Av 2 course fixed price £13.95
Accommodation (Min) s£53 d£58

POWMILL Perth & Kinross — Map 11 NT09

Gartwhinzean Hotel
POWMILL
FK14 7NW ☎ 01577 840595
Situated between the Ochil Hills and the Cleish Hills, this hotel's specials board features haddock Cairnfold, home-made steak pie, and various steak grills. Other main courses include smoked chicken with lemon and Vermouth sauce, guinea fowl with black cherry and orange sauce, and veal with apricot and sherry sauce. **Principal beers:** Maclay 70/-, 80/-.
Directions A977 to Kincardine Bridge road, for approx 7m to the vilage of Powmill, hotel at the end of village
Brewery/Company Free House
Open 7-12
Bar food 12-9.30 Av main course £6
Restaurant 12-2.30 6.30-9.30 Av 3 course à la carte £21
Accommodation (Min) s£50 d£65

Renfrewshire

HOUSTON Renfrewshire — Map 10 NS46

Fox & Hounds
HOUSTON
South St PA6 7EL ☎ 01505 612448
An 18th-century coaching inn, with its own micro-brewery, set in a conservation village. Tuna and scallop kebabs, and steak, mushroom and ale pie are offered in the bar. Restaurant dishes include seared fillet of salmon with spring onion mash, and chicken 'rusty nail'. **Principal beers:** Killelan, Barochan, Jack Frost, guest ales.
Directions M8 - Glasgow Airport. A737- Houston
Brewery/Company Free House
Open 11-12 (Fri-Sat 11-1am/food 12-10 Sat & Sun)
Bar food 12-2.30 5.30-10 Av main course £7
Restaurant 12-2.30 5.30-10 Av 3 course à la carte £18

Scottish Borders

EDDLESTON *Map 11 NT24*
Scottish Borders

Horse Shoe Inn
EDDLESTON
EH45 8QP ☎ 01721 730225 & 730306
Surrounded by Border hills and beautiful countryside, this low, whitewashed building was once a blacksmith's forge and coaching stop. Spacious and well-furnished bar area, and an extensive menu featuring good pub favourites, and specials like osso bucco, herrings in oatmeal, baked halibut bonne femme, and lamb with tomato and red wine sauce. **Principal beers:** Belhaven Best.
Directions On A703 S of Edinburgh. From M74 to Biggar, then A72 to Peebles & A703 N to Eddleston
Brewery/Company Free House
Open 7.30am-3 5.30-12
Bar food 12.30-3 5.30-9.30 Av main course £8.50
Restaurant 12.30-3 5.30-9.30 Av 3 course à la carte £11
Accommodation (Min) s£25 d£40

GALASHIELS *Map 12 NT43*
Scottish Borders

Abbotsford Arms
GALASHIELS
63 Stirling St TD1 1BY ☎ 01896 752517
Ideal of local golf and touring the beautiful Borders countryside, this family-run, stone-built hotel offers comfortable accommodation and traditional bar food. Expect an extensive menu supplemented by home-made specials, perhaps cock-a-leekie soup, chicken Balmoral and sticky toffee pudding. **Principal beers:** John Smiths.

Directions Turn off A7 down Ladhope Vale, turn L opposite the Bus Station
Brewery/Company Free House
Open 11-11 (Fri-Sat 11-12)
Bar food 12-6 6-9 Av main course £5
Restaurant 12-6 6-9 Av 3 course à la carte £6
Accommodation (Min) s£35 d£50

Kingsknowles
GALASHIELS
1 Selkirk Rd TD1 3HY ☎ 01896 758375
19th-century mansion splendidly situated in three and a half acres in the beautiful Scottish Borders, overlooking the River Tweed and Sir Walter Scott's ancestral home. Poached Tweed salmon is among the favourite restaurant dishes, as are Border sirloin steak, beef and Traquair ale pie and locally caught Eyemouth haddock. **Principal beers:** McEwans - 60/- & 70/-, John Smiths.

Directions Off A7 at Galashiels/ Selkirk rdbt
Brewery/Company Free House
Open 7.15am-midnight
Bar food 12-2 5.45-9.30 Av main course £5.50
Restaurant 12-2 5.45-9.30 Av 5 course fixed price £19.25
Accommodation (Min) s£42 d£60

INNERLEITHEN *Map 11 NT33*
Scottish Borders

Traquair Arms Hotel
INNERLEITHEN
Traquair Rd EH44 6PD ☎ 01896 830229
A traditional stone-built inn and hotel situated in the tranquil Scottish Borders. Expect a cosy bar, blazing log fires and a relaxed atmosphere. As well as high teas, the varied menu offers broccoli and cheese flan, spiced lamb and vegetable casserole, steak pie, pan-fried duckling with redcurrant jus, and bread-and-butter

contd.

pudding. **Principal beers:** Traquair Bear, Broughton Greenmantle & Blackdouglas.
Directions 6m E of Peebles on A72. Hotel 100metres from junc with B709
Brewery/Company Free House
Open 11-11.30
Bar food 12-9 Av main course £5.50
Accommodation (Min) s£45 d£58

KELSO Scottish Borders Map 12 NT73

Queens Head Hotel NEW
KELSO
Bridge St TD5 7JD ☎ 01573 224636
Situated between the cobbled square and Rennie's Bridge over the Tweed, this 18th-century Georgian coaching inn has historical connections with Kelso Abbey and Bonnie Prince Charlie. Home-cooked food, served in the comfortable lounge and restaurant includes lambs' liver and onion, Smailholm pie, pan-fried monkfish and bacon, and Dover sole. **Principal beers:** Morland Old Speckled Hen, Marstons Pedigree, Broughton Greenmantle Ale.
Brewery/Company Free House
Open 11-2.45 4.45-11
Bar food 12-2 6-9 Av main course £4.50
Restaurant 12-2 6-9 Av 3 course à la carte £12.50 Av 3 course fixed price £12.50
Accommodation (Min) s£35 d£50

LAUDER Scottish Borders Map 12 NT54

Lauderdale Hotel NEW
LAUDER
1 Edinburgh Rd TD2 6TW
☎ 01578 722231
Traditional stone Victorian building at the foot of the Lammermuir Hills, close to the Southern Upland Way and Thirlestane Castle. Cheerful lounge bar and a good range of generously served food. Dishes may include tagliatelle carbonara, steak pie, cod steak in black butter, vension with pepper and port sauce, and chargrilled steaks. High teas. **Principal beers:** Broughton Ales.
Directions on the main A68 25m S of Edinburgh
Brewery/Company Free House
Open 8.30-11 (Thu-Sat 8.30-12)
Bar food 12-2 5.30-9.30 Av main course £5.35
Restaurant 12-2 5.30-9.30 Av 3 course à la carte £15.25
Accommodation (Min) s£32 d£49

MELROSE Scottish Borders Map 12 NT53

Burts Hotel
MELROSE
Market Square TD6 9PN
☎ 01896 822285
Set in Melrose's 18th-century market square, Burts retains much of its period charm. The bar with its welcoming fire and the elegant restaurant reflect a serious approach to good food. Interesting combinations of ingredients are evident in pigeon, rabbit and venison mousse, or beef with marinated beansprouts and chilli jam. Decent traditional bar food. **Principal beers:** Belhaven 80/-, Bass.
Directions A6091, 2m from A68 3m South of Earlsdon
Brewery/Company Free House
Open 11-2.30 5-11
Bar food 12-2 6-9.30 Av main course £6.25
Restaurant 12-2 7-9 Av 3 course à la carte £24.75 Av 3 course fixed price £25
Accommodation (Min) s£46 d£60

ST BOSWELLS Scottish Borders Map 12 NT53

Buccleuch Arms Hotel
ST BOSWELLS
The Green TD6 0EW ☎ 01835 822243
Perfectly situated at the heart of the Scottish Borders, this historic 16th-century inn offers a varied menu to suit every palate. There is a selection of blackboard specials, and main courses include grilled loin of Border lamb, lightly grilled fillet of Tweed salmon, and a choice of sizzle platters. **Principal beers:** Broughton Greenmantle.
Directions on A68, 8m N of Jedburgh
Brewery/Company Free House
Open 7am-11pm
Bar food 12-11 Av main course £6
Accommodation (Min) s£30 d£60

SWINTON Scottish Borders Map 12 NT84

Wheatsheaf Hotel
SWINTON
Main St TD11 3JJ ☎ 01890 860257
Situated close to the River Tweed, this characterful country inn makes an ideal base for touring the beautiful Scottish Borders. Good quality local produce

features prominently on the varied menu. Sample the seared fillet of codling from the bar menu or try the fillet of Highland venison in the restaurant. **Principal beers:** Caledonian 80/- & Deuchers IPA, Broughton Greenmantle Ale.
Directions 6m N of Duns on A6112
Brewery/Company Free House
Open 11-2.30 6-11 (closed Mon)
Bar food 11.45-2.30 6-9 Av main course £6.50
Restaurant 11.45-2 6-9 Av 3 course à la carte £18
Accommodation (Min) s£35 d£60

TIBBIE SHIELS INN Scottish Borders *Map 11 NT22*

Tibbie Shiels Inn
TIBBIE SHIELS INN
St Mary's Loch TD7 5NE
☎ 01750 42231

On the route of the Southern Upland Way, overlooking St Mary's Loch, this historic coaching inn is named after the wife of Lord Napier's mole catcher who started the business in 1826. Sir Walter Scott and Robert Louis Stephenson reputedly stayed here. Bar meals include local trout, chilli, and mushroom and hazelnut crumble. **Principal beers:** Broughton Greenmantle Ale, Belhaven 80/-.
Directions From Moffat take A708. Inn is 14m on R
Brewery/Company Free House
Open 11-11
Bar food 12.30-2.30 6.30-8.30 Av main course £5
Restaurant 6.30-8.30 Av 3 course à la carte £11.65
Accommodation (Min) s£27 d£48

TUSHIELAW INN Scottish Borders *Map 11 NT31*

Tushielaw Inn
TUSHIELAW INN
7D7 5HT ☎ 01750 62205

A 19th-century coaching inn with an idyllic location on the banks of Ettrick Water. Traditional home-made fare is offered along with inventive specials, such as salmon steak in creamy turmeric sauce and lamb chops with mint sauce. **Principal beers:** Broughton, McEwans.
Directions At junction of B709 & B711(W of Hawick)
Brewery/Company Free House
Open 12-2.30 6-11 (Sun 7-11)
Bar food 12-2.30 6-11 Av main course £5.95
Restaurant 12-2.30 6-11 Av 3 course à la carte £16
Accommodation (Min) s£22 d£25

TWEEDSMUIR Scottish Borders *Map 11 NT12*

The Crook Inn
TWEEDSMUIR
ML12 6QN ☎ 01899 880272

Scotland's first licensed coaching inn, dating back to 1604, this is where Robert Burns wrote his 'Willie Wastles Wife' poem. The River Tweed flows along the bottom of the garden. The appetising bar menu might include double venison burgers, deep-fried scampi tails, home-cooked ham and egg, and savoury mushroom crêpes. **Principal beers:** Broughton Greenmantle.
Brewery/Company Free House
Open 9am-12midnight
Bar food 12-9.30 Av main course £6.50
Accommodation (Min) s£36 d£52

South Ayrshire

SYMINGTON South Ayrshire *Map 10 NS33*

Wheatsheaf Inn
SYMINGTON
Main St KA1 5QB ☎ 01563 830307

17th-century village inn converted from an old farmhouse which still has its original walls and fires. Fresh fish highlights the menu, possibly including fillet of salmon with cracked pepper and orange sauce, creamy seafood lasagne, and fillet of sole mornay. Various steaks, salads and vegetarian dishes are also available. **Principal beers:** Calders 70/-, Caledonian 80/-.
Brewery/Company Belhaven
Open 11-midnight (closed Sun eve Nov-Mar)
Bar food 12-9.30 Av main course £5.95
Accommodation (Min) s£36

For Pubs with AA food rosettes see page 430

Stirling

BRIG O'TURK Stirling Map 11 NN50

The Byre Inn
BRIG O'TURK
FK17 8HT ☎ 01877 376292
Carefully converted 18th-century stone cattle byre peacefully located on the edge of the Queen Elizabeth Forest Park. Popular with outdoor types, it features traditional Scottish music, log fires and imaginative home-cooking using fresh local produce. Expect hearty soups and sandwiches, game casserole, haggis, and venison with red wine and redcurrant jus. **Principal beers:** Maclay 70/- & Wallace IPA.
Brewery/Company Free House
Open 12-3 6-11 (closed Tue)
Bar food 12.30-2.30 6.30-9 Av main course £10
Restaurant 12.30-2.30 6.30-9 Av 3 course à la carte £25

DRYMEN Stirling Map 11 NS48

Clachan Inn
DRYMEN
2 Main St G63 0BG ☎ 01360 660824
Quaint, white-painted cottage situated in a small village on the West Highland Way. Locate the appealing lounge bar for freshly-made food, the varied menus listing filled baked potatoes, salads, chicken and mushroom pasta bake, fish and chips, sirloin steak with bacon and Roquefort sauce, and good daily specials. **Principal beers:** Caledonian Deuchars IPA, Belhaven.
Brewery/Company Free House
Open 11-12
Bar food 12-4 6-10 Av main course £4.85
Restaurant 12-4 6-10 Av 3 course à la carte £15

KIPPEN Stirling Map 11 NS69

Cross Keys Hotel NEW
KIPPEN
Main St FK8 3DN ☎ 01786 870293
Welcoming, family-run, 18th-century country inn retaining much of its traditional charm within spacious bars and the stone-walled restaurant. Home-made specials (pork Wellington, duck with plum sauce, fresh haddock in batter) enhance printed menu fare, the latter featuring lamb stovies, liver and bacon, venison burgers, and cloutie dumpling. **Principal beers:** Broughton Greenmantle.
Brewery/Company Free House
Open 12-2.30 5.30-11 (Sun 12.30-11)
Bar food 12-2 5.30-9.30 Av main course £5.50
Restaurant 7-8.45 Av 3 course à la carte £18.95
Accommodation (Min) s£19.50

STRATHBLANE Stirling Map 11 NS57

Kirkhouse Inn
STRATHBLANE
Glasgow Rd GG3 9AA ☎ 01360 770621
17th-century coaching inn nestling beneath the jagged scarp of the Campsie Fells, a rolling patchwork of green volcanic hills and picturesque villages. Interesting menu offers International cuisine as well as traditional British dishes. Sample steak and Guinness pie or try the smoked haddock in creamy Stilton sauce. **Principal beers:** Maclay, Tennents.
Directions A81 Aberfoyce rd from Glasgow city centre through Bearsden & Milngavie, Strathblane on junct with A891
Brewery/Company
Open 11-midnight
Bar food 12-2.30 6-9.30 Av main course £7.35
Restaurant 12-2.30 7-9.30
Accommodation (Min) s£30 d£50

THORNHILL Stirling Map 11 NN60

Lion & Unicorn NEW
THORNHILL
FK8 3PS ☎ 01786 850204
Droving inn dating from 1635, frequented by Rob Roy MacGregor. Reliable and freshly cooked food may feature steak and Guinness pie and salmon with lobster sauce, alongside filled baguettes and ostrich burger in the bar, to rack of lamb with apricot and rosemary glaze, and smoked sea trout with coriander butter in the restaurant. **Principal beers:** Inveralmond Independence & Ossians, Belhaven IPA, Caledonian Deuchars IPA, Caledonian 80/-.
Directions On A873 Blair Drummond to Aberfoyle
Brewery/Company Free House
Open 12-1am
Bar food 12-5 5-10 Av main course £6
Restaurant 12-5 5-10 Av 3 course à la carte £19 Av 2 course fixed price £10

West Lothian

LINLITHGOW Map 11 NS97
West Lothian

Champany Inn NEW
LINLITHGOW
Champany EH49 7LU ☎ 01506 834532
16th-century inn two miles from the ruins of Linlithgow Palace, birthplace of Mary Queen of Scots and James V. Noted for its Aberdeen Angus steaks. The appetising menu consists of various starters, a selection of burgers and several fish dishes. Grain-fed chicken and Scottish salmon are among the specialities. **Principal beers:** Belhaven.
Brewery/Company Free House
Open 12-11
Bar food 12-2 6.30-10 Av main course £20
Restaurant 12.30-2 7-10 Av 3 course à la carte £40 Av 2 course fixed price £16.75
Accommodation (Min) s£95 d£95

Western Isles

LOCHBOISDALE Map 13 NF71
Western Isles

Polochar Inn
LOCHBOISDALE
Polochar HS8 5TT ☎ 01878 700215
Overlooking a magnificent sandy beach with breathtaking views of Eriskay and Barra, this 17th-century inn is superbly situated and enjoys beautiful sunsets. The bar menu offers fresh seafood dishes, and steaks with various sauces, while restaurant fare includes supreme of chicken, and seared king scallops with lime and ginger marmalade.
Principal beers: no real ale.

Directions From Lochboisdale travel W & take B888. Hotel at end of road
Brewery/Company Free House
Open 11-11 (Thu-Fri 11-12.45am, Sat 11-11.45)
Bar food 12.30-2.30 6.30-9.30 Av main course £4.60
Restaurant 6.30-9.30 Av 3 course à la carte £22.50 Av 4 course fixed price £14.95
Accommodation (Min) s£35 d£55

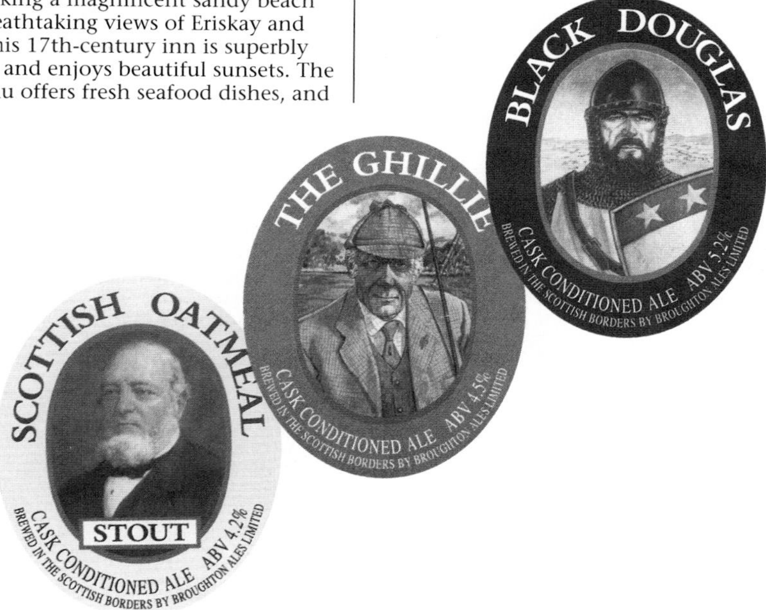

KEY TO ATLAS

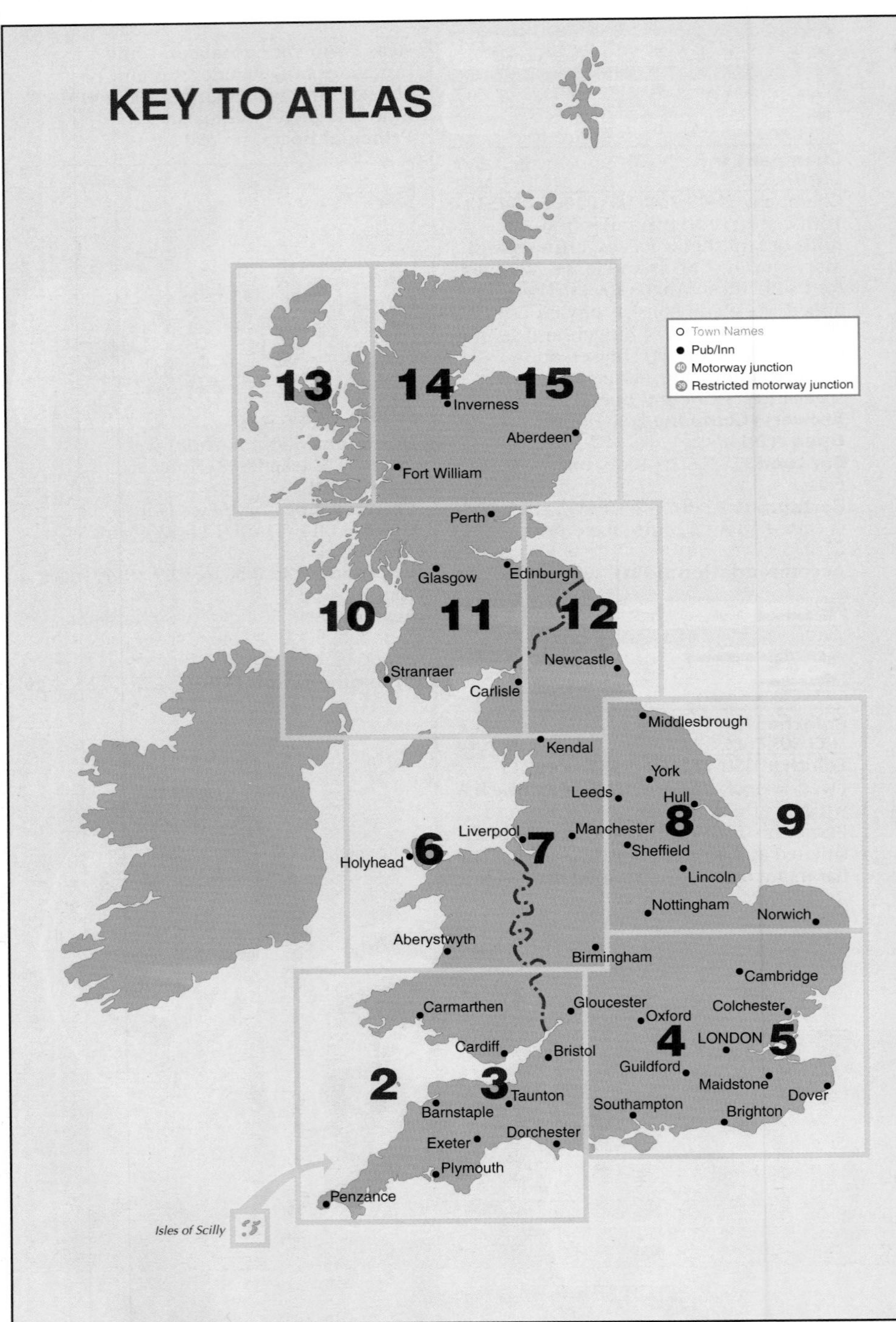

Town Names
Pub/Inn
Motorway junction
Restricted motorway junction
13
14
15
Inverness
Aberdeen
Fort William
Perth
Glasgow
Edinburgh
10
11
12
Newcastle
Stranraer
Carlisle
Middlesbrough
Kendal
York
Leeds
Hull
8
9
Liverpool
Manchester
7
6
Holyhead
Sheffield
Lincoln
Nottingham
Norwich
Aberystwyth
Birmingham
Cambridge
Carmarthen
Gloucester
Oxford
Colchester
LONDON
4
5
Cardiff
Bristol
Guildford
Maidstone
2
3
Taunton
Dover
Barnstaple
Southampton
Brighton
Dorchester
Exeter
Plymouth
Penzance
Isles of Scilly

Greater London

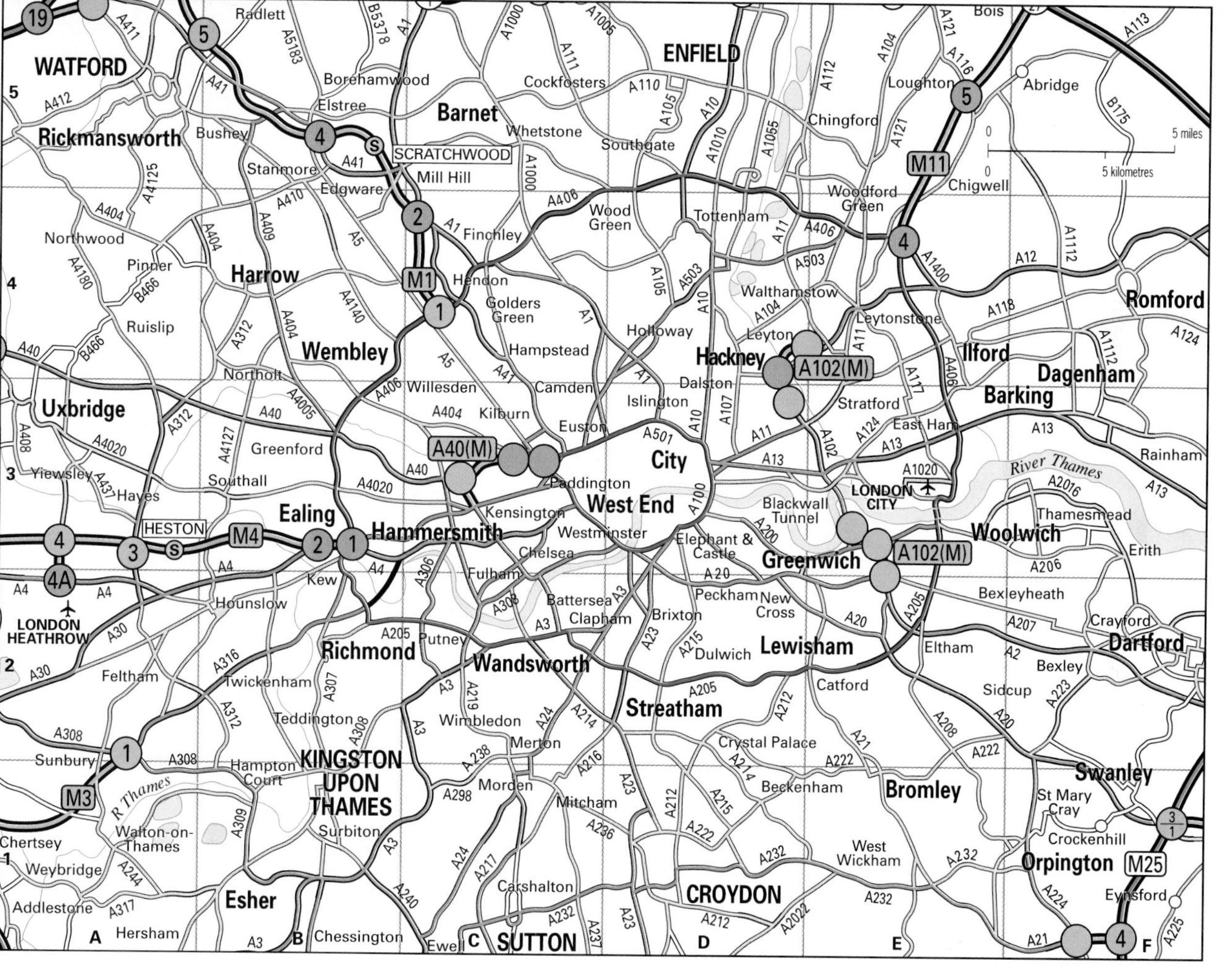

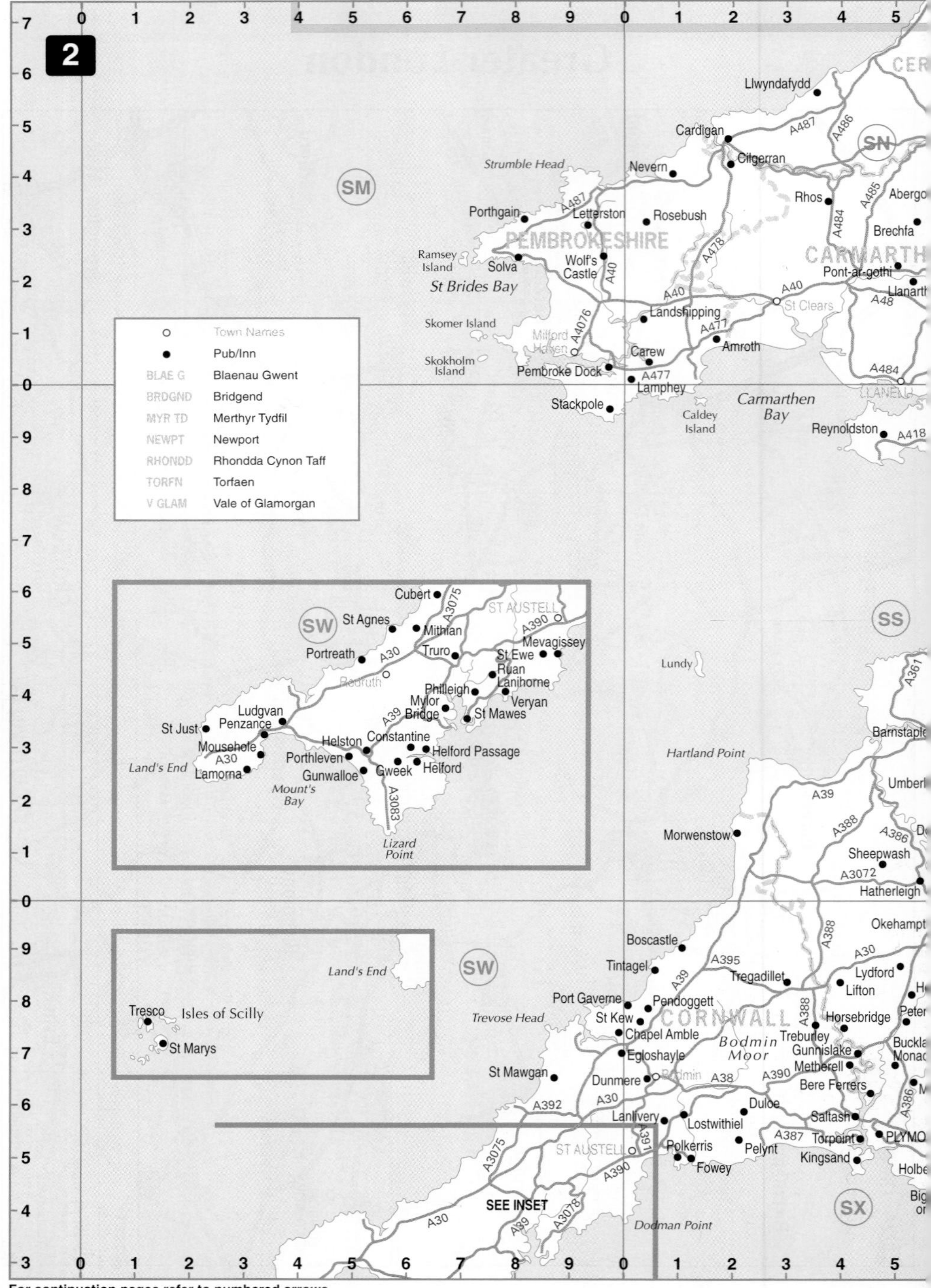

For continuation pages refer to numbered arrows

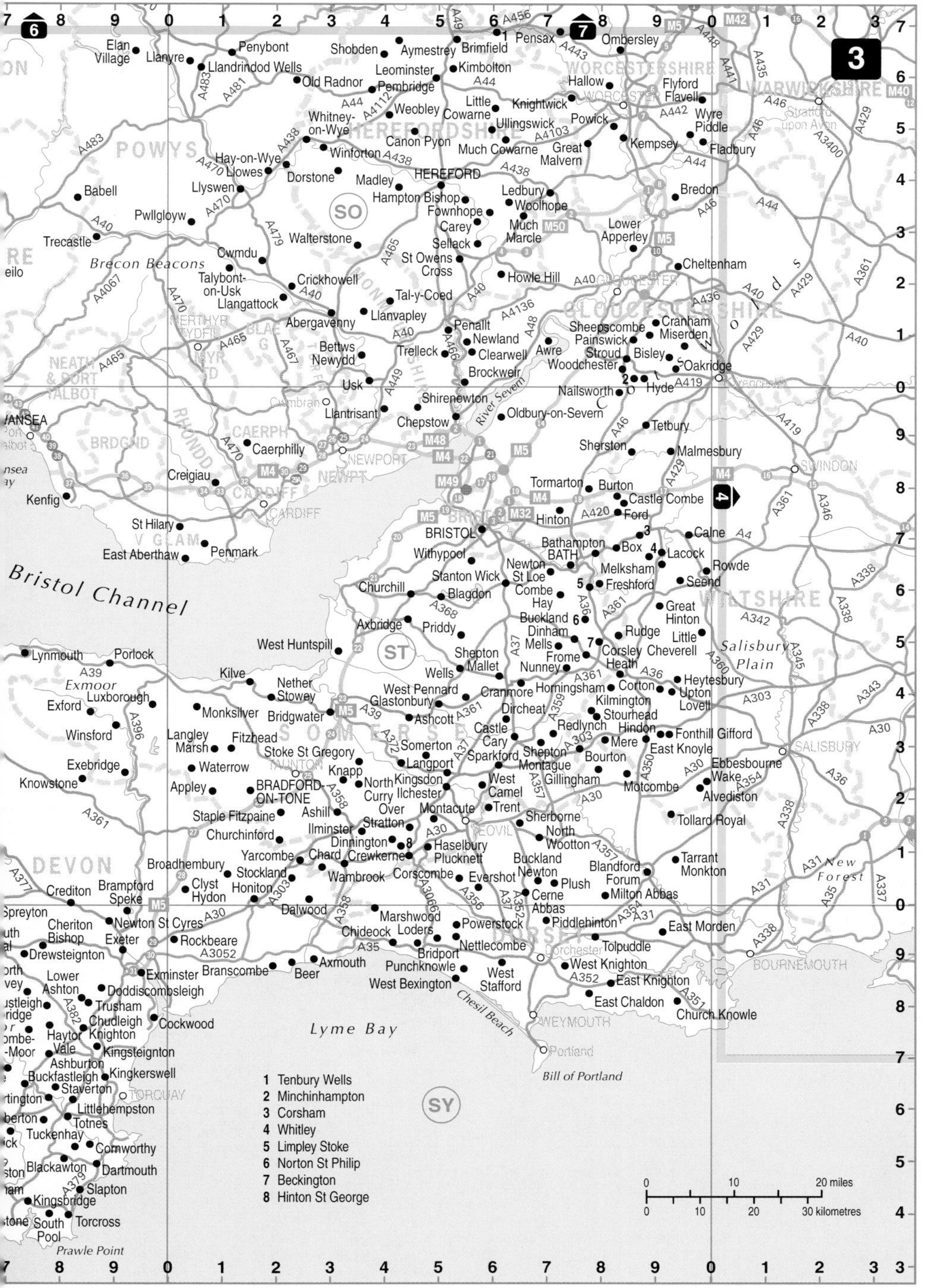

3
Elan Village
Llanyre
Penybont
Llandrindod Wells
Old Radnor
Shobden
Aymestrey
Brimfield
Pensax
Ombersley
Leominster
Kimbolton
Pembridge
WORCESTERSHIRE
Hallow
Flyford Flavell
WARWICKSHIRE
Stratford upon Avon
Weobley
Little Cowarne
Knightwick
Powick
Wyre Piddle
Whitney-on-Wye
Ullingswick
HEREFORDSHIRE
Canon Pyon
Much Cowarne
Great Malvern
Kempsey
Fladbury
POWYS
Hay-on-Wye
Llowes
Winforton
Dorstone
Madley
HEREFORD
Bredon
Babell
Llyswen
Hampton Bishop
Ledbury
Fownhope
Woolhope
Pwllgloyw
Carey
Much Marcle
Lower Apperley
Trecastle
Walterstone
Sellack
Cwmdu
St Owens Cross
Cheltenham
Brecon Beacons
Talybont-on-Usk
Crickhowell
Howle Hill
Llangattock
Tal-y-Coed
GLOUCESTER
GLOUCESTERSHIRE
Abergavenny
Llanvapley
Penallt
Sheepscombe
Cranham
Newland
Painswick
Miserden
Bettws Newydd
Trelleck
Clearwell
Awre
Stroud
Bisley
Woodchester
Oakridge
Brockweir
Usk
Nailsworth
Hyde
Cotswolds
Cirencester
Llantrisant
Shirenewton
River Severn
Oldbury-on-Severn
SWANSEA
Chepstow
Tetbury
Caerphilly
NEWPORT
Sherston
Malmesbury
Creigiau
SWINDON
Tormarton
Burton
CARDIFF
Castle Combe
Kenfig
Hinton
Ford
St Hilary
BRISTOL
Calne
Bathampton
Box
Lacock
East Aberthaw
Penmark
Withypool
BATH
Rowde
Newton St Loe
Melksham
Seend
Bristol Channel
Stanton Wick
Combe Hay
Freshford
Churchill
Blagdon
Great Hinton
WILTSHIRE
Buckland Dinham
Axbridge
Priddy
Rudge
Little Cheverell
Mells
Salisbury Plain
West Huntspill
Lynmouth
Porlock
Shepton Mallet
Frome
Corsley Heath
Nunney
Wells
Exmoor
Kilve
Heytesbury
Nether Stowey
West Pennard
Cranmore
Horningsham
Corton
Upton Lovell
Luxborough
Glastonbury
Kilmington
Exford
Monksilver
Bridgwater
Ashcott
Dircheat
Stourhead
Castle Cary
Redlynch
Hindon
Winsford
Langley Marsh
Fitzhead
Somerton
SOMERSET
Mere
Fonthill Gifford
East Knoyle
Stoke St Gregory
Sparkford
Shepton Montague
Bourton
SALISBURY
Exebridge
Waterrow
TAUNTON
Knapp
Langport
Ebbesbourne Wake
Kingsdon
West Camel
Gillingham
Knowstone
Appley
BRADFORD-ON-TONE
North Curry
Ilchester
Motcombe
Alvediston
Over Stratton
Montacute
Trent
Staple Fitzpaine
Ashill
YEOVIL
Sherborne
Tollard Royal
Churchinford
Ilminster
North Wootton
Dinnington
Haselbury Plucknett
DEVON
Broadhembury
Yarcombe
Chard
Crewkerne
Buckland Newton
Blandford Forum
Tarrant Monkton
New Forest
Stockland
Wambrook
Corscombe
Evershot
Plush
Crediton
Brampford Speke
Clyst Hydon
Honiton
Cerne Abbas
Milton Abbas
Spreyton
Dalwood
Marshwood
Cheriton Bishop
Newton St Cyres
Chideock
Loders
Powerstock
DORSET
Piddlehinton
East Morden
Exeter
Rockbeare
Nettlecombe
Drewsteignton
Bridport
Dorchester
Tolpuddle
Axmouth
Punchknowle
West Knighton
BOURNEMOUTH
Lower Ashton
Exminster
Branscombe
Beer
West Stafford
East Knighton
West Bexington
Doddiscombsleigh
Trusham
East Chaldon
Chudleigh Knighton
Cockwood
Chesil Beach
Church Knowle
WEYMOUTH
Haytor Vale
Lyme Bay
Kingsteignton
Portland
Ashburton
Bill of Portland
Kingkerswell
Buckfastleigh
Staverton
TORQUAY
Littlehempston
Totnes
Tuckenhay
Cornworthy
Blackawton
Dartmouth
Slapton
Kingsbridge
South Pool
Torcross
Prawle Point
SO
ST
SY
1 Tenbury Wells
2 Minchinhampton
3 Corsham
4 Whitley
5 Limpley Stoke
6 Norton St Philip
7 Beckington
8 Hinton St George
0 10 20 miles
0 10 20 30 kilometres

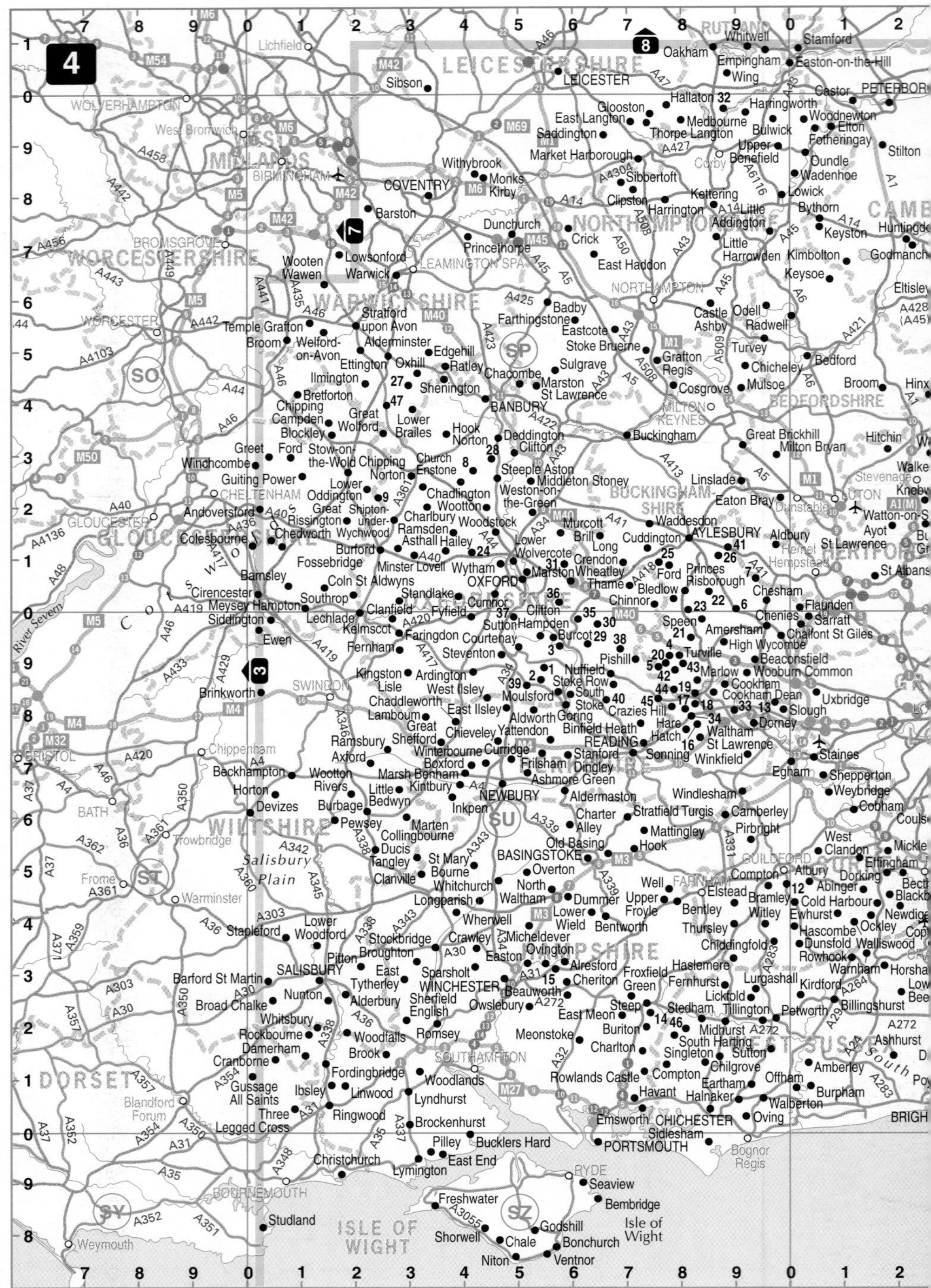

For continuation pages refer to numbered arrows

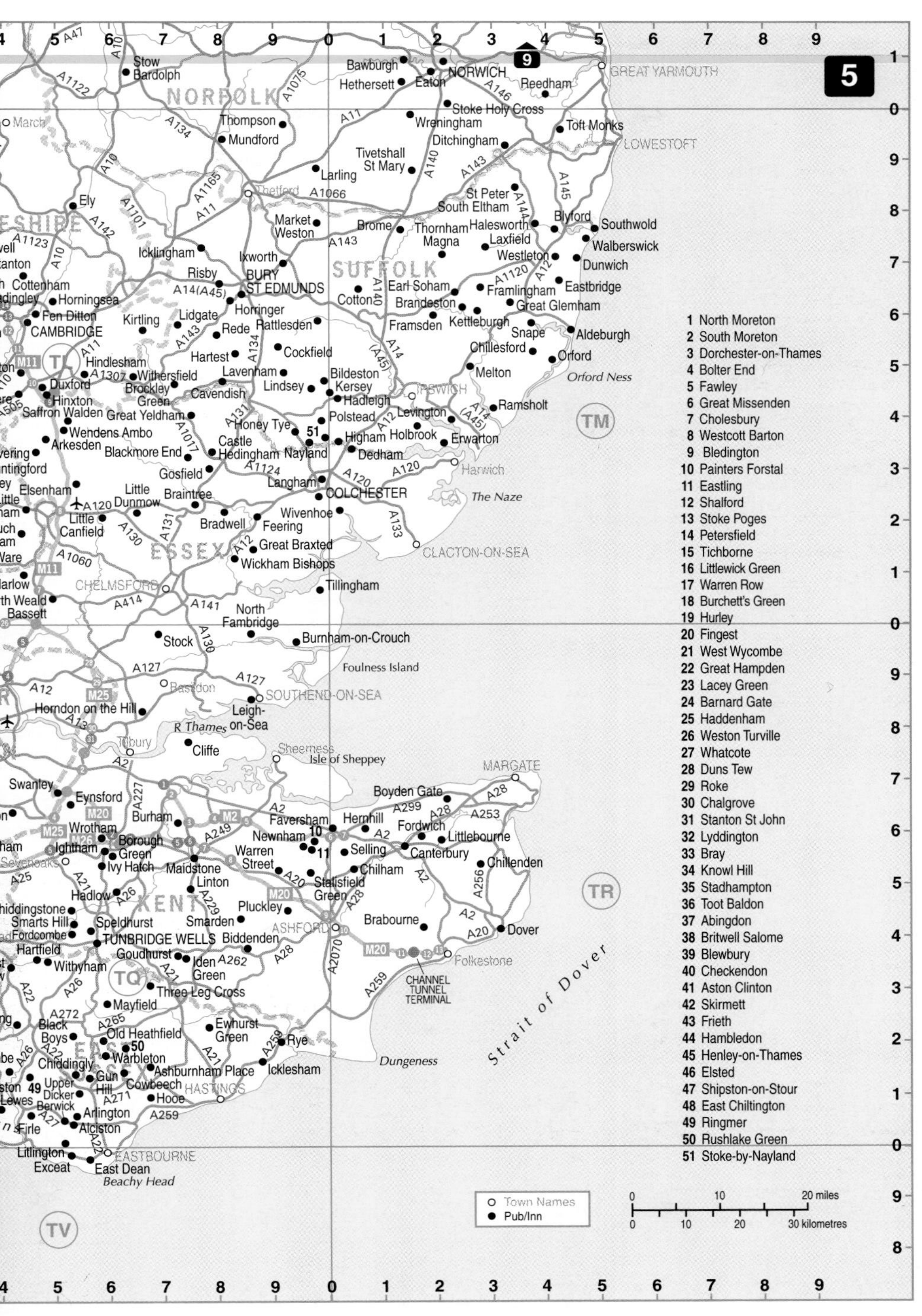
5
NORFOLK
SUFFOLK
ESSEX
KENT
NORWICH
GREAT YARMOUTH
LOWESTOFT
BURY ST EDMUNDS
CAMBRIDGE
COLCHESTER
IPSWICH
CHELMSFORD
CLACTON-ON-SEA
SOUTHEND-ON-SEA
MARGATE
TUNBRIDGE WELLS
HASTINGS
EASTBOURNE
Strait of Dover
Orford Ness
The Naze
Foulness Island
R Thames
Isle of Sheppey
Dungeness
Beachy Head
CHANNEL TUNNEL TERMINAL
1 North Moreton
2 South Moreton
3 Dorchester-on-Thames
4 Bolter End
5 Fawley
6 Great Missenden
7 Cholesbury
8 Westcott Barton
9 Bledington
10 Painters Forstal
11 Eastling
12 Shalford
13 Stoke Poges
14 Petersfield
15 Tichborne
16 Littlewick Green
17 Warren Row
18 Burchett's Green
19 Hurley
20 Fingest
21 West Wycombe
22 Great Hampden
23 Lacey Green
24 Barnard Gate
25 Haddenham
26 Weston Turville
27 Whatcote
28 Duns Tew
29 Roke
30 Chalgrove
31 Stanton St John
32 Lyddington
33 Bray
34 Knowl Hill
35 Stadhampton
36 Toot Baldon
37 Abingdon
38 Britwell Salome
39 Blewbury
40 Checkendon
41 Aston Clinton
42 Skirmett
43 Frieth
44 Hambledon
45 Henley-on-Thames
46 Elsted
47 Shipston-on-Stour
48 East Chiltington
49 Ringmer
50 Rushlake Green
51 Stoke-by-Nayland
Town Names
Pub/Inn
0 10 20 miles
0 10 20 30 kilometres

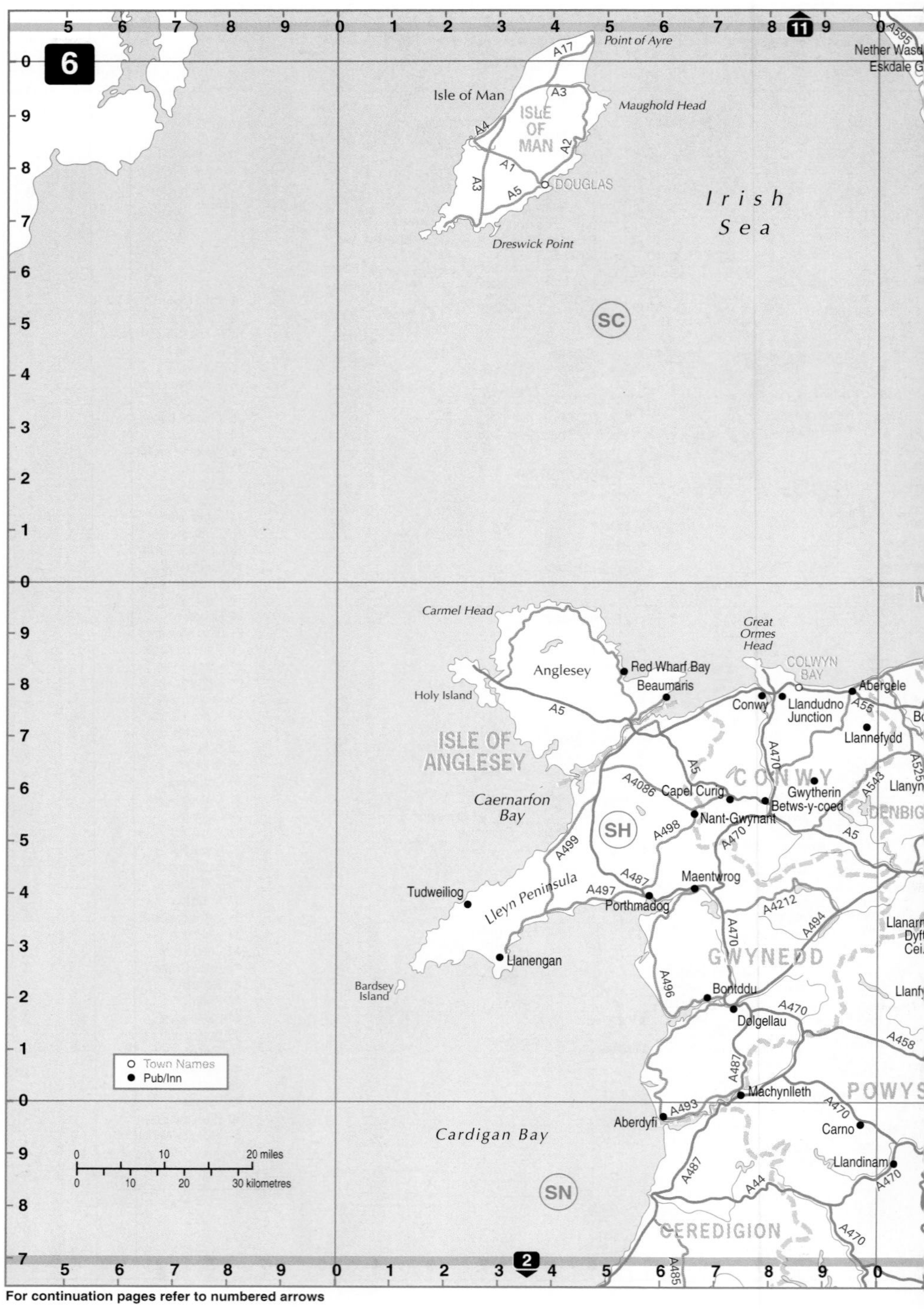

For continuation pages refer to numbered arrows

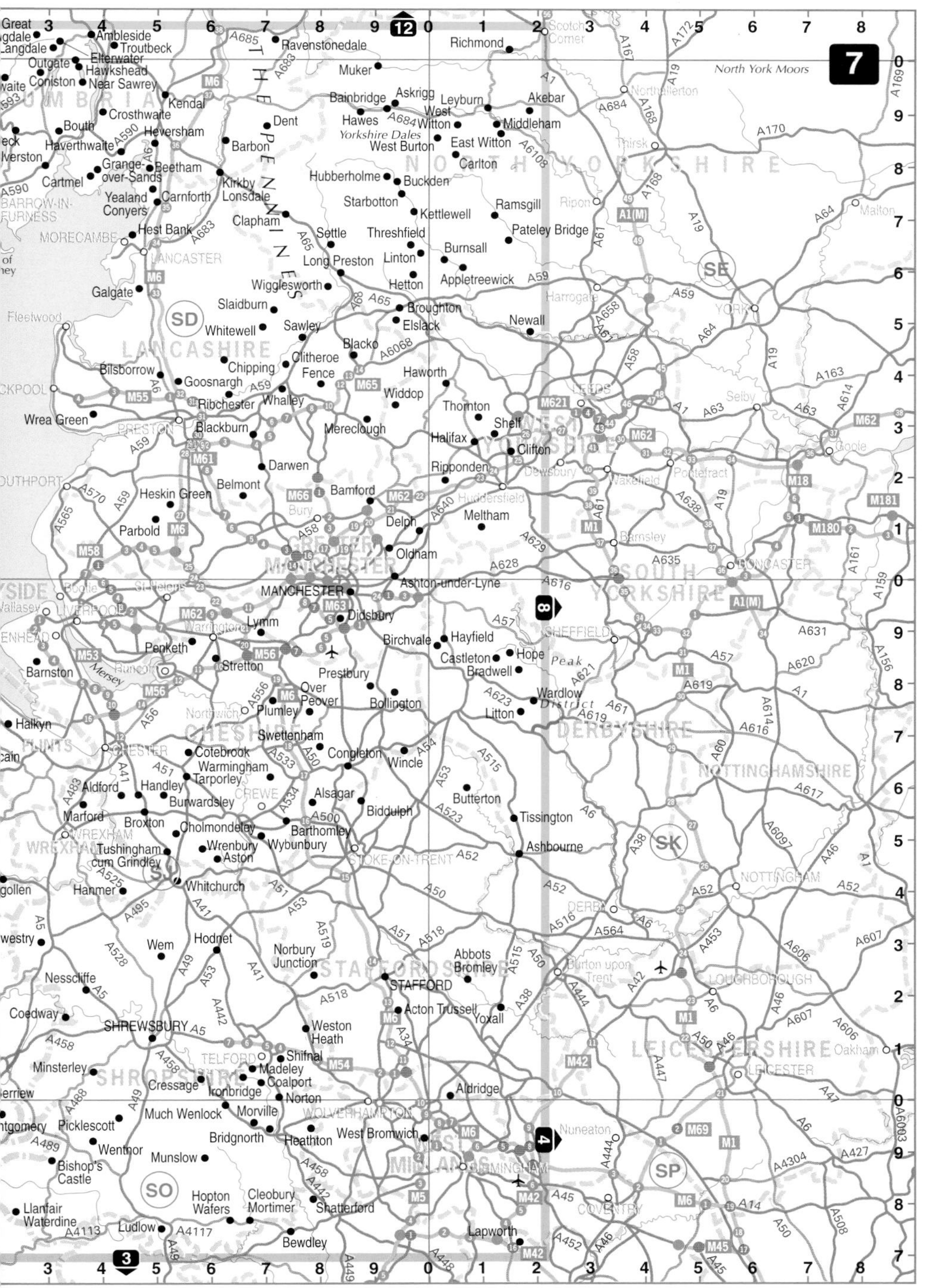
7
12
8
4
3
North York Moors
NORTH YORKSHIRE
Yorkshire Dales
THE PENNINES
CUMBRIA
LANCASHIRE
WEST YORKSHIRE
GREATER MANCHESTER
SOUTH YORKSHIRE
CHESHIRE
DERBYSHIRE
NOTTINGHAMSHIRE
STAFFORDSHIRE
SHROPSHIRE
LEICESTERSHIRE
WEST MIDLANDS
FLINTS
WREXHAM
Peak District
SD
SE
SJ
SK
SO
SP
Great Langdale
Langdale
Ambleside
Troutbeck
Elterwater
Outgate
Hawkshead
Coniston
Near Sawrey
Kendal
Crosthwaite
Bouth
Haverthwaite
Ulverston
Heversham
Grange-over-Sands
Beetham
Cartmel
Barrow-in-Furness
Yealand Conyers
Carnforth
Hest Bank
Morecambe
Lancaster
Galgate
Fleetwood
Blackpool
Ravenstonedale
Dent
Barbon
Kirkby Lonsdale
Clapham
Settle
Long Preston
Wigglesworth
Slaidburn
Whitewell
Sawley
Chipping
Bilsborrow
Goosnargh
Ribchester
Clitheroe
Whalley
Preston
Wrea Green
Blackburn
Darwen
Belmont
Southport
Heskin Green
Parbold
Bury
Bamford
Delph
Oldham
Manchester
Ashton-under-Lyne
Didsbury
Lymm
Warrington
Penketh
Stretton
Runcorn
Widnes
St Helens
Bootle
Liverpool
Wallasey
Birkenhead
Barnston
Mersey
Halkyn
Chester
Northwich
Plumley
Over Peover
Prestbury
Bollington
Swettenham
Cotebrook
Warmingham
Tarporley
Congleton
Wincle
Alsagar
Crewe
Biddulph
Barthomley
Wybunbury
Alford
Handley
Burwardsley
Marford
Wrexham
Broxton
Cholmondeley
Wrenbury
Aston
Tushingham cum Grindley
Whitchurch
Hanmer
Llangollen
Oswestry
Wem
Hodnet
Nesscliffe
Coedway
Shrewsbury
Minsterley
Cressage
Ironbridge
Telford
Shifnal
Madeley
Coalport
Norton
Much Wenlock
Morville
Bridgnorth
Heathton
Picklescott
Wentnor
Bishop's Castle
Munslow
Hopton Wafers
Cleobury Mortimer
Shatterford
Bewdley
Ludlow
Llanfair Waterdine
Stoke-on-Trent
Norbury Junction
Stafford
Acton Trussell
Weston Heath
Wolverhampton
West Bromwich
Birmingham
Lapworth
Aldridge
Abbots Bromley
Yoxall
Burton upon Trent
Derby
Ashbourne
Tissington
Butterton
Litton
Wardlow
Hope
Castleton
Bradwell
Hayfield
Birchvale
Sheffield
Barnsley
Doncaster
Meltham
Huddersfield
Dewsbury
Wakefield
Pontefract
Ripponden
Halifax
Clifton
Shelf
Thornton
Haworth
Widdop
Mereclough
Fence
Blacko
Elslack
Broughton
Hetton
Linton
Threshfield
Burnsall
Appletreewick
Kettlewell
Starbotton
Buckden
Hubberholme
Muker
Bainbridge
Askrigg
Hawes
West Witton
West Burton
Leyburn
Middleham
East Witton
Carlton
Akebar
Richmond
Scotch Corner
Northallerton
Thirsk
Ripon
Ramsgill
Pateley Bridge
Newall
Harrogate
York
Leeds
Selby
Goole
Malton
Nottingham
Loughborough
Leicester
Oakham
Nuneaton
Coventry
Mercy
M6
M55
M61
M65
M66
M62
M58
M56
M53
M63
M60
M621
M1
M18
M180
M181
M42
M54
M5
M69
M45
A1(M)
A1
A6
A19
A64
A59
A61
A65
A66
A168
A170
A684
A685
A683
A590
A6108
A629
A628
A616
A57
A623
A6068
A58
A556
A534
A500
A52
A50
A51
A53
A41
A49
A5
A458
A488
A489
A4113
A4117
A442
A458
A449
A448
A34
A38
A515
A518
A519
A444
A42
A452
A45
A14
A46
A47
A607
A606
A6006
A4304
A427
A5199
A508
A6003
A159
A631
A156
A620
A614
A616
A617
A6097
A60
A619
A621
A61
A638
A635
A163
A63
A161
A172
A167
A1069
A570
A565
A525
A495
A528
A523
A54
A453
A564
A516
A453
A447

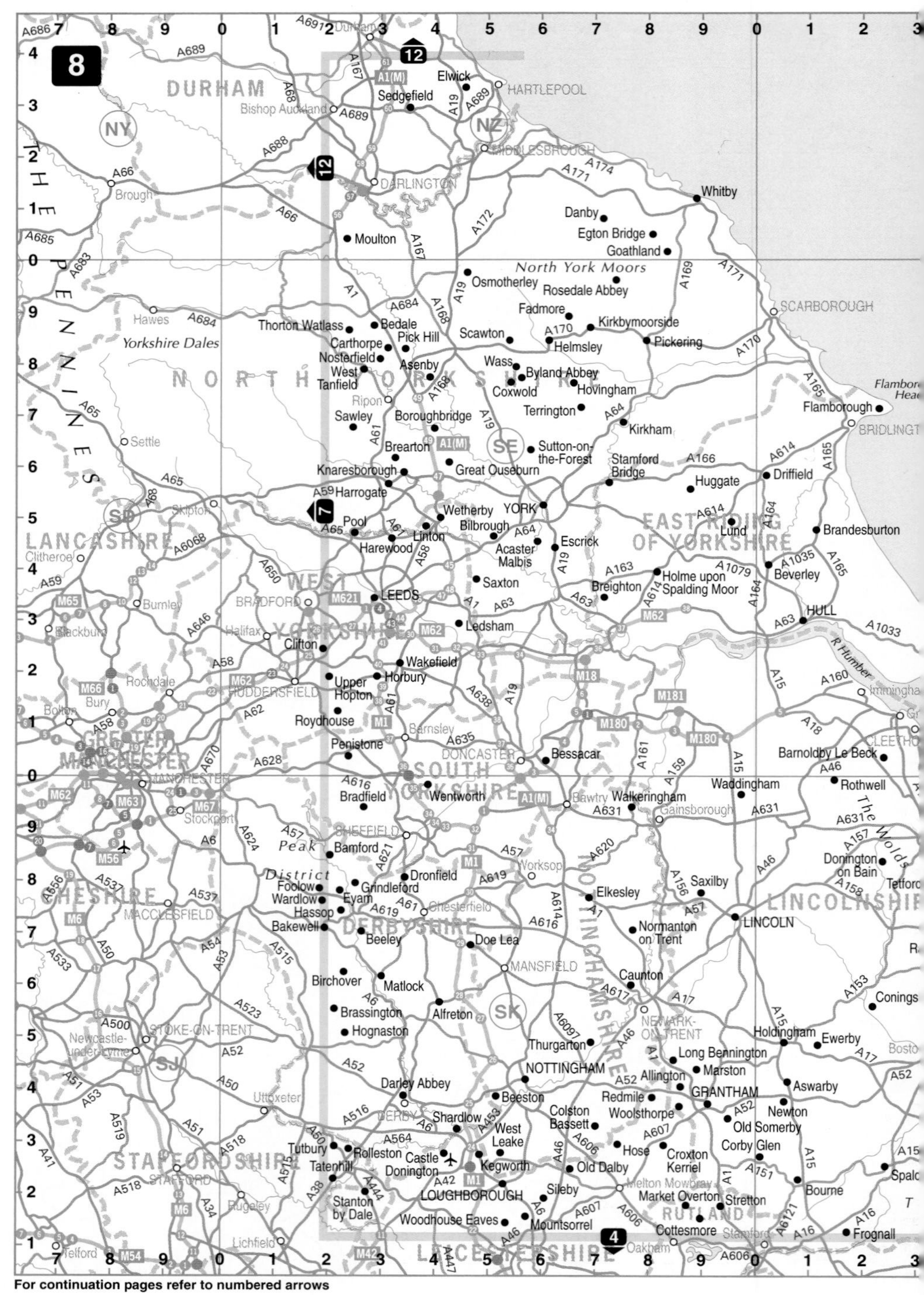

For continuation pages refer to numbered arrows

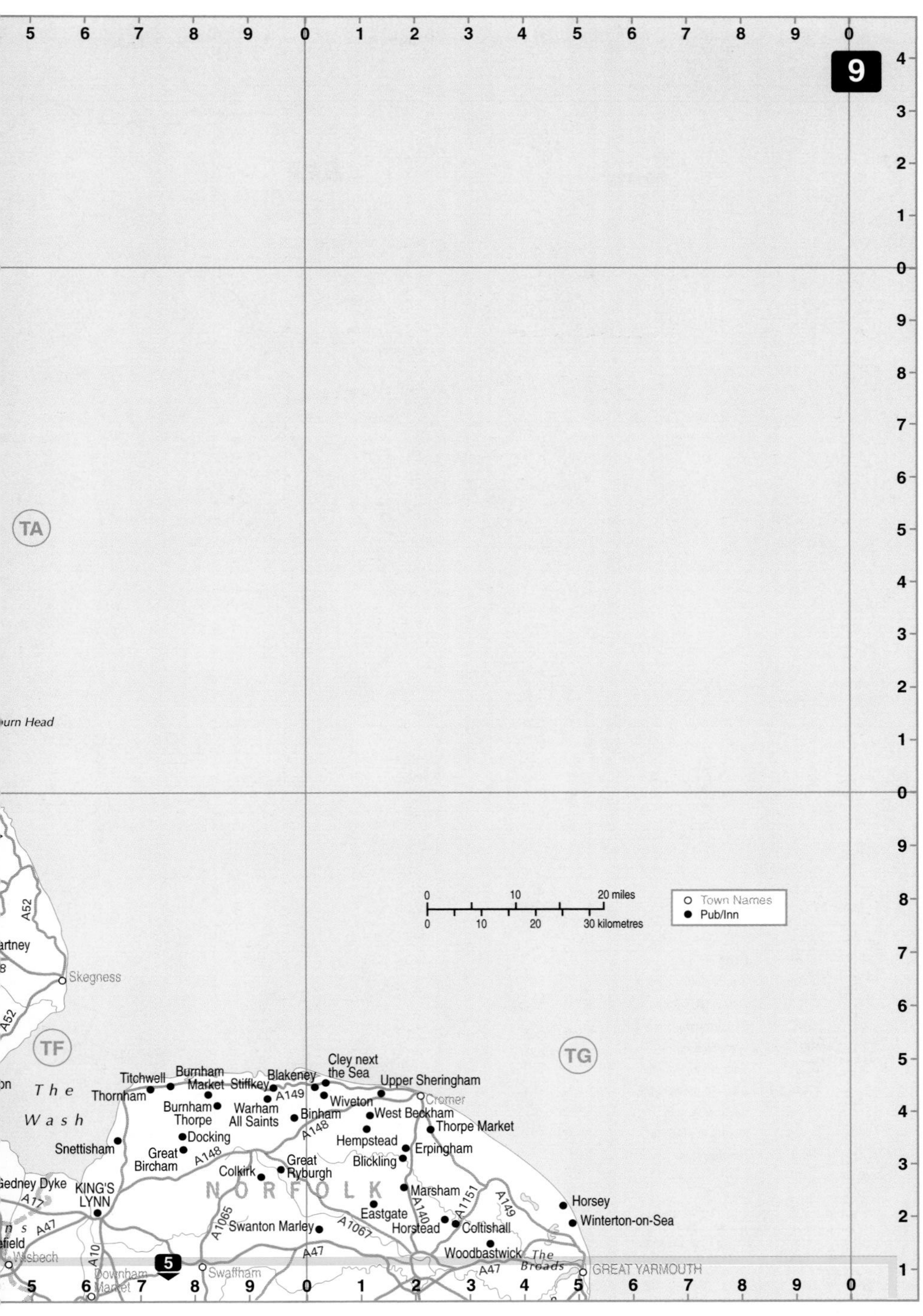
9
TA
TF
TG
The Wash
NORFOLK
Skegness
Titchwell
Burnham Market
Stiffkey
Blakeney
Cley next the Sea
Upper Sheringham
Cromer
Thornham
Burnham Thorpe
Warham All Saints
Binham
Wiveton
West Beckham
Thorpe Market
Docking
Hempstead
Erpingham
Snettisham
Great Bircham
Colkirk
Great Ryburgh
Blickling
KING'S LYNN
Marsham
Eastgate
Horsey
Winterton-on-Sea
Swanton Marley
Horstead
Coltishall
Woodbastwick
The Broads
GREAT YARMOUTH
Swaffham
Downham Market
Wisbech
Gedney Dyke
A149
A148
A1065
A1067
A140
A1151
A47
A10
A17
A52
0 10 20 miles
0 10 20 30 kilometres
Town Names
Pub/Inn

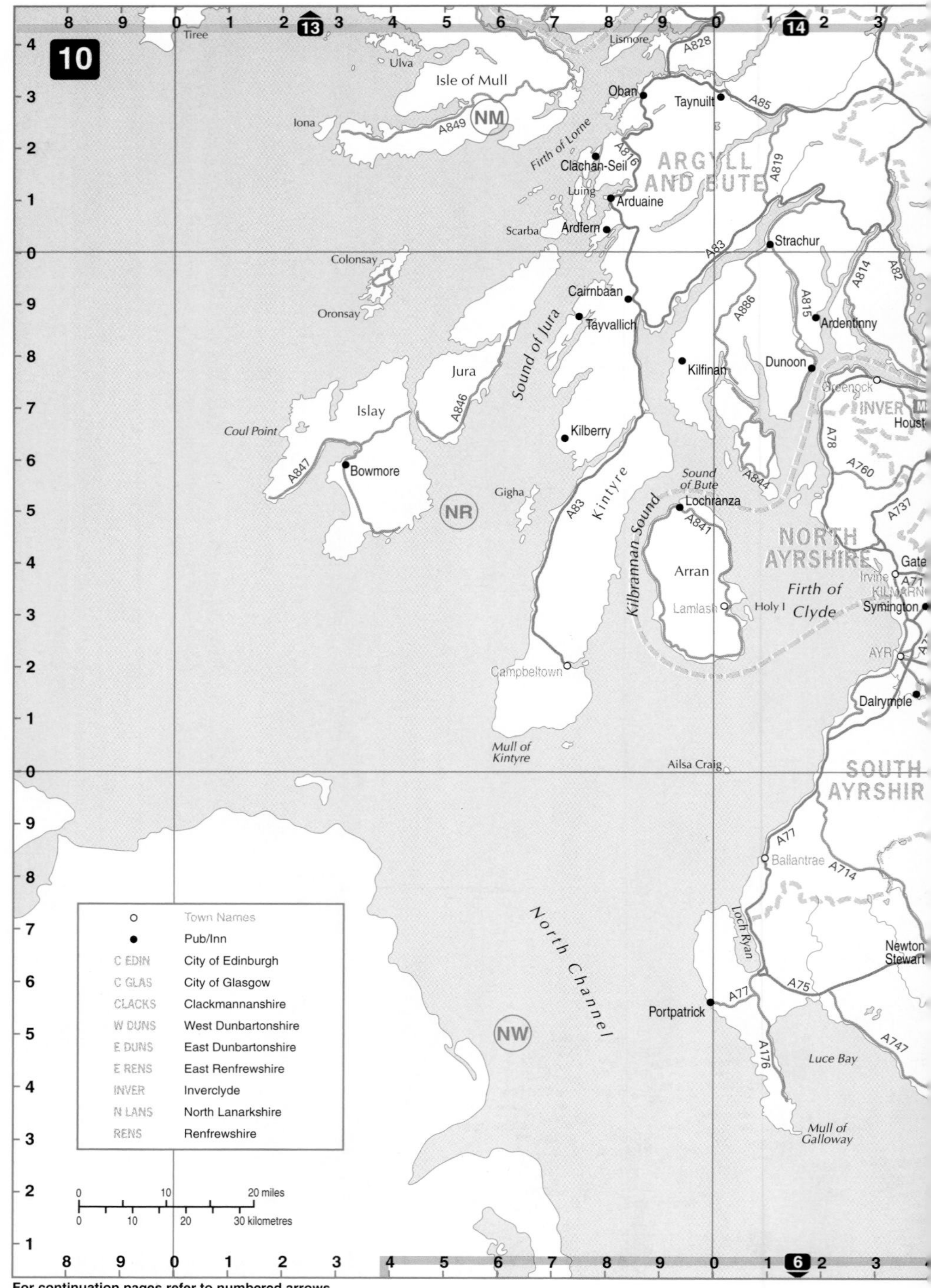

For continuation pages refer to numbered arrows

11
PERTH AND KINROSS
Burrelton
DUNDEE
Arbroath
DUNDEE CITY
Almondbank
PERTH
Firth of Tay
St Andrews Bay
St Andrews
Glenfarg
Glendevon
FIFE
Fife Ness
NORTH SEA
Kinross
Kinnesswood
Lower Largo
Markinch
Isle of May
STIRLING
Thornhill
CLACKS
Powmill
Cleish
Dysart
Kirkcaldy
Kippen
O'Turk
Firth of Forth
FALKIRK
South Queensferry
Dunbar
Castlecary
Linlithgow
WEST
EDINBURGH
C EDIN
Ratho
EAST LOTHIAN
St Abb's Head
GLASGOW
N LANS
LOTHIAN
MIDLOTHIAN
Penicuik
Lammermuir Hills
Newton Mearns
East Kilbride
Berwick-upon-Tweed
Eddleston
Holy Island
SOUTH LANARKSHIRE
Uplands
Galashiels
Coldstream
Innerleithen
BORDERS (SCOTTISH)
EAST AYRSHIRE
Tweedsmuir
Tibbie Shiels Inn
Tushielaw Inn
Jedburgh
The Cheviot Hills
Hawick
Alnwick
Moffat
Southern
DUMFRIES AND GALLOWAY
Otterburn
NORTHUMBERLAND
Morpeth
Dumfries
Eaglesfield
Canonbie
New Abbey
Corbridge
Hexham
CARLISLE
Consett
Blencogo
Solway Firth
Wigtown Bay
Abbey Head
Whithorn
Bassenthwaite
DURHAM
WORKINGTON
Mungrisdale
Penrith
Thornthwaite
Keswick
Scales
Yanwath
Dockray
Watermillock
CUMBRIA
Loweswater
Thirlspot
North Head
Buttermere
Lake District
Wasdale Head
Grasmere

For continuation pages refer to numbered arrows

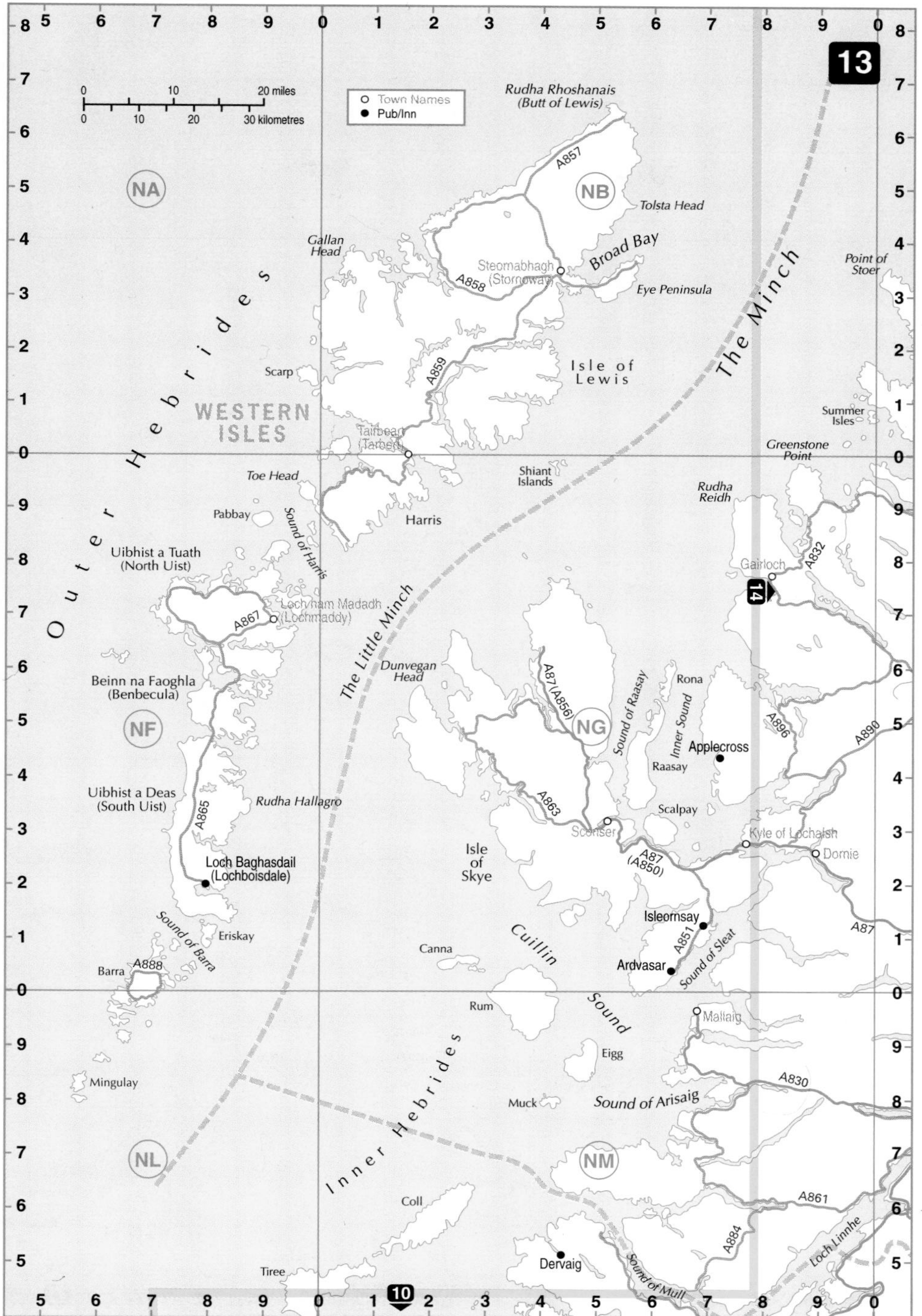

13
Town Names
Pub/Inn
0 10 20 miles
0 10 20 30 kilometres
NA
NB
NF
NG
NL
NM
Rudha Rhoshanais
(Butt of Lewis)
A857
Tolsta Head
Gallan Head
Broad Bay
Steornabhagh
(Stornoway)
A858
Eye Peninsula
The Minch
Point of Stoer
Isle of Lewis
Scarp
A859
Outer Hebrides
WESTERN ISLES
Tairbeart
(Tarbert)
Summer Isles
Greenstone Point
Toe Head
Shiant Islands
Rudha Reidh
Pabbay
Sound of Harris
Harris
Uibhist a Tuath
(North Uist)
Gairloch
A832
14
Lochmaddy
A867
The Little Minch
Beinn na Faoghla
(Benbecula)
Dunvegan Head
A87 (A856)
Sound of Raasay
Rona
Inner Sound
A896
A890
Applecross
Raasay
Uibhist a Deas
(South Uist)
Rudha Hallagro
A865
A863
Scalpay
Sconser
Kyle of Lochalsh
Dornie
A87
(A850)
Isle of Skye
Loch Baghasdail
(Lochboisdale)
Isleornsay
Sound of Barra
Eriskay
Cuillin Sound
A851
Sound of Sleat
Canna
Ardvasar
Barra
A888
Rum
Mallaig
Eigg
Mingulay
A830
Inner Hebrides
Muck
Sound of Arisaig
Coll
A861
A884
Loch Linnhe
Dervaig
Sound of Mull
Tiree
10

14
Rudha Rhoshanais
(Butt of Lewis)
Cape Wrath
Whiten
Head
Pentland Firth
Strathy
Point
A857
A838
A836
Handa Island
Tolsta Head
NB
NC
Steornabhagh
(Stornoway)
Broad Bay
The Minch
Point of
Stoer
Kylesku
A894
A838
Altnaharra
A836
A897
Eye Peninsula
A837
Isle of
Lewis
Summer
Isles
Achiltibuie
A835
Greenstone
Point
A839
A9
A837
Shiant
Islands
Ullapool
Rudha
Reidh
Dundonnell
Dornoch
A832
A836
Tain
Gairloch
North West Highlands
A835
A9
NH
A832
A832
A832
Garve
Contin
Rona
Sound of Raasay
Inner Sound
13
A87
NG
A896
HIGHLAND
A890
A9
Cawdor
Portree
Raasay
INVERNESS
A939
A863
A831
A82
Scalpay
Plockton
A9
Sconser
Kyle of Lochalsh
Dornie
Isle
of
Skye
A87
Carrbridge
A938
Glenelg
Cuillin
A851
A87
Monadliath
Mountains
Aviemore
Sound of Sleat
A887
Fort Augustus
A9
Rum
A87
Sound
Mallaig
Eigg
A86
A830
Glenfinnan
A82
Muck
Sound of Arisaig
NM
NN
Grampian Mou
Fort William
A9
Onich
North Ballachulish
PERTH
AND
KINROSS
Killiecrankie
A861
Glencoe
Tobermory
Loch Linnhe
Pitlochry
A884
A82
Sound of Mull
Port
Appin
Aberfeldy
10
11
For continuation pages refer to numbered arrows

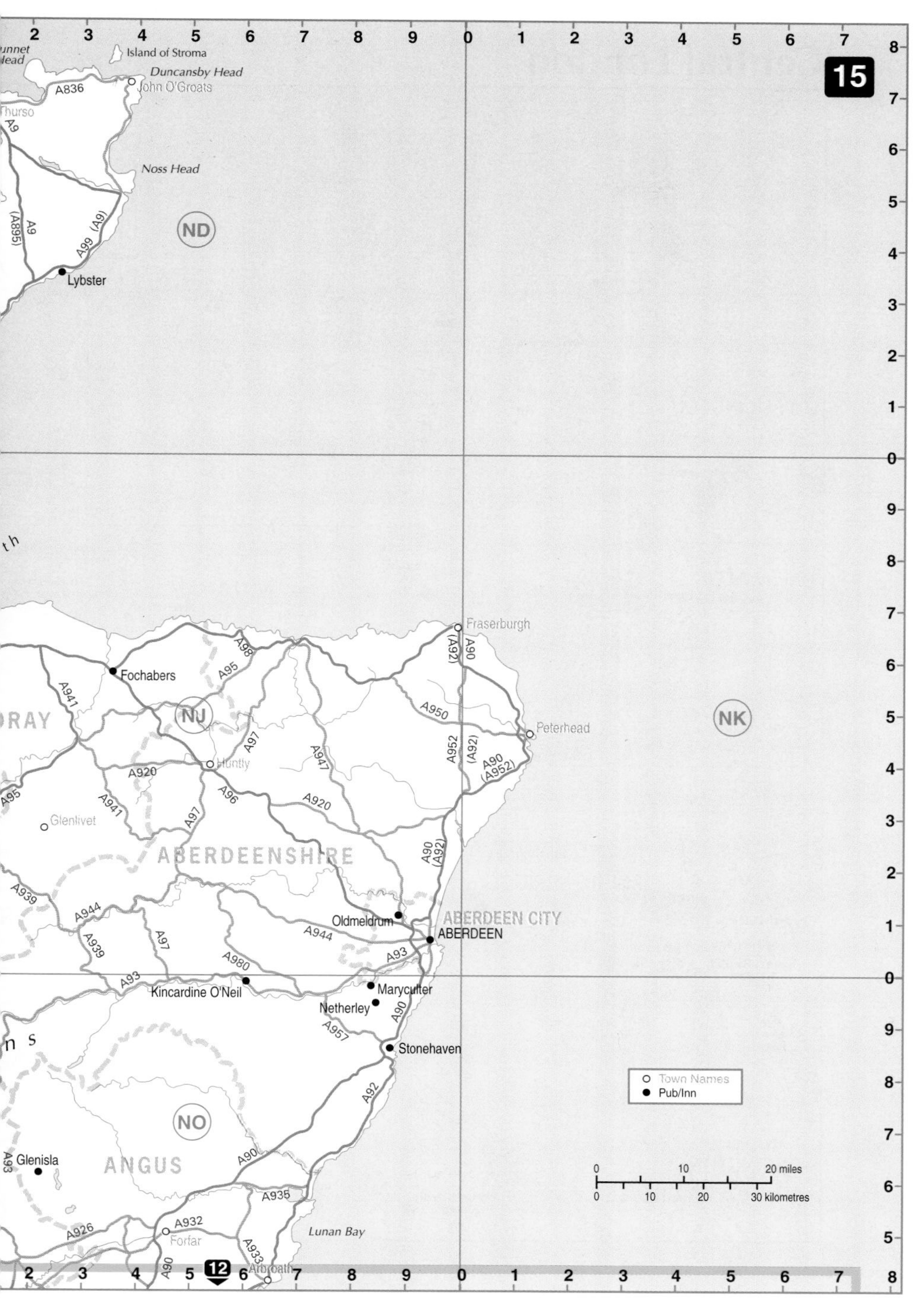

15
Island of Stroma
Duncansby Head
John O'Groats
Thurso
Noss Head
ND
Lybster
Fraserburgh
Fochabers
NJ
Peterhead
NK
Huntly
Glenlivet
ABERDEENSHIRE
Oldmeldrum
ABERDEEN CITY
ABERDEEN
Kincardine O'Neil
Maryculter
Netherley
Stonehaven
Town Names
Pub/Inn
NO
Glenisla
ANGUS
Forfar
Lunan Bay
Arbroath
12
20 miles
30 kilometres

Central London

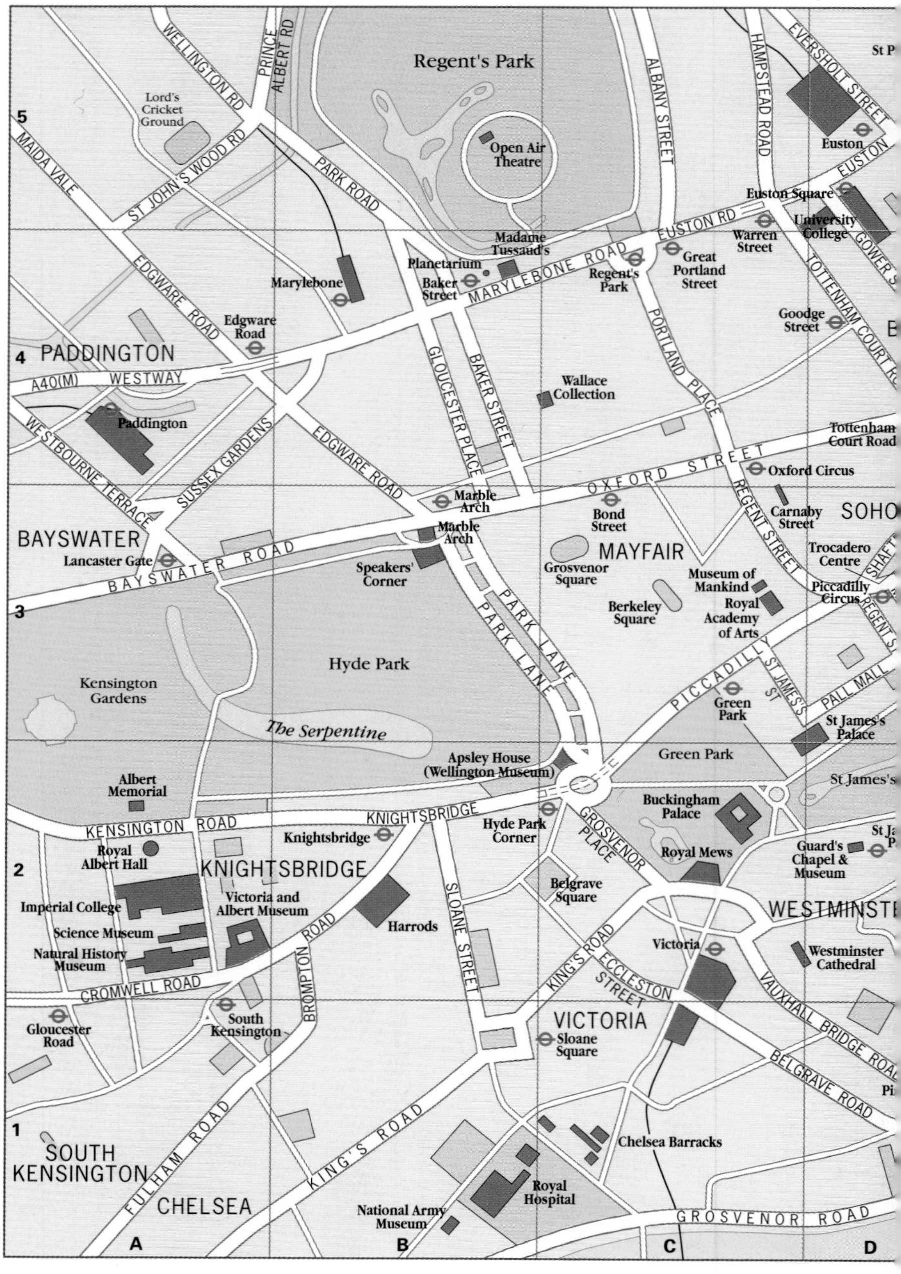

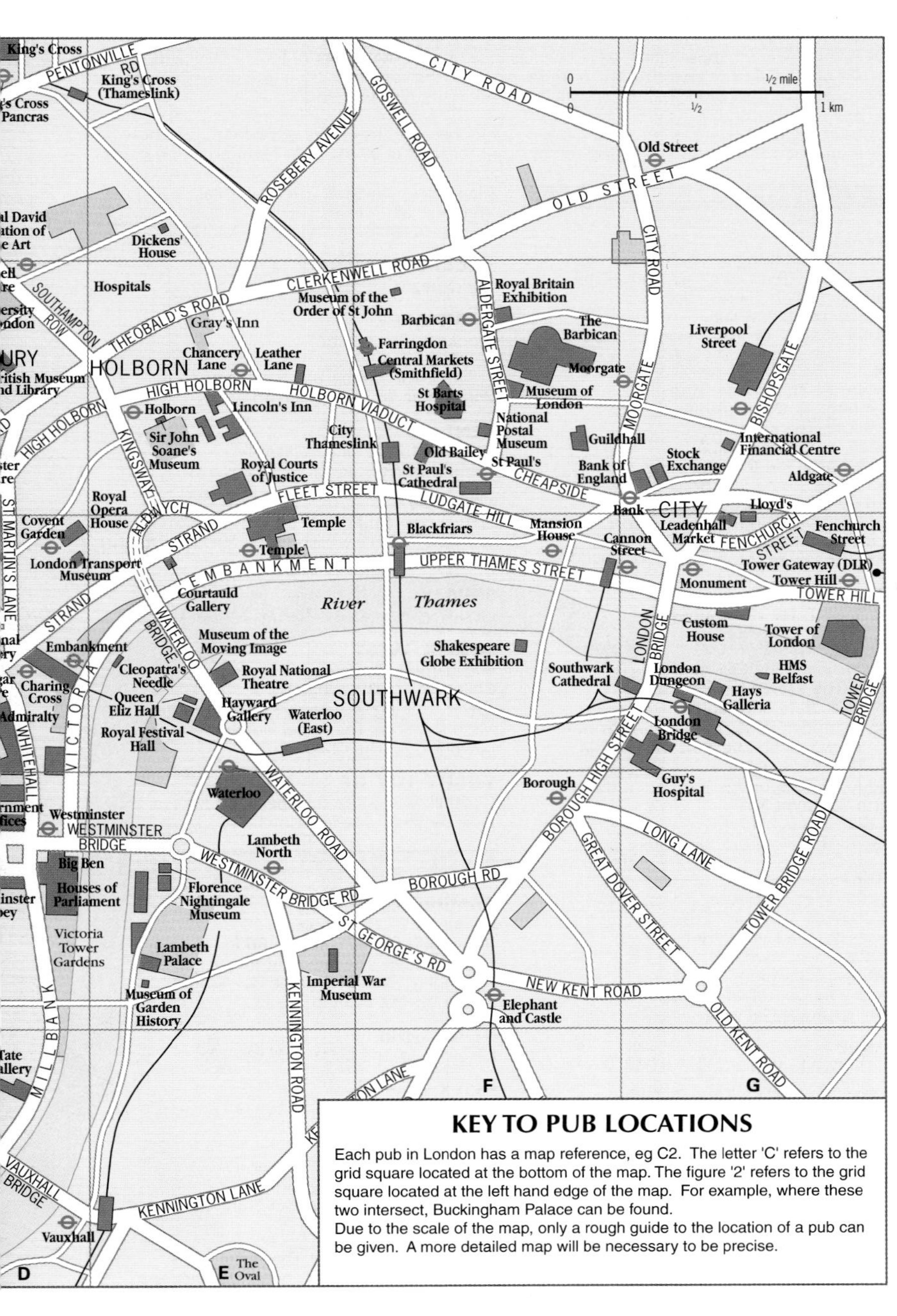

KEY TO PUB LOCATIONS

Each pub in London has a map reference, eg C2. The letter 'C' refers to the grid square located at the bottom of the map. The figure '2' refers to the grid square located at the left hand edge of the map. For example, where these two intersect, Buckingham Palace can be found.
Due to the scale of the map, only a rough guide to the location of a pub can be given. A more detailed map will be necessary to be precise.

PUBS WITH AA ROSETTE AWARDS

The pubs listed below are those which have been assessed by the AA's team of highly qualified inspectors and have been awarded one or more rosettes (the scale runs from one up to five) for the notable quality of their food. Full details will be found in the directory entries.

All the pubs in the guide have been chosen at least partly because they serve good food, but those in this list - around 150 - represent the top ten per cent for food of all the pubs featured in the guide.

WEST COUNTRY

CORNWALL
Constantine, ❀❀ Trengilly Wartha Inn
Mousehole, ❀❀ The Old Coastguard Hotel
Port Gaverne ❀ Port Gaverne Hotel
St Mawes ❀ The Rising Sun
Tresco, Isles of Scilly ❀ The New Inn

DEVON
Branscombe ❀ The Masons Arms
Broadhembury ❀ Drewe Arms
Haytor Vale ❀ The Rock Inn
Lifton ❀❀❀ The Arundell Arms
Lydford ❀ Castle Inn & Hotel
Lynmouth ❀❀ Rising Sun Hotel
Plymouth ❀ Langdon Court Hotel
Rockbeare ❀❀ Jack in the Green Inn
Staverton ❀❀ The Sea Trout
Totnes ❀ The Durant Arms

DORSET
Powerstock ❀ Three Horseshoes Inn

GLOUCESTERSHIRE
Ampney Crucis ❀ The Crown of Crucis
Blockley ❀ The Crown Inn & Hotel
Chedworth ❀ Hare & Hounds
Chipping Campden ❀❀ The Noel Arms Hotel
Coln St-Aldwyns ❀❀ The New Inn at Coln
Ewen ❀ The Wild Duck
Fossebridge ❀ Fossebridge Inn
Nailsworth ❀ Egypt Mill
Paxford ❀❀ Churchill Arms
Stroud ❀ Bear of Rodborough Hotel

SOMERSET
Axbridge ❀ The Oak House
Beckington ❀❀ Woolpack Inn
Castle Cary ❀ The George Hotel
Exford ❀❀ The Crown Hotel
Frome ❀ The Talbot Inn
Nunney ❀ The George at Nunney
Withypool ❀ Royal Oak Inn

WILTSHIRE
Ford ❀ The White Hart
Hindon ❀ Grosvenor Arms
Hindon ❀ Lamb at Hindon,The
Little Bedwyn ❀❀ The Harrow Inn
Malmesbury ❀ Horse & Groom
Rowde ❀❀ The George and Dragon

SOUTH AND SOUTH-EAST ENGLAND

BEDFORDSHIRE
Bedford ❀ Knife & Cleaver

BERKSHIRE
Burchett's Green ❀ The Crown
Cookham Dean ❀ The Inn on the Green
Marsh Benham ❀❀ The Water Rat
Winkfield ❀ Rose & Crown
Yattendon ❀❀❀ The Royal Oak Hotel

BUCKINGHAMSHIRE
Haddenham ❀ The Green Dragon

HAMPSHIRE
Brook ❀ The Bell Inn
Bucklers Hard
❀❀ The Master Builders House Hotel
Winchester ❀ The Wykeham Arms

KENT
Littlebourne ❀ King William IV
Tunbridge Wells, Royal ❀❀ Royal Wells Inn

LONDON
EC1 ❀ The Eagle
W2 ❀❀ The Cow Saloon Bar & Dining Rooms
W6 ❀ Anglesea Arms

SURREY
Ockley ❀ Bryce's At The Old School House

SUSSEX, WEST
Burpham ❀❀ George & Dragon
Chilgrove ❀ The White Horse
Lower Beeding ❀ Jeremy's at the Crabtree
Midhurst ❀❀ The Angel Hotel
Rowhook ❀ The Chequers Inn

WIGHT, ISLE OF
Godshill ❀ Cask & Taverners
Seaview ❀❀ Seaview Hotel

CENTRAL ENGLAND & EAST ANGLIA

CAMBRIDGESHIRE
Fowlmere ❀ The Chequers
Huntingdon ❀❀ The Old Bridge Hotel
Keyston ❀❀ The Pheasant Inn
Madingley ❀❀ The Three Horseshoes
Stilton ❀ The Bell Inn

DERBYSHIRE
Bakewell ❀ The Rutland Arms Hotel

ESSEX
Great Yeldham ❀❀ The White Hart

LINCOLNSHIRE
Bourne ❀❀ The Black Horse Inn
Lincoln ❀ The Wig & Mitre
Stamford ❀ The George at Stamford

NORFOLK
Burnham Market ❀❀ The Hoste Arms
Stoke Holy Cross ❀❀ The Wildebeest Arms
Titchwell ❀ Titchwell Manor Hotel

NORTHAMPTONSHIRE
Castle Ashby ❀ Falcon Hotel

OXFORDSHIRE
Burford ❀ The Inn for All Seasons
Burford ❀❀ The Lamb Inn
Chalgrove ❀ The Red Lion Inn
Chinnor ❀❀ Sir Charles Napier
Dorchester-On-Thames ❀ The George
Faringdon ❀ The Lamb at Buckland
Middleton Stoney ❀ The Jersey Arms
Shipton-Under-Wychwood ❀ The Lamb Inn
Shipton-Under-Wychwood
❀ The Shaven Crown Hotel
Stadhampton ❀❀ The Crazy Bear
Woodstock ❀ Kings Head Inn
Woodstock ❀❀❀ Feathers Hotel

RUTLAND
Stretton ❀ Ram Jam Inn

STAFFORDSHIRE
Acton Trussell ❀ The Moat House

SUFFOLK
Lavenham ❀ Angel Hotel
Nayland ❀❀ White Hart
Polstead ❀ The Cock Inn
Southwold ❀ Crown Hotel

WALES & THE MARCHES

ANGLESEY, ISLE OF
Beaumaris ❀❀ Ye Olde Bulls Head Inn

CARDIFF
Creigiau ❀ Caesars Arms

CONWY
Abergele ❀❀ Kinmel Arms

GWYNEDD
Aberdyfi ❀ Penhelig Arms Hotel

HEREFORDSHIRE
Brimfield ❀ The Roebuck Inn
Hereford ❀❀ The Ancient Camp Inn

MONMOUTHSHIRE
Abergavenny
❀ Llanwenarth Arms Hotel & Restaurant
❀❀❀ Walnut Tree Inn

POWYS
Crickhowell ❀❀ Gliffaes Country House Hotel
Crickhowell ❀ Nantyffin Cider Mill
Crickhowell ❀❀ The Bear
Hay-On-Wye ❀ Kilverts Hotel
Llyswen ❀ The Griffin Inn
Montgomery ❀ Dragon Hotel
New Radnor ❀ Red Lion Inn
Pwllgloyw ❀❀ Seland Newydd

SHROPSHIRE
Oswestry ❀ The Old Mill Inn

WREXHAM
Llanarmon Dyffryn Ceiriog ❀ The West Arms Hotel

NORTHERN ENGLAND

CUMBRIA
Ambleside ❀ Drunken Duck Inn
Appleby-In-Westmorland ❀ Tufton Arms Hotel
Eskdale Green ❀ Bower House Inn
Mungrisdale ❀ The Mill Inn
Ravenstonedale ❀❀ Black Swan Hotel
Troutbeck ❀❀ Queens Head Hotel
Ulverston ❀❀ Bay Horse Hotel

CO DURHAM
Romaldkirk ❀❀ Rose and Crown

GREATER MANCHESTER
Manchester ❀❀ Mash & Air
Oldham ❀❀ The White Hart Inn

LANCASHIRE
Blackburn ❀ Millstone Hotel
Sawley ❀❀ The Spread Eagle

NORTHUMBERLAND
Blanchland ❀ Lord Crewe Arms

YORKSHIRE, NORTH
Asenby ❀❀ Crab & Lobster
Askrigg ❀❀ Kings Arms Hotel
Buckden ❀❀ The Buck Inn
Burnsall ❀ The Red Lion
Carlton ❀ Foresters Arms
Harrogate ❀❀ The Boar's Head Hotel
Helmsley ❀ The Feversham Arms Hotel
Hetton ❀❀ The Angel
Hovingham ❀❀ The Worsley Arms Hotel
Kirkbymoorside ❀ George & Dragon Hotel
Knaresborough ❀❀ The General Tarleton Inn
Moulton ❀ Black Bull Inn
Pickering ❀ The Fox & Hounds Country Inn
Pickering ❀ The White Swan
Ramsgill ❀❀ The Yorke Arms
Rosedale Abbey ❀❀ The Milburn Arms Hotel
West Witton ❀ The Wensleydale Heifer Inn

SCOTLAND

ARGYLL & BUTE
Arduaine ❀❀ Loch Melfort Hotel
Kilfinan ❀❀❀ Kilfinan Hotel Bistro Bar
Strachur ❀ Creggans Inn

CITY OF GLASGOW
Glasgow ❀❀ Buttery
Glasgow ❀ Ubiquitous Chip

DUMRIES & GALLOWAY
Newton Stewart ❀ Creebridge House Hotel

HIGHLAND
Dundonnell ❀❀ Dundonnell House
Fort William ❀ The Moorings Hotel
Glenfinnan ❀ The Prince's House
Isle Ornsay ❀ Hotel Eilean Iarmain

LOTHIAN, WEST
Linlithgow ❀❀ Champany Inn

PERTH & KINROSS
Killiecrankie ❀❀ The Killiecrankie Hotel

SCOTTISH BORDERS
Melrose ❀❀ Burts Hotel
Swinton ❀ Wheatsheaf Hotel

Index

A

B

Index

C

D

E

F

G

H

I

J

K

L

M

N

O

S

T

U

V

W

Y

Picture Credits

The following photographs are held in the Association's own photo library (AA PHOTO LIBRARY) and were taken by the following photographers:
20 P Baker; 21 R Moore; 90a D Forss; 90b W Voysey; 168 A Perkins; 169 T Souter; 258 R Newton; 259 V & S Bates; 296 C Lees; 297 S Day; 354 J Henderson; 355 J Beazley.